Elementary Particle Physics and Field Theory

BRANDEIS UNIVERSITY SUMMER INSTITUTE LECTURES IN THEORETICAL PHYSICS

K. W. Ford, *Editor*

1960 Lectures

C. Møller • P. T. Matthews • J. Schwinger • N. Fukuda • J. J. Sakurai

1961 Lectures

Vol. 1
R. J. Eden • J. C. Polkinghorne • G. Källén • J. J. Sakurai

Vol. 2
M. E. Rose • E. C. G. Sudarshan

1962 Lectures

Vol. 1—Elementary Particle Physics and Field Theory
T. Fulton • G. Källén • J. D. Jackson • C. Fronsdal

Vol. 2—Astrophysics and the Many-Body Problem
E. N. Parker • J. S. Goldstein • A. A. Maradudin • V. Ambegaokar

Vol. 3—Statistical Physics
G. E. Uhlenbeck • N. Rosenzweig • A. J. F. Siegert • E. T. Jaynes • S. Fujita

Brandeis Summer Institute 1962

ELEMENTARY PARTICLE PHYSICS AND FIELD THEORY

1

T. Fulton
G. Källén
J. D. Jackson
C. Fronsdal

Notes by

R. Gudmundsson
E. Sarachik

W. A. BENJAMIN, INC. *New York* *Amsterdam*

1963

ELEMENTARY PARTICLE PHYSICS AND FIELD THEORY
Volume 1 of the 1962 Brandeis Summer Institute
Lectures in Theoretical Physics

Library of Congress Catalog Card Number 61-18591
Manufactured in the United States of America

Final manuscript was received on October 15, 1962; this volume was published June 21, 1963

Dr. Fulton personally supervised the preparation of camera copy for his paper. Dr. Jackson prepared the equations for his lecture; Brandeis University produced the displayed material for the papers by Dr. Källén and Dr. Fronsdal.

W. A. BENJAMIN, INC.
2465 Broadway, New York 25, New York

Foreword

It is the purpose of these notes to make widely available, in an informal presentation, material from a group of lectures covering the main areas of particle physics, delivered by experts, at the 1962 Brandeis Summer Institute in Theoretical Physics. Reasonably self-contained and up-to-date presentations in quantum electrodynamics, weak interactions, strong-interaction phenomenology, and group theoretic treatments of symmetries are contained in this volume.

The notes of each lecture series were prepared either by the lecturers themselves or under their direct supervision.

The Institute was supported by the National Science Foundation.

Saul Barshay
Co-Director of the 1962 Institute

Contents

Elementary Particle Physics
and
Field Theory

RESONANCES IN STRONG INTERACTION PHYSICS

THOMAS FULTON
Johns Hopkins University

Notes by the lecturer

CONTENTS

I. INTRODUCTION

Many resonances have been experimentally observed recently, particularly within the last year or so. They have been seen to involve different kinds of particles as decay products: two and three π mesons, a K and a π meson, a hyperon and a π meson. In addition, a number of resonances seem well established in the π-N system—the well-known (3, 3) resonance, as well as resonances at higher energies. In table 1 below, a tentative list of these resonances is given (as of June, 1962), with all that is known of their zoology as of now. The table is based on one circulated by A. Rosenfeld.

Figure (I. 1) presents the same data in the form of an elementary particle spectrum. For the sake of completeness, the long-lived elementary particles are included (solid lines) as well as the short-lived particles -- the resonances (dotted lines). The numbers in parentheses after the long-lived particles give their masses in Nambus (units of $m_e/\alpha \approx 70$ Mev, where m_e is the mass of the electron and α the fine structure constant). The fact that all these particles have masses in Nambus which are integers or half integers may be significant, and at the very least it is a convenient aid to memory.

Which of the resonances are real? This is hard to tell, but some will probably disappear. At the moment the ζ is not in very good standing. Conversely, it is more than likely that the list is not yet complete. There are suspicious bumps in various spectra: for example, in the 2π spectrum at 420 Mev, which may upon further examination turn out to be resonances. Better resolution may show further fine structure in already existing resonances; finally, the higher-energy regions are yet to be explored.

There are some interesting numerological features of the resonances, which can be termed "degenerate spectral characteristics" (for example, $m_\omega \approx m_\rho$ and $m_\eta \approx m_\zeta$). There have been a number of recent attempts to relate members of the above pairs possessing significant 3π and 2π decay modes, respectively. Another interesting correspondence exists between masses of resonances and corresponding thresholds for two-particle channels. This is summarized in Table 2 (originally due to Salam). Again, these features may be significant or may serve only as aids to memory.

We have adopted the expedient (but not necessarily correct) convention that a resonance is nothing but a short-lived particle. From this point of view, a resonance is an accident of the energy spectrum: if decay channels to particles with strong interactions are energetically available, then we have a resonance. In any case, whether we label them as particles or not, we hope that the exist-

Table 1

Tentative List of Resonances

Particle	Mass	Width Γ	I spin	Spin & parity	Principal decay modes
ξ	560	< 70	1	?	2π
ρ	750	100	1	1^{-+}	2π
η	548	< 12	0(?)	0^{-+} (?)	{ 3π Neutrals
ω	788	< 12	0	1^{--}	3π
K*	888	50	1/2	?	Kπ
N^*_1	1238	145	3/2	3/2+	Nπ
N^*_2	1512	130	1/2	3/2-	{ Nπ Others
N^*_3	1688	140	1/2	5/2+	{ Nπ Others
N^*_4	1922	185	3/2	?	?
Y^*_1	1385	≤50	1	?	{ Λπ Σπ < 4%
Y^*_0	1405	50	0	?	{ Σπ Λ 2π
Y**	1520	16	0	3/2	{ Σπ Λ 2π K^0N K^-P
Y***	1815	120	0	≥3/2	Many
Ξ^{-*}	1535	> 7 <	1/2		{ Σπ Others (?)

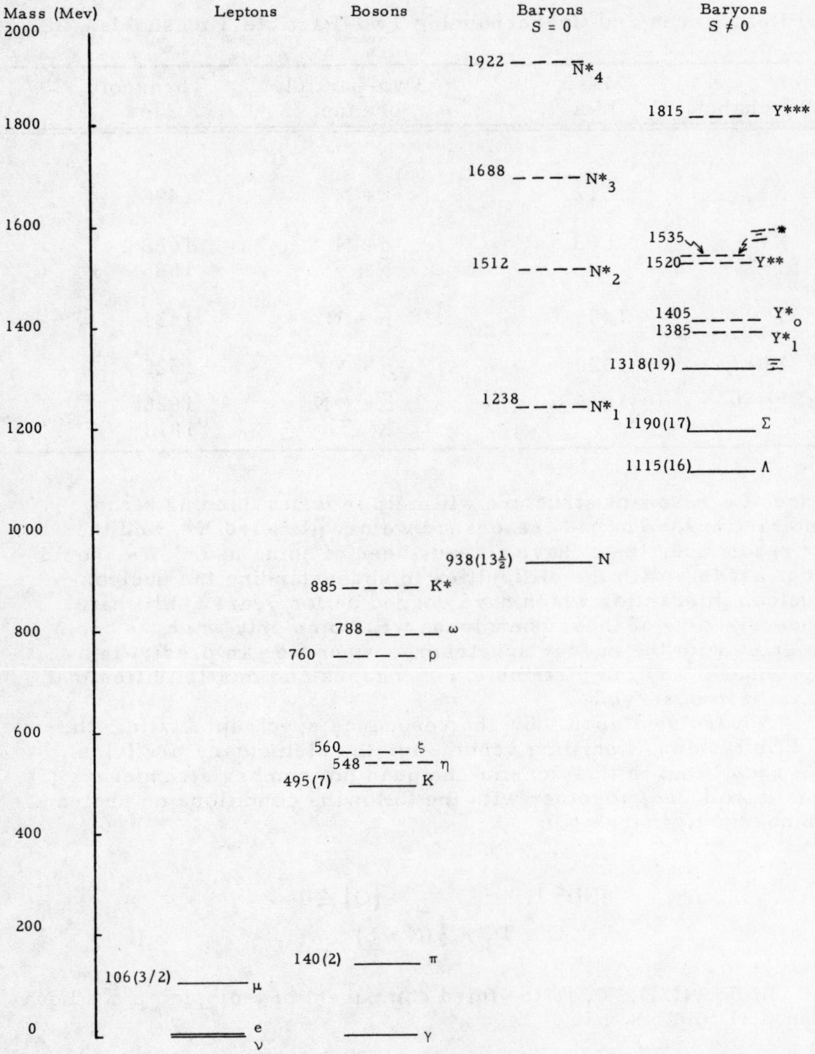

Fig. I.1 Elementary Particle Spectrum

Table 2

Resonances and Corresponding Two-Particle Thresholds

Resonance	Mass, Mev	Two-particle channel	Threshold, Mev
N^*_2	1512	$\xi + N$	1498
N^*_3	1688	$\rho + N$ $\bar{K} + \Sigma$	1688 1685
Y^*_o	1405	$\bar{K} + N$	1433
Y^{**}	1520	$\pi + Y^*_1$	1525
Y^{***}	1815	$\bar{K}^* + N$ $K + \Xi$	1826 1813

ence of a resonant structure will help in understanding strong interactions. The π-N resonance we have labeled N^*_1 and the 2π resonance, the ρ, have already been of some use.[1] We should contrast this with the difficulties in understanding the nucleon-nucleon interaction which have dogged us for years. Ultimate understanding of these phenomena will come only when we come to grips with the energy spectrum -- when we can predict in a systematic way the distribution of masses and multiplicities that have been observed.

A word next about how the resonance spectrum fits into the old Gell-Mann-Nishijima scheme for the elementary particles. We recall that in this scheme the quantum number strangeness (S) was introduced, together with the following conditions on nucleon number (N), charge (Q):

$$|N| \leq 1, \qquad |Q| \leq 1$$

$$Q = T_3 + \tfrac{1}{2}(N + S) \tag{I. 1}$$

In Eq. (I. 1), T_3 is the third component of isotopic spin. Equation (I.1) implies that

$$|S| \leq 3 \tag{I. 2}$$

In terms of the above conditions, the following holes still exist in the Gell-Mann-Nishijima scheme [sets of quantum numbers (N, S, T, Q) to which no particle assignments have as yet been made]:

Table 3

Available Sets of Quantum Numbers in the Gell-Mann-Nishijima Scheme

	Particle	N	S	T	Q
Mesons	π^{00}	0	0	0	0
	$D^{\pm}$	0	± 2	0	± 1
Baryons	Z^{+}	1	1	0	1
	Z^{-}	-1	-1	0	-1
	Ω^{-}	1	-3	0	-1
	Ω^{+}	-1	+3	0	+1

If one defines, with Schwinger, the hypercharge Y, where:

$$Y = N + S \tag{I.3}$$

and further demands, as Schwinger does, that

$$|Y| \leq 1$$

then all but the π^{00} are automatically excluded from consideration.

With the possible exception of the η particle, none of the resonances seen so far fits into the above list of missing particles. In any case, we see particles that possess two units of charge, which would exclude them from the above list. This does not imply that the Gell-Mann scheme is incorrect, but we must broaden the scheme somewhat. In particular, if we allow spin values other than 0 for bosons and 1/2 for fermions, we immediately include all the presently observed boson resonances and most of the baryon resonances in the scheme. If, in addition, we relax the condition $|Q| \leq 1$, we can include the remaining resonances. Possibly, however, at least some of the baryon resonances should be treated on a different footing from the boson resonances.

At present, there are two general approaches that aim at an understanding of the relations between the various particles on some more fundamental level. They are:

Regge pole approach. This approach is a development of dispersion relation techniques. Analyticity properties of scattering amplitudes are postulated in the complex angular momentum plane, in analogy with the behavior of such amplitudes in potential scattering. An attempt is made to relate particles and resonances that have all quantum numbers but spin identical -- they are said to lie on the same "Regge trajectory." This approach has so far had nothing to say about the characteristic distributions of these Regge trajectories, nor has it been too specific about predicting the mass spectrum of a group of particles related by lying on the same Regge trajectory.

Symmetry approach. Assuming certain symmetries, based on suitable groupings of masses, we can allocate particles to various dimensional representations of different groups and, depending on the existence of some unfilled slots, predict the existence of as yet undiscovered particles. One can even generate interactions from generalized gauge invariance arguments. Although this approach has some rather attractive features, it too has nothing to say about the explicit character of the mass spectrum or about why and how the postulated symmetries are removed.

Our concern shall be with neither of these approaches in the lectures which follow; instead, we shall use elementary methods to discuss questions such as the following: What is a resonance in reactions with more than one final channel? How does one deduce from experimental observations that a resonance exists? Is it possible that experiment suggests the existence of a resonance, when, in fact, one does not exist? How is one to relate resonances to other phenomena in a simple-minded effective range-theory approach? What role, in particular, do multipion resonances play in other phenomena -- such as the nucleon form factor?

It is useful to discuss such questions in the present incomplete state of our factual knowledge. It can assist the experimenter in sorting out and relating his data. It can help the theorist in systematizing the information to be channeled into a more sophisticated or fundamental theory.

References:

Below is a by no means exhaustive list of references to experimental reports of the resonances. Additional references may be found in these papers.

1. ζ: Barloutaud et al., Phys. Rev. Letters, 8, 32 (1962).

2. ρ: Anderson et al., Phys. Rev. Letters, 6, 365 (1961); Stonehill et al., Phys. Rev. Letters, 6, 624 (1961); Erwin, March, Walker, and West, Phys. Rev. Letters, 6, 628 (1961).

3. η: Pevsner et al., Phys. Rev. Letters, 7, 421 (1961).

4. ω: Maglić, Alvarez, Rosenfeld, and Stevenson, Phys. Rev. Letters, 7, 178 (1961).

5. K*: Alston et al., Phys. Rev. Letters, 6, 300 (1961).

6. $N^*_{1,2,3}$: Moyer, Rev. Mod. Phys., 3, 367 (1961).

7. N^*_4: Falk-Vairant and Valladas, Proceedings of 1960 Rochester Conference, Interscience, New York, p. 38.

8. Y^*_1: Alston and Ferro-Luzzi, Rev. Mod. Phys., 3, 416 (1961).

9. Y^*_0: Alston et al., Phys. Rev. Letters, 6, 698 (1961); Bastien et al., Phys. Rev. Letters, 6, 702 (1961).

10. Y**: Ferro-Luzzi, Tripp, and Watson, Phys. Rev. Letters, 8, 28 (1962).

11. Y***: Kerth, Rev. Mod. Phys., 3, 389 (1961).

12. π and nucleon isobars: Detoeuf, Proceedings of Aix-en-Provence Conference, Saclay, Paris, 1961, pp. 57ff.

13. Strange particle isobars: Schmitz, Proceedings of Aix-en-Provence Conference, Saclay, Paris, 1961, pp. 177ff.

The following references may also be found useful in connection with the material presented in this section:

14. Salam, Review Lecture at High Energy Physics Conference of Physical Society, Imperial College, London, March, 1962 (preprint).

15. Regge poles: Regge, Nuovo Cimento, 14, 951 (1959); ibid., 18, 947 (1960); Chew and Frautschi, Phys. Rev. Letters, 8, 41 (1962); Blankenbecler and Goldberger (in press); Frautschi, Gell-Mann, and Zachariasen, Phys. Rev. (in press).

16. Symmetries: Glashow and Sakurai, Nuovo Cimento (in press); Gell-Mann, Cal. Tech. Report TSL-20 1961; Yang and Lee, Phys. Rev., 122, 1954 (1961); Ward and Salam, Nuovo Cimento, 11, 568 (1959).

II. THE S MATRIX—RESONANCES AND CUSPS

1. Review of General Properties of the S Matrix

The review which follows is partly to introduce notation. Another purpose is to carry out a partial wave analysis from the Dirac point of view of states, rather than from the more old-fashioned view of wave functions. This approach makes the relativistically covariant character of the parametrization more apparent.

Consider the complete set of orthonormal Heisenberg basis vectors at time $t = -\infty$ and $t = +\infty$. These are defined as the "in" and "out" states, respectively:

$$|b^{in}\rangle = |b(t)\rangle\Big|_{t=-\infty}$$

$$|a^{out}\rangle = |a(t)\rangle\Big|_{t=+\infty} \qquad \text{(II. 1. 1)}$$

The S matrix is the transition amplitude representing an overlap between an in and out state:

$$S_{ab} = \langle a^{out}|b^{in}\rangle \qquad \text{(II. 1. 2)}$$

We define the S operator by the equation

$$|b^{in}\rangle = S|b^{out}\rangle \quad \text{or} \quad S^{-1}|b^{in}\rangle = |b^{out}\rangle \qquad \text{(II. 1. 3)}$$

The transition amplitude S_{ab} becomes:

$$S_{ab} = \langle a^{out}|S|b^{out}\rangle = \langle a^{in}|S|b^{in}\rangle \qquad \text{(II. 1. 4)}$$

Next, we turn to the unitarity of the S matrix. "Unitarity" is another way of stating the conservation of probability. Since both the in and out states form a complete orthonormal set of basis vectors, we have for the out states

$$\langle b'^{out}|b^{out}\rangle = \delta_{bb'} = \sum_a \langle b'^{out}|a^{in}\rangle \underbrace{\langle a^{in}|b^{out}\rangle}_{\langle b^{out}|a^{in}\rangle^*} =$$

$$= \sum_a S_{b'a} S^*_{ba} = \sum_a S_{b'a} S^+_{ab} \qquad \text{(II. 1. 5)}$$

In operator notation, Eq. (II. 1. 5) becomes

$$SS^{+} = \underset{\approx}{1} \tag{II. 1. 6}$$

Alternatively, we can demonstrate unitarity, using orthonormality of the in states:

$$\langle a'^{in} | a^{in} \rangle = \delta_{a'a} = \sum_b \underbrace{\langle a'^{in} | b^{out} \rangle}_{\langle b^{out} | a'^{in} \rangle^*} \langle b^{out} | a^{in} \rangle$$

$$= \sum_b S^*_{ba'} S_{ba} = \sum_b S^{+}_{a'b} S_{ba} \tag{II. 1. 7}$$

In operator notation, we have:

$$S^{+}S = \underset{\approx}{1} \tag{II. 1. 8}$$

We define the operator T by the expression:

$$S = \underset{\approx}{1} + iT \tag{II. 1. 9}$$

The unitarity relation (II. 1. 6) or (II. 1. 8) in terms of T or its inverse becomes:

$$T - T^{+} = iTT^{+}$$

or

$$i(T^{-1} - T^{+\,-1}) = \underset{\approx}{1} \tag{II. 1. 10}$$

So far, no statement has been made about the number of particles in the incoming or outgoing state. From now on, we shall restrict ourselves to scattering: that is, we shall consider two particles in all channels, both incoming and outgoing, though the identity of the particles need not remain unchanged in the course of the reaction. For example, we do not exclude a process like $K^- + P \to \pi^0 + \Lambda$.

The symbol "a" in our state vectors denotes specific eigenvalues of a complete set of commuting operators. We now specify "a" in more detail:

$$|a\rangle = |p_{1_\mu}, p_{2_\nu}; \alpha\rangle \tag{II. 1. 11}$$

where α denotes everything but the 4-momenta of the two particles (p_{1_μ}, p_{2_ν}), for example, the spins and z components of the spins of the particles, their isotopic spins and charges, their particle character, etc. Further, we take the volume V which enters the usual normalization of the particle states to be unity. We recall that S_{ab} and S are relativistic invariants, and so is T. It is customary at this point to define still a third invariant operator, T_P, by explicitly exhibiting the normalization factors and conservation of energy and momentum:

$$\langle a|T|b\rangle = (2\pi)^4 \left(\prod_j \frac{\eta_j}{2\omega_j}\right)^{\frac{1}{2}} \delta^4(P_a - P_b) \langle\alpha|T_P|\beta\rangle \tag{II. 1. 12}$$

The product which appears is over all four particles in the states a and b; ω_j are their energies, and $\eta_j = 1$ for bosons, $\eta_j = 2m_j$ for fermions (m_j is the fermion mass). P_a and P_b are the total 4-momenta of a and b.

If we observe that

$$(2\pi)^4 \delta(P_a - P_b) = V \cdot T \to 1 \cdot T \tag{II. 1. 13}$$

where T is a time interval, the transition probability per unit time from a to b, with $a \neq b$, is given by:

$$w_b = \sum_a w_{ab} =$$

$$= (2\pi)^4 \sum_a \left(\prod_j \frac{\eta_j}{2\omega_j} \right) \delta^4(P_a - P_b) \langle \beta | T_P^+ | \alpha \rangle \langle \alpha | T_P | \beta \rangle \tag{II. 1. 14}$$

Next, we proceed to do the phase-space integrals:

$$\rho = \sum_a \delta^4 (P_a - P_b) |\alpha\rangle\langle\alpha| =$$

$$= \sum_\alpha \int \frac{d^3 \underset{\sim}{p}_1{}^a}{(2\pi)^3} \frac{d^3 \underset{\sim}{p}_2{}^a}{(2\pi)^3} \delta^4(P_a - P_b) |\alpha\rangle\langle\alpha|$$

If we go to center-of-mass and relative coordinates, $P_a = p_1^a + p_2^a$ and k_a, so that

$$d^3 \underset{\sim}{p}_1{}^a d^3 \underset{\sim}{p}_2{}^a = d^3 \underset{\sim}{k}_a d^3 \underset{\sim}{p}_a \quad \text{and} \quad \frac{dE_a}{dk_a} = \frac{k_a E_a}{\omega_1^a \omega_2^a} \tag{II. 1. 15}$$

With E_a the total c. m. energy in state a, we obtain

$$\rho = \frac{1}{(2\pi)^6} \frac{1}{\eta_1^a \eta_2^a} \cdot$$

$$\cdot \sum_\alpha \int \underbrace{k_a{}^2 \frac{dk_a}{dE_a}}_{\frac{k_a \omega_1^a \omega_2^a}{E_a}} d\Omega_a dE_a \, \delta(E_a - E_b) |\alpha\rangle\langle\alpha| \tag{II. 1. 16}$$

with $d\Omega_a$ representing the angular integrations in relative coordinates. Substitution into (II. 1. 14) gives ($E_a = E_b = E$):

$$w_b = \frac{1}{(2\pi)^2} \frac{\eta_1^b \eta_2^b}{16\omega_1^b \omega_2^b} \sum_{\alpha} \frac{k_a}{E} \int d\Omega_a \langle \beta | T_P^+ | \alpha \rangle \langle \alpha | T_P | \beta \rangle \tag{II. 1. 17}$$

In order to obtain the total cross section for the process with initial state $|b\rangle$, we divide w_b by the incident flux $\mathfrak{F}$, where:

$$\mathfrak{F} = \left| \frac{\underset{\sim}{p}_1^b}{\omega_1^b} - \frac{\underset{\sim}{p}_2^b}{\omega_2^b} \right| \eta_1^b \eta_2^b = \frac{k_b E}{\omega_1^b \omega_2^b} \eta_1^b \eta_2^b \tag{II. 1. 18}$$

and average over the initial spins S_1^b, S_2^b:

$$\sigma_b = \left(\frac{w_b}{\mathfrak{F}} \right)_{\text{Av. } S^b} = \left\{ \frac{1}{(8\pi)^2} \frac{1}{(2S_1^b + 1)(2S_2^b + 1)} \frac{1}{E^2} \right\} \cdot \sum_{S^b, \alpha} \frac{k_a}{k^b} \int d\Omega_a \langle \beta | T_P^+ | \alpha \rangle \langle \alpha | T_P | \beta \rangle \tag{II. 1. 19}$$

Further details and collateral information may be found in the following references:

1. Jauch and Rohrlich, The Theory of Photons and Electrons, Addison-Wesley, Reading, Mass., 1955, particularly Chaps. 7 and 8.

2. Blatt and Weisskopf, Theoretical Nuclear Physics, Wiley, New York, 1952, Chap. 10.

2. Unitarity Condition and the Submatrix for Given J and Parity

We are now ready to carry out a partial wave analysis by suitably projecting out states of given total J and parity. We begin with the unitarity condition and express the unit operator in terms of the complete set of states as:

$$i(T^{-1} - T^{+\,-1}) = \sum_n |n\rangle\langle n| \qquad \text{(II. 2. 1)}$$

The representations of a and b we considered previously were implicitly plane-wave representations [cf. Eq. (II. 1. 11)]. If we are to consider partial waves, it is most convenient to keep a plane-wave representation for $|n\rangle$ but take matrix elements of Eq. (II. 2. 1) with $|d\rangle$ and $\langle e|$ in a representation described by quantum numbers c and χ, where c denotes J, M, T, T_3, parity and χ is the channel number. (Thus for a given c, χ is an index denoting the $\Lambda\pi$, $\Sigma\pi$, and $\overline{K}N$ channels, for example.) We implicitly restrict ourselves to two-particle channels. We thus take

$$|n\rangle = |p_1^{(n)}, p_2^{(n)}; \nu\rangle = |p_1^{(n)}, p_2^{(n)}\rangle|\nu\rangle$$

$$|d\rangle = |P_d, c, \chi\rangle \quad = |P_d\rangle|c, \chi\rangle \quad = |P_d\rangle|c\rangle\,|\chi\rangle \qquad \text{(II. 2. 2)}$$

and the matrix element of Eq. (II. 2. 1) becomes [using the definition of Eq. (II. 1. 12)]:

$$i\langle c\chi|T_P^{-1} - T_P^{+\,-1}|c'\chi'\rangle =$$

$$= \sum_\nu \frac{1}{\eta_1^{(n)}\eta_2^{(n)}} \int \frac{d^3 \underset{\sim}{p}_1^{(n)}}{(2\pi)^3} \frac{d^3 \underset{\sim}{p}_2^{(n)}}{(2\pi)^3} (2\pi)^4 \,\cdot$$

$$\cdot\ \delta^4(P_d - P_n)\, \frac{\eta_1^{(n)}\eta_2^{(n)}}{4\omega_1^{(n)}\omega_2^{(n)}} \langle c\chi|n\rangle\langle n|c'\chi'\rangle \qquad \text{(II. 2. 3)}$$

Since the reaction conserves J, M, T, T_3, and parity (π), the left-hand side of Eq. (II. 2. 3) simplifies to

$$i\,\delta_{cc'}\,\langle \chi |\, T^{-1}_{c,P} - T^{+\,-1}_{c,P} \,|\chi' \rangle \tag{II. 2. 4}$$

The situation is simpler than indicated by Eq. (II. 2. 4), since T in fact does not depend on M and T_3, due to invariance under rotation in space and i-spin space.

Digression: Proof of independence of M and T_3. We shall outline derivation for M. Suppress all other indices but M. We then have:

$$\langle M | T | M' \rangle = \delta_{MM'} T_M \tag{II. 2. 5}$$

because of conservation of z component of angular momentum. We shall in fact show that T_M is independent of M. Since the T matrix is invariant under rotations, characterized by the operator R, we have:

$$RTR^{-1} = T$$

$$\delta_{MM'} T_M = \langle M | T | M' \rangle = \langle M | R^{-1} (RTR^{-1}) R | M' \rangle =$$

$$= \langle M | R^{-1} T R | M' \rangle = \sum_{M'', M'''} \langle M | R^{-1} | M'' \rangle \langle M'' | T | M''' \rangle .$$

$$\cdot \langle M''' | R | M' \rangle = \sum_{M''} \langle M | R^{-1} | M'' \rangle \, T_{M''} \, \langle M'' | R | M' \rangle \tag{II. 2. 6}$$

But

$$R = e^{i \underset{\sim}{J} \cdot \underset{\sim}{\theta}} \tag{II. 2. 7}$$

where

$$\underset{\sim}{J} \cdot \underset{\sim}{\theta} = J_+ \theta_+ + J_- \theta_- + J_Z \theta_Z \qquad \text{(II. 2. 8)}$$

and

$$\langle M' | J_+ | M \rangle = \delta_{M', M+1} C_M \qquad \text{(II. 2. 9)}$$

If, in particular, we take an infinitesimal rotation, with only θ_+ different from zero (θ_+ is a real parameter),

$$R = 1 + iJ_+ \theta_+$$

$$R^{-1} = 1 - iJ_+ \theta_+ \qquad \text{(II. 2. 10)}$$

Substitution in Eq. (II. 2. 6) gives

$$\delta_{MM'} T_M = \delta_{MM'} T_M + i\theta_+ (\delta_{M, M'+1} C_{M'} T_M - \delta_{M, M'+1} C_{M'} T_{M'})$$

Cancellation gives

$$T_M - T_{M'} = 0 \qquad M = M' + 1 \qquad \text{(II. 2. 11)}$$

and so T_M is independent of M. A similar proof can be made for T_3.

We return now to the main line of argument. We shall denote by a single subscript J, the variables P, J, T, and parity. We then have,

$$\delta_{cc'} \langle \chi | T^{-1}_{c, P} - T^{+ \, -1}_{c, P} | \chi' \rangle = \delta_{cc'} \langle \chi | T_J^{-1} - T_J^{+ \, -1} | \chi' \rangle \qquad \text{(II. 2. 12)}$$

Turning now to the evaluation of the right-hand side of Eq. (II. 2. 3), we have in the center-of-mass frame:

$$\sum_{\nu} \int \frac{d^3 p_1^{(n)}}{(2\pi)^3} \frac{d^3 p_2^{(n)}}{(2\pi)^3} (2\pi)^4 \delta^4(P_a - P_n) \frac{1}{4\omega_1^{(n)}\omega_2^{(n)}} \langle c\chi | n\rangle \langle n | c\chi'\rangle$$

$$= \delta_{TT'}\delta_{T_3T'_3} \quad \delta_{\pi\pi'}\delta_{\chi\chi'} \frac{1}{(4\pi)^2} \frac{k_\chi}{E} \, .$$

$$\underbrace{\sum_{\text{spins}} \int d\Omega_n \langle JM | \hat{k}^{(n)}, \text{spins}\rangle \langle \hat{k}^{(n)}, \text{spins} | J'M'\rangle}_{\delta_{JJ'}\delta_{MM'}}$$

(II. 2. 13)

where k_χ is the center-of-mass relative momentum in the χ channel.

The unitarity condition, in terms of submatrices of the T matrix which are operators in channel space only, thus becomes, for a given total energy, spin, parity, and isotopic spin:

$$i(T_J^{-1} - T_J^{+\,-1}) = \frac{1}{(4\pi)^2} \frac{\mathbf{k}}{E} \qquad \text{(II. 2. 14)}$$

with

$$\langle \chi | \mathbf{k} | \chi'\rangle = \delta_{\chi\chi'} k_\chi \qquad \text{(II. 2. 15)}$$

If states of more than two particles would have been involved in this analysis, the $T^{-1}_{c,P}$ would have been infinite dimensional and the relation between $T^{-1}_{c,P}$ and $T_{c,P}$ would have been an integral equation of the first kind.

Equation (II. 2. 14) serves to determine the imaginary part of T_J^{-1}. Unitarity clearly provides no restriction on the real part of T_J^{-1}. In terms of operators in channel space, we can therefore define a real matrix $\mathcal{K}_J^{-1}$, and a complex matrix $\mathcal{T}_J^{-1}$, by

$$T_J^{-1} = \frac{1}{2(4\pi)^2 E} \left(\mathcal{K}_J^{-1} - ik \right) \equiv \frac{1}{2(4\pi)^2 E} \quad \mathcal{T}_J^{-1}$$

(II. 2. 16)

We can now express σ_b in terms of $\mathcal{T}_J$ by using completeness conditions for $|c, \chi\rangle$. We rewrite Eq. (II. 1. 19) as:

$$\sigma_b = \underbrace{\{\ \}\sum_{\mathfrak{s}}}_{\text{repeated indices}} \frac{k_a}{k_b} \int d\Omega_a \ \langle \beta | c\, \chi \rangle \langle c\, \chi | T_P^+ | c'\, \chi' \rangle \cdot$$

$$\cdot \langle c'\, \chi' | \alpha \rangle \ \langle \alpha | c''\, \chi'' \rangle \ \langle c''\, \chi'' | T_P | c'''\, \chi''' \rangle \langle c'''\, \chi''' | \beta \rangle$$

(II. 2. 17)

The following relations hold as obvious consequences of what has been demonstrated previously:

$$\langle c\, \chi | T_P | c'\, \chi' \rangle = 2(4\pi)^2 E \delta_{cc'} \langle \chi | \mathcal{T}_J | \chi' \rangle \qquad \text{(II. 2. 18)}$$

$$\sum_\alpha k_a \ \langle c\, \chi | \alpha \rangle \ \langle \alpha | c'\, \chi' \rangle = k_\chi \ \delta_{cc'} \delta_{\chi\chi'} \qquad \text{(II. 2. 19)}$$

$$\langle \beta | c\, \chi \rangle = \delta_{\chi_b \chi} \sqrt{\frac{2J+1}{4\pi}} \qquad \text{(II. 2. 20)}$$

Substituting Eqs. (II. 2. 18) to (II. 2. 20) in (II. 2. 17) yields

$$\sigma_b = \sum_a \frac{2J+1}{(2S_1{}^b + 1)(2S_2{}^b + 1)} \ \sigma_{ba}^{(J)} \qquad \text{(II. 2. 21)}$$

where

$$\sigma_{ba}^{(J)} = 4\pi \ \frac{k_a}{k_b} |\langle \chi_b | \mathcal{T}_J | \chi_a \rangle|^2 \qquad \text{(II. 2. 22)}$$

and all the extraneous numerical and energy factors have canceled out correctly.

It will be useful for future reference to define one more quantity, by removing the explicit k_a dependence. We define:

$$\mathbb{T}_J = \mathbf{k}^{\frac{1}{2}} \mathfrak{T}_J \mathbf{k}^{\frac{1}{2}} \tag{II. 2. 23}$$

Correspondingly, we have

$$\mathbb{T}_J^{-1} = \mathbf{k}^{-\frac{1}{2}} \mathfrak{T}_J^{-1} \mathbf{k}^{-\frac{1}{2}} \tag{II. 2. 24}$$

and a real matrix $\mathbb{K}_J$, where

$$\mathbb{T}_J^{-1} = (\mathbb{K}_J^{-1} - i\underset{\approx}{1}) \tag{II. 2. 25}$$

The cross section for a given channel has the form:

$$\sigma_{ab}^{(J)} = \frac{4\pi}{k_b^2} |\langle \chi_b | \mathbb{T}_J | \chi_a \rangle|^2 \tag{II. 2. 26}$$

We emphasize in conclusion that the derivation has been in terms of states rather than wave functions, and that nowhere has a nonrelativistic approximation been made. From now on, we shall suppress the subscript J in the $\mathfrak{T}$-s and $\mathbb{T}$-s and the related K matrices, when no confusion can arise from such suppression.

To make contact with familiar things, consider the case of a single final channel, identical with the incoming channel (elastic scattering). The matrices in channel space are just numbers now. $\mathbb{K}$ is some real number. We can therefore define with full generality:

$$\mathbb{K}_J^{-1} = \cot \delta_J \qquad \text{(II. 2. 27)}$$

where δ_J is a real number. For this case, $k_a = k_b = k$ and $\mathbb{T}_J$ becomes:

$$\mathbb{T}_J = e^{i\delta_J} \sin \delta_J \qquad \text{(II. 2. 28)}$$

The parametrization of the relativistic S matrix in the one-channel case is now completed.

References:

1. Matthews and Salam, Nuovo Cimento, 13, 381 (1959).
2. Feldman, Matthews, and Salam, Nuovo Cimento, 16, 549 (1960).

3. Single-Channel Resonance and Wigner's Theorem

We are now ready to ask, at least for the single-channel case, what a resonance is. The cross section is given by

$$\sigma = \frac{4\pi}{k^2} \sin^2 \delta \qquad \text{(II. 3. 1)}$$

A resonance occurs when

$$\mathcal{H} = \frac{k^2 \sigma}{4\pi} \qquad \text{(II. 3. 2)}$$

is a maximum, that is,

$$\delta_{res} = (2n + 1) \frac{\pi}{2} \qquad n = 0, \pm 1, \ldots \qquad \text{(III. 3. 3)}$$

An additional condition which must be satisfied at resonance is that the phase shift must increase through these values of δ:

$$\left.\frac{d\delta}{dk}\right|_{res} \equiv \dot{\delta}_{res} > 0 \tag{II. 3. 4}$$

These conditions provide the simplest way of finding a resonance in an elastic scattering; in fact, the π-N (3, 3) resonance was found by using these conditions. One must simply obtain the phase shifts from the scattering data and find where a particular phase shift goes through $\pi/2$.

Why the additional condition given in Eq. (II. 3. 4)? Physically, a resonance is one that is observed -- that is, it must be moderately narrow. As a necessary condition, it must at least be much narrower than it is distant from the threshold (zero kinetic energy).

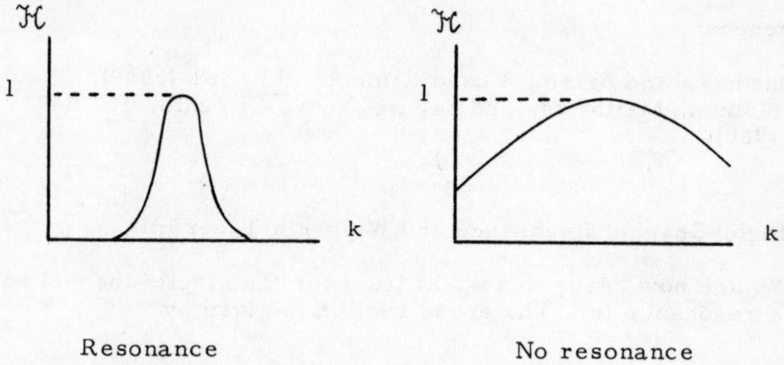

Fig. II. 1 Conditions under which a resonance is stated to exist.

We can write down a dimensionless condition for the existence of a narrow resonance. A necessary condition for a resonance to exist at a momentum k_0 is that

$$\sin^2 \delta(k_o) = 1 \tag{II. 3. 5}$$

The narrowness condition is expressed by the inequality

$$\left| k^2 \frac{d^2\mathcal{H}}{dk^2} \right|_{k_o} >> 2 \tag{II. 3. 6}$$

Equation (II. 3. 6) is merely a condition that the curvature at resonance is large compared with the distance from threshold. We can simplify Eq. (II. 3. 6) by explicit calculation:

$$\frac{d\mathcal{H}}{dk} \equiv \dot{\mathcal{H}} = 2\,\dot{\delta}\,\sin\delta\cos\delta \qquad \text{(II. 3. 7)}$$

$$\left.\frac{d^2\mathcal{H}}{dk^2}\right|_{k_o} = -\,2\sin^2\delta\,\dot{\delta}^2\Big|_{k_o} = -2[\,\dot{\delta}(k_o)]^2 \qquad \text{(II. 3. 8)}$$

The narrowness condition thus becomes

$$|k_o\,\dot{\delta}(k_o)| >> 1 \qquad \text{(II. 3. 6a)}$$

That is, we have above a condition on the slope of δ.

Wigner's theorem is in fact a condition on the slope of δ. Unfortunately, it applies only to potential scattering. It thus has the same status as Levinson's theorem concerning bound states:

$$\delta(0) - \delta(\infty) = n\pi \qquad \text{(II. 3. 9)}$$

where n is the number of bound states. It would be helpful if we had field-theoretical proofs of both of these theorems. The discussion below will, for simplicity's sake, refer to a spinless particle in a potential well.

Wigner's theorem: If the potential vanishes beyond a certain distance R, $\dot{\delta}_\ell$ is bounded below. In fact, the inequality satisfied by $\dot{\delta}_\ell$ is:

for S waves

$$\dot{\delta}_S > -R + \frac{1}{2k}\sin 2(\delta_S + kR) \qquad \text{(II. 3. 10)}$$

for P waves

$$\dot{\delta}_P > -R + \frac{1}{k^2R}[1 - \cos 2(\delta_P + kR)] - \frac{1}{2k}\sin 2(\delta_P + kR) \qquad \text{(II. 3. 11)}$$

Proof: Consider the local, spherically symmetric potential $V(r)$, which is sufficiently nonsingular at the origin (i. e., it behaves better than $1/r^2$ at the origin), and vanishes identically for $r \geq R > 0$. If the solution for the radial part is $\Phi(r)$, we define

$$u_\ell(r) = r\Phi_\ell(r) \tag{II. 3. 12}$$

and the Schroedinger equation has the form

$$-u'' + \left[V + \frac{\ell(\ell+1)}{r^2} - k^2\right] u_\ell = 0, \quad u' \equiv \frac{du}{dr} \tag{II. 3. 13}$$

We want a solution that vanishes at the origin as $r^{\ell+1}$. This solution can be written in the form

$$\varphi_\ell(k, r) = \frac{1}{2ik^{\ell+1}} \left[(-1)^\ell f_\ell(k) f_\ell(-k, r) - f_\ell(-k) f_\ell(k, r)\right] \tag{II. 3. 14}$$

where $f_\ell(k, r)$ satisfies the boundary conditions

$$f_\ell(k, r) = i^\ell e^{-ikr} \qquad r \geq R \tag{II. 3. 15}$$

and

$$\lim_{r \to 0} f_\ell(k, r) \sim \frac{1}{(kr)^\ell} \tag{II. 3. 16}$$

The function $f_\ell(k)$ is defined by

$$f_\ell(k) = \lim_{r \to 0} (kr)^\ell \frac{f_\ell(k, r)}{(2\ell - 1)!!}$$

$$(2\ell - 1)!! = (2\ell - 1)(2\ell - 3) \ldots 3.1 \tag{II. 3. 17}$$

From the boundary conditions and the reality of the differential equation, we have

$$f^*_\ell(k, r) = (-1)^\ell f_\ell(-k, r) \tag{II. 3. 18}$$

and therefore

$$f^*_\ell(k) = f_\ell(-k) \tag{II. 3. 19}$$

Asymptotically

$$\varphi_\ell(k, r) \sim \frac{1}{2(ik)^{\ell+1}} [f_\ell(k)e^{ikr} - (-1)^\ell f_\ell(-k)e^{-ikr}] \equiv$$

$$\equiv \Psi_\ell(k, r) \tag{II. 3. 20}$$

and the ℓ-th channel S matrix is the overlap between outgoing and incoming waves:

$$\mathfrak{S}_\ell(k) \equiv e^{2i\delta_\ell} = \frac{f_\ell(k)}{f_\ell(-k)} \tag{II. 3. 21}$$

Multiplication of the Schroedinger equation for $f_\ell(k, r)$ by $\varphi_\ell(k', r)$ and subtraction of the resulting expression from the Schroedinger equation for $\varphi_\ell(k', r)$, multiplied by $f_\ell(k, r)$ gives:

$$\frac{d}{dr} W[f_\ell(k, r), \varphi_\ell(k', r)] =$$

$$= (k^2 - k'^2) f_\ell(k, r)\, \varphi_\ell(k', r) \tag{II. 3. 22}$$

where the Wronskian of two functions g and h is defined by

$$W[g, h] = gh' - g'h \qquad \text{(II. 3. 23)}$$

Differentiating with respect to k' and then setting k = k' gives, after integration,

$$W[f_\ell(k, r), \dot{\varphi}_\ell(k, r)] =$$

$$= -2k \int_0^r f_\ell(k, r')\, \varphi_\ell(k, r')\, dr' \qquad \text{(II. 3. 24)}$$

where $\dot{\varphi} = d\varphi/dk$, and integrand is finite at 0.

Setting k = k' in Eq. (II. 3. 22) and integrating yields

$$W[f_\ell(k, r), \varphi_\ell(k, r)] = \text{const.} \qquad \text{(II. 3. 25)}$$

We evaluate the constant by resorting to the asymptotic condition and find

$$W[f_\ell(k, r), \varphi_\ell(k, r)] = \frac{f_\ell(k)}{k^\ell} \qquad \text{(II. 3. 26)}$$

Differentiating Eq. (II. 3. 26) with respect to k and using Eq. (II. 3. 24), we get

$$\dot{f}_\ell(k) = \frac{\ell f_\ell(k)}{k} + k^\ell W[f_\ell(k, r), \varphi_\ell(k, r)]$$

$$- 2k^{\ell+1} \int_0^r f_\ell(k, r')\, \varphi_\ell(k, r')\, dr' \qquad \text{(II. 3. 27)}$$

We note that

$$\dot{\delta}_{\ell} = \frac{1}{2i} \frac{d}{dk} \ln \mathcal{S}_{\ell} = \frac{1}{2i} \left[\frac{\dot{f}_{\ell}(k)}{f_{\ell}(k)} - \frac{\dot{f}_{\ell}(-k)}{f_{\ell}(-k)} \right] \tag{II. 3. 28}$$

We shall therefore evaluate:

$$\dot{f}_{\ell}(k) f_{\ell}(-k) - \dot{f}_{\ell}(-k) f_{\ell}(k) =$$

$$= k^{\ell} \left\{ W[\dot{f}_{+}, \varphi] \, f(-k) - (-1)^{\ell} W[\dot{f}_{-}, \varphi] \, f(k) \right\} -$$

$$- 2k^{\ell+1} \int_{0}^{r} f_{+} \varphi f(-k) - (-1)^{\ell} f_{-} \varphi f(k) \tag{II. 3. 29}$$

where we have defined $\varphi = \varphi(k, r)$, $f_{\pm} = f(\pm k, r)$ and have suppressed the subscripts ℓ.

The second term on the right-hand side is [multiply and divide by $-2ik^{\ell+1}$ and use Eq. (II. 3. 14)]

$$4ik^{2(\ell+1)} \int_{0}^{r} \varphi^{2}(k, r')\,dr' \tag{II. 3. 30}$$

The whole right-hand side of Eq. (II. 3. 29) is independent of r. Thus we can evaluate it for $r_0 \geq R$. The first term on the right-hand side then has a simple form. Note that in the asymptotic region

$$\dot{f}_{\ell}(\pm k, r) = \mp i(i)^{\ell} r e^{\mp ikr} \tag{II. 3. 31}$$

$$f'_{\ell}(\pm k, r) = \mp i(i)^{\ell} k e^{\mp ikr} \tag{II. 3. 32}$$

or

$$\dot{f}_{\pm} = \frac{r}{k} f'_{\pm} \tag{II. 3. 33}$$

The term in brackets in Eq. (II. 3. 29) thus reduces to

$$\{\ \}_{r_o} = W[\frac{r}{k}(f'_+ f(-k) - (-1)^\ell f'_- f(k)),\ \varphi]_{r_o}$$

$$= -2ik^{\ell+1} W[\frac{r}{k}\Psi',\ \Psi] \qquad \text{(II. 3. 34)}$$

Substitution of Eqs. (II. 3. 30) and (II. 3. 34) in Eq. (II. 3. 29) yields

$$\dot{\delta}_\ell = \frac{k^{2\ell}}{|f(k)|^2}\left[-W(r\Psi',\Psi)_{r_o} + 2k^2\int_0^{r_o}\varphi^2(k,r')dr'\right] \qquad \text{(II. 3. 35)}$$

Since the last term in Eq. (II. 3. 35) is positive, we have as our final result the inequality

$$\dot{\delta}_\ell > \frac{-k^{2\ell}}{|f(k)|^2} W[r\Psi',\Psi] \qquad r_o \geq R \qquad \text{(II. 3. 36)}$$

If Eq. (II. 3. 36) is evaluated for S states, for which

$$\frac{\Psi_S(k,r)}{|f(k)|} = \frac{1}{k}\sin(kr+\delta) \qquad \text{(II. 3. 37)}$$

the result for $r_0 = R$ is the previously quoted one, namely,

$$\dot{\delta}_S > -R + \frac{1}{2k}\sin 2(kR+\delta_S) \qquad \text{(II. 3. 10)}$$

The condition for P waves, Eq. (II. 3. 11) is obtained in a similar manner.

Now let us apply Wigner's theorem to the narrowness condition for a resonance. Since we are going to apply our results to field theory, R would be associated with the mass of the lightest particle responsible for the interaction. Then the potential concept can only be valid if $kR << 1$. If we take $k_{max} = 1/2R$ as the limit of validity of our expressions for field theory, we then have

$$k\dot{\delta}_S > -1 \qquad k \leq k_{max} \tag{II. 3. 38}$$

For $\dot{\delta} < 0$ we therefore obtain, if our resonance lies below k_{max},

$$|k_0 \dot{\delta}_S(k_0)| < 1 \tag{II. 3. 39}$$

which violates our narrowness condition. Thus, at least for the present case, condition (II. 3. 4) must be satisfied for a narrow resonance. In what follows, we shall assume that this is so in general.

In conclusion, we remark that an interesting light is shed by the preceding analysis on the physical significance of a resonance, at least for S waves. To show this we rewrite Eq. (II. 3. 35) in a somewhat different form by noting that

$$W[r\Psi', \Psi] = r(\Psi'^2 - \Psi''\Psi) - \Psi'\Psi = r(\Psi'^2 + k^2\Psi^2) - \Psi'\Psi$$

or

$$\frac{d}{dr} W[r\Psi', \Psi] = 2k^2\Psi^2 \tag{II. 3. 40}$$

Thus Eq. (II. 3. 35) can be written for S waves as

$$\dot{\delta}_S(k) = \frac{2k^2}{|f(k)|^2} \int_0^\infty [\varphi^2(k, r') - \Psi^2(k, r')]\, dr' + \frac{\sin 2\delta_S(k)}{2k} \tag{II. 3. 41}$$

Equations (II. 3. 4) and (II. 3. 6a) imply that $\delta_S(k_0)$ is large and positive at a resonance. This fact in turn implies that the integrand in Eq. (II. 3. 41) is large and positive. This requirement has a simple physical meaning: At a resonance, the probability is large that the particle will be found inside the region of interaction. This simple-minded argument can be carried out only for S waves, since for P and higher waves Ψ has a singularity at the origin.

References:

1. Wigner, Phys. Rev., 98, 145 (1955).
2. Lüders, Z. Naturforsch., 10a, 581 (1955).
3. Newton, Jour. Math. Phys., 1, 319 (1960).

4. Parametrization of the Many-Channel S Matrix -- Multichannel Resonances

We turn once more to the multichannel case. Recall that we restricted our analysis to the case where there were two particles in each channel. This is not an academic problem. Examples of such coupled systems include:

Real cases:

$$\begin{pmatrix} \pi N \\ \gamma N \end{pmatrix} \quad \begin{pmatrix} \bar{K}N \\ \Lambda\pi \\ \Sigma\pi \end{pmatrix}$$

Slightly artificial cases:

$$\begin{pmatrix} \pi N \\ \pi N^* \\ \rho N \end{pmatrix} \quad \begin{pmatrix} \pi\pi \\ \rho\rho \\ \pi\eta \end{pmatrix}$$

We first tackle the problem of parametrization in the multichannel case. Our starting point is Eq. (II. 2. 25). We shall assume that the analysis is carried out at an energy for which all channels are open.

Under Wigner time reversal, we have

$$T_W \,|J, m, \chi\rangle = \langle J, -m, \chi| \tag{II. 4. 1}$$

If the interactions are time-reversal invariant, so is S (that is, $T_W^{-1} S T_W = S$) and therefore so is $\mathbb{K}$. Suppressing unnecessary indices wherever possible, we have

$$\langle \chi | \mathbb{K}_J^{-1} | \chi' \rangle = \langle Jm\chi | \mathbb{K}_J^{-1} | Jm\chi' \rangle$$

$$= \langle Jm\chi | T_W^{-1} \underbrace{T_W \mathbb{K}_J^{-1} T_W^{-1}}_{\mathbb{K}_J^{-1}} T_W | Jm\chi' \rangle$$

$$= \langle Jm\chi' | \mathbb{K}_J^{-1} | Jm\chi \rangle = \langle \chi' | \mathbb{K}_J^{-1} | \chi \rangle \qquad \text{(II. 4. 2)}$$

Thus $\mathbb{K}_J^{-1}$ is symmetric, as well as real. It can therefore be diagonalized by an orthogonal transformation. It follows from Eq. (II. 2. 25) that $\mathbb{T}_J^{-1}$, and therefore $\mathbb{T}_J$, is diagonalized by the same transformation. Finally, defining the S matrix for angular momentum J as

$$\mathbb{S}_J = 1 + 2i\mathbb{T}_J \qquad \text{(II. 4. 3)}$$

$\mathbb{S}_J$ is also diagonalized by the same transformation.

To simplify matters, let us think of the two-particle channels $|\varphi\rangle$ and $|\xi\rangle$, and let $|\Psi_1\rangle$ and $|\Psi_2\rangle$ be the states that diagonalize the $\mathbb{S}_J$ matrix. $|\Psi_1\rangle$ and $|\Psi_2\rangle$ will be some orthonormal linear combinations of the states $|\varphi\rangle$ and $|\xi\rangle$; in other words, we shall have a rotation of the basis vectors in two dimensions:

$$|\Psi_1\rangle = \cos\eta |\varphi\rangle + \sin\eta |\xi\rangle$$
$$\qquad \text{(II. 4. 4)}$$
$$|\Psi_2\rangle = -\sin\eta |\varphi\rangle + \cos\eta |\xi\rangle$$

where η is real. We shall also suppress subscript J. For a matrix $\mathbb{M}$ where $\mathbb{M}$ is any of $\mathbb{S}, \mathbb{T}, \mathbb{K}$, or their inverse, we can write

$$\mathbb{M} = \tilde{u}\mu u \qquad \text{(II. 4. 5)}$$

where

$$\mu = \begin{pmatrix} m_1 & 0 \\ 0 & m_2 \end{pmatrix} \qquad \text{(II. 4. 6)}$$

and

$$u = \begin{pmatrix} \cos\eta & \sin\eta \\ -\sin\eta & \cos\eta \end{pmatrix} \qquad \text{(II. 4. 7)}$$

Explicitly,

$$\mathbb{M} = \begin{pmatrix} \cos^2\eta m_1 + \sin^2\eta m_2 & \sin\eta\cos\eta(m_1 - m_2) \\ \sin\eta\cos\eta(m_1 - m_2) & \sin^2\eta m_1 + \cos^2\eta m_2 \end{pmatrix}$$

(II. 4. 8)

The natural parametrization can again be accomplished in terms of the $\mathbb{K}^{-1}$ matrix:

$$\kappa^{-1} = \begin{pmatrix} \kappa_1^{-1} & 0 \\ 0 & \kappa_2^{-1} \end{pmatrix} \quad \text{where } \kappa_j^{-1} = \cot\delta_j, \text{ and } j = 1, 2 \qquad \text{(II. 4. 9)}$$

The δ_J are the eigenphase shifts and are real; a third real parameter, η, characterizing the mixture of eigenstates that give the physical states, is also necessary. The corresponding diagonal S matrix is

$$\sigma = \begin{pmatrix} \sigma_1 & 0 \\ 0 & \sigma_2 \end{pmatrix} \qquad \sigma_J = e^{2i\delta_j} \text{ and } j = 1, 2 \qquad \text{(II. 4. 10)}$$

We are now ready to generalize the definition of a resonance to multichannel cases. The important point is that we expect intuitively that the incoming system will determine whether a resonance exists or not. That is, at the right energy a compound system is formed (in nuclear physics -- compound nucleus), which can then decay into various channels. Thus, on the basis of our physical intuition, we get the following important principle: At a resonance, all channels should show a characteristic resonant behavior.

We shall show that a sufficient condition for such behavior is that one of the eigenphases, say δ_1, should resonate. In addition, we shall attach the condition provided by Wigner's theorem. Both may be summarized by saying that, in the neighborhood of the resonance,

$$\tan \delta_1 = \frac{\frac{1}{2}\Gamma}{E_r - E} \qquad \text{(II. 4. 11)}$$

and Γ is a slowly varying function of E.

By this choice of resonance condition, we assure that we go over to the proper one-channel condition, as we let the channel coupling η go to zero.

It remains to identify the coefficient η near resonance. We take

$$\cos^2\eta = \frac{\Gamma_\varphi}{\Gamma} \qquad \sin^2\eta = \frac{\Gamma_\xi}{\Gamma} \qquad \Gamma = \Gamma_\varphi + \Gamma_\xi \qquad \text{(II. 4. 12)}$$

Γ_φ and Γ_ξ are both assumed to be slowly varying functions of the energy near resonance. As we shall see, Γ_φ, Γ_ξ and Γ play the role of partial and total widths, respectively, at resonance.

Typical $\mathbb{K}$ matrix elements near resonance are given by

$$\mathbb{K}_{\varphi\varphi} = \frac{\frac{1}{2}\Gamma_\varphi}{E_r - E} + V_{\varphi\varphi} \qquad \mathbb{K}_{\varphi\xi} = \frac{\frac{1}{2}\sqrt{\Gamma_\varphi \Gamma_\xi}}{E_r - E} + V_{\varphi\xi} \qquad \text{(II. 4. 13)}$$

where $V_{\varphi\varphi}$ and $V_{\varphi\xi}$ are nonresonant; in the Breit-Wigner theory these elements are called "potential scattering" terms.

The cross sections near resonance -- neglecting potential scattering -- are typically:

$$\sigma_{\varphi\varphi} = \frac{\pi}{k_\varphi^2} \frac{\Gamma_\varphi^2}{(E_r - E)^2 + \frac{1}{4}\Gamma^2} \quad \text{elastic } \varphi \text{ channel} \qquad \text{(II. 4. 14)}$$

and

$$\sigma_{\varphi\xi} = \frac{\pi}{k_\varphi^2} \frac{\Gamma_\varphi \Gamma_\xi}{(E_r - E)^2 + \frac{1}{4}\Gamma^2} \quad \varphi \to \xi \text{ reaction} \qquad \text{(II. 4. 15)}$$

These expressions are in agreement with the Breit-Wigner formalism.

Thus, our resonance criterion in terms of the eigenphase shift has turned out to be equivalent to the intuitive requirement that all channels show a resonance. For computational purposes, it is convenient to put this in terms of a simple criterion in terms of the various matrices $\mathbb{M}$ associated with scattering. For a single channel, many criteria could be used (limits are assumed approached from below):

$$\lim_{E \to E_r^-} \mathbb{K} \to +\infty \qquad \lim_{E \to E_r^-} \mathbb{K}^{-1} \to 0^+$$

$$\text{(II. 4. 16)}$$

$$\lim_{E \to E_r^-} \mathbb{S} \to -1 + i\epsilon \qquad \lim_{E \to E_r^-} \mathbb{T} \to i + \epsilon$$

The only criterion passing over simply to the multichannel case is the condition that every element of the $\mathbb{K}$ matrix be infinite at resonance. This is most simply put in the form

$$\det \mathbb{K}^{-1}(E_r) = \prod_j \cot \delta_j(E^-_r) = 0^+ \qquad \text{(II. 4. 17)}$$

The criterion of simultaneous resonance in all channels seems like a sensitive test of resonance in multichannel cases; in fact, it is characteristically observed in case of the (3, 3) π-N resonance, which is seen in both the π-N elastic and the photoproduction channels. However, another feature can complicate the observation of resonances in different channels: the branching ratio, characterized by the relative magnitudes of Γ_φ and Γ_ξ above. If Γ_ξ is small, the resonance in $\sigma_{\varphi\xi}$ may be not observed for purely experimental reasons. Thus, for $Y_1{}^*$, we should have both $\Lambda\pi$ and $\Sigma\pi$ decay modes; the fact that the $\Sigma\pi$ mode has not so far been definitely established could be due to the fact that the $Y_1{}^*$ is not a true resonance, or to the fact that $\Gamma_{\Sigma\pi}/\Gamma_{\Lambda\pi} << 1$. The latter assumption is generally made in dealing with this state.

For the sake of completeness, using our notation, we shall review some significant features of the π-N (3, 3) resonance. Because photoproduction is an e. m. process, we can make approximations based on perturbation theory, neglect corrections of order $e^2 = \alpha$ and take

$$\begin{aligned} \delta_1 &= \delta_\pi & \cos\eta &= 1 + O(e^2) \approx 1 \\ \delta_2 &= \delta_\gamma = O(e^2) \approx 0 & \sin\eta &= O(e) \approx \eta \end{aligned} \qquad \text{(II. 4. 18)}$$

In this approximation, the $\mathbb{T}$ matrix is given by

$$\mathbb{T} \cong \begin{array}{c} \\ \end{array} \begin{array}{cc} \pi N & \gamma N \end{array}$$

$$\mathbb{T} \cong \begin{pmatrix} e^{i\delta_\pi} \sin \delta_\pi & \eta e^{i\delta_\pi} \sin \delta_\pi \\ \eta e^{i\delta_\pi} \sin \delta_\pi & 0 \end{pmatrix} \begin{array}{c} \pi N \\ \gamma N \end{array} \qquad \text{(II. 4. 19)}$$

We see in Eq. (II. 4. 19) a characteristic of $\mathbb{T}$ stressed by Gell-Mann and Watson in their review article, namely, that the phase of the $\mathbb{T}$ matrix in photoproduction is the same as that for π-N scattering. Equation (II. 4. 19) also maintains a property not apparent from their analysis, -- that is, it exhibits the resonant behavior of all elements of the $\mathbb{T}$ matrix. We obtain Gell-Mann and Watson's form of $\mathbb{T}$ if we set

$$\eta \sin \delta_\pi = \gamma \cos \delta_\pi$$

For the sake of completeness, we shall review another parametrization used in the multichannel case. This parametrization involves the introduction of complex phase shifts and is basically an asymmetric way of characterizing reactions. We look at a given incident channel $|i\rangle$. Accessible to it are an outgoing channel $\langle i|$ and "inelastic" channels, states orthogonal to $\langle i|$. We are concerned only with describing the elastic scattering and the attenuation in $|i\rangle$. We introduce

$$\delta_{ii} = \Delta + i\rho \tag{II. 4. 20}$$

and define

$$X = e^{-2\rho} \tag{II. 4. 21}$$

$$Y = \cos 2\Delta \tag{II. 4. 21}$$

To derive the familiar relations in terms of complex phase shifts, we make contact with our previous description of reactions in terms of eigenphases. Illustrating with the two-channel case, with $|i\rangle = |1\rangle$, and in addition, another channel, $|2\rangle$, we can easily identify, by equating the (1 1) element of the S matrix

$$e^{2i\delta_{ii}} = \cos^2 \eta \, e^{2i\delta_1} + \sin^2 \eta \, e^{2i\delta_2} \tag{II. 4. 22}$$

$$X = \left\{1 - [\sin 2\eta \sin (\delta_1 - \delta_2)]^2\right\}^{\frac{1}{2}} \tag{II. 4. 23}$$

$$Y = \frac{1}{X}[\cos(\delta_1 + \delta_2)\cos(\delta_1 - \delta_2)$$

$$- \cos 2\eta \sin(\delta_1 + \delta_2)\sin(\delta_1 - \delta_2)] \qquad \text{(II. 4. 24)}$$

As expected, we have $0 \leq X \leq 1$, corresponding to $\rho \geq 0$, and $X \to 1$ when $\eta \to 0$, that is, when the coupling vanishes. Using our previous definitions for σ and substituting expressions (II. 4. 23) and (II. 4. 24) for X and Y, we have

$$\sigma_{e\ell} \equiv \sigma_{11} = \frac{4\pi}{k_1^2}|t_{11}|^2 = \frac{\pi}{k_1^2}(X^2 - 2XY + 1) \qquad \text{(II. 4. 25)}$$

$$\sigma_{in} \equiv \sigma_{12} = \frac{4\pi}{k_1^2}|t_{12}|^2 = \frac{\pi}{k_1^2}(1 - X^2) \qquad \text{(II. 4. 26)}$$

$$\sigma_{tot} \equiv \sigma_{in} + \sigma_{e\ell} = \frac{2\pi}{k_1^2}(1 - XY) \qquad \text{(II. 4. 27)}$$

The optical theorem can be seen to follow rather simply:

$$\text{Im}\,\mathbb{T}_{11} = \tfrac{1}{2}(1 - XY) \equiv \frac{k_1^2}{4\pi}\sigma_{tot} \qquad \text{(II. 4. 28)}$$

The unitarity limit for elastic scattering is the maximum of $|t_{11}|^2$ for fixed X. It occurs when Y = -1 and gives a value of $|t_{11}|^2$:

$$|t_{11}|^2_{max} = \frac{1}{4}(1 + X)^2 \qquad \text{(II. 4. 29)}$$

The maximum value of the magnitude of the inelastic amplitude occurs for X = 0 and is

$$|t_{12}|^2_{max} = \frac{1}{4}$$

When X = 0, independent of Y, we have

$$\sigma_{e\ell}(X = 0) = \sigma_{in}(X = 0) = \frac{\pi}{k_1^2} \qquad \text{(II. 4. 30)}$$

This parametrization of the scattering is not as convenient for describing a resonance as eigenphases are. We shall have occasion to make use of it later, however, in discussing the Ball-Frazer mechanism for accounting for peaks in some cross sections.

References:

1. Blatt and Weisskopf, Theoretical Nuclear Physics, Wiley, New York, 1952, Chaps. 8 and 10.
2. Dalitz, Rev. Mod. Phys., 33, 471 (1961).
3. Wali, Fulton, and Feldman, Phys. Rev. Letters, 6, 644 (1961).
4. Feldman, Fulton, and Wali, Effective Range Theory for Scattering in States of Strangeness ±1 (unpublished).
5. Gell-Mann and Watson, Ann. Rev. Nuclear Sci., 4, 219 (1954).

5. Complex Scattering Lengths and Cusps

Another simple consequence of a multichannel S matrix is the existence of complex scattering lengths. Consider Eq. (II. 2. 25) and single out a particular channel, say (11). We can write (using $\mathfrak{T}$, not $\mathbb{T}$, since we are interested in the scattering length -- expanding the analogue of k cot δ, not cot δ),

$$\mathfrak{T}^{-1} = \begin{pmatrix} c - ik_1 & \tilde{\vec{B}} \\ \vec{B} & \underset{\approx}{t}^{-1} \end{pmatrix} \qquad \text{(II. 5. 1)}$$

If $\mathfrak{T}^{-1}$ is an $n \times n$ matrix, $\vec{B}$ is an (n - 1) dimensional column vector and $\underset{\approx}{t}^{-1}$ is an $(n - 1) \times (n - 1)$ symmetric matrix of the form

$$\underset{\approx}{t}^{-1} = \underset{\approx}{\kappa}^{-1} - i\underset{\approx}{\rho} \qquad \text{(II. 5. 1)}$$

where $\underset{\approx}{\kappa}^{-1}$ is real and symmetric and

$$\underset{\approx}{\rho} = \begin{pmatrix} k_2 & 0 & & \\ 0 & k_3 & & \\ & & \cdot & \\ & & & \cdot \\ & & & & \cdot \end{pmatrix} \qquad \text{(II. 5. 3)}$$

ρ is a diagonal matrix involving the relative momenta of all channels except (11). Inverting, we have

$$\mathfrak{T} = \frac{1}{D}\begin{pmatrix} 1 & -\tilde{\vec{B}}\cdot\underset{\approx}{t} \\ -\underset{\approx}{t}\cdot\vec{B} & \underset{\approx}{\Sigma} \end{pmatrix} \qquad \text{(II. 5. 3)}$$

where $\underset{\approx}{\Sigma}$ is some matrix of no interest at the moment, $\vec{B}$ is a column, and $\tilde{\vec{B}}$ a row vector.

D is defined by

$$D = (c - ik_1) - \tilde{\vec{B}}\cdot\underset{\approx}{t}\cdot\vec{B} = \frac{\det \mathfrak{T}^{-1}}{\det t^{-1}} \qquad \text{(II. 5. 4)}$$

<u>Proof:</u> $\det \mathfrak{T}^{-1} = (c - ik_1) \det t^{-1} - B_i B_j \operatorname{cof} t_{ij}^{-1}$

$$= (c - ik_1) \det t^{-1} - \det t^{-1}\, \tilde{\vec{B}}\cdot\underset{\approx}{t}\cdot\vec{B}$$

[Q. E. D.]

We shall use Dalitz's sign convention, namely, for one channel, scattering length "a" is defined by

$$k \cot \delta = \frac{1}{a} + \tfrac{1}{2} r_o k^2 + \dots \tag{II. 5. 5}$$

(Recall that, for nucleon-nucleon scattering, the customary definition is

$$k \cot \delta = - \frac{1}{a} + \dots)$$

If we consider the (11) elastic channel only, we can define

$$\frac{1}{A} = (c - \widetilde{\vec{B}} \cdot \underset{\approx}{t} \cdot \vec{B})_o \tag{II. 5. 6}$$

where $(\quad)_o$ means that all quantities are evaluated at threshold for the (11) channel. Equation (II. 5. 6) has been applied recently to the analysis of $\overline{K}N$ scattering lengths. For $\overline{K}N$ scattering in the T = 0 state, there are two channels: $(\overline{K}N)$, $(\Sigma\pi)$; in the T = 1 state, there are three: $(\overline{K}N)$, $(\Sigma\pi)$, $(\Lambda\pi)$. In particular, for the two-channel case, $\vec{B}$ and $\underset{\approx}{t}^{-1}$ are numbers:

$$t^{-1} = d - ik_{\Sigma\pi} \qquad B = b \tag{II. 5. 7}$$

$$\frac{1}{A^{(o)}_{\overline{K}N}} = c - \frac{b^2}{d - ik_{\Sigma\pi}} \Bigg|_{\left(k_{\overline{K}N}\right) = 0} \tag{II. 5. 8}$$

$$\sigma^{(o)}_{\overline{K}N} = 4\pi \left| A^{(o)}_{\overline{K}N} \right|^2 \tag{II. 5. 9}$$

Since c, b, and d are real, $A^{(o)}_{\overline{K}N}$ is clearly complex.

We turn now to a brief discussion of cusps. They will occur in various physical observables for a given reaction -- the cross section and polarization, for example. They are discontinuities in the first derivative (of the function representing the observable) with respect to energy at the threshold energy for a competing channel.

In order to proceed, we need a statement of analyticity. We shall treat this statement as an assumption, if you wish, a fundamental postulate. The scattering amplitude T_P can be expressed, in general, in terms of a sum of invariant form factors (functions of scalars under Lorentz transformation constructed from the 4-momenta) multiplied by explicit expressions depending on spin and isotopic spin. The Mandelstam assumption is that these form factors are analytic functions of their variables (which for scattering are the total energy squared and the square of the momentum transfer), except for cuts and poles for real values of these variables. Furthermore, the discontinuity across these cuts is twice the imaginary part of the form factor. In terms of the angular momentum J component of the scattering amplitude, the postulate is equivalent to the statement that $\mathcal{T}_J$ (<u>not</u> $\mathbb{T}_J$) is an analytic function of the energy, with cuts and poles for real energy, and discontinuities in the imaginary part of $\mathcal{T}_J$ across cuts. Since this is not a review of dispersion theory, these statements will be taken for granted. Even if we had time, we could produce only partial proofs -- analyticity for forward scattering, or for potential scattering, or to suitable order of perturbation theory only. No general proof of the validity of the Mandelstam representation exists at present.

If one forgets about poles for the moment, it is clear that $\mathcal{T}_J^{-1}$ will have the same cuts as $\mathcal{T}_J$. Suppressing J, we write

$$\mathcal{T}^{-1} = \mathcal{K}^{-1} - ik \qquad \text{(II. 5. 10)}$$

It follows from the symmetry of $\mathcal{T}$ and the above unitarity condition that $\mathcal{K}^{-1}$ is an analytic function of E near the physical thresholds for the various processes. In other words, we can write

$$\mathcal{K}^{-1}(E) = \mathcal{K}^{-1}(E_o) + E\left[\frac{d}{dE}\mathcal{K}^{-1}(E)\right]_{E_o} + \cdots \qquad \text{(II. 5. 11)}$$

The analytic continuation of $\mathcal{K}^{-1}$ below threshold is therefore trivial.

The analytic continuation of a particular channel momentum k_j below threshold can be easily carried out, too. As we go below threshold, k_j becomes imaginary:

$$k_j \to \pm i |k_j| \tag{II. 5. 12}$$

In order to determine which branch of k_j to choose, we note that k_j above threshold is associated with an outgoing wave, and below threshold must be exponentially damped -- that is, above threshold the amplitude goes asymptotically as $e^{ik_j r}$. To get damping asymptotically, we must therefore choose the positive sign in Eq. (II. 5. 12).

We may also note that the cut is no longer present below threshold; that is, all $\mathcal{T}$ matrix elements connecting to a state below threshold are real. Of course, in the cross sections, energy conservation conditions are also appended, together with the assumption that we have real particles with energies $\omega_j \geq m_j$. Thus, the elements of the $\mathcal{T}$ matrix connecting to and from states below threshold are of no interest.

We shall now obtain the relevant $\mathcal{T}$ matrix below but near the threshold for one of the channels in terms of the $\mathcal{T}$ matrix above but near the threshold, by means of analytic continuation, and show that a cusp will arise in the cross section.

Consider $\mathcal{T}^{-1}$ as given by Eq. (II. 5. 1), with $\underset{\approx}{t}^{-1}$ as defined in Eq. (II. 5. 2). Assuming that we are near threshold for channel (1), c and the elements of B and γ^{-1} are all real and constant to $O(E_1)$.

Analytic continuation requires that we change $c - ik_1 \to c + |k_1|$ when we go below threshold. Everything else remains as it was above threshold.

The truncated $\mathcal{T}$ matrix, $\mathcal{T}_{tr}$, which relates the still-open channels below the threshold of channel (1), is an $(n - 1) \times (n - 1)$ matrix of the form

$$\mathcal{T}_{tr} = \frac{\underset{\approx}{\Sigma}'}{D'} \tag{II. 5. 13}$$

The primes are appended to signify the replacement $-ik_1 \to |k_1|$ as we go below threshold whenever k_1 occurs in Σ and D.

Now we must be more explicit about Σ. The condition that $\mathfrak{T}$ be the inverse of $\mathfrak{T}^{-1}$ requires that Σ be a symmetric matrix and satisfy the equations

$$[\Sigma - (c - ik_1)t] \cdot \vec{B} = 0 \qquad (II.5.14)$$

$$t^{-1}\Sigma - \vec{B}\tilde{\vec{B}} \cdot t = 1D \qquad (II.5.15)$$

We have used dyadic notation in Eq. (II.5.15); that is, we define

$$(\vec{B}\tilde{\vec{B}} \cdot t)_{mn} = \sum_{\ell} B_m B_\ell t_{\ell n} \qquad (II.5.16)$$

Again in dyadic notation, one can easily show that

$$\Sigma = tD + (t \cdot \vec{B})(\tilde{\vec{B}} \cdot t) \qquad (II.5.17)$$

so that the $\mathfrak{T}$ matrix of interest can be written

$$\mathfrak{T}_{tr} = t + \frac{1}{D'}(t \cdot \vec{B})(\tilde{\vec{B}} \cdot t) \qquad (II.5.18)$$

As a special example, consider the case where $\mathfrak{T}$ is a 2×2 matrix, with parameters as defined before. The truncated matrix now refers to only a single open channel and is a number

$$\mathfrak{T}_{tr} = \frac{c + |k_1|}{(c + |k_1|)(d - ik_2) - b^2} \qquad (II.5.19)$$

We can further observe that, in general, inversion of Eq. (II. 5. 18) gives

$$\mathcal{T}^{-1}_{tr} = \underset{\approx}{t}^{-1} - \frac{1}{c + |k_1|} \vec{B}\,\tilde{\vec{B}} \qquad \text{(II. 5. 20)}$$

Since the second term is a real matrix, we get

$$\text{Im}\, \mathcal{T}^{-1}_{tr} = \text{Im}\, t^{-1} \qquad \text{(II. 5. 21)}$$

and $\mathcal{T}_{tr}$ is in fact unitary, as it ought to be.

One final identity that will be useful later is

$$\det \mathcal{K}^{-1}_{tr} = \det \kappa^{-1} - \frac{1}{c + |k_1|} B_i B_j \,\text{cof}\, \kappa^{-1}_{ij}$$

$$= \det \kappa^{-1} \left(1 - \frac{1}{c + |k_1|} \tilde{\vec{B}} \cdot \kappa \cdot \vec{B}\right)$$

or

$$(c + |k_1|) \det \mathcal{K}^{-1}_{tr} = \det \mathcal{K}'^{-1} \qquad \text{(II. 5. 22)}$$

Consider now the scattering amplitude $T_{\ell m}$, where neither ℓ nor m refers to channel (1), at an energy slightly above threshold. We can expand 1/D [cf. Eq. (II. 5. 4)] near threshold:

$$\frac{1}{D} \cong \frac{1}{D_o - ik_1} \approx \frac{1}{D_o} + \frac{ik_1}{D_o^2} \qquad \text{(II. 5. 23)}$$

From the expression for $\mathcal{T}$, Eq. (II. 5. 3), we have immediately:

$$\mathfrak{T}_{\ell m} \cong \mathfrak{T}^{\circ}_{\ell m} + \frac{ik_1}{D_o^2} (\underset{\approx}{t}^{\circ} \cdot \vec{B})_{\ell} (\widetilde{\vec{B}} \cdot \underset{\approx}{t}^{\circ})_m$$

$$= \mathfrak{T}^{\circ}_{\ell m} + \mathfrak{T}^{\circ}_{\ell 1} ik_1 \mathfrak{T}^{\circ}_{1m} \qquad 1, m \neq 1 \tag{II. 5. 24}$$

That is, near threshold the transition takes place either directly from ℓ to m or via the intermediate state (1) (ik_1 is a density-of-states factor). For the sake of simplicity, write $\mathfrak{T}_{\ell m} \equiv f$. Then, using the analytic continuation rule $ik_1 \to |k_1|$, we have

$$f = \begin{cases} f_o + ik_1 g_o & \text{above threshold} \\ f_o - |k_1| g_o & \text{below threshold} \end{cases} \tag{II. 5. 25}$$

We then have, to order $|k_1|$,

$$\frac{k_\ell}{8\pi k_m} (\sigma_{\ell m} - \sigma^o_{\ell m}) \cong \begin{cases} k_1 \operatorname{Im} g^*_o f_o & \text{above threshold} \\ -|k_1| \operatorname{Re} g^*_o f_o & \text{below threshold} \end{cases} \tag{II. 5. 26}$$

Since the coefficients of k_1 and $|k_1|$ will not in general be the same, there will be a discontinuity in the first derivative at threshold.

Cusps have been observed in some nuclear reactions and, recently, in the process

$$\pi^- + p \to \Lambda + K \tag{II. 5. 27}$$

near the ΣK threshold. The experiments were done in the hope of determining the relative parity of the Λ and Σ. Near threshold, the ΣK system will be in the $S_{1/2}$ state. The cusp in reaction (II. 5. 27) occurs in both the differential cross section and the polarization distribution of the Λ, and must clearly appear in the same total J and parity state as the $(\Sigma K)S_{1/2}$ state. Thus, if $P_{\Lambda\Sigma} = +1$, the cusp will occur in the $S_{1/2}K\Lambda$ state, while if $P_{\Lambda\Sigma}$ is odd, the cusp will occur in the $P_{1/2}K\Lambda$ state.

Efforts to determine $P_{\Lambda\Sigma}$ in this fashion have been somewhat inconclusive, since the number of partial waves present in ΛK scattering at the ΣK threshold is too large to allow for a clear-cut determination of the angular-momentum state in which the cusp occurs.

Another interesting conjecture, particularly in view of the extensive correspondence between thresholds for two-particle channels and the observed "resonances" (cf. Table 2), is the possibility that these bumps in the cross section labeled "resonances" are in fact cusps. Of course, a cusp can appear as

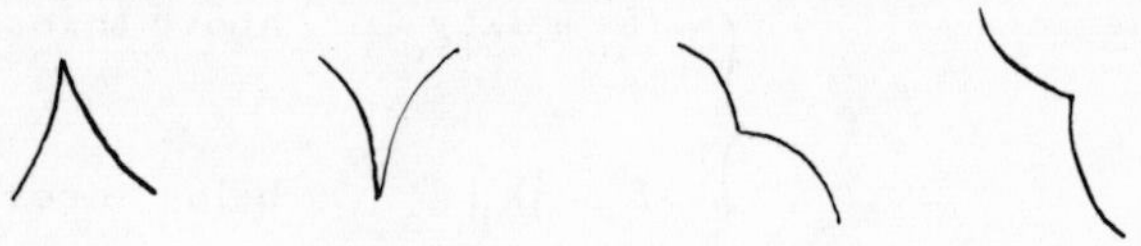

etc., and in only one of these cases do we get a bump that looks like a resonance. Another problem is the question of widths. Pais and Nauenberg have argued that if one or more of the "particles" in the two-particle channel at threshold is itself a resonance, one may expect the cusp to get rounded or "woolly," with a width at least of the order of the width of the resonance. The assumption that S-wave production at threshold predominates provides a severe limitation on the spins of the particles which could play a role in such a phenomenon. Thus, there can be a cusp in the $D_{3/2}$ state of πN scattering (corresponding to N^*_2) at the ξN threshold if ξ is 1^-, but not if it is 1^+ or has spin 0, and the $F_{5/2}\pi N$ peak (N^*_3) can be related to the $N\rho$ threshold only if there is a sizable P-wave production at this threshold.

References:

1. Dalitz, Revs. Modern Phys., 33, 471 (1961).
2. Matthews and Salam, Nuovo Cimento 13, 381 (1959).
3. Pais, CERN Seminars, 1961, p. 119 ff (CERN 61-30).
4. Wigner, Phys. Rev., 73, 1002 (1948).
5. Adair, Phys. Rev., 111, 632 (1958).
6. Nauenberg and Pais, Phys. Rev., 123, 1958 (1961).

III. APPLICATION OF DISPERSION THEORY TO RESONANCES AND RELATED PHENOMENA

1. Review of Dispersion Relations; Effective Range Theory and "Pology"

We shall discuss approximations to dispersion relations for elastic and inelastic two-particle processes. Our aim is to be somewhat more than descriptive. We hope to show how resonances can arise from spectral properties and to connect them to other measurable phenomena -- scattering lengths, for example.

As stated previously, we shall postulate the existence of dispersion relations; nonetheless, in this section some relevant aspects of dispersion theory will be reviewed in more detail than they were dealt with in our discussion of cusps. We shall begin by demanding that S and T satisfy: (1) unitarity, (2) Lorentz invariance, and (3) analyticity.

Perhaps a few comments on these three points are in order. We have already discussed the unitarity conditions briefly. As far as Lorentz invariance is concerned, the demand that S and T be Lorentz invariant can be shown to lead to the Lorentz invariance of T_P; in fact, T_P must be a scalar.

Let us turn next to the postulate of analyticity. Consider the following diagram representing a scattering process:

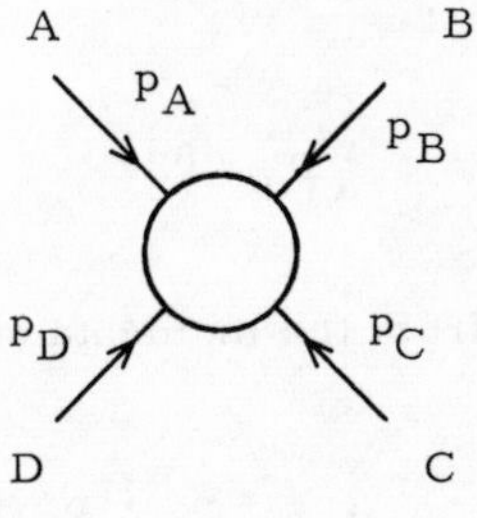

Fig.III.1

All the 4-momenta are chosen to be for incoming particles. The diagram above can refer to three scattering processes:

	Initial 4-momenta	Final 4-momenta
$A + B \leftrightarrow C + D$	$\pm (p_A, p_B)$	$\mp (p_C, p_D)$
$A + C \leftrightarrow B + D$	$\pm (p_A, p_C)$	$\mp (p_B, p_D)$
$A + D \leftrightarrow B + C$	$\pm (p_A, p_D)$	$\mp (p_B, p_C)$

(III. 1. 1)

where the top signs refer to the arrow going right, and the bottom signs the arrow going left, and the momenta of incoming particles have + signs in front.

The scattering amplitude can be expressed in terms of invariant form factors that are scalar functions of invariants constructed from the 4-momenta. All 4-momenta are taken on their mass shell; that is,

$$p_\alpha^2 = -m_\alpha^2 \qquad \alpha = A, B, C, D \tag{III. 1. 2}$$

and energy momentum is conserved:

$$\sum_\alpha p_\alpha = 0 \tag{III. 1. 3}$$

Invariants constructed from the momenta all have the form

$$A_{\alpha\beta} = p_\alpha \cdot p_\beta \tag{III. 1. 4}$$

There are ten such invariants for a scattering process. Since Eqs. (III. 1. 2) and (III. 1. 3) represent eight equations of constraint, one can consider two of the above invariants that are linearly independent as the variables describing the scattering process. It is not surprising that there are two such variables, since in the c. m. system, two variables E and θ completely characterize the scattering. A systematic definition of these variables is

$$s_1 \equiv s = -(p_A + p_B)^2$$

$$s_2 \equiv t = -(p_A + p_C)^2 \qquad \text{(III. 1. 5)}$$

$$s_3 \equiv u = -(p_A + p_D)^2$$

Since there are only two independent invariants, there is in fact a linear relationship among the three s_i:

$$\sum_{i=1}^{3} s_i = \sum_{\alpha=1}^{4} m_\alpha^2 \qquad \text{(III. 1. 6)}$$

If A and B are the incident particles, then s is the square of the c. m. energy and t the square of the c. m. momentum transfer; taking $m_A = m_B = m_C = m_D = M$, we have

$$s = 4(\underset{\sim}{q}^2 + M^2)$$

$$t = -2\underset{\sim}{q}^2(1 - \cos\theta) \qquad \text{(III. 1. 7)}$$

where $\underset{\sim}{q}$ is the c. m. momentum and θ is the angle between the incident A and outgoing C.

The Mandelstam analyticity conjecture can be summarized by the relation

$$A(s_1, s_2, s_3) = \sum_{i,\ell} \frac{g_{\ell i}^2}{s_i - m_{\ell i}^2}$$

$$+ \sum_{i \neq j} \int_{c_i}^{\infty} ds'_i \int_{c_j}^{\infty} ds'_j \frac{\rho_{ij}(s'_i s'_j)}{(s_i - s'_i)(s_j - s'_j)} \qquad \text{(III. 1. 8)}$$

where A is an invariant form factor, and $g^2_{\ell i}$ are residues of poles in s_i at $m^2_{\ell i}$ and are real constants. The c_i are positive constants. In general, the limit of integration is a curve in the s_i-s_j plane, asymptotic to c_i and c_j. A is real for real s_i, provided that we are not near cuts. The discontinuity in A across the cut is equal to twice the imaginary part of A.

The simple rule for obtaining the location of cuts and poles is to consider perturbation theory with renormalized masses and coupling constants. The singularities of the exact amplitude will have the same location as those of perturbation theory.

The important point is that A is a single analytic function, which is postulated to describe scattering processes where any one of the three s_i can be taken as the energy. Since it is analytic, it can also be continued for unphysical values of the variables -- that is, values which cannot occur in any real scattering process. This remark will have significance later, when we shall refer to extrapolation procedures from physical scattering to certain unphysical points.

Finally, one can obtain partial-wave dispersion relations for a given scattering process from the full amplitude by deciding on the variable one chooses to call the energy and then suitably projecting the relevant partial wave. Such a projection involves an integration over cos θ. For a spinless system, we require $\int_{-1}^{1} d(\cos\theta) \cdot P_\ell(\cos\theta)\, A(s_1, s_2, s_3)$. If spins are involved, such as in the π-N problem, the process is equally simple in principle but involves somewhat tedious mathematics.

Before writing down the general partial-wave dispersion relation, we shall illustrate the location of cuts and poles for the $^3S_1$ partial-wave neutron-proton scattering. Figure II. 2 sets forth the diagrams that can be used to describe N-P scattering.

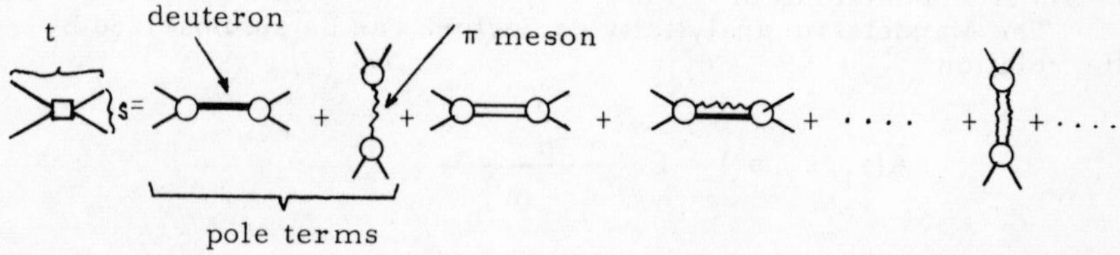

Fig. III. 2

Only diagrams with one or two particles in intermediate states have been drawn. The deuteron pole occurs only in the $^3S_1$ state. The variables are as defined in Eq. (III. 1. 7). (We have neglected the N-P mass difference.)

Consider the pole terms first. The deuteron pole is of the form $(\Gamma\delta_{J^\pi,1^+})/(s - M_D^2)$ in the total amplitude, where δ indicates that the term appears only in the $^3S_1$ state. In the $^3S_1$ partial wave, the amplitude is $\Gamma/(s - M_D^2)$. M_D is the mass of the deuteron and Γ a real constant. In terms of the c. m. momentum required (q^2) and the binding energy of the deuteron (ϵ), the pole will occur at

$$4(q^2 + M^2) \cong (2M - \epsilon)^2 \quad \text{or} \quad q^2 = -\epsilon(M - \frac{\epsilon}{4})$$
$$= -0.106 \qquad \text{(III. 1. 9)}$$

in units of the square of the π mass (μ^2).

The one-meson pole is of the form $G/(t - \mu^2)$, where G is a suitable invariant but where all the form factors appearing in G are in fact constants, since there are no free variables depending only on scalars made out of 4-momenta at a vertex where all three particles are on their mass shells. In the partial-wave amplitude this pole will turn into a cut. In fact,

$$A^{(1\ \text{meson})}_{^3S_1} = \frac{R}{2}\int_{-1}^{1} \frac{d(\cos\theta)}{-2q^2(1 - \cos\theta) - \mu^2}$$

$$= -\frac{R}{4q^2} \ln \frac{\mu^2 + 4q^2}{\mu^2} \qquad \text{(III. 1. 10)}$$

R is a numerical factor times g^2/M, where g is the π-N coupling constant. Thus the one-meson exchange term leads to a cut beginning at $q^2 = -1/4$ in units of μ^2.

For exchanges of more than one meson in momentum transfer, since $\cos\theta : -1 \to 1$ implies $t = -4q^2 \to 0$, we have cuts in the partial-wave amplitude beginning at

$$-4q^2 = (n\mu)^2 \qquad n \text{ integer} \qquad \text{(III. 1. 11)}$$

or at

$$q^2 = -\frac{1}{4}, -1, -\frac{9}{4}, \ldots \qquad \text{(III. 1. 12)}$$

For exchanges of two or more particles in the s channel, we have cuts in the total amplitude and at the same values of q^2 in the partial wave. Thus, for the deuteron, we have cuts beginning at

$$4(q^2 + M^2) = (2M)^2, (M_D + 1)^2, (2M + 1)^2, \ldots \qquad \text{(III. 1. 13)}$$

In other words, cuts begin at

$$q^2 = 0, (1 - \epsilon)\left[M - \frac{1}{4}(1 - \epsilon)\right], (M + \frac{1}{4}), \ldots \qquad \text{(III. 1. 14)}$$

These values of q^2 correspond to the thresholds for various physical processes: the first one being the threshold for elastic N-P scattering, and the subsequent ones being thresholds for various inelastic processes such as $N + P \to \pi + D$, $N + P \to N + N + \pi$, etc. We can thus represent the singularities of the $^3S_1$ partial-wave amplitude in terms of two cuts and one pole in the q^2 plane:

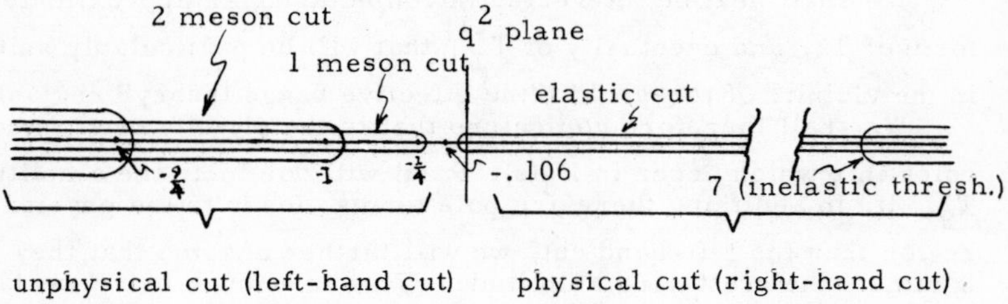

Fig. III. 3

There will in general be the same pattern of singularities; thus the Mandelstam representation will lead to the partial-wave dispersion relation for T_J:

$$T_J(s) = P_J(s) + \frac{1}{\pi}\int_L \frac{\operatorname{Im} T_J(s')\ ds'}{s' - s} + \frac{1}{\pi}\int_R \frac{\operatorname{Im} T_J(s')\ ds'}{s' - s} \qquad \text{(III. 1. 15)}$$

where the T_J can in general be matrices in channel space, the relationship between s and q^2 has been given previously, and $P_J(s)$ refer to any pole terms that may appear due to one-particle intermediate states in the dispersion diagrams. Since $P_J(s)$ arise from perturbation theory and time-reversal invariance holds, they will naturally be symmetric matrices. The integrals are over the unphysical (left L) and physical (right R) cuts, respectively, and the right-hand cut begins at the lowest physical threshold. The physical scattering amplitude is obtained by approaching the right-hand cut from above, that is, for $\lim_{\epsilon \to 0} s + i\epsilon$ with s real and above threshold.

If we restrict ourselves to two-particle channels only, on the right hand cut we can make use of the unitarity relation derived previously in Eq. (II. 2. 14) to get

$$\mathrm{Im}\, T_J = \frac{1}{2(4\pi)^2 E_T} T_J \, k \, T_J^+ \qquad \text{(III. 1. 16)}$$

We shall next be interested in conjecturing an approximate form of T_J, and eventually of T_J^{-1}, that will be particularly suitable in the vicinity of threshold ("the effective range theory" region).

We shall therefore conjecture that in the vicinity of s_B, the poles in s which occur in $P_J(s)$, $P_J(s)$ will dominate the amplitude T_J. If, in addition, there are pole terms closer to the physical region than the left-hand cut, we will further assume that they will dominate the scattering amplitude. This is a much more weakly based conjecture and tacitly assumes severe limits on the size and character of Im T_J on the left-hand cut: namely, that Im $T_J(s')$ is not too large for the effective s' which contribute significantly to the integrals and that $|s' - s| >> |s_B - s|$ for threshold s and effective contributing s'. For some applications of polology -- the Chew-Low approximation, for example -- we can relax the second conjecture by assuming only that, near threshold, the contribution of the left-hand cut does not vary rapidly with s and can be approximated by a constant. But in the effective range region, we shall completely neglect the left-hand cut if there are poles present

Now that we have taken such a large leap, we may as well continue to live dangerously and postulate a dispersion relation for the inverse amplitude. We can expect the inverse amplitude to have the same cuts as T_J. In addition, we can expect singularities to arise corresponding to zeros of T_J. These we shall ignore.(!!!)

We can summarize the requirements our approximation to T_J must satisfy by demanding that

1. $\mathrm{Im}\, T_J^{-1} = - \dfrac{k}{2(4\pi)^2 E_T}$

2. $T_J = \widetilde{T}_J$

3. $(T_J(s))_{if} = (P_J(s))_{if}$ in the neighborhood of the poles of $[P_J(s)]_{if}$

4. $(T_J(s))_{if} \sim k_i^{\ell} k_f^{\ell'}$ for small k_i and k_f, where ℓ and ℓ' are the orbital angular momenta of the initial and final states, respectively

The first two conditions are to satisfy the demands of unitarity and time-reversal invariance. The last two have to do with the short-range character of the interaction. Condition 4 is introduced to help eliminate spurious singularities in the T_J^{-1} dispersion relations, arising from zeros of T occurring because of the vanishing of partial waves for higher-than-zero orbital angular momentum. The assumption of analyticity, aside from the singularities implied by the list above, essentially represents a neglect of all but the longest-range interactions.

A dispersion relation that satisfies all our requirements can be written simply in terms of quantities with the low energy and momentum dependence projected out. With this aim in mind, we define Q, $\overline{T}$, and $\overline{P}$ by

$$Q_{mn} = k_m^{\ell_m} \delta_{mn}$$

$$T_J = Q\overline{T}_J Q \qquad \text{(III. 1. 17)}$$

$$P_J = Q\overline{P}_J Q$$

and postulate the dispersion relation

$$\overline{T}_J^{-1}(s) = \overline{P}_J^{-1}(s) + \frac{1}{\pi} \overline{P}_J^{-1}(s) \cdot$$

$$\int_R \frac{\overline{P}_J(s') \operatorname{Im} \overline{T}_J^{-1}(s') \overline{P}_J(s')}{s' - s} ds' \, \overline{P}_J^{-1}(s) \qquad \text{(III. 1. 18)}$$

We shall suppress the index J from now on.

To show that condition 3 is met, we prove first that if a single element of $\overline{P}$, say $\overline{P}_{ik}[s_B^{(ik)}]$, equals ∞, the i-th row and k-th column of $\overline{P}^{-1}[s_B^{(ik)}]$ vanishes. For example, $(\overline{P}^{-1})_{im}$, for m = 1, . . . , n, can be written

$$(\overline{P}^{-1})_{im} = \frac{(\text{cof } \overline{P})_{im}}{\det \overline{P}} \qquad \det \overline{P} \equiv \sum_{\ell} \overline{P}_{i\ell}(\text{cof } \overline{P})_{i\ell} \tag{III. 1. 19}$$

The cofactor of $\overline{P}_{im}$, namely, $(\text{cof } \overline{P})_{im}$, does not contain $\overline{P}_{ik}$ and so the numerator is finite and the denominator is infinite at $s = s_B^{(ik)}$. A similar argument holds for $\overline{P}^{-1}_{mk}$.

For the sake of simplicity, let us assume that

$$\overline{P}_{ik}(s) = \frac{R_{ik}(s)}{s - s_B^{(ik)}} \tag{III. 1. 20}$$

Use of the above lemma leads to

$$(\overline{T}^{-1})_{im} = [s - s_B^{(ik)}]\, M_{im}(s) \tag{III. 1. 21}$$

$$(\overline{T}^{-1})_{mk} = [s - s_B^{(ik)}]\, M_{mk}(s) \tag{III. 1. 22}$$

R_{ik}, M_{im}, and M_{mk} do not have zeros or poles at $s = s_B^{(ik)}$. Near $s = s_B^{(ik)}$,

$$(\overline{T}^{-1})_{ik} = (\overline{P}^{-1})_{ik} + O[s - s^{(ik)}]^2 \tag{III. 1. 23}$$

where

$$(\overline{P}^{-1})_{ik} \approx \frac{s - s_B^{(ik)}}{R_{ik}} \tag{III. 1. 24}$$

Thus, for $s \to s_B^{(ik)}$,

$$\overline{T}_{ik} = \frac{(\mathrm{cof}\ \overline{T}^{-1})_{ik}}{\det \overline{T}^{-1}} \tag{III. 1. 25}$$

But

$$\det \overline{T}^{-1} = (\overline{T}^{-1})_{ik}\ \mathrm{cof}\ (\overline{T}^{-1})_{ik} + O[s - s_B^{(ik)}]^2 \tag{III. 1. 26}$$

so that

$$\overline{T}_{ik} \approx P_{ik} \tag{III. 1. 27}$$

when $s \to s_B^{(ik)}$ as condition 3 requires.

Condition 2 is obviously satisfied by Eq. (III. 1. 18). Condition 4 is met, since $\overline{P}$ arises from Born approximation terms that necessarily satisfy this condition. Thus, at channel thresholds, $\overline{T}_J^{-1}$ is finite and the condition is satisfied.

The convenience of Eq. (III. 1. 18) lies in the simplicity of the first, unitarity condition. Since $\overline{P}$ is known, $\overline{T}^{-1}$ is easily calculable. An inconvenience of Eq. (III. 1. 18) is that the indicated integral is frequently divergent; however, since Eq. (III. 1. 18) is meant to apply to low energies only, a cutoff can certainly be introduced.

Use of Eq. (III. 1. 18) can be quite cumbersome. It is sufficient to meet conditions 1 - 4 but is not necessary. Simpler forms can sometimes be found which satisfy these four conditions for specific pole locations in $\overline{P}$ and are essentially of the same character as Eq. (III. 1. 18). We shall not discuss them further.

Finally, we remark that the Regge approach has no bearing on the above discussion. We are dealing here with a crude approximation in a limited energy range. The Regge approach is particularly useful if we consider the scattering amplitude over a wide energy range, particularly in the limit of large energies in crossed channels.

References:

1. Dispersion relations: There is an extensive literature. Perhaps a good starting point from which to obtain other references is the monograph by Chew: S-Matrix Theory of Strong Interactions, Benjamin, New York, 1961; elementary expositions of dispersion relations are also given by Jackson and Chew in their Edinburgh lectures: Scottish Universities' Summer School (1960), Interscience, New York.
2. Feldman, Matthews, and Salam, Nuovo Cimento, 16, 549 (1960).
3. Feldman, Fulton, and Wali, Effective Range Theory for Scattering in States of Strangeness ±1 (unpublished).

2. Two Simple Applications

a. N-P scattering in the $^3S_1$ state. The point of this illustration is to indicate the reasonable character of the approximations. We are dealing with a single channel here, and $\overline{T} = T$, $\overline{P} = P$. The variable q^2 is more convenient to use than s. Since we are interested in a non relativistic approximation, $E_T \approx 2M$ and can be removed from under the integrals. We can then just as well deal with $\mathfrak{T}$, and the corresponding $\mathfrak{P}$, rather than T and P, since they only differ by constant factors and since unitarity is simpler in terms of $\mathfrak{T}$ than T. Consistent with our approximations, we neglect the unphysical cut and consider only the pole due to the deuteron. That is,

$$\mathfrak{P} = \frac{\Gamma}{q^2 + \alpha^2} \quad \text{with } \alpha^2 = +0.106 \text{ in units of } \mu^2 \tag{III. 2. 1}$$

Equation (III. 1. 18) becomes

$$\mathfrak{T}^{-1}(q^2) = (q^2 + \alpha^2)\left[\frac{1}{\Gamma} - \frac{1}{\pi}(q^2 + \alpha^2) \cdot \int_0^\infty \frac{q'd(q'^2)}{(q'^2 + \alpha^2)^2(q'^2 - q^2 - i\epsilon)}\right] \tag{III. 2. 2}$$

The integration can easily be converted into a contour integral in q'. The result is

$$\mathcal{J}^{-1}(q^2) = (q^2 + \alpha^2)\left(\frac{1}{\Gamma} + \frac{1}{2\alpha}\right) - \alpha - iq \tag{III. 2. 3}$$

In terms of our previous parametrization, we have

$$q \cot \delta = (q^2 + \alpha^2)\left(\frac{1}{\Gamma} + \frac{1}{2\alpha}\right) - \alpha \tag{III. 2. 4}$$

This is of the effective range form

$$q \cot \delta = -\frac{1}{a} + \tfrac{1}{2} r_o q^2 \tag{III. 2. 5}$$

(We are now using the nuclear-physics, rather than the high-energy physics, sign convention for the scattering length.) In fact, the result is precisely effective range theory. To show this, we identify

$$\tfrac{1}{2} r_o = \frac{1}{\Gamma} + \frac{1}{2\alpha} \tag{III. 2. 6}$$

We can look upon this equation as defining Γ in terms of α and r_o. Substitution and further identification gives

$$-\frac{1}{a} = \tfrac{1}{2} r_o \alpha^2 - \alpha = -\frac{1}{R} + \tfrac{1}{2} r_o \frac{1}{R^2} \tag{III. 2. 7}$$

To obtain the standard effective range formula for N-P scattering, we have used the fact that, by definition, α is the inverse radius of the deuteron (cf. Blatt and Weisskopf, for example.)

b. π^+-P scattering and the (3, 3) resonance. This case will serve to illustrate how a typical one-channel resonance can be imagined as arising.

The pole term is given by the diagram of Fig. III. 4.

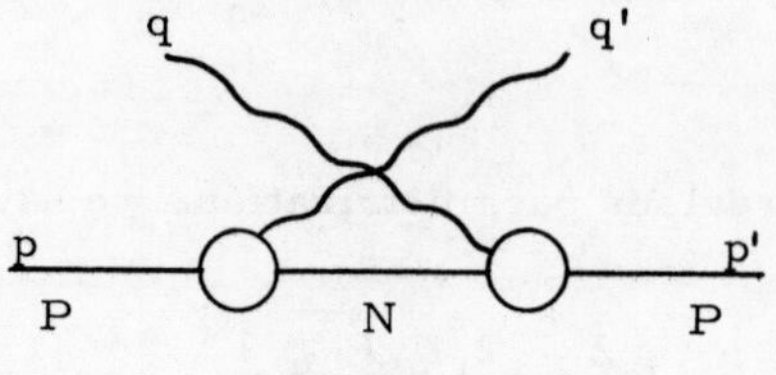

Fig. III. 4

giving a matrix element

$$T = -2g^2\bar{u}(p')\,\gamma_5\,\frac{M - i\gamma\cdot(p - q')}{(p - q')^2 + M^2}\,\gamma_5\,u(p)$$

$$= 2g^2\bar{u}(p')\,\frac{\frac{1}{2}i\gamma\cdot(q + q')}{(p - q')^2 + M^2}\,u(p) \qquad \text{(III. 2. 8)}$$

(note that g is normally defined as the coupling constant of π^o; then $\sqrt{2}g$ is the coupling to $\pi^{\pm}$) with u(p) satisfying the equation

$$(M + i\gamma\cdot p)\,u(p) = 0 \qquad \text{(III. 2. 9)}$$

and having the explicit form

$$u(p) = \sqrt{\frac{M + \epsilon}{2M}}\begin{pmatrix} 1 \\ \frac{\vec{\sigma}\cdot\vec{p}}{M + \epsilon}\end{pmatrix}\eta_i \qquad \text{(III. 2. 10)}$$

in terms of the two component spinors

$$\eta_1 = \begin{pmatrix} 1 \\ 0 \end{pmatrix} \quad \text{and} \quad \eta_2 = \begin{pmatrix} 0 \\ 1 \end{pmatrix} \qquad \text{(III. 2. 11)}$$

The mass M is the mass of the physical proton, and ϵ is the nucleon energy. In terms of the two-component spinors, in the c.m. coordinate frame the matrix element becomes

$$M = 4\pi\eta'(f_1 + f_2\, \sigma \cdot \hat{q}\, \sigma \cdot \hat{q}')\, \eta \tag{III. 2.12}$$

where

$$f_1 = \frac{-2g^2}{4\pi} \frac{(\epsilon + M)(W - M)}{4W(\epsilon\omega + q^2 \hat{q}' \cdot \hat{q} - \frac{\mu^2}{2})} \tag{III. 2.13}$$

$$f_2 = -\frac{2g^2}{4\pi} \frac{(\epsilon - M)(W + M)}{4W(\epsilon\omega + q^2 \hat{q} \cdot \hat{q}' - \frac{\mu^2}{2})} \tag{III. 2.14}$$

and ω and W are the pion and total c.m. energies, respectively. A simple calculation yields (see Sakurai, 1961 Brandeis Summer Institute Lectures, with a few additional trivial steps)

$$f_1 = \sum_{\ell=0}^{\infty} (f_\ell^+ P'_{\ell+1} - f_\ell^- P'_{\ell-1}) \tag{III. 2.15}$$

$$f_2 = \sum_{\ell=0}^{\infty} (f_\ell^- - f_\ell^+)\, P'_\ell \tag{III. 2.16}$$

In the above equations

$$P'_\ell(\cos\theta) = \frac{d}{d(\cos\theta)} P_\ell(\cos\theta) \tag{III. 2.17}$$

and the partial waves f_ℓ^+ are associated with total $J = \ell + \frac{1}{2}$, f_ℓ^- with $J = \ell - \frac{1}{2}$.

We need the inverse of Eqs. (III. 2.15) and (III. 2.16) -- that is, the projection of f_ℓ^+, f_ℓ^- from f_1 and f_2. One can easily confirm this to be (taking $z = \cos\theta$)

$$f_\ell^+ = \frac{1}{2}\int_{-1}^{1} [\, f_1(z) P_\ell(z) + f_2(z) P_{\ell+1}(z)]\, dz \qquad \text{for all } \ell \tag{III. 2. 18}$$

$$f_\ell^- = \frac{1}{2}\int_{-1}^{1} [\, f_1(z) P_\ell(z) + f_2(z) P_{\ell-1}(z)]\, dz \qquad \text{for } \ell \neq 0 \tag{III. 2. 19}$$

In the low-energy limit,

$$f_1 \approx - \frac{g^2}{4\pi} \; \frac{1}{M} \left(1 - \frac{q^2 z}{M\omega} + \ldots\right) \tag{III. 2. 20}$$

$$f_2 \approx - \frac{g^2}{4\pi} \; \frac{q^2}{2M^2\omega} \left(1 - \frac{q^2 z}{M\omega} + \frac{q^4 z^2}{M^2 \omega^2} + \ldots\right) \tag{III. 2. 21}$$

so that

$$f_o^+ \cong -4Mf^2 \tag{III. 2. 22}$$

$$f_1^- \cong - \frac{2}{3} f^2 \, \frac{q^2}{\omega} \tag{III. 2. 23}$$

$$f_1^+ \cong \frac{4}{3} f^2 \, \frac{q^2}{\omega} \tag{III. 2. 24}$$

where

$$f^2 = \frac{g^2}{4\pi} \; \frac{1}{4M^2} = 0.08 \tag{III. 2. 25}$$

Once again we use the nonrelativistic approximations to Eq. (III. 1 . 18), $[s \cong M^2 + \mu^2 + 2M\omega]$, and further note that $q^2 \overline{\mathcal{T}}_{\frac{3}{2}} = \mathcal{T}_{\frac{3}{2}}$ so that we have for the $P_{3/2}$ state

$$\mathrm{Re}\, \overline{\mathcal{T}}_{\frac{3}{2}}^{-1} = q^3 (\cot \delta_{33} - i) \tag{III. 2. 26}$$

and the dispersion relation can be written in terms of ω:

$$q^3 \cot \delta_{33} = \frac{1}{\frac{4}{3} f^2}\, \omega - \frac{\omega^2}{\pi} \mathrm{P.V.} \int_{\mu}^{C} \frac{q'^3}{\omega'^2 (\omega' - \omega)}\, d\omega' \tag{III. 2. 27}$$

A cutoff, C, is now necessary, since the integral is diverent. The expression above is just the familiar Chew-Low expression for the (3, 3) resonance, neglecting crossing (which has to do with the neglect of the left-hand cut). It can be written in the form

$$\frac{4}{3} f^2 \frac{q^3}{\omega} \cot \delta_{33} = 1 - \frac{\omega}{\omega_r} \tag{III. 2. 28}$$

Comments:

Equation (III. 2. 28) is clearly a resonance formula, since $q \cot \delta_{33}$ can vanish. This is made possible by opposite relative signs on the right-hand side of Eq. (III. 2. 27). This is a statement independent of any adjustable parameters we have in the problem -- that is, the coupling constant. Note that in the $P_{1/2}$ wave the two terms on the right-hand side have the same (negative) sign, so no resonance is possible. For the S wave, in the nonrelativistic approximation, there is no pole term, so the formalism does not apply.

If we adjust $\omega_r \approx 2\mu$, the observed value of the resonance, the cutoff required is $C \approx 8\mu$, which is quite reasonable. If the effect of crossing were included, the magnitude of the cutoff would be reduced somewhat. Once ω_r is given, the width of the resonance can be calculated (cf. Eqs. (II. 4. 8), (II. 4. 11), and III. 4. 12)] by using the known coupling constant; this gives

$$\Gamma = \frac{8}{3} f^2 q^3{}_r \approx 1 \tag{III. 2. 29}$$

which is not out of line with the value actually observed.

If we elevate the various resonances to the status of particles, two additional pole terms appear for unphysical ω.

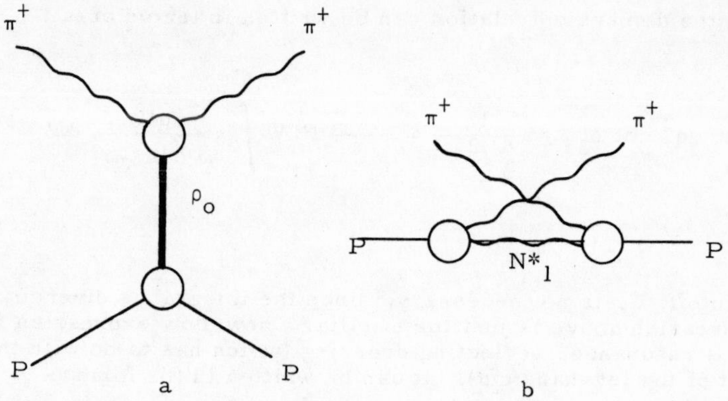

Fig. III. 5

The proper invariants must be constructed for the vertices, so that the spins and i-spins of the new "particles" are taken into account.

The uncrossed form of Fig. III. 5b is precisely the sought for (3, 3) resonance in the physical region. Figure III. 5b is merely a way of including the effects of crossing; Figure III. 5a gives rise to a pole that is too distant to affect the (3, 3) dispersion relations. It also gives rise to a pole for the S state. Fubini and others have indicated that it could be used to properly account for the behavior of S waves in the two i-spin states.

References:

1. Matthews, Proceedings of the Aix-en-Provence Conference, Saclay, Paris, 1961, p. 87.
2. Sakurai, Brandeis Summer Institute Lectures in Theoretical Physics, Benjamin, New York, 1961, p. 282.
3. Fubini, Revs. Modern Phys., 33, 455 (1961).

3. Multichannel Effective Range Theory and Resonances

The cases of particular interest here are the coupled two-particle channels with S = -1. These are $\Lambda\pi$, $\Sigma\pi$, and $\bar{K}N$ channels for T = 1, and $\Sigma\pi$ and $\bar{K}N$ channels for T = 0. There are related one-channel cases, such as $\Sigma\pi$ elastic scattering in T = 2 states for S = -1, and KN elastic scattering for S = +1.

There is a great deal of experimental information available (or to be available soon) in the effective range theory region of these channels, listed below:

1. $\bar{K}N$ complex S-wave scattering lengths for T = 0 and T = 1 states
2. Branching ratios of K^-P threshold. If we define $\Sigma^+ \equiv \sigma(K^- + P \rightarrow \Sigma^+ + \pi^-)$, etc., there are three independent ratios, which are customarily defined as

$$R \equiv \frac{\Sigma^+ + \Sigma^-}{\Sigma^o + \Lambda}$$

$$S \equiv \frac{\Lambda}{\Sigma^o + \Lambda}$$

$$T \equiv \frac{\Sigma^-}{\Sigma^+}$$

3. KN, $S_{\frac{1}{2}}$, $P_{\frac{1}{2}}$, and $P_{3/2}$ scattering lengths for T = 0 and 1
4. The energies and widths of the resonances Y^*_1 and Y^*_o, both below but near the $\bar{K}N$ threshold, and the branching ratio of the decay into the $\Sigma\pi$ and $\Lambda\pi$ mode for Y^*_1.

This comprises a list of 18 separate pieces of experimental data. The multichannel effective-range theory corresponding to the processes listed, if it is to treat particles and resonances on the same footing, would have to take into account pole diagrams of the form in Fig. III. 6.

The generic symbol Y has been used for Λ and Σ above, and Y* for their isobars. The symbol Ω is generic for any multipion resonance -- ρ, ω, η, ζ, etc. Following the pattern of the π-N resonance analysis, Y* has been included only where it appears at unphysical energies. For physical energies, we hope to establish the presence of isobars from effective range theory.

When the above diagrams are analyzed in detail, the nearest singularities are located as indicated on Fig. III. 7. The singularities are calculated on the assumption that $m_\Sigma = m_\Lambda = Y$. The variable ω is chosen so that the total energy W is given by $W = Y + \omega$.

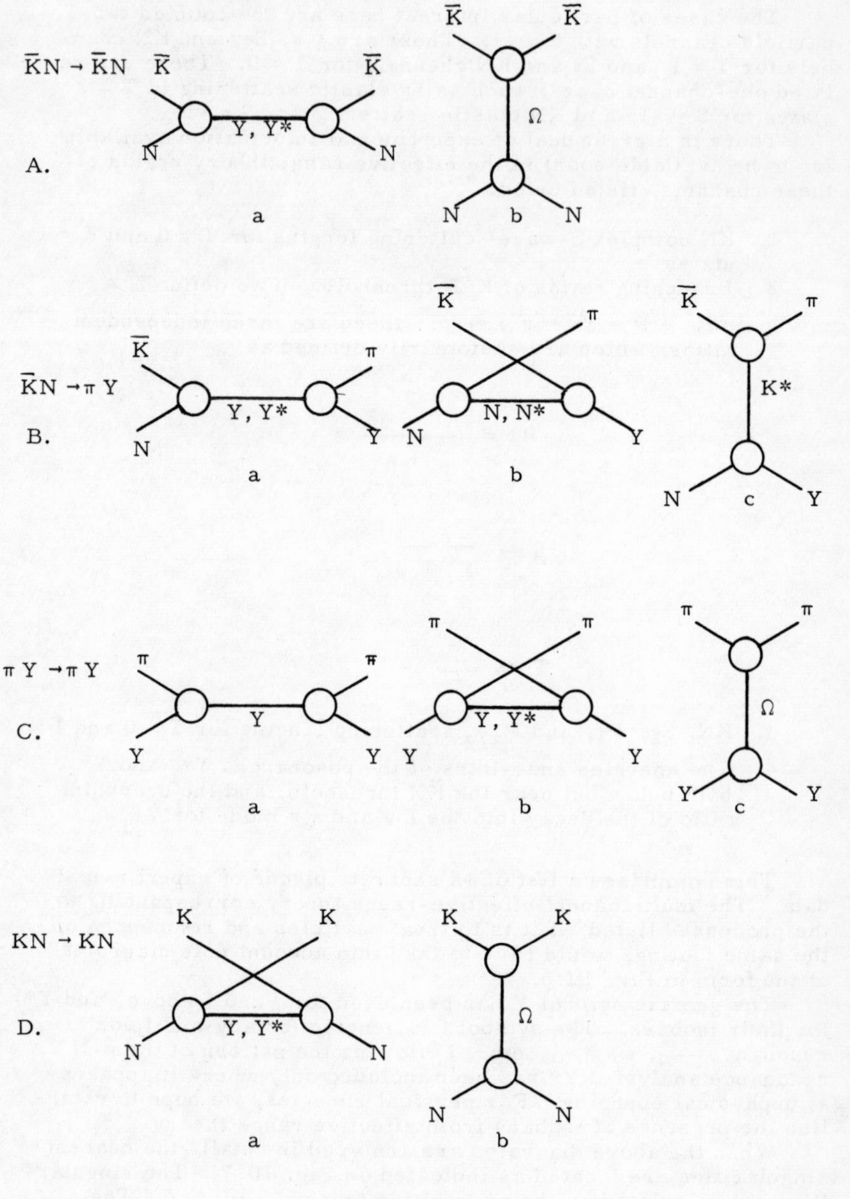

Fig. III. 6

The effective range theory as outlined above can then be used to take into account the shaded cuts (corresponding to the various elastic and two-particle inelastic channels) and poles. The results finally depend only on the coupling constants $g_{\pi\Lambda\Sigma}$, $g_{\pi\Sigma\Sigma}$, $g_{\pi NN}$, $g_{\Lambda KN}$, $g_{\Sigma KN}$, and G_Ω where G_Ω is the product of Ω coupling to K-s and nucleons, for each Ω. The pion-nucleon coupling is known. The determination of the remaining couplings depends on the further assumptions we make: for example, if the assumption of global symmetry is made, we must choose $g_{\pi NN} = g_{\pi\Lambda\Sigma} = g_{\pi\Sigma\Sigma}$ and the Λ-Σ parity must be taken as even. Amati, Vitale, and Stanghellini have considered the coupled $\pi\Sigma$ and $\pi\Lambda$ channels for this case, below the $\bar{K}N$ threshold. The situation is very similar to the π-N case; and using the analysis outlined above, together with Eq. (II. 4. 17), one can show that there is a resonance in the J = 3/2 state. The nearness of the $\bar{K}N$ channel could perhaps significantly alter these results, but since not much is known about the P wave $\bar{K}N$ channels near threshold, one cannot calculate anything explicitly.

The situation is different if one assumes the K-Λ and the Λ-Σ parity both to be opposite. The $S_{1/2}$ $\bar{K}N$ and $\pi\Lambda$ channels are now coupled to the $P_{1/2}$ $\pi\Sigma$ channels. One can now use the $\bar{K}N$ low-energy data to study this channel both above threshold and below it, employing the analytic continuation procedures outlined above. The hyperon, K, and boson resonance coupling constants are now free parameters, subject only to the qualitative conditions that, since we are dealing with strong interactions, the coupling for pseudoscalar interactions be of the order of the π-N coupling constant and the scalar couplings be somewhat smaller than their pseudoscalar counterparts. The number of free parameters is considerably smaller than the number of experimental data. One can now use Eq. (II. 5. 22) continued below threshold to see if there is a resonance corresponding to Y^*_1 and Y^*_0. About a year ago Wali, Feldman, and this writer indeed found that an $S_{1/2}$ resonance corresponding to the Y^*_1 could exist. We found no resonance corresponding to the Y^*_0. The data, of course, are still shifting (value of $\bar{K}N$ scattering lengths has been changing; the η, ζ, and ω have been discovered since the time our analysis was made; the Y^*_1 spin is not known, etc.).

In any case, there seems to be strong indication from these calculations that the $\bar{K}N$ channel has a critical effect on the resonance behavior of the other channels. Dalitz has found similar results, using nuclear physics techniques to extrapolate from the $\bar{K}N$ scattering lengths to a $\bar{K}N$ bound state that can be identified with the Y^*_1.

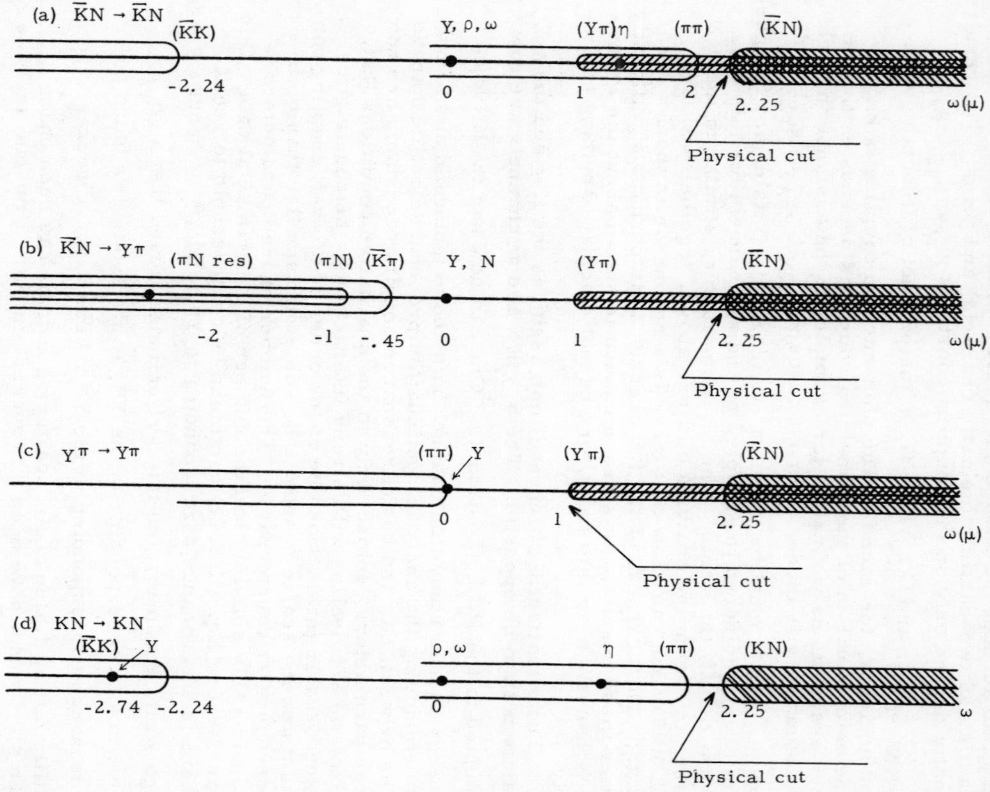
(a) $\bar{K}N \to \bar{K}N$
$(\bar{K}K)$
-2. 24
Y, ρ, ω
(Yπ)η
(ππ)
$(\bar{K}N)$
0
1
2
2. 25
ω(μ)
Physical cut
(b) $\bar{K}N \to Y\pi$
(πN res)
(πN)
$(\bar{K}\pi)$
Y, N
(Yπ)
$(\bar{K}N)$
-2
-1
-. 45
0
1
2. 25
ω(μ)
Physical cut
(c) Yπ → Yπ
(ππ)
Y
(Y π)
$(\bar{K}N)$
0
1
2. 25
ω(μ)
Physical cut
(d) KN → KN
$(\bar{K}K)$
Y
ρ, ω
η
(ππ)
(KN)
-2. 74
-2. 24
0
2. 25
ω
Physical cut

Fig. III. 7

References:

1. Amati, Stanghellini, and Vitale, Nuovo Cimento, 13, 1143(1959)
2. Wali, Fulton, and Feldman, Phys. Rev. Letters, 6, 644 (1961).
3. Dalitz, Phys. Rev. Letters, 6, 239 (1961).
4. Feldman, Fulton, and Wali, Effective Range Theory for Scattering in States of Strangeness ±1 (1961, unpublished).
5. Dalitz and Tuan, Ann. Phys., 8, 100 (1959).
6. Dalitz, Revs. Modern Phys., 33, 471 (1961).
7. Björken, Phys. Rev. Letters, 4, 473 (1960).
8. Salam, Proceedings of the Aix-en-Provence Conference, Saclay, Paris, 1961, p. 191.

4. "Polology" for Inelastic Processes

We shall not go into further general discussion of "polology" (the study of the role of pole-term contributions to scattering amplitudes); in particular, we shall not discuss polology in elastic processes. They have been extensively discussed and reviewed, in connection with the problem of determining parities and coupling constants and have been used to take into account the tail of the nucleon-nucleon potential. We shall concern ourselves with an application potentially useful in studying resonances and their interactions. The proposal, originally due to Goebel and to Chew and Low, is to consider inelastic processes mediated by a single virtual intermediate particle. These authors conjecture quite reasonably that "dispersion-perturbation theory" can adequately describe these processes. That is, diagrammatically, if quantum numbers allow it, we can write

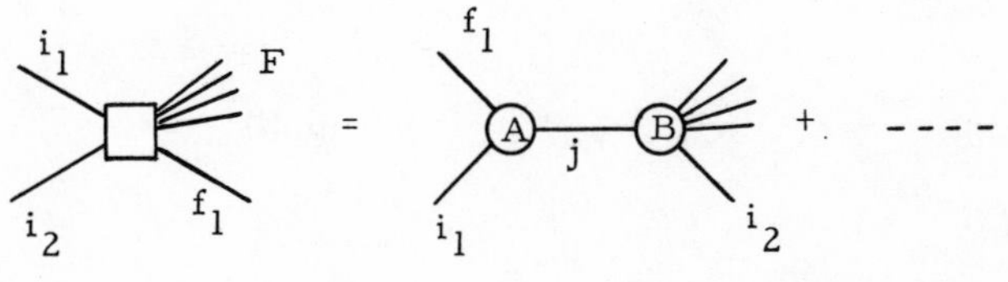

Fig. III. 8

where j is a single-particle state. Thus, poles at unphysical values of the variables can occur if conservation laws permit them. It is further conjectured that in the vicinity of the poles, the pole term alone dominates the process. At the pole, the bubble

A of Fig. III. 8 becomes the physical vertex for $i_1 \rightarrow j + f_1$, and B the amplitude for the process $j + i_2 \rightarrow F$, where all particles are now on their mass shells ($p_i^2 = -m_i^2$). This idea has had further extensions by Salzmann and Salzmann and by Drell to high-energy inelastic scattering, but we shall not be concerned with this here.

To be specific, as an illustration we shall consider pion production in π-N collisions and, in particular, shall take the process

$$\pi^- + P \rightarrow \pi^- + \pi^0 + P \qquad \text{(III. 4. 1)}$$

There will be a pole contribution for this process, given by the diagram

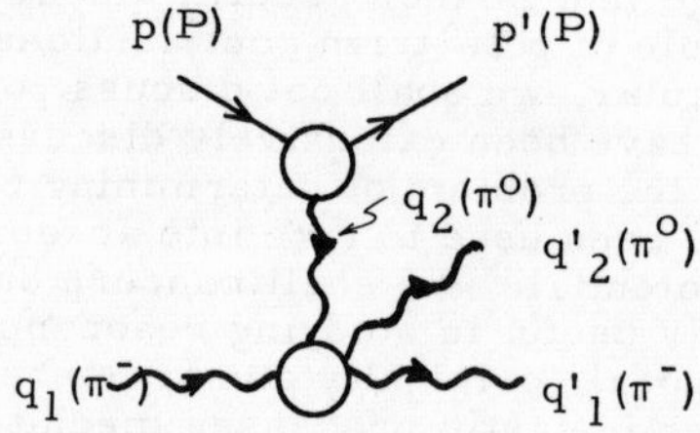

Fig. III. 9

Energy conservation gives at the two vertices:

$$p = q_2 + p' \qquad p = (\vec{p}, E) \qquad \text{(III. 4. 2)}$$

and

$$q_1 + q_2 = q'_1 + q'_2 \qquad q_1 = (\vec{q}_1, \omega_1), \text{ etc.}$$

Of course, since q_2 corresponds to a virtual π^0, it is not on its mass shell for physical p and p'. This is easiest to see in the frame in which the initial proton is at rest ("proton lab frame," to be denoted by putting a bar under all symbols).

$$\Delta^2 \equiv q_2{}^2 = (p - p')^2 = 2M(\underline{E}' - M)$$

$$> 0 \neq -\mu^2 \qquad \text{(III. 4. 3)}$$

The transition matrix for the above diagram (we are writing T_P, as defined previously) is

$$T_{in} = V(p, p') \frac{1}{\Delta^2 + \mu^2} G(s, t, \Delta^2) \qquad \text{(III. 4. 4)}$$

where

$$s = -(q'_1 + q'_2)^2$$

$$\qquad \text{(III. 4. 5)}$$

$$t = -(q_1 - q'_1)^2$$

$$V(p, p') = ig(\Delta^2)\bar{u}(p')\gamma_5 u(p) \qquad \text{(III. 4. 6)}$$

In the limit $\Delta^2 \to -\mu^2$, G becomes the elastic $\pi^-\pi^0$ T_P matrix (cf. Fig. III. 9).

The nucleon vertex is easily handled. $|V|^2$ summed over final and averaged over initial spins gives

$$4\pi\,\Gamma(\Delta^2) = \overline{|V|^2} = -\frac{g^2}{2} \mathrm{Tr}\, \frac{(M - i\gamma p)}{2M}\gamma_5 \frac{(M - i\gamma p')}{2M}\gamma_5$$

$$= \frac{g^2}{4M^2}\Delta^2 = 4\pi f^2 \frac{\Delta^2}{\mu^2} \qquad \text{(III. 4. 7)}$$

We must carry out the usual phase space integrals over $|T_{in}|^2$

and divide by the incident flux, to obtain the inelastic cross section. Before doing this, we recall (cf. Jauch and Rohrlich, Theory of Photons and Electrons) that the flux can be written

$$\mathfrak{F} = \frac{F}{\omega_1 E} \tag{III. 4. 8}$$

where F is an invariant, and that the phase space integral can also be put in an invariant form, for example,

$$\int \frac{d^3 q_1}{2\omega_1} = \int d^4 q_1 (\theta q_{1o}) \delta(q_1{}^2 + \mu^2) \tag{III. 4. 9}$$

Writing the integration over the meson phase space in covariant form and dividing by the incident flux, we find that the inelastic cross section in the proton lab frame is in the vicinity of $\Delta^2 = -\mu^2$.

$$\sigma_{in} \underset{\Delta^2 \to -\mu^2}{=} \frac{M\underline{\omega}_1}{M\underline{q}_1} \int \frac{d^3 \underline{p}'}{(2\pi)^3} \frac{M^2}{2M\underline{E}'\underline{\omega}_1}$$

$$\left[\int \frac{d^4 q'_1}{(2\pi)^3} \theta(q'_{10}) \delta(q'_1{}^2 + \mu^2) \frac{d^4 q'_2}{(2\pi)^3} \theta(q'_{2o}) \right.$$

$$\left. \delta(q'_2{}^2 + \mu^2) \cdot \delta^4(q_1 + q_2 - q'_1 - q'_2) \overline{|T_{in}|^2} \right] \tag{III. 4. 10}$$

where

$$\overline{|T_{in}|^2} = 4\pi f^2 \frac{\Delta^2}{\mu^2} \frac{1}{(\Delta^2 + \mu^2)^2} |G(s, t; \Delta^2)|^2 \tag{III. 4. 11}$$

and the expression in brackets is manifestly an invariant.

We shall next make a suitable change of variables. We note that, if we write the total energy-momentum vector (a constant), as P, we have in the proton lab frame

$$s = -(P - p')^2 = -(P^2 - M^2) - 2P_o E' + 2|q_1||p'| \cos \theta' \qquad \text{(III. 4. 12)}$$

where

$$\cos \theta' = \frac{\vec{p}' \cdot \vec{q}_1}{|\vec{p}'|\,|\vec{q}_1|} \qquad \text{(III. 4. 13)}$$

Using Eqs. (III. 4. 12) and (III. 4. 3), we find

$$J\left(\frac{\Delta^2, s}{E', \cos \theta'}\right) = 4Mq_1 p' \qquad \text{(III. 4. 14)}$$

so that

$$d^3p' = E'p' \, d\varphi' \, d(\cos \theta') \, dE' =$$

$$= \frac{E'}{4Mq_1} \, d\varphi' \, d\Delta^2 \, ds \qquad \text{(III. 4. 15)}$$

But, the total elastic $\pi^-\pi^o$ cross section is given by(some of the terms in the incident flux are cancelled by the normalization of the incoming mesons)

$$\sigma_{\pi^-\pi^o}(s) = \frac{4}{F_{\pi\pi}} \int \frac{d^4q'_1}{(2\pi)^3} \frac{d^4q'_2}{(2\pi)^3} \cdot$$

$$\cdot \, \theta(q'_{10})\theta(q'_{20}) \, \delta(q'^2_1 + \mu^2) \, \delta(q'^2_2 + \mu^2)$$

$$\delta^4(q_1 + q_2 - q'_1 - q'_2) \, |G(s, t; -\mu^2)|^2 \qquad \text{(III. 4. 16)}$$

and is an invariant. Evaluating $F_{\pi\pi}$ in the "meson lab frame" (the frame in which the initial π meson is at rest),

$$F_{\pi\pi} = q_1\mu = \tfrac{1}{2}\sqrt{s^2 - 4\mu^2 s} \qquad \text{(III. 4. 17)}$$

Finally, we obtain

$$\left.\frac{\partial^2\sigma_{in}}{\partial\Delta^2\partial s}\right|_{\Delta^2\to\mu^2} = \frac{f^2}{4\pi}\,\frac{\sqrt{s^2 - 4\mu^2 s}}{q_1^2}$$

$$\sigma_{\pi^-\pi^o}(s)\,\frac{\Delta^2}{\mu^2}\,\frac{1}{(\Delta^2 + \mu^2)^2} \qquad \text{(III. 4. 18)}$$

The more general case of particles with spin and more than three final particles can also be simply treated.

As a matter of practical consideration, with our present technology we can produce π beams but not π targets. (In principle, two colliding π beams are possible, but presently available particle fluxes are far too low to make such experiments practicable.) Thus, we can study π-N scattering directly but π-π scattering only indirectly. Extrapolating the differential cross section given in Eq. (III. 4. 18) to values of momentum transfer equal to $-\mu^2$, together with the knowledge of the π-N coupling constant available from other experiments, enables us to indirectly obtain $\sigma_{\pi^-\pi^o}$ from experiment.

We are now in a position to obtain information about 2π resonances. Assuming that we have a 2π resonance at a given energy, we can determine its spin by observing that at resonance

$$(\sigma_{\pi\pi})_J^{(res)} = (2J + 1)\,\frac{4\pi}{k^2_{res}} \qquad \text{(III. 4. 19)}$$

This limit is reached only if there are no inelastic channels open. It is only an upper limit above inelastic thresholds.

Alternatively, we can turn the argument around, and if we know the spin of the dominant π-π state at a certain energy, we can establish whether a resonance exists or not.

In their initial report on the ρ, Walker and coworkers determined $\sigma_{\pi\pi}$ by a method based on Eq. (III. 4. 18). They did not carry out an extrapolation but merely assumed that Eq. (III. 4. 18) was the dominant contribution to the inelastic cross section and neglected off-shell effects in $\sigma_{\pi\pi}$ for small positive Δ^2. They found that

$$(\sigma_{\pi\pi})^{(res)} \approx \frac{12\pi}{k_1^{\ 2}} \qquad \text{(III. 2. 40)}$$

but is slightly below it. Assuming that a small $2\pi \to 4\pi$ inelastic cross section somewhat reduces the height of the resonance peaks and that they are dealing with a resonance, and thus a single value of J dominates $\sigma_{\pi\pi}$, they find $J_\rho = 1$. We can turn their arguments around. Evidence exists that $J_\rho = 1$ from other experiments involving angular correlations between the initial π and the final π-s. If this fact is used in looking at Walker's $\sigma_{\pi\pi}$, and if we assume that J = 1 dominates $\sigma_{\pi\pi}$ and that a small inelastic cross section somewhat reduces the unitarity limit, there is a strong indication that the ρ in fact is a true resonance and not just a bump in $\sigma_{\pi\pi}$.

This approach of Chew and Low has been developed and extended by Drell, Salzmann and Salzmann, and others to more complicated high-energy processes and has come to be known as the "theory of peripheral collisions." We do not have the space to discuss further the various interesting results obtained in the peripheral approximation.

References:

1. Goebel, Phys. Rev. Letters, 1, 337 (1958).
2. Chew and Low, Phys. Rev., 113, 1640 (1959).
3. F. and G. Saltzmann, Phys. Rev., 120, 599 (1960); ibid., 121, 1941 (1961).
4. Drell and Zachariasen, Phys. Rev. Letters, 5, 66 (1960).
5. Drell, Phys. Rev. Letters, 5, 342 (1960).
6. Moravcsik, Dispersion Relations, Scottish Universities' Summer School, Interscience, New York, 1960, p. 117.

5. Nonresonant Mechanisms for Producing Peaks in Cross Sections

Next we shall review two suggestions made recently to account for the sharp structure seen in cross sections. The first mechanism is another application of "dispersion perturbation theory." It was suggested by R. Peierls and expanded somewhat by Pais and Nauenberg. Consider a particle X that can decay into two others, Y and Z. If we let X, Y, and Z stand for the masses, we then have X > Y + Z. Unlike in every other polology situation we have discussed, a pole will occur in the crossed-momentum transfer variable for X-Y scattering with an intermediate Z but for physical values of the variables.

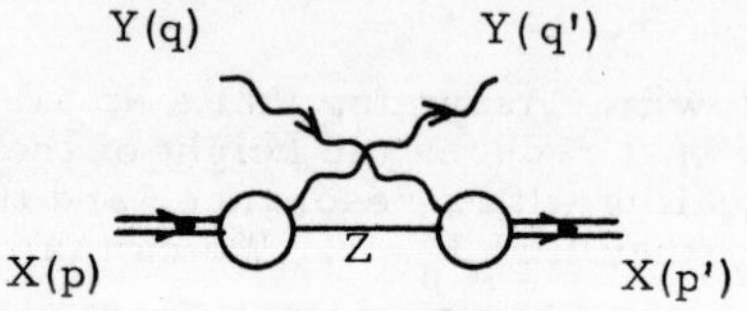

Fig. III.10

Of course, the cross section will not actually diverge for these values since the lifetime (width) associated with the decay will serve to broaden and reduce the peak produced.

In general, there will be other singularities (other "dispersion-perturbation" terms) near the physical region that would perhaps be dominant. So the peaking produced by the above diagram would not necessarily stand out against the "background." The point is that it could possibly occur.

Specific examples of X, Y, and Z are: (a) $X = N^*_1$, $Y = \pi$, $Z = N$ (π - N^*_1 scattering to produce N^*_2); (b) $X = \zeta$, $Y = \pi$, $Z = \pi$ (π-ζ scattering to produce the ω).

To illustrate the mechanism, we consider a situation where all particles have both vanishing spin and isotopic spin. If we assume that the mass of X is

$$X^* = X - \tfrac{1}{2} i\Gamma$$

where X is the real part of the mass and Γ the full width (an expression suggested by the Breit-Wigner form of the X* resonance), the scattering amplitude due to Fig. III.10 is

$$T = \frac{g^2}{u - Z^2} \qquad \text{(III. 5. 1)}$$

where

$$u - Z^2 = -(p - q')^2 - Z^2$$

$$= -(s - s_o) + 2\underset{\sim}{q}^2(i - \cos\theta) - i\Delta \qquad \text{(III. 5. 2)}$$

in the c. m. system, with

$$s = \left(\sqrt{X^2 + \underset{\sim}{q}^2} + \sqrt{Y^2 + \underset{\sim}{q}^2}\right)^2 \qquad \text{(III. 5. 3)}$$

$$s_0 = 2(X^2 + Y^2) - Z^2 \qquad \text{(III. 5. 4)}$$

$$\Delta(s) = 2\Gamma X \frac{X^2 - Y^2}{s + X^2 - Y^2} \qquad \text{(III. 5. 5)}$$

Terms of order Γ^2 have been neglected above. The expressions are given in the X-Y c. m. system, and g is the coupling constant.

The differential cross section will be proportional to

$$\sigma(s, \cos\theta) \sim \frac{1}{[s - s_o - 2\underset{\sim}{q}^2(1 - \cos\theta)]^2 + \Delta^2} \qquad \text{(III. 5. 6)}$$

Integration over cos θ gives

$$\sigma(s) \sim \frac{1}{2\underset{\sim}{q}^2\Delta} \tan^{-1} \frac{4\underset{\sim}{q}^2\Delta}{\Delta^2 + \frac{Z^2}{s}(s - s_o)(s - s_1)} \qquad \text{(III. 5. 7)}$$

where

$$s_1 = \frac{(X^2 - Y^2)^2}{Z^2} \qquad \text{(III. 5. 8)}$$

and we have used the identity

$$4\underset{\sim}{q}^2 = s - s_o - \frac{Z^2}{s}(s - s_1) \qquad \text{(III. 5. 9)}$$

If we consider particles with nonvanishing spin and isotopic spin, the essential features remain the same, but $\sigma(s, \cos\theta)$ will have some additional spin dependence.

Note that for πN^*_1 scattering, $s_1/s_o \approx 1$, while for π-ζ scattering, $s_1/s_o >> 1$. Thus for π-N^*_1 scattering it is clear that $\sigma(s)$ will have a peak near $s \approx s_o \approx s_1$. This is less clear for the second case; however, there is still a peak near $s \approx s_o$. When $s \approx s_1$, the energy dependence of Δ serves to cut down the expected peaking.

Why can't a peak of this type in the ζ-π scattering be considered a proper resonance? In fact, Pais and Nauenberg find that the peak energy is quite close to the mass of the ω:

1. It does not occur in a unique channel in angular momentum.
2. It does not occur in a unique channel in isotopic spin.
3. It does not have a resonant shape (that is, it is not of Breit-Wigner form). To elucidate: In general, $s_o \neq s_1$ and Δ is not too large, so that near $s = s_o$ the term multiplied by $(1 - \cos\theta)^2$ will dominate the denominator and many angular momenta will play a role. Further, since we are dealing with crossed channels, it is clear that in general for isotopic spins T_1 and T_2 for the incoming particles, all total isospins from $T_1 + T_2$ to $|T_1 - T_2|$ will appear. Since one of the salient characteristics of a particle (resonance) is its unique J and T, the above argument precludes our considering peaks arising in this fashion as resonances.

The situation is not so bad when we consider the N^*_2. For one thing, since $s_o \approx s_1$, the angular dependence of the denominator of Eq. (III. 5. 6) near the peak is not too great. Strictly speaking, we do not have a proper resonance, but from a practical point of view the interaction between N^*_1 and π is predominantly in an S state, so the peak would be most apparent in one angular momentum state. Moreover, in point of fact experimentally, a rapid energy dependence is observed for both T = 1/2 and T = 3/2 (a peak and a dip, respectively) near the N^*_2 energy and could be the result of the constructive and destructive interference, respectively, of the peak to background.

We shall not give details of how the peak in the π-N^*_1 scattering affects π-N scattering, but it is clear that π-N^*_1 scattering plays a role in both the process $\pi N \to (\pi N^*_1) \to \pi N^*_1$ and the process $\pi N \to (\pi N^*_1) \to \pi N$. To state it somewhat vaguely -- the π-N^*_1 and π-N channels are coupled through unitarity.

Another mechanism to account for some peaks in cross sections, specifically in πN and K^-P scattering, has been suggested by Ball and Frazer. Again these peaks are not resonances. They are produced above inelastic thresholds in the elastic channel only, when there is a rapid rise in the inelastic channel to total absorption. Our intuitive conception of a resonance is that it is a compound state of the system. The elastic and inelastic processes at resonance in this picture can be considered as two possible decay modes of the same state; hence both of them should exhibit a peaking at resonance. We have in fact given an analytic statement of this condition for two-particle channels (the eigenphase shifts must increase through an odd half-integral multiple of π. The picture is somewhat more complicated if there are more than two particles in a channel, but its essential features must be the same. The peaks predicted by Ball and Frazer (unlike those of Peierls) do, of course, occur for unique T and J.

The approximation of Ball and Frazer belongs under the heading of effective range theory in the sense that they neglect all unphysical singularities, cuts and poles. They assume that they can calculate or obtain experimentally the inelastic scattering (effectively using "dispersion-perturbation theory" for the example they discuss and treating it as input information). We recall the parametrization in terms of complex phase shifts, $\delta = \Delta + i\rho$ [Eqs. (II. 4. 21) to (II. 4. 26) and (II. 4. 29)]. We now demand that the scattering amplitude be (1) analytic for all $\nu = q^2$, except for a cut for positive real ν; (2) real for negative real ν, and (3) satisfy unitarity in the sense that a δ exists such that

$$t = \frac{1}{2i}\left(e^{2i\delta} - 1\right) \quad \text{and} \quad \sigma_{el} = \frac{4\pi}{\nu}|t|^2 \qquad \text{(III. 5. 10)}$$

A δ satisfying the above conditions is

$$\delta = \frac{k}{\pi}\int_{\nu_i}^{\infty} \frac{\rho(\nu')}{k'(\nu' - \nu)}\, d\nu'$$

where ν_i is the value of the inelastic threshold. If $k^2\sigma_{in}/4\pi$ increases rapidly to its limit (1/4), as shown on the diagram, the corresponding elastic unitarity limit for $k^2\sigma_{el}/4\pi$ must decrease rapidly to 1/4. Ball and Frazer show that their mechanism gives a rapidly rising δ below and immediately above threshold. Thus, there is a rapid rise in σ_{el}, giving the low-energy side of the peak, until the unitarity limit is reached. The subsequent rapid fall in σ_{el}, giving the high-energy side of the peak, is dictated by the unitarity limit

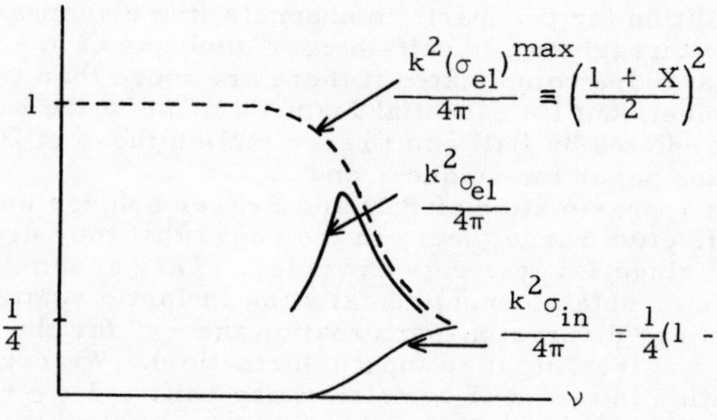

Fig. III. 11

In the foregoing discussion, we may seem to have stressed unduly a distinction between a peak which is a resonance and one which is not. The distinction is not an academic one. Although an energy-dependent structure for particle cross sections is in itself interesting, the particle concept can only be associated with resonances. Thus resonances may have a more fundamental role to play in an ultimate physical theory (based on symmetry considerations or on some other principle) that is to account for the spectrum of elementary particles.

References:

1. R. Peierls, Phys. Rev. Letters, 6, 641 (1961).
2. Nauenberg and Pais, Phys. Rev. Letters, 8, 82 (1962).
3. Ball and Frazer, Phys. Rev. Letters, 7, 204 (1961).

6. The Role of π Resonances in the Nucleon Form Factors

One of the great successes of dispersion relations has been the prediction of the need for sharp peaks in the π-π cross section to explain the structure of the nucleon form factors. In fact, the prediction of such striking structure in the π-π scattering stimulated the experimental search for it.

We shall not discuss the nucleon form factors in detail, their general structure from invariance arguments, dispersion relations for them, etc., but shall only outline briefly what role multipion resonances play in nucleon structure, from the simple-minded "dispersion perturbation" point of view.

Consider the elastic scattering of a nucleon by an electron. If we assume that electrodynamics is adequate to describe the interaction of electrons and photons, we can use perturbation theory for the electrodynamic part of the process, and the exchange of one virtual photon will describe the scattering to lowest order in the fine-structure constant. We can represent the process by the graph of Figure III. 12.

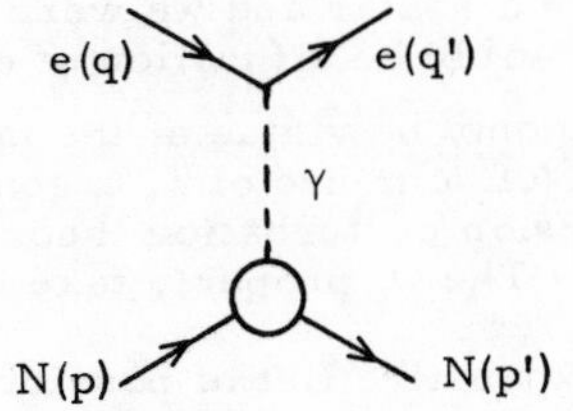

Fig. III. 12

and the corresponding T matrix

$$\langle e_2 N_2 | T_P | e_1 N_1 \rangle = \frac{[\bar{u}_e(q')\gamma_\mu u_e(q)] \langle N_2 | J_\mu | N_1 \rangle}{k^2}$$

$$k^2 = (p - p')^2 = -t \qquad \text{(III. 6. 1)}$$

Note that the above graph is not a "dispersion perturbation" graph but is ordinary perturbation theory for the electrodynamic part. The photon propagator $\delta_{\mu\nu}/q^2$ appears, and clearly we are considering a virtual photon -- one which has both longitudinal and scalar components and which is not on the mass shell ($q^2 \neq 0$). The symbol J_μ is justified to describe the nucleon vertex, since it is always a current that is coupled to an e. m. field. (The term $J_\mu A_\mu$ appears in the interaction Lagrangian.) Of course, the current is not that due to a point nucleon alone but includes the effects of virtual mesons and other particles.

We can now assert what the general structure of the vertex $\langle N_2 | J_\mu | N_1 \rangle$ must be from invariance arguments. The current, a hermitian four-vector, has the structure

$$\langle N_2 | J_\mu | N_1 \rangle = \bar{u}_N(p') \left[\sum_i a_i(q^2) O_i \right] u_N(p) \qquad \text{(III. 6. 2)}$$

If the vertex were a scalar and we were dealing with spinless particles, clearly J_μ would be a function of q^2 only. It would not be a constant function only by virtue of the fact that the photon is not on its mass shell (cf. our use of g, a constant to describe the π-N vertex in "dispersion perturbation theory," with all particles on their mass shell). The O_i properly take into account the spins involved.

A by no means exhaustive list of possible O_i follows:

$$O: \ (p' - p)_\mu \equiv k_\mu \ ; \quad (p + p')_\mu \equiv K_\mu$$

$$i\gamma_\mu ; \ i\sigma_{\mu\nu} k_\nu ; \ i\sigma_{\mu\nu} K_\nu ; \ i\gamma_\mu \gamma \cdot p' ; \ i\gamma \cdot p \gamma_\mu \ \gamma \cdot p' ; \ \ldots$$

$$\left(\sigma_{\mu\nu} = \frac{1}{2i} [\gamma_\mu , \gamma_\nu] \right) \qquad \text{(III. 6. 3)}$$

If we use the Dirac equation for the physical nucleons, we can eliminate some of the O_i. For example, using

$$\{\gamma_\mu , \gamma_\nu\} = 2\delta_{\mu\nu} \qquad \text{(III. 6. 4)}$$

then

$$\bar{u}(p')\gamma_\mu \gamma\cdot p'u(p) = \bar{u}(p')[-iM\gamma_\mu + 2p'_\mu]\ u(p) =$$

$$= \bar{u}(p')[-Mi\gamma_\mu + (K_\mu - k_\mu)]\ u(p)$$

$$\bar{u}(p')\gamma\cdot pi\gamma_\mu \gamma\cdot p'u(p) = \bar{u}(p')[-2MK_\mu + (3M^2 + k^2)i\gamma_\mu]\ u(p)$$

$$\bar{u}(p')i\sigma_{\mu\nu}K_\nu u(p) = \bar{u}(p')\ k_\nu\ u(p)$$

$$\bar{u}(p')i\sigma_{\mu\nu}k_\nu u(p) = \bar{u}(p')[-2iM\gamma_\mu + K_\mu]\ u(p)$$

(III. 6. 5)

This partial list of O_i can be reduced to the form

$$\langle N_2 | J_\mu | N_1 \rangle =$$

$$i\bar{u}(p')[G_1(t)\gamma_\mu + G_2(t)\sigma_{\mu\nu}k_\nu + iG_3(t)k_\mu]\ u(p) \qquad \text{(III. 6. 6)}$$

Any more complicated expressions, containing additional $\gamma\cdot p$-s or $\gamma\cdot p'$-s can be reduced to the above expression by moving the $\gamma\cdot p$-s to the right and $\gamma\cdot p'$-s to the left and letting them act on $u(p)$ and $\bar{u}(p')$, respectively.

The above expression can be further simplified by using current conservation, that is,

$$\langle N_2 | k_\mu J_\mu | N_1 \rangle = 0 \qquad \text{(III. 6. 7)}$$

Since

$$\sigma_{\mu\nu} k_\mu k_\nu \equiv 0 \qquad \text{(III. 6. 8)}$$

and

$$\bar{u}(p') \gamma \cdot k u(p) = 0$$

it follows that

$$G_3(t)t = 0 \qquad \text{(III. 6. 9)}$$

since in general $t \neq 0$, $G_3(t)$ must vanish identically. A somewhat more elegant proof of this fact follows from time-reversal invariance, but it would require a more extensive discussion to give it here.

The remaining form factors G_1 and G_2 can be shown to be real. They are still operators in isotopic-spin space. Since the photon is neutral, the initial and final nucleon must have the same charge. The most general way in which this requirement is met is by taking

$$G_i = G_i^s + G_i^v \tau_3 \qquad i = 1, 2 \qquad \text{(III. 6. 10)}$$

where τ_3 is the third component of the i-spin Pauli operator, and the superscripts s and v denote scalar and vector, respectively. The proton and neutron form factors in terms of G^s and G^v are

$$G_i^P = G_i^s + G_i^v$$

$$G_i^N = G_i^s - G_i^v \qquad \text{(III. 6. 11)}$$

For a point charge proton and uncharged neutron,

$$G_1^s = G_1^v = \frac{e}{2} \qquad \text{(III. 6. 12)}$$

Even for extended nucleons, for t = 0 we have the conditions

$$G_1^{P}(0) = e \qquad G_2^{P}(0) = \frac{e}{2M}(\tfrac{1}{2}g_P - 1) = \frac{e\kappa_P}{2M}$$

$$G_1^{N}(0) = 0 \qquad G_2^{N}(0) = \frac{e}{2M}(\tfrac{1}{2}g_N - 1) = \frac{e\kappa_N}{2M} \tag{III. 6. 13}$$

where g_P and g_N are the proton and neutron gyromagnetic ratios.

One can normalize the form factors by introducing F-s to give

$$\langle N_2 | J_\mu | N_1 \rangle = \bar{u}(p')\, e[\, F_1(t)\gamma_\mu + \frac{\kappa}{2M} F_2(t)\sigma_{\mu\nu}k_\nu] \; u(p) \tag{III. 6. 14}$$

With this normalization, all $F_i(0) = 1$.

If we insert the above explicit form in T_P, square and carry out suitable phase space integrations, we end up with the so-called "Rosenbluth formula" for the cross section in electron-nucleon scattering:

$$\frac{d\sigma}{d\Omega} = \left(\frac{d\sigma}{d\Omega}\right)_0 [\, F_1{}^2 + \frac{t}{2M^2}(F_1 + \kappa F_2)^2 \tan^2 \frac{\theta}{2} + \kappa^2 F_2{}^2] \tag{III. 6. 15}$$

where $(d\sigma/d\Omega)_0$ is the differential cross section of an electron scattered by a point nucleon of unit charge and no anomalous magnetic moment, and θ is the scattering angle of the electron. This is the formula used in obtaining the form factors from the experimental e-P scattering data.

Turning to the further analysis of the nucleon vertex, let us consider what types of dispersion diagrams would contribute to such a function of a single variable, t. But since we are taking a dispersion theory viewpoint, we can consider the scattering of a nucleon by an off-mass-shell photon on the same footing as the related process of the annihilation of a nucleon-antinucleon pair into a single virtual photon. We must simply choose suitable ranges of the momentum transfer t to describe both processes with a single amplitude ($t > 4M^2$ for $\bar{N}N$ annihilation,-time-like momentum transfers; $t \gtrsim 0$ for N scatter,-space-like momentum transfers). From the point of view of indicating the roles π resonances play in the description of the form factors, $\bar{N}N$ annihilation is more convenient. Typical diagrams involving exchange of lowest mass intermediate particles are

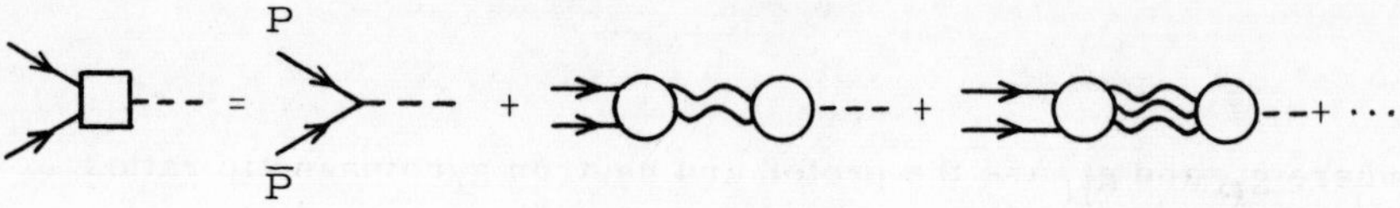

Fig. III. 13

where the intermediate particles drawn are π mesons. (Note that a single π meson cannot couple to a γ ray.) To clarify the picture further, note that a perturbation diagram giving a contribution like that of the second diagram of the right-hand side of Fig. III. 13, looked at from the scattering point of view is

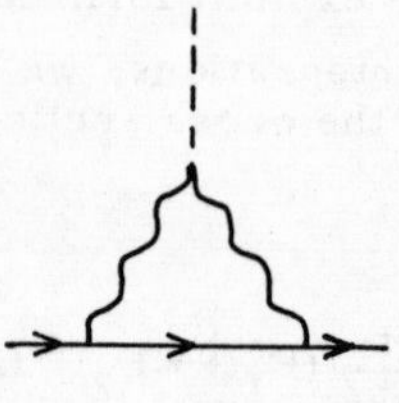

Fig. III. 14

Suppose the only significant contribution to the dispersion diagrams above (in addition to the direct PPγ interaction) came from resonant multipion states. The dispersion diagrams would then all have the structure

Fig. III. 15

where the intermediate state is an effective one-particle state.

These new particles must be vector particles, in order to be able to convert into a photon with a non vanishing coupling. Since there is both an isoscalar and isovector form factor, there must be a corresponding isoscalar and isovector particle. Since the photon carries no charge, only the third component of the isovector particle plays a role in the nucleon form factor. The relevant terms in the Lagrangian describing the interaction of the isoscalar and isovector bosons S_ν and V_ν with the nucleon and the photon have the following simplest invariant form, capable of accounting for both the charge and anomalous moment of the nucleons:

$$L_{SN} = ig_1{}^s \bar{\Psi} \gamma_\mu \Psi S_\mu + \frac{g_2{}^s}{4M} \bar{\Psi} \sigma_{\mu\nu} \Psi (\partial_\mu S_\nu - \partial_\nu S_\mu) \qquad \text{(III. 6. 16)}$$

$$L_{VN} = ig_1{}^v \bar{\Psi} \vec{\tau} \gamma_\mu \Psi \cdot \vec{V}_\mu + \frac{g_2{}^v}{4M} \bar{\Psi} \sigma_{\mu\nu} \vec{\tau} \cdot \Psi (\partial_\mu \vec{V}_\nu - \partial_\nu \vec{V}_\mu) \qquad \text{(III. 6. 17)}$$

$$L_A = ef^s S_\mu A_\mu + ef^v V_{3\mu} A_\mu \qquad \text{(III. 6. 18)}$$

Let us further assume that, to take into account intermediate states other than the one-particle states listed, it is sufficient to add a constant to the nucleon form factors. (The constants may of course be zero, and to illustrate both possibilities, they shall be set equal to zero for the anomalous moment form factors.) The form factors must be normalized to their values at t = 0. The procedure just outlined is equivalent to carrying out one subtraction in the dispersion relations for F_1 and none for F_2, and it leads to the result

$$F_1{}^j(t) = \tfrac{1}{2}\left(1 + \frac{a_j t}{t - M_j{}^2}\right)$$

$$a_j = \frac{-2g_1{}^j f^j}{M_j{}^2} \qquad j = S,\ V \qquad \text{(III. 6. 19)}$$

$$F_2^{\,j}(t) = \frac{b_j}{t - M_j^{\,2}}$$

$$b_j = -g_2^{\,j} f^j = -\kappa^j M^{j^2} \qquad \text{(III. 6. 20)}$$

If there is more than one V_ν or S_ν, we have a summation rather than a single term on the right-hand side of the above equations.

One additional condition is sometimes placed on $F_1^{\,N}(t)$. Since the low-energy neutron-electron interaction can be well accounted for in terms of the anomalous magnetic moment alone, the effective charge radius of the neutron vanishes. This is equivalent to putting

$$\lim_{t \to 0} \frac{1}{t} F_1^{\,N}(t) = 0$$

In addition, Sachs has proposed that the form factors should also be required to satisfy suitable asymptotic conditions for high t, but we shall not discuss these here.

Before discussing the experimental fit to the form factors with the above assumptions, we must digress to discuss what decay properties S_μ and V_μ must have. In the Cartesian components of the isotopic spin, the π fields, described in terms of charge, have the form

$$\pi_+ = \frac{1}{\sqrt{2}} (\pi_1 + i\pi_2)$$

$$\pi_- = \frac{1}{\sqrt{2}} (\pi_1 - i\pi_2)$$

$$\pi_o = \pi_3 \qquad \text{(III. 6. 21)}$$

The π^o is self-charge conjugate and the π^+ and π^- are the conjugates of each other, so that, in terms of the charge conjugation operator,

$$\pi_1 \overset{C}{\rightarrow} \pi_1$$

$$\pi_2 \overset{C}{\rightarrow} -\pi_2$$

$$\pi_3 \overset{C}{\rightarrow} \pi_3 \qquad \text{(III. 6. 22)}$$

Consider next the charge symmetry operator

$$R = e^{i\pi I_2}$$

which represents a rotation of 180° around the y axis in isospace. When applied to the π-s, this gives

$$\pi_1 \overset{R}{\rightarrow} -\pi_1$$

$$\pi_2 \overset{R}{\rightarrow} \pi_2$$

$$\pi_3 \overset{R}{\rightarrow} -\pi_3 \qquad \text{(III. 6. 23)}$$

The product of the two transformations is called the G parity operator:

$$G = CR \qquad \text{(III. 6. 24)}$$

A one-π-meson state then is clearly an eigenstate of G parity, with eigenvalue -1. N π-s are eigenstates with eigenvalue $(-1)^N$.

Consider S_ν and V_ν next. Since they are both coupled to A_μ, on the assumption that the Lagrangian is charge-conjugation invariant, S_ν and V_ν must behave like the photon under charge conjugation, that is,

$$\begin{Bmatrix} S_\nu \\ V_\nu \end{Bmatrix} \overset{C}{\rightarrow} - \begin{Bmatrix} S_\nu \\ V_\nu \end{Bmatrix} \tag{III. 6. 25}$$

The isotopic spin assignments immediately give the behavior under R:

$$S_\nu \overset{R}{\rightarrow} S_\nu$$

$$V_{3\nu} \overset{R}{\rightarrow} -V_{3\nu} \tag{III. 6. 26}$$

It follows that under G

$$S \overset{G}{\rightarrow} -S$$

$$V_{3\nu} \overset{G}{\rightarrow} +V_{3\nu} \tag{III. 6. 27}$$

Thus, if i-spin is conserved in the decay of the boson resonances, S_ν must decay into an odd number (minimum of 3) of π mesons and V_ν into an even number (minimum of 2) of π mesons. Candidates for V_ν are the ρ meson and ξ, if it exists and has spin parity, $J^P = 1^-$. Candidates for S_ν are ω and, if it has spin-parity 1^-, the η.

If the experimental results for the form factors are to be fitted, there appears to be a need for an isoscalar 1^- particle of the mass of the η. In their initial analysis of the form factors using dispersion relations, Frazer and Fulco showed that, while nucleon structure could be explained in terms of boson resonances (their particular concern was F^V and 2π resonances), the momentum transfer dependence of the form factors could not be accounted for if a non resonant behavior was assumed for the 2π system.

Of course, the multipion resonances also play a role in N-N scattering. Their exchange between nucleons gives rise to poles in momentum transfer. One can again write down the usual "dispersion-perturbation theory" for this case. In order to be able to compare them with the conventional treatments of the nucleon-nucleon interaction, one must convert the expressions obtained to an effective potential in two-component spinor notation. There is no time to present details, but amazingly enough the π resonances, among other effects, give rise to a spin-orbit interaction that, depending on the relative magnitudes and the signs of the coupling constants, can be either attractive or repulsive. A spin-orbit interaction was introduced by Signell and Marshak in their analysis of N-N scattering in terms of phenomenological potentials and was found necessary to account for the data.

References:

1. Drell and Zachariasen, Electromagnetic Structure of Nucleons, Oxford, New York, 1961; an excellent review of both the theoretical and experimental aspects of nucleon form factors is presented in this short monograph.
2. Frazer and Fulco, Phys. Rev. Letters, 2, 365 (1959); Phys. Rev., 115, 1763 (1959); ibid., 117, 1609 (1960).
3. Fubini, Proceedings of Aix-en-Provence Conference, Saclay, Paris, 1961, p. 33
4. Matthews, Proceedings of Aix-en-provence Conference, Saclay, Paris, 1961, p. 87 (N-N scattering).
5. Marshak and Signell, Phys. Rev., 106, 832 (1957).
6. Wali, Effect of High Energy Limits on the Nucleon Form Factors, Nuovo Cimento (1962) (in press).

IV. THE DECAY MODES

In this series of lectures so far, I have attempted briefly and on a quite pedestrian and semiqualitative level to discuss what a resonance means, how it can arise, and what role it plays in various strong interaction processes. The "dispersion-perturbation theory" approach provides a quick way of indicating such connections between data. If you wish, it can almost be used to help classify such data into simpler correlated groupings. Very likely, however, this "theory" bears little resemblance to any really satisfactory final version which will be used to account for the phenomena discussed.

I have said almost nothing as yet about one of the most significant properties of the various resonances -- their decay modes. It is ultimately in terms of their decay products that all the resonances are observed. In fact, with the exception of the π-N (3, 3) resonance, where a detailed phase-shift analysis indicates the existence of the resonance, and in the case of the ρ, where a Chew-Low extrapolation is attempted, the resonances are stated to be such when a sharp peak is observed in cross sections, as a function of the invariant mass of the resonance

$$M^2_{Res} = - (\Sigma p_i)^2 \qquad \text{(III. 6. 28)}$$

(p_i is the 4-momentum of the i-th decay product), and this peak is above any structure expected from phase space analysis, or its use in combination with simple models, such as the impulse approximation. The assumption that a resonance exists is strengthened if further experimental study shows that the postulated particle, or resonance, associated with this peak possesses unique spin, parity, and (possibly) isotopic spin. Such information can be obtained indirectly by studying the branching ratios of various possible decay modes and the energy and angular distributions and angular correlations of the particles composing such decay modes. I propose briefly to review some aspects of the applied field theory associated with such analyses.

1. Applications of the Density Matrix to Elementary Particle Interactions

As my next topic, I propose to discuss the density matrix, with particular emphasis on its applications to elementary particle interactions. I will, however, make my remarks moderately self-contained, since comparatively few discussions of the general subject of density matrices exist. Most discussions of the density matrix starting from first principles have a statistical mechanical bias, and a certain degree of notational awkwardness from the point of view of particle physics.

Density matrix techniques, particularly when combined with invariance arguments, provide a powerful technique for analyzing strong interactions. They have been applied typically to nucleon-nucleon scattering and to various decay processes and have been used to describe the general structure of the relevant S-matrix elements. This structure provides us with predictions concerning angular correlations which, when compared with the experimental results, can yield us information concerning the spins, parities, etc., of the particles and resonances participating in the various reactions; hence, the relevance of the topic in the present context.

In general, density matrix techniques are useful when there is less than maximum information available about a system. We specify a quantum mechanical state by a complete set of commuting observables. We have to resort to the use of a density matrix when one or more physical observables are not precisely specified. In such cases, we could alternatively introduce all the possible quantum mechanical states that enter, with random phases attached, carry out the required calculations, and then average over phases. This second approach is a great deal more awkward than the use of density-matrix techniques.

Consider an ensemble of quantum mechanical systems. A beam of particles is an example of such an ensemble. Each system is in a given state that need not be an eigenstate of a particular set of commuting operators but a pure state, that is, an eigenstate of some (not necessarily known) complete set of commuting operators. The state of the j-th system is $|\Psi_j\rangle$. By the superposition principle, we can expand $|\Psi_j\rangle$ in a set of basis states $|n\rangle$

$$|\Psi_j\rangle = \sum_n a_{n_j} |n\rangle \qquad \text{(IV. 1. 1)}$$

The quantum mechanical probability that the eigenstate $|n\rangle$ appears in $|\Psi_j\rangle$ is $|a_{n_j}|^2$ for discrete states (suitable generalization is necessary to include continuum states). Note that $|\Psi_j\rangle$ describes a single system; thus calculations can give rise to interference phenomena. However, the ensemble refers to different systems that are incoherent and cannot give rise to interference.

The ensemble will in general consist of a number of states $|\Psi_j\rangle$, $j = 1, \ldots, N$, because not all eigenvalues are specified. For example, an incoming particle beam may be prepared by appropriate momentum selection but without preparing the beam in a particular spin state. We can specify the state of the system by providing a list of the pure states that can appear, together with the statistical mechanical probability of getting a particular state $|\Psi_j\rangle$, that is,

$$
\begin{array}{ll}
|\Psi_1\rangle & \mathcal{P}_1 \\
|\Psi_2\rangle & \mathcal{P}_2 \\
\vdots & \vdots \\
|\Psi_r\rangle & \mathcal{P}_r \\
\vdots & \vdots
\end{array}
\qquad \text{(IV. 1. 2)}
$$

From the defition of $\mathcal{P}_j$, $\mathcal{P}_j$ is real and positive, and

$$\sum_{j=1}^{N} \mathcal{P}_j = 1 \qquad \text{(IV. 1. 3)}$$

Note that although the $|\Psi_j\rangle$ are normalized they need not be orthogonal or span the space completely. Different $|\Psi_j\rangle$ refer to different systems.

As an example, let us discuss the spin state of a spin 1/2 system. The complete set of orthonormal basis states, with the quantization direction being the z axis, is given by

$$|\uparrow\rangle_z = \begin{pmatrix} 1 \\ 0 \end{pmatrix} \quad \text{and} \quad |\downarrow\rangle_z = \begin{pmatrix} 0 \\ 1 \end{pmatrix} \qquad \text{(IV. 1. 4)}$$

A particular eigenstate, quantized along the y axis, is given by $|\uparrow\rangle_y = \frac{1}{\sqrt{2}}\begin{pmatrix} 1 \\ i \end{pmatrix}$. An arbitrary normalized pure state is given by

$$|\Psi\rangle = \begin{pmatrix} a \\ b \end{pmatrix} \qquad |a|^2 + |b|^2 = 1 \qquad \text{(IV. 1. 5)}$$

where, suppressing an overall phase, we can define

$$a = \cos\tfrac{1}{2}\theta \qquad \text{and} \qquad b = \sin\tfrac{1}{2}\theta\, e^{i\varphi} \qquad \text{(IV. 1. 6)}$$

in terms of real parameters θ and φ.

There exists some hermitean operator of which Eq. (IV. 1. 5) is an eigenstate. We can perform a rotation of coordinates such that $|\Psi\rangle$ becomes the spin up eigenstate along some new z axis, z'. In fact, since the expectation value of the spin is given by

$$\vec{P} \equiv \langle\Psi|\vec{\sigma}|\Psi\rangle = \hat{i}\sin\theta\cos\varphi + \hat{j}\sin\theta\sin\varphi + \hat{k}\cos\theta \qquad \vec{P}^2 = 1 \tag{IV. 1. 7}$$

the axis z' is defined by the following diagram:

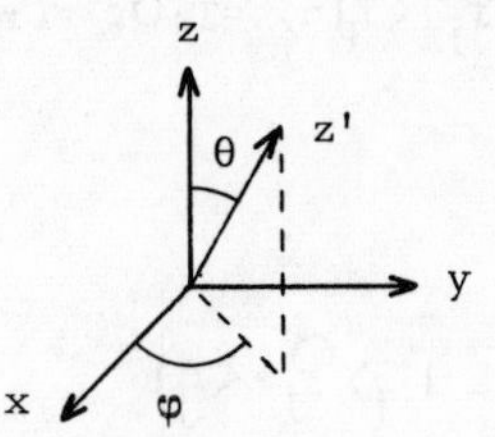

Fig. IV. 1

On the other hand, a specific mixed state of spin 1/2 particles is defined by

$$|\Psi_1\rangle = |\uparrow\rangle_z \qquad \mathcal{P}_1 = \frac{1}{4}$$

$$|\Psi_2\rangle = |\downarrow\rangle_z \qquad \mathcal{P}_2 = \frac{1}{2}$$

$$|\Psi_3\rangle = |\uparrow\rangle_y \qquad \mathcal{P}_3 = \frac{1}{4} \tag{IV. 1. 8}$$

The essential distinction between a pure and a mixed state comes from the definition of the expectation value of an operator. The average value of an observable O for an ensemble of states is given by

$$\overline{\langle O \rangle} = \sum_{j=1}^{N} \mathcal{P}_j \langle O \rangle_j \qquad \langle O_j \rangle = \langle \Psi_j | O | \Psi_j \rangle \tag{IV. 1. 9}$$

Expansion in an orthonormal set of basis states yields

$$\overline{\langle O \rangle} = \sum_{j,n} \mathcal{P}_j \langle \Psi_j | n \rangle \langle n | O | \Psi_j \rangle =$$

$$\sum_{j,n} \langle n | O | \Psi_j \rangle \mathcal{P}_j \langle \Psi_j | n \rangle = \mathrm{Tr}\, O\rho = \mathrm{Tr}\, \rho O \tag{IV. 1. 10}$$

where

$$\rho = \sum_j | \Psi_j \rangle \mathcal{P}_j \langle \Psi_j | \tag{IV. 1. 11}$$

$$\rho_{nm} = \sum_j \langle n | \Psi_j \rangle \mathcal{P}_j \langle \Psi_j | m \rangle \tag{IV. 1. 12}$$

The form of ρ does not arise uniquely from a given ensemble. Many different ensembles (that is, prepared in different ways) can give rise to the same ρ.

It follows immediately from the reality of $\mathcal{P}_j$ [Eq. (IV. 1. 3)], and from the fact that the $|\Psi_j\rangle$ are normalized, that

$$\rho^{+} = \rho \tag{IV. 1.13}$$

and

$$\mathrm{Tr}\ \rho = \sum_j \mathcal{P}_j \langle \Psi_j | \Psi_j \rangle = 1 \tag{IV. 1. 14}$$

Since ρ is hermitean, it can be diagonalized by means of a unitary transformation. In other words, for every ρ, there exists a basis $|\ell\rangle$, not necessarily equal to $|n\rangle$, in which

$$\rho = \sum_{\ell=1}^{M} \mathcal{P}'_\ell |\ell\rangle\langle\ell| \qquad \mathcal{P}'_\ell \geq 0 \qquad \text{(IV. 1. 15)}$$

The second condition in Eq. (IV. 1. 15) follows, since in any representation the expectation value of finding the system in a particular basis state $|k\rangle$ is given by

$$\mathrm{Tr}\,\rho\,\mathbb{P}_k = \mathrm{Tr}\,\rho|k\rangle\langle k| = \sum_j \langle k|\Psi_j\rangle \mathcal{P}_j \langle\Psi_j|k\rangle =$$
$$\sum_j \mathcal{P}_j |\langle\Psi_j|k\rangle|^2 = \langle k|\rho|k\rangle$$

But this expectation value is the probability of the state $|k\rangle$ and is therefore positive. Thus the diagonal elements of ρ are positive in any representation.

We can now distinguish between pure and mixed states. We shall prove the following theorem: the density matrix ρ represents a pure state if, and only if,

$$\rho^2 = \rho \qquad \text{(IV. 1. 16)}$$

To show that Eq. (IV. 1. 16) is satisfied by a ρ arising from a pure state, we note that such a ρ is given by

$$\rho = |\Psi\rangle\langle\Psi|$$

Equation (IV. 1. 16) follows immediately from this form by explicit computation.

To show that Eq. (IV. 1. 16) implies that we have a pure state, we make use of the diagonal form of the density matrix, Eq. (IV. 1. 15). Evaluation of ρ^2 yields

$$\rho = \sum_{\ell} \mathcal{P}'_{\ell} \, |\ell\rangle\langle\ell| \tag{IV. 1. 18}$$

$$\rho^2 = \sum_{\ell, \ell'} \mathcal{P}'_{\ell} \mathcal{P}'_{\ell'} \, |\ell\rangle\langle\ell|\ell'\rangle\langle\ell'| = \sum_{\ell} \mathcal{P}'^2_{\ell} |\ell\rangle\langle\ell| \tag{IV. 1. 19}$$

Thus, we have as a consequence of Eq. (IV. 1. 16) that

$$\mathcal{P}'^2_{\ell} = \mathcal{P}'_{\ell} \qquad \text{for all } \ell \tag{IV. 1. 20}$$

The only possible solutions of Eq. (IV. 1. 20), in view of Eq. (IV. 1. 15), are

$$\mathcal{P}'_{\ell} = \begin{cases} 0 \\ 1 \end{cases} \tag{IV.1.21}$$

Therefore, unless the density matrix vanishes identically, only one $\mathcal{P}'_{\ell}$, say $\mathcal{P}'_{\ell_0}$, can be different from zero, and then its value is unity. The density matrix thus becomes in this case

$$\rho = |\ell_0\rangle\langle\ell_0| \tag{IV.1. 22}$$

and we have to do with a pure state.

In general, if the density matrix does not describe a pure state,

$$\mathrm{Tr}\, \rho^2 \leq \mathrm{Tr}\, \rho = 1$$

since $\mathcal{P}'^2_{\ell} \leqq \mathcal{P}'_{\ell}$ for each ℓ. (IV.1. 23)

Thus, in any representation,

$$\mathrm{Tr}\,\rho^2 = \sum_{n,n'} |\langle n|\rho|n'\rangle|^2 \leq 1 \qquad \text{(IV. 1. 24)}$$

The above relation serves to limit the magnitude of all the elements of ρ.

Examples of density matrices:

a. Spin 1/2 system. The most general ρ is a 2 x 2 matrix. Since its trace is unity, it can depend at most on three real parameters; and since the operators 1, σ_x, σ_y, and σ_z are linearly independent, we can write the general density matrix for spin 1/2 as

$$\rho^{(1/2)} = \tfrac{1}{2}(1 + \vec{P}\cdot\vec{\sigma}) \qquad \text{(IV. 1. 25)}$$

Since $\vec{\sigma}$ is a pseudovector operator, $\vec{P}$ is a pseudovector with real components. The condition on $\mathrm{Tr}\,\rho^2$ serves to limit the values of $|\vec{P}|$. We get by substituting $\rho^{(1/2)}$ in Eq. (IV. 1. 24) that $|\vec{P}|^2 \leq 1$.

b. Two spin 1/2 systems. The density matrix, which can be used to describe N-N scattering, is the product of two spin 1/2 density matrices:

$$\rho = \rho_1^{(1/2)}\rho_2^{(1/2)} = \tfrac{1}{2}(1 + \vec{P}_1\cdot\vec{\sigma}_1)\tfrac{1}{2}(1 + \vec{P}_2\cdot\vec{\sigma}_2)$$

$$[\vec{\sigma}_1, \vec{\sigma}_2] = 0 \qquad \text{(IV.1. 26)}$$

c. Spin 1 system. ρ is a 3 x 3 matrix, depending on eight real parameters. If the spin operator is defined as S_i, 1, S_x, S_y, and S_z and five of the six $\{S_i, S_j\}$ are linearly independent. The most general density matrix describing the state of a vector particle is

$$\rho^{(1)} = \frac{1}{3}(1 + \vec{P} \cdot \vec{S} + \vec{S} \cdot \underset{\approx}{Q} \cdot \vec{S}) \qquad \text{(IV.1.27)}$$

where we are again employing the dyadic notation. $\vec{P}$ is a pseudovector with real components and $\underset{\approx}{Q}$ is a real, symmetric, traceless tensor. The values of $\vec{P}$ and $\underset{\approx}{Q}$ are suitably limited through the condition given by Eq. (IV. 1. 24)

Although the spin of the photon is unity, since it is transverse, its density matrix depends on fewer parameters. We shall not discurs the photon further; any results we derive for spin 1 particles will not in general apply to it.

The vector $\vec{P}$ in all the cases illustrated above can be identified with the polarization. By definition, the polarization is given in terms of the expectation value of the spin:

$$\vec{P} \equiv \overline{\langle \vec{\sigma} \rangle} = \mathrm{Tr}\, \rho^{(1/2)} \vec{\sigma} \qquad \text{(IV. 1. 28)}$$

for spin 1/2, or

$$\vec{P} \equiv \frac{3}{2} \overline{\langle \vec{S} \rangle} = \frac{3}{2}\, \mathrm{Tr}\, \rho^{(1)} \vec{S} \qquad \text{(IV. 1. 29)}$$

for spin 1. These results follow since the trace of an odd number of $\vec{\sigma}$-s or $\vec{S}$-s vanishes and

$$\mathrm{Tr}\ \sigma_i\, \sigma_j = \mathrm{Tr}\, S_i S_j = \delta_{ij} \qquad \text{(IV. 1. 30)}$$

As an example, a state of zero polarization in the spin 1/2 case is described by $\rho = 1/2\, \underset{\approx}{1}$, while the state of 100 percent polarization in the z direction is given by

$$\rho_z^{(1/2)} = 1/2(\underset{\approx}{1} + \sigma_z) \qquad \text{(IV. 1. 31)}$$

which in the $|\uparrow\rangle_z$, $|\downarrow\rangle_z$ representation is

$$\rho_z^{(1/2)} = \begin{pmatrix} 1 & 0 \\ 0 & 0 \end{pmatrix} \tag{IV. 1.32}$$

As expected, it is a pure state.

For a spin 1 particle, in addition to polarization, there is another characteristic associated with the spin, its orientation, which is also needed to describe the state of the system. Thus, if $\rho^{(1)}$ is diagonal in the m representation, so that

$$\rho^{(1)} = \begin{pmatrix} \mathcal{P}_1 & 0 & 0 \\ 0 & \mathcal{P}_0 & 0 \\ 0 & 0 & \mathcal{P}_{-1} \end{pmatrix} \tag{IV. 1. 33}$$

a state of zero polarization is one for which $\mathcal{P}_1 = \mathcal{P}_{-1}$, and one of zero orientation is one for which

$$\mathcal{P}_0 = \tfrac{1}{2}(\mathcal{P}_1 + \mathcal{P}_{-1}) \tag{IV.1. 35}$$

We turn next to the study of reactions involving particles with spin, in terms of density matrices. Consider an ensemble of initial states $|i\rangle$ and a corresponding density matrix ρ_{in}, $\rho_{in} = \sum_i |i\rangle \mathcal{P}_i \langle i|$. Let M denote the transition operator to some final state. For the sake of simplicity, we shall focus our attention on a single channel and consider two types of reactions: scattering and decay processes. In the case of scattering, the identity of the initial and final particles is the same. M is a square matrix and is the transition matrix T_P (defined earlier) written as a matrix in spin space. M need not be square for decay processes.

A given final state f, arising from an initial state $|i\rangle$, is

$$|\varphi_f\rangle = M|i\rangle \tag{IV. 1. 36}$$

The relative final probability in terms of the initial probability $\mathcal{P}_i$ is

$$\langle \varphi_f | \varphi_f \rangle \mathcal{P}_i = \langle i | M M^+ | i \rangle \mathcal{P}_i \qquad \text{(IV. 1. 37)}$$

Consequently, the final distribution Δ_f in terms of the initial density matrix is given by

$$\Delta_f = \sum_f \mathcal{P}_f' = \sum_i \langle i | M^+ M | i \rangle \mathcal{P}_i = \mathrm{Tr}\ M \rho_i M^+ \qquad \text{(IV. 1. 38)}$$

Suitable phase space integrations and divisions by incident fluxes, as required, will convert Δ_f into a cross section or an inverse lifetime, as the case may be. [In what is to follow, we may call the right-hand side of Eq. (IV. 1. 38) a cross section or an inverse lifetime, always implying that the required additional operations are performed to make them so.]

To convert $M\rho_{in} M^+$ into a density matrix for the final states, we have to normalize suitably. First, we must use normalized states, that is,

$$|\varphi_f\rangle \to |f\rangle = \frac{|\varphi_f\rangle}{\sqrt{\langle \varphi_f | \varphi_f \rangle}} = \frac{M|i\rangle}{[\langle i | M^+ M | i \rangle]^{1/2}} \qquad \text{(IV. 1. 39)}$$

Second, we must normalize the probabilities

$$\mathcal{P}_f' \to \mathcal{P}_f \qquad \Sigma \mathcal{P}_f = 1$$

or

$$\mathcal{P}_f = \frac{\mathcal{P}_f'}{\Sigma \mathcal{P}_f'} = \frac{\langle i | M^+ M | i \rangle \mathcal{P}_i}{\sum_{i'} \langle i' | M^+ M | i' \rangle \mathcal{P}_{i'}} \qquad \text{(IV. 1. 40)}$$

The density matrix for the final states is

$$\rho_f = \sum_f |f\rangle \mathcal{P}_f \langle f| = \sum_i \frac{M|i\rangle}{[\langle i|M^+ M|i\rangle]^{\frac{1}{2}}}$$

$$\frac{\langle i|M^+ M|i\rangle \mathcal{P}_i}{\sum_{i'} \langle i'|M^+ M|i'\rangle \mathcal{P}_{i'}} \frac{\langle i|M^+}{[\langle i|M^+ M|i\rangle]^{\frac{1}{2}}}$$

or

$$\rho_f = \frac{M\rho_i M^+}{\mathrm{Tr}\, M\rho_i M^+} \qquad \text{(IV.1.41)}$$

Since we shall make use of it later, we shall also give the final polarization $\vec{P}^{(f)}$ of a spin 1/2 particle that has the initial polarization $\vec{P}^{(i)}$:

$$\vec{P}^{(f)} = \langle\vec{\sigma}\rangle_f = \mathrm{Tr}\, \rho_f \vec{\sigma} = \frac{\mathrm{Tr}\, M\rho_i M^+ \vec{\sigma}}{\mathrm{Tr}\, M\rho_i M^+}$$

Substituting the general form for ρ_i, Eq. (IV.1.25), we get

$$P_j^{(f)} = \frac{\mathrm{Tr}\, MM^+ \sigma_j + P_\ell^{(i)}\, \mathrm{Tr}\, M\sigma_\ell M^+ \sigma_j}{\mathrm{Tr}\, MM^+ + P_\ell^{(i)} \mathrm{Tr}\, M\sigma_\ell M^+} \qquad \text{(IV.1.42)}$$

If we deal with a decay or production process, the final density matrix will not in general be of the same dimensions as the initial matrix. It is always a square matrix, however.

One may well ask why we did not use the S matrix instead of the transition matrix M to define the final density matrix. We are only interested in the changed part of the wave (the scattered or decayed part), not the straight through term. In fact, if we took $|f\rangle$ to be

$$|f\rangle = S|i\rangle$$

the final states and probabilities would be automatically normalized. (This is how the unitarity of S was derived.) Thus ρ_f would be given by

$$\rho_f = S\rho_i S^+$$

S therefore merely produces a unitary transformation of ρ_i and only serves to change its form but not its content.

We shall now proceed to specific applications of density matrices to various reactions.

a. Scattering processes. In addition to density matrices, we shall have to make use of invariance arguments. Since T_P is a scalar in four dimensions, it is necessary (but not sufficient) that T_P be a scalar in three dimensions as well. Let us consider N-N elastic scattering as an example. The transition amplitude M is then a matrix in the product of two spin 1/2 spaces. We work in the center-of-mass system. In addition to the vector operators, only the initial and final relative momenta $\vec{k}_i$, $\vec{k}_f$ are available to make scalars.

The most general operator in the product spin 1/2 space of the two nucleons is a sum of products of scalar form factors that are functions of $\vec{k}_f$, $\vec{k}_i$, and k^2 ($|\vec{k}_i| = |\vec{k}_f| = k$) and scalar operators in spin space.

We define the orthonormal triplet of vectors

$$\hat{e}_1 = \frac{\hat{k}_i \times \hat{k}_f}{|\hat{k}_i \times \hat{k}_f|} \equiv \hat{n} \qquad \hat{e}_2 = \frac{\hat{k}_i - \hat{k}_f}{|\hat{k}_i - \hat{k}_f|} \qquad \hat{e}_3 = \hat{e}_1 \times \hat{e}_2 \tag{IV.1.43}$$

$\hat{e}_1$ is a pseudovector, while $\hat{e}_2$ and $\hat{e}_3$ are vectors. One can then make a list of all possible scalar operators:

1.	1	6.	$\vec{\sigma}_1 \cdot \hat{e}_2 \vec{\sigma}_2 \cdot \hat{e}_2$
2.	$\vec{\sigma}_1 \cdot \vec{\sigma}_2$	7.	$\vec{\sigma}_1 \cdot \hat{e}_3 \vec{\sigma}_2 \cdot \hat{e}_3$
3.	$\vec{\sigma}_1 \cdot \hat{e}_1$	8.	$\vec{\sigma}_1 \cdot \hat{e}_2 \vec{\sigma}_2 \cdot \hat{e}_3$
4.	$\vec{\sigma}_2 \cdot \hat{e}_1$	9.	$\vec{\sigma}_1 \cdot \hat{e}_3 \vec{\sigma}_2 \cdot \hat{e}_2$
5.	$(\vec{\sigma}_1 \times \vec{\sigma}_2) \cdot \hat{e}_1$		(IV. 1.44)

Examples of terms that cannot appear are:

1. Pseudoscalars: $\vec{\sigma}_1 \cdot \hat{e}_2$, $\vec{\sigma}_1 \cdot \hat{e}_2 \vec{\sigma}_2 \cdot \hat{e}_1$

2. The term $\vec{\sigma}_1 \cdot \hat{e}_1 \vec{\sigma}_2 \cdot \hat{e}_1$ because

$$\vec{\sigma}_1 \cdot \hat{e}_1 \vec{\sigma}_2 \cdot \hat{e}_1 + \vec{\sigma}_1 \cdot \hat{e}_2 \vec{\sigma}_2 \cdot \hat{e}_2 + \vec{\sigma}_1 \cdot \hat{e}_3 \vec{\sigma}_2 \cdot \hat{e}_3 = \vec{\sigma}_1 \cdot \vec{\sigma}_2 \qquad \text{(IV. 1. 45)}$$

Thus, only two of the terms on the left-hand side of the equation above are linearly independent. They are already listed as items 6 and 7 above.

Time-reversal invariance reduces the list further. Under Wigner time reversal,

$$\sigma_j \to -\sigma_j \qquad \vec{k}_i \to -\vec{k}_f \qquad \vec{k}_f \to -\vec{k}_i$$

and therefore

$$\hat{e}_1 \to -\hat{e}_1 \qquad \hat{e}_2 \to \hat{e}_2 \qquad \hat{e}_3 \to -\hat{e}_3$$

Thus, items 5, 8, and 9 are not time-reversal invariant and must be dropped from the list.

The most general N-N scattering matrix, using invariant form factors A . . . F, can be written

$$M = A1 + B(\vec{\sigma}_1 \cdot \vec{\sigma}_2 - 1) +$$

$$C(\vec{\sigma}_1 + \vec{\sigma}_2) \cdot \hat{e}_1 + D(\vec{\sigma}_1 - \vec{\sigma}_2) \cdot \hat{e}_1 +$$

$$E\vec{\sigma}_1 \cdot \hat{e}_2 \vec{\sigma}_2 \cdot \hat{e}_2 + F\vec{\sigma}_1 \cdot \hat{e}_3 \vec{\sigma}_2 \cdot \hat{e}_3 \qquad \text{(IV.1.46)}$$

If we deal with P-P scattering, the S matrix, and therefore M, must be symmetrical under the interchange of the two nucleons, and so D must vanish. Thus five complex functions -- A, B, C, E, and F -- completely determine the S matrix for P-P scattering. Since the overall phase is unimportant, nine scalar functions need to be measured to determine S completely for this case.

Various straightforward consequences follow immediately from the simple form of M. First, note that the differential cross section (distribution) of an unpolarized beam of nucleons scattered by unpolarized target nucleons is given by

$$\sigma_0(\theta) = \frac{1}{4} \operatorname{Tr} MM^+ \qquad \text{(IV.1.47)}$$

where Tr means a trace with respect to the spin space of both nucleons. The polarization produced by such a scattering is

$$\vec{P}_1 = \frac{\operatorname{Tr} \vec{\sigma}_1 MM^+}{\operatorname{Tr} MM^+} \qquad \text{(IV.1.48)}$$

The differential cross section of a partially polarized beam of nucleons, scattered by unpolarized target nucleons is

$$\sigma(\theta) = \frac{1}{4}\,\mathrm{Tr}\;MM^+ + \vec{P}_1^{\,(i)} \cdot \frac{1}{4}\,\mathrm{Tr}\;M\vec{\sigma}_1 M^+ \tag{IV. 1. 49}$$

For the specific form of M given in Eq. (IV. 1. 46), we have

$$\mathrm{Tr}\;\vec{\sigma}MM^+ = \mathrm{Tr}\;M\,\vec{\sigma}\,M^+ \tag{IV. 1. 50}$$

This relation is not a trivial identity. It would not hold if we had included the terms violating time-reversal invariance in M.

We can thus write Eq. (IV. 1. 49) in the form

$$\sigma(\theta) = \sigma_0(\theta)\,[1 + \vec{P}^{(i)} \cdot \vec{P}^{(f)}]$$

where by $\vec{P}_f$ we mean the polarization that would be produced for the same $\vec{k}_i$ and $\vec{k}_f$ as occur in the present reaction, but where the incident beam would be unpolarized. By invariance arguments, $\vec{P}_f$ must necessarily be a vector normal to the plane of scattering (since $\hat{n}$ is the only pseudovector that can be made to arise from $\vec{k}_f$ and $\vec{k}_i$. We can therefore write the cross section in the final form

$$\sigma(\theta) = \sigma_0(\theta)\,[\,1 + |\vec{P}^{(f)}|\,\vec{P}^{(i)} \cdot \hat{n}\} \tag{IV. 1. 51}$$

It is easy to see from Eq. (IV. 1. 51) how a scattering can act as a polarization detector. Consider the following two experiments:

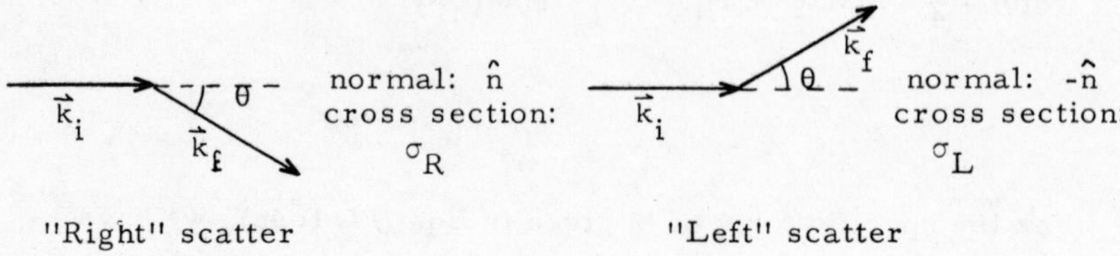

Fig. IV. 2

Define

$$\epsilon = |\vec{P}^{(f)}|\ \vec{P}^{(i)} \cdot \hat{n} \qquad \text{(IV. 1. 52)}$$

There will be a difference in the cross section of a partially polarized beam of particles scattered by an unpolarized target to the right and to the left:

$$\epsilon = \frac{\sigma_R(\theta) - \sigma_L(\theta)}{\sigma_R(\theta) + \sigma_L(\theta)} \qquad \text{(IV. 1. 53)}$$

The cross section is sensitive to the polarization.

We shall not go into further detail on the uses of left-right scattering as a polarization analyzer that can help determine the S matrix. In order to make such a determination, one must perform various double- and triple-scattering experiments at various energies and scattering angles. One must also introduce magnetic fields suitably between scatterings to rotate the polarizations. [One of the consequences of the form in Eq. (IV. 1. 51) is that polarizations $\vec{P}_i$ along the incident beam direction are not detectable by a subsequent scattering.] There have been many such experiments in the last few years.

It turns out that multiple scattering experiments, even if magnetic fields are introduced to rotate polarizations, cannot be used to determine completely the S matrix in N-N scattering. It is necessary to resort to the measurement of spin correlations, that is, observations of quantities like

$$\overline{\langle \vec{\sigma}_1 \cdot \vec{\sigma}_2 \rangle} - \overline{\langle \vec{\sigma}_1 \rangle} \cdot \overline{\langle \vec{\sigma}_2 \rangle}$$

and

$$\overline{\langle \vec{\sigma}_1 \cdot \hat{q}\, \vec{\sigma}_2 \cdot \hat{q} \rangle} - \overline{\langle \vec{\sigma}_1 \cdot \hat{q} \rangle}\ \overline{\langle \vec{\sigma}_2 \cdot \hat{q} \rangle}$$

where $\hat{q}$ is some unit vector.

b. Decays. As the second example, I shall consider the somewhat simpler problem of the measurement of the relative Σ - Λ parity by the study of the polarizations of the outgoing particles in the reaction

$$\Sigma^o \to \Lambda^o + \gamma \qquad \text{(IV. 1. 54)}$$

Since this decay proceeds electromagnetically, one assumes that parity is conserved. The process can therefore be used to measure the relative parity. Since both the Λ and the Σ have spin 1/2, the transition amplitude is a matrix in spin 1/2 space. Since we are considering an electrodynamic process to lowest order, the transition amplitude should be linear in the polarization vector of the photon, $\hat{\varepsilon}^{(\alpha)}$. The only other vector available is $\vec{q}$, the relative γ - Λ momentum in the Σ rest frame. We can make only one scalar operator in spin space for either odd or even parity. The transition amplitudes are

$$M_{even} = A\vec{\sigma} \cdot (\hat{\varepsilon}^{(\alpha)} \times \hat{q}) \qquad \text{(IV. 1. 55)}$$

$$M_{odd} = A' \vec{\sigma} \cdot \hat{\varepsilon}^{(\alpha)} \qquad \text{(IV. 1. 56)}$$

where A and A' are the form factors and are functions of q^2. Because of the transverse polarization of the photon,

$$\hat{\varepsilon}^{(\alpha)} \cdot \hat{q} = 0 \qquad \alpha = 1, 2$$

Substitution of the two transition matrices in Eq. (IV. 1. 42) gives

$$\vec{P}_{\Lambda}\,(\text{even}) = -\vec{P}_{\Sigma} + 2(\hat{\varepsilon}^{(\alpha)} \times \hat{q})[\vec{P}_{\Sigma} \cdot (\hat{\varepsilon}^{(\alpha)} \times \hat{q})] \qquad \text{(IV. 1. 57)}$$

and

$$\vec{P}_{\Lambda}(\text{odd}) = -\vec{P}_{\Sigma} + 2\,\hat{\varepsilon}^{(\alpha)}(\vec{P}_{\Sigma} \cdot \hat{\varepsilon}^{(\alpha)}) \qquad \text{(IV. 1. 58)}$$

The polarization of the Σ is perpendicular to the production plane. The polarization of the Λ can be determined from the asymmetry of the decay distribution. Thus, if we can determine the polarization of the decay photon, we can establish the relative Σ - Λ parity. Consider, for example, $\hat{q}$ in the plane of production, and for simplicity look at the following two special cases:

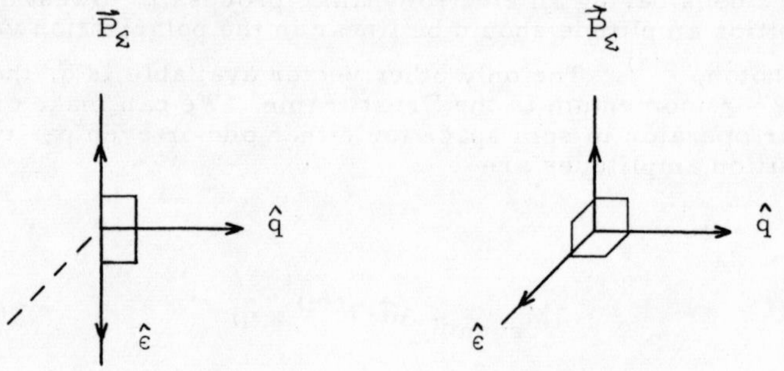

Case I Case II

Fig. IV. 3

Substitution in Eqs. (IV. 1. 57) and (IV. 1. 58) gives

Case I	Case II
$\vec{P}_\Lambda(\text{even}) = -\vec{P}_\Sigma$	$\vec{P}_\Lambda(\text{even}) = +\vec{P}_\Sigma$
$\vec{P}_\Lambda(\text{odd}) = +\vec{P}_\Sigma$	$\vec{P}_\Lambda(\text{odd}) = -\vec{P}_\Sigma$

(IV. 1. 59)

In practice, the polarization of the photon is difficult to measure. It is more convenient to consider the reaction

$$\Sigma^0 \rightarrow \Lambda^0 + e^+ + e^- \qquad \text{(IV. 1. 60)}$$

The polarization of the virtual photon in this reaction is reflected in the angular distribution of the plane of the electron-positron pair. One then studies the correlations of this angle with $\vec{P}_\Lambda$. Presently this approach to measure $P_{\Sigma\Lambda}$ is being pursued experimentally.

Since the photon polarization is difficult to measure, perhaps one could still consider reaction (IV. 1. 54) and sum over the polarizations in Eqs. (IV. 1. 57) and (IV. 1. 58). Unfortunately, the distinction between the two different choices of Λ - Σ parities disappears. Using dyadic notation, and noting that

$$\sum_{\alpha=1}^{2} \hat{\varepsilon}^{(\alpha)} \hat{\varepsilon}^{(\alpha)} = 1 - \hat{q}\hat{q} \qquad \text{(IV. 1. 61)}$$

we obtain, after summation over the photon polarization,

$$\vec{P}_\Lambda = -\hat{q}(\vec{P}_\Sigma \cdot \hat{q}) \qquad \text{(IV. 1. 62)}$$

for both possible choices of parities. Averaging over all decay directions yields

$$\vec{P}_\Lambda = -\frac{1}{3}\vec{P}_\Sigma \qquad (IV.1.63)$$

Although this result does not serve to determine $P_{\Sigma\Lambda}$, it can be used in any given experiment involving Σ^o decay, to determine the polarization of the Σ^o. This input data can be used in the subsequent polarization analysis.

As a final example of the application of density matrix techniques to elementary particle interactions, we shall consider the decay of a spin 1 boson, U. The general density matrix describing the state of such a boson is given by Eq. (IV.1.27). The quantities $\vec{P}$ and $\underset{\approx}{Q}$ are determined by the production process for the boson. If $\vec{k}$ and $\vec{k}'$ are two independent vectors associated with the production process (for example, in the production reaction $\pi + N \to U + N$, $\vec{k}$ and $\vec{k}'$ would be the initial and final relative momenta), $\vec{P}$ will typically have the form

$$\vec{P} = f\vec{k} \times \vec{k}' \qquad (IV.1.64)$$

where f is a scalar form factor. $\underset{\approx}{Q}$ has a somewhat more complicated form in general. If, however, one observes only the direction $\vec{k}$ of the boson in the production process, Q_{ij} must have the simple form

$$\underset{\approx}{\overline{Q}} = g(\hat{k}\,\hat{k} - \frac{1}{3}\underset{\approx}{1}) \qquad (IV.1.65)$$

The boson U can have various decay modes. (We have boson resonances like the ω_j, η, and ρ in mind.) A partial list of final states is: 3π, 2π, $\pi\gamma$, $\gamma\gamma$, $\bar{L}L$, $\pi\bar{L}L$, and $\gamma\bar{L}L$, where L is a generic symbol for e or μ. Let $|U\rangle$ be the state vector of the boson and $U_i \equiv \langle i|u\rangle$ its components in a Cartesian representation of the boson's spin state. We work in the rest frame of the decaying particle. The transition matrix element for the decay of U into any available final state $\langle \alpha\,\vec{a}|$ is

$$\langle \alpha\,\vec{a}|M|U\rangle = \sum_i \langle \alpha\,\vec{a}|M|i\rangle \langle i|U\rangle = \vec{A}^\alpha \cdot \vec{U} \qquad (IV.1.66)$$

The symbol $\vec{a}$ denotes the various momentum vectors available in the final state while α runs over the other degrees of freedom (e.g., photon polarization, lepton spins, etc.). We also used the definition

$$A_i^{\alpha} \equiv \langle \alpha \, \vec{a} \,|\, M \,|\, i \rangle \tag{IV.1.67}$$

for the representation of the transition amplitude.

The spin operator has a simple Cartesian representation, namely,

$$\langle \ell | S_m | n \rangle = i \epsilon_{\ell m n} \tag{IV.1.68}$$

where $\epsilon_{\ell mn}$ is the third-rank Levi-Civita tensor density. The general spin 1 density matrix can therefore be written as

$$\langle \ell | \rho_{in} | n \rangle = \frac{1}{3} (\delta_{\ell n} + i \sum_m P_m \epsilon_{\ell m n} - 2Q_{\ell n}) \tag{IV.1.69}$$

in the Cartesian representation, where we have used the identities

$$\sum_m \epsilon_{\ell i m} \epsilon_{m j n} = 2(\delta_{\ell j} \delta_{in} - \delta_{\ell n} \delta_{ij}) \tag{IV.1.70}$$

and

$$\sum_{ij} \delta_{ij} Q_{ij} = 0 \tag{IV.1.71}$$

Using Eqs. (IV.1.66) and (IV.1.69), we obtain

$$\Theta \equiv \langle \alpha | M \rho_{in} M^{+} | \beta \rangle = A_{\ell}^{\alpha} \langle \ell | \rho_{in} | n \rangle A_n^{+\beta}$$

$$= \frac{1}{3} [\vec{A}^{\alpha} \cdot \vec{A}^{+\beta} - i\vec{P} \cdot (\vec{A}^{\alpha} \times \vec{A}^{+\beta} - 2\vec{A}^{\alpha} \cdot \underset{\approx}{Q} \cdot \vec{A}^{+\beta}] \tag{IV.1.72}$$

with

$$\rho_f = \frac{\Theta}{\mathrm{Tr}\,\Theta}$$

Thus, a change in the dimension of ρ in a decay is no more difficult to consider than the case when the initial and final ρ have the same dimensions.

We shall next consider what form the A-s would have for the various decay modes, using the usual invariance arguments, and shall obtain the corresponding ρ-s.

1. $U \to 3\pi$. There are no spin degrees of freedom in the final state, so Θ and ρ_f are just numbers. Because of momentum conservation, there are only two independent vectors $\hat{p}_1$ and $\hat{p}_2$, which we can choose to be unit vectors in the directions of two of the π mesons in the U rest frame. For this mode, $\vec{A}^{\alpha}$ is given by $\vec{A}_{\pm}$ where

$$\vec{A}_- = F\hat{p}_1 \times \hat{p}_2 \equiv F\vec{n} \tag{IV.1.73}$$

if U is a polar vector, and

$$\vec{A}_+ = F_1\hat{p}_1 + F_2\hat{p}_2 \tag{IV.1.74}$$

for U an axial vector. The functions F, F_1, and F_2 are invariant functions of the meson energies ω_1 and ω_2. Use of Eq. (IV.1.72) leads to the final distributions

$$\Delta_- = \mathrm{Tr}\,\Theta_- = \Theta_- = \frac{1}{3}|F|^2|\vec{n}|^2\,[\underset{\approx}{1} - 2\hat{n}\cdot\underset{\approx}{Q}\cdot\hat{n}] \tag{IV.1.75}$$

and

$$\Delta_+ = A' + B'\vec{P}\cdot\hat{n} + c'\hat{p}_1\cdot\underset{\approx}{Q}\cdot\hat{p}_1 + D'\hat{p}_2\cdot\underset{\approx}{Q}\cdot\hat{p}_2 + E'\hat{p}_1\cdot\underset{\approx}{Q}\cdot\hat{p}_2$$

(IV.1.76)

where A' . . . E' are real form factors related to F_1 and F_2, but they are of no detailed interest here. It is also instructive to average the final distribution over the directions of one of the decay mesons, say $\hat{p}_1$. If f denotes some arbitrary form factor that is a function of ω_1 and ω_2 (observe that $\hat{p}_1 \cdot \hat{p}_2$ is a function of ω_1 and ω_2 because of the conservation of energy; the phase space integration $\int d^3p_1 d^3p_2 \delta(M - \sum_{i=1}^{3} \omega_i)$ ultimately reduces to $\int d\Omega_1 d\Omega_2 d\omega_1$) and if $\int_1 f$ denotes the integral over $\hat{p}_1$, we have:

$$\int_1 \hat{p}_1 f = 0 \tag{IV. 1. 77}$$

$$\int_1 \hat{p}_1\hat{p}_1 f = \tfrac{1}{2}\Big\{(\underset{\approx}{1}_2 - \hat{p}_2\hat{p}_2)\int_1 f + (3\hat{p}_2\hat{p}_2 - \underset{\approx}{1}_2)\int_1 \hat{p}_1 \cdot \hat{p}_2 f\Big\} \tag{IV. 1. 78}$$

The second form above may be checked by taking the trace of both sides and by dotting $\hat{p}_2$ into the dyadics from the left and right on both sides of the expression.

Thus, using Eq. (IV. 1. 78), we have

$$\int_1 |F|^2 \vec{n} \cdot \underset{\approx}{Q} \cdot \vec{n} = \int_1 |F|^2 \epsilon_{ik\ell}\epsilon_{jmn} Q_{ij} p_{1k} p_{2\ell} p_{1m} p_{2n} =$$

$$= \tfrac{1}{2} Q_{ij} \epsilon_{ik\ell}\epsilon_{jmn} p_{2\ell} p_{2n} \delta_{km} \int_1 [\underset{\approx}{1} - (\hat{p}_1 \cdot \hat{p}_2)^2] \, |F|^2$$

$$= -\tfrac{1}{2}\hat{p}_2 \cdot \underset{\approx}{Q} \cdot \hat{p}_2 \int_1 |F|^2 |\vec{n}|^2 \tag{IV. 1. 79}$$

By similar arguments, we finally obtain

$$\overline{\Delta}_{\mp} = C\ [\ 1 + K_{\mp}\ \hat{p}_2 \cdot \underset{\approx}{Q} \cdot \hat{p}_2] \qquad \text{(IV. 1. 80)}$$

where $K_{-} = 1$ and C is an average over appropriate form factors.

2. $U \to \gamma\pi^o$. Let $\hat{q}$ be a unit vector in the photon direction in the U rest frame. In addition, there are photon polarization degrees of freedom. The transition amplitude must be linear in the photon polarization vector $\hat{\varepsilon}^{(\alpha)}$ and is given by

$$\vec{A}_{-}^{(\alpha)} = H(\hat{\varepsilon}^{(\alpha)} \times \hat{q}) \qquad \text{(IV. 1. 81)}$$

and

$$\vec{A}_{+}^{(\alpha)} = H'\ \hat{\varepsilon}^{(\alpha)} \qquad \text{(IV. 1. 82)}$$

for a 1^- and 1^+ U, respectively. The index α runs over 1 and 2. Substitution into Eq. (IV. 1. 72) yields

$$\Theta_{-}^{\alpha\beta} = \frac{1}{3}\ |H|^2 \Big\{ \delta_{\alpha\beta} - i\vec{P}\cdot[(\varepsilon^{(\alpha)} \times \hat{q}) \times (\hat{\varepsilon}^{(\beta)} \times \hat{q})] - $$

$$- 2(\hat{\varepsilon}^{(\alpha)} \times \hat{q}) \cdot \underset{\approx}{Q} \cdot (\hat{\varepsilon}^{(\beta)} \times \hat{q}) \Big\} \qquad \text{(IV. 1.83)}$$

$$\Theta_{+}^{\alpha\beta} = \frac{1}{3}|H'|^2 \Big\{ \delta_{\alpha\beta} - i\vec{P} \cdot (\hat{\varepsilon}^{(\alpha)} \times \hat{\varepsilon}^{(\beta)}) - 2\hat{\varepsilon}^{(\alpha)} \cdot \underset{\approx}{Q} \cdot \hat{\varepsilon}^{(\beta)} \Big\}$$

(IV. 1.84)

3. $U \rightarrow L\bar{L}$. We list only $\vec{A}^{\alpha}$ for this case, to illustrate decays where fermion pairs can occur. We think of this decay, to lowest order in electrodynamics, as due to a U decaying into a virtual photon, which then creates the pair. The interaction at the photon-pair vertex is the usual point electrodynamic interaction. The process can be illustrated by the diagram

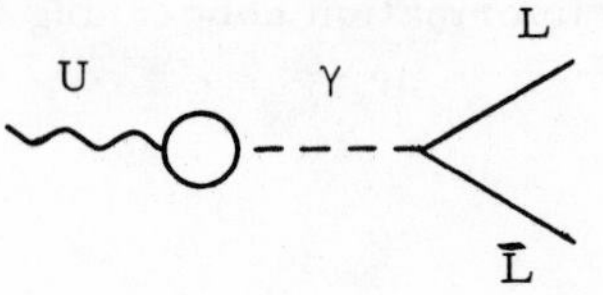

Fig. IV. 4

This mode can occur only for a 1^- boson, to lowest order in the e. m. interaction. The corresponding $\vec{A}^{\alpha}$ is

$$\vec{A}^{tt'} = C\bar{u}_t(r)\,\vec{\gamma}v_{t'}(s) \tag{IV.1.85}$$

where $u_t(r)[v_{t'}(s)]$ are the particle (antiparticle) spinors for 4-momenta r(s).

To illustrate applications of these distributions, consider the decay process $U \rightarrow 3\pi$. The distributions (IV. 1. 75) and (IV. 1. 76) could be used to help determine the spin and parity of U. The existence of an angular correlation of the decay π-s with the direction of the U would be proof that the spin of the U was other than zero. If, further, one took a decay in which the direction of the incident U lay in the plane of the decay, as shown in the accompanying figure, then Δ_- would lead to no angular dependence, since

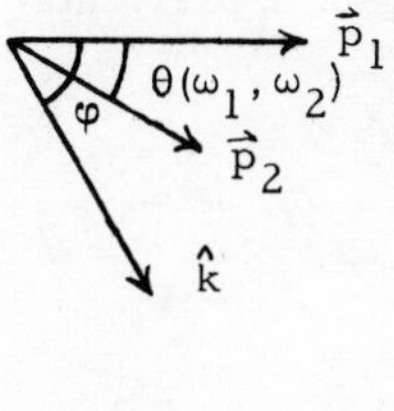

Fig. IV. 5

$\hat{n} \cdot \hat{k} = 0$ for the configuration sketched. On the other hand, Δ_+ would in general (for nonzero $\bar{Q}$) lead to an angular correlation dependent on the angle φ defined in Figure IV. 5. Thus, if one experimentally detected such an angular correlation, one would be able to assert that the spin is other than 0 and 1^-.

These arguments can be turned around, too. Suppose, for example, the spin of the U were known to be 1^-. One could then utilize $\overline{\Delta}_-$ as given by Eq. (IV. 1. 80) to determine Q, which in turn would provide us with information concerning the production process of the U.

References:

General information on density matrices:

1. Fano, Rev. Mod. Phys., 29, 74 (1957).
2. Ter Haar, Reports on Progress in Physics, 24, 304 (1961).

Specific applications:

3. Dalitz, Proc. Roy. Soc. (London), A65, 175 (1952).
4. Wolfenstein and Ashkin, Phys. Rev., 85, 947 (1952).
5. Feldman and Fulton, Nuc. Phys., 8, 106 (1958).
6. Feldman, Fulton, and Wali, Nuovo Cimento, 24, 278 (1962).

2. Selection Rules and Decay Modes of Boson Resonances

In conclusion, I would like to illustrate briefly the direct use of selection rules in the determination of spins and parities. I will restrict myself to the boson resonances, partly because resonances are the topic under discussion and partly because, by listing the various possible decay modes of a boson resonance, we ring many changes on the application of selection rules to various reactions.

Before giving a table of decay modes, I would like to summarize some properties of the various decay channels, or of particles involved in them, with respect to parity (π), charge conjugation (C), spin (J), isotopic spin (T), and G parity (G). The numbers in Table 2 are eigenvalues of the systems with respect to the operator under which they are listed. The symbol ~ denotes that the system is not an eigenvalue of the operator in question. A space is left blank if the listing of a particular eigenvalue is not relevant to the subsequent discussion.

Table 2

Eigenvalue Table of Particles and Systems

	Operator					
Particle	π	C	J	T	G	
γ	-	-	1	~	~	
π^o	-	+	0	1	-	
$\pi^{\pm}$	-	~	0	1	-	
$2\pi^o$	+	+	even	0, 2	+	(1)
$\pi^+\pi^-$	+	+	even	0, 2	+	(1)
	-	-	odd	1	+	(1)
$\pi^o\gamma$		-		~	~	(2)
$\gamma\gamma$		+	$\neq 1$	~	~	(3)
$3\pi^o$	$(-1)^{\ell+L+1}$	+		$\neq 0$	-	(4)
$\pi^+\pi^-\pi^o$	$(-1)^{\ell+L+1}$				-	

Clarifying remarks:

1. The 2π system, because we deal with two identical bosons, must be symmetric overall. Let us denote the state of a π meson by $\vec{\pi}$, where the vector refers to isotopic spin space. Forgetting about normalizations, the T=0, 1, and 2 states of 2π-s must be a scalar, a vector, and a symmetric tensor in i-spin space, respectively. By invariance arguments, they must have the form given in Table 3.

Table 3

T	Invariant structure	Symmetry of π^+ and π^- exchange	Spatial symmetry
0	$\vec{\pi}\cdot\vec{\pi}$	Symmetric	Symmetric
1	$\vec{\pi}\times\vec{\pi}$	Antisymmetric	Antisymmetric
2	$A\{\pi_i, \pi_j\} + B\delta_{ij}\vec{\pi}\cdot\vec{\pi}$	Symmetric	Symmetric

We may also note that $T = 1$ contains no $2\pi^o$ state. Lines 4 to 6 of Table 2 summarize various relevant consequences of the above statements.

2. The symbol ℓ denotes the orbital angular momentum of the $\pi^o\gamma$ system.

3. The significant point of this line is that a spin 1 particle cannot decay into two photons. The simplest way to show this is by an invariance argument. The decay amplitude can depend on $\vec{k}$, the relative momentum of the two photons in the c. m. system of the boson, and must depend linearly on the polarization of each photon. The only scalar we can construct will arise from an $\vec{A}^{\alpha\beta}$:

$$\vec{A}^{\alpha\beta} = F(k^2)\hat{k}(\hat{\varepsilon}_1^{(\alpha)} \cdot \hat{\varepsilon}_2^{(\beta)})$$

(Note that $\hat{k} \times (\hat{\varepsilon}_1 \times \hat{\varepsilon}_2) = (\hat{k} \cdot \hat{\varepsilon}_2)\hat{\varepsilon}_1 - (\hat{k} \cdot \hat{\varepsilon}_1)\hat{\varepsilon}_2$ is ruled out because real photons are transverse.) Because of Bose statistics, $\vec{A}^{\alpha\beta}$ must be symmetric under the interchange of the two photons. But $\hat{k}$ goes into $-\hat{k}$ under such interchange, and so $\vec{A}^{\alpha\beta}$ is in fact antisymmetric.

4. The $T = 0$ state of 3π-s must be of the form $(\vec{\pi} \times \vec{\pi}) \cdot \vec{\pi}$, and therefore no $3\pi^o$ state can have $T = 0$. The symbol ℓ refers to the relative angular momentum of two of the π^o-s, and L to the angular momentum of the third π^o relative to the center of mass of the other two.

We next consider the various decay possibilities of a resonance U, one of whose observed decay modes is $\pi^+\pi^-\pi^o$, and which has no observed 3π decay mode that possesses a net charge. The assumption will therefore be made that U has $T = 0$; consequently, the eigenvalues of G and C to be assigned to this resonance must be the same. The spin-parity assignment 0^+ does not appear in the table below, since the decay $U(0^+) \rightarrow \pi^+\pi^-\pi^o$ violates parity conservation and therefore will not occur. (Since the resonance decays by other than β-decay interactions -- as is indicated by the measured widths -- we shall assume that P and C must be conserved separately in all decays.) Thus, we are not interested in any other decay modes of this particular spin-parity assignment. The various modes involving lepton pairs are not listed below since these modes are not particularly relevant as far as the determination of the spin-parity of U from selection rules is concerned.

The symbols A, F, W, and E in the table below denote, respectively, that the decay is allowed, forbidden, weak (that is, it does not conserve G parity or isotopic spin), or electromagnetic

[E = $0(e^2)$]. The symbol in parenthesis after F denotes at least one of the conservation laws that are violated, or else refers to a note of further explanation. A given decay may violate several conservation laws, but only one is listed in Table 4.

Table 4

Possible Decay Modes of a T=0 Boson with Decay Mode $\pi^+\pi^-\pi^o$

Quantum numbers of the U			Decay Modes						
J	π	C=G	$\pi^+\pi^-\pi^o$	$3\pi^o$	$\pi^+\pi^-\gamma$	$\pi^+\pi^-$	$2\pi^o$	$\pi^o\gamma$	$\gamma\gamma$
0	-	-	A	F(C)	E	F(P)	F(P)	F(*)	F(C)
0	-	+	W	W	E	F(P)	F(P)	F(*)	E^2
1	+	-	A	F(C)	E	F(P)	F(J)	E	F(J)
1	+	+	W	W	E	F(P)	F(J)	F(C)	F(J)
1	-	-	A	F(C)	E	W	F(J)	E	F(J)
1	-	+	W	W	E	F(C)	F(J)	F(C)	F(J)

Remarks:

(*) This decay involves the emission of a γ-ray in a transition $U \rightarrow \pi^o$ which is a J=0 to J=0 transition. Such transitions are absolutely forbidden. A simple argument for showing this is the following: Take the axis of quantization along the direction of the γ. Because the γ is transverse, $m_S = \pm 1$ ($m_S = 0$ is excluded). Since U is assumed to have spin zero, $m_U = 0$ and because of the choice of quantization direction, the z component of the orbital angular momentum of the final state vanishes ($m_L = 0$). Therefore, the azimuthal quantum number cannot be conserved in such a decay.

I should like to make a few comments on the relevance of the above table to the problem of the spin of the η. Because of the need for a particle with $J^{\pi}_T = 1^-_0$ to play a role in the nucleon form factors, the η was assumed initially to have $J^{\pi G}_T = 1^{--}_0$. G was taken to be -1, since it is natural to have the decay of the resonance conserve G and T. However, as can be seen from the structure $(\vec{\pi} \times \vec{\pi}) \cdot \vec{\pi}$ for a T = 0 3π meson state, the transition amplitube must be antisymmetric in the momenta of any two π mesons, and the probability distribution must therefore be symmetric in such interchange. This was not observed to be the case for the initial data, so 1_0^{--} was at least tentatively abandoned as a possible quantum-number assignment. To allow for nonsymmetric distributions, it was natural to choose a G conservation violating $\pi^+\pi^-\pi^o$ decay; that is, G = +1 for the η. Interest then centered on the quantum number assignment 0_0^{-+}, which corresponded to an open slot in a representation of one of the symmetry groups (Gell-Mann's "eight-fold way"). A particle with such quantum number assignments could decay into four π-s, but the η has too small a mass to do this. The 2π mode is forbidden, leaving only $\pi^+\pi^-\pi^o$ and $\pi^+\pi^-\gamma$ as possible modes with no more than two charged decay products. It is not possible to estimate the expected branching ratio into these modes with any precision, but it is not unreasonable to expect, on the basis of the calculations performed, that the $\pi^+\pi^-\pi^o$ mode could dominate the $\pi^+\pi^-\gamma$ decay by a factor of 10 or so. The crucial question is the character of the decay modes of η with all neutral particles. These neutral decay modes are experimentally observed to occur about three times as frequently as the $\pi^+\pi^-\pi^o$ decay. From Table 3 one can see that if at least part of this neutral decay is in the 2γ mode, the quantum numbers of the η must be 0^{-+} (provided the possibility that the spin of the η is greater than 1 is excluded), since this decay is strictly forbidden for all other spin assignments listed in the table. On the other hand, if the $\pi^o\gamma$ mode is seen, the spin of the η cannot be 0^{-+}. In the course of these lectures, a preprint has appeared by the Cambridge bubble-chamber group. The authors claim that they have observed the 2γ decay mode of the η. Thus, the spin of the η appears to be 0^{-+} (if possible spins greater than 1 are excluded from consideration).

References on invariance principles:

1. Wick, Ann. Rev. Nuc. Sci., 8, 1 (1958).
2. Marshak and Sudarshan, Introduction to Elementary Particle Physics, Interscience, New York, 1961.

TOPICS IN QUANTUM ELECTRODYNAMICS

G. Källén
University of Lund

Notes by R. Gudmundsson

CONTENTS

CONTENTS (continued)

1. INTRODUCTION

This course intends to give a survey of some of the standard problems in quantum electrodynamics treated by techniques which perhaps are not quite standard. After a short summary of the properties of free fields, we shall discuss the polarization of the vacuum, the anomalous magnetic moment of the electron, the Lamb shift, and electron-proton scattering, making extensive use of general arguments such as invariances of different kinds and causality. This line of reasoning leads naturally to spectral representations for various quantities, and the weight functions in these formulae are computed with perturbative expansions.

We feel that such an exposition is of value not only for those immediately interested in applications of the formalism but perhaps even more for students who want to investigate the general properties of quantized fields. The spectral representations and the related analyticity properties we are working with here play an essential role in such a general abstract approach. Someone working with the general formalism but without a good understanding of how it looks in practical application is liable either to flounder in very sophisticated mathematical problems or —what is nearly the same thing—to be doing complete nonsense. At the same time we hope to demonstrate that this way of handling practical problems is no more complicated than the standard techniques.

The course is intended to be a short survey and does not attempt to encompass all problems in the field. Consistency problems, especially those related to a nonperturbative treatment, are not discussed. Some of the pitfalls which exist for the special problems of vacuum polarization were discussed in a course given by the author at the Brandeis summer school of 1961. For a fuller account of these and other problems not mentioned here, we refer the reader to the article "Quantenelektrodynamik" in Handbuch der Physik, Band V, Teil 1, Springer-Verlag, 1958. References to original papers usually are not given in this course but can be found in the above-mentioned article.

2. FREE DIRAC FIELD

2-1. Equation of Motion; Lagrangian

The Dirac equation for the free electron is

$$\left(\gamma \frac{\partial}{\partial x} + m\right) \psi(x) = 0 \tag{2.1}$$

The state vector $\psi(x)$ has four components; $\psi_1(x), \ldots, \psi_4(x)$, and γ_μ are 4 x 4 matrices which satisfy the relations

$$\{\gamma_\mu, \gamma_\nu\} \equiv \gamma_\mu \gamma_\nu + \gamma_\nu \gamma_\mu = 2\delta_{\mu\nu} \tag{2.2}$$

If we write out the matrix multiplications in detail, the Dirac equation reads

$$\sum_{\beta=1}^{4} \left[\sum_{\mu=1}^{4} (\gamma_\mu)_{\alpha\beta} \frac{\partial}{\partial x_\mu} + m\,\delta_{\alpha\beta} \right] \psi_\beta(x) = 0 \qquad \text{for } \alpha = 1, \ldots, 4 \tag{2.3}$$

In the following, we shall use the short hand notation of Eq. (2.1). In most cases the explicit form of the γ matrices is not needed. When we need explicit expressions for γ_μ, we shall use the following representations:

$$\gamma_4 = \begin{pmatrix} 1 & 0 \\ 0 & -1 \end{pmatrix} = \begin{pmatrix} 1 & 0 & 0 & 0 \\ 0 & 1 & 0 & 0 \\ 0 & 0 & -1 & 0 \\ 0 & 0 & 0 & -1 \end{pmatrix} \tag{2.4}$$

$$\gamma_k = \begin{pmatrix} 0 & -i\sigma_k \\ i\sigma_k & 0 \end{pmatrix} \qquad k = 1, 2, 3. \tag{2.5}$$

Here, σ_K are the 2 x 2 Pauli spin matrices:

$$\sigma_1 = \begin{pmatrix} 0 & 1 \\ 1 & 0 \end{pmatrix} \qquad \sigma_2 = \begin{pmatrix} 0 & -i \\ i & 0 \end{pmatrix} \qquad \sigma_3 = \begin{pmatrix} 1 & 0 \\ 0 & -1 \end{pmatrix} \tag{2. 6}$$

If we take the complex conjugate of Eq. (2. 1) and multiply it by γ_4 from the right, we get the equation

$$-\frac{\partial \bar{\Psi}(x)}{\partial x} \gamma + m \bar{\Psi}(x) = 0 \tag{2. 7}$$

for the quantity

$$\bar{\Psi}(x) = \Psi^*(x) \gamma_4 \tag{2.7a}$$

With the representation of γ_μ given above, we can find plane-wave solutions

$$\Psi_\alpha(x) = e^{ipx} U_\alpha(\bar{P}) \tag{2.8}$$

to the Dirac equation (we use the metric $px = \bar{p}\bar{x} - p_o x_o$). If we put this Ψ (x) into Eq. (2. 1), we get an eigenvalue problem. For every $\bar{p}$, p_o has to satisfy the equation

$$P_o^2 = \bar{P}^2 + m^2 = E^2 \quad ; \quad E = +\sqrt{\bar{p}^2 + m^2} \tag{2. 9}$$

Hence, we get two possible p_o values, namely, $\pm$ E. To every $\bar{p}$ and p_o we get two independent solutions $u_\alpha^{(r)}(\bar{p})$. Together we have four independent solutions, which we can summarize in Table 1. The solutions with r = 1, 2 correspond to p_o = +E, while the other two solutions correspond to p_o = -E. The constant $\sqrt{(m+E)/2E}$ has been chosen in such a

Table 1

α \ r	1	2	3	4
1	1	0	$\frac{-p_z}{m+E}$	$\frac{-p_x+ip_y}{m+E}$
2	0	1	$\frac{-p_x-ip_y}{m+E}$	$\frac{p_z}{m+E}$
3	$\frac{p_z}{m+E}$	$\frac{p_x-ip_y}{m+E}$	1	0
4	$\frac{p_x+ip_y}{m+E}$	$\frac{-p_z}{m+E}$	0	1

$$\times\sqrt{\frac{m+E}{2E}} \tag{2.10}$$

way that the solutions $u_\alpha^{(r)}(\bar{p})$ are normalized; that is, they satisfy the relation

$$\sum_{\alpha=1}^{4} u_\alpha^{*(r)}(\bar{p})\, u_\alpha^{(s)}(\bar{p}) = \delta_{rs} \tag{2.11}$$

From the table above, one can easily show that

$$\sum_{r=1}^{4} u_\alpha^{*(r)}(\bar{p})\, u_\beta^{(r)}(\bar{p}) = \delta_{\alpha\beta} \tag{2.12}$$

which means that our solutions are complete. In the applications, one often needs the sum over only two r values, namely, over the first two or the last two. These sums are given by

$$\sum_{r=1}^{2} \bar{u}_\alpha^{(r)}(\bar{p})\, u_\beta^{(r)}(\bar{p}) = \frac{-1}{2E}(i\gamma p - m)_{\beta\alpha} \tag{2.13}$$

$$\sum_{r=3}^{4} \bar{U}_{\alpha}^{(r)}(\bar{P})\, U_{\beta}^{(r)}(\bar{P}) = \frac{-1}{2E}(i\gamma P + m)_{\beta\alpha} \tag{2.14}$$

where

$$\bar{U}(\bar{P}) = U^{*}(\bar{P})\,\gamma_{4} \tag{2.15}$$

and

$$P = (\bar{P}, +E) \tag{2.16}$$

The theory outlined so far is good enough for many problems. For instance, one can calculate the energy levels of the hydrogen atom, and the fine structure comes out in very good (even if not complete) agreement with the observations. However, the interpretation of the negative-energy solutions makes difficulties; one cannot simply disregard them. For instance, if ordinary positive-energy electrons are moving along the negative x axis in a potential $V(x)$, which is 0 for $x < o$ and V_o for $x > o$, one finds that there are also negative energy solutions in the region where $x > o$ if $V_o > 2m$ (m = electron mass). This is known as the "Klein paradox." Therefore, we must have some interpretation of the negative-energy solutions. As is well known, the most elegant method is "second quantization," where we treat $\psi(x)$ as an operator instead of as a state vector. But before doing this, we want to reformulate the theory in terms of a Lagrangian formalism. This is only formal mathematics and, in itself, adds nothing to the physical interpretation.

The equation of motion, Eq. (2.1), can be obtained from the Euler-Lagrange equations

$$\frac{\partial}{\partial x_{\mu}} \frac{\partial \mathcal{L}}{\partial \frac{\partial \varphi_{\alpha}}{\partial x_{\mu}}} = \frac{\partial \mathcal{L}}{\partial \varphi_{\alpha}} \tag{2.17}$$

if we choose

$$\mathcal{L} = -\bar{\psi}(x)\left(\gamma \frac{\partial}{\partial x} + m\right)\psi(x) \tag{2.18}$$

as Lagrange function. One could perhaps think that this Lagrangian is identically zero, since $(\gamma\, \partial/\partial x + m)\, \psi(x) = 0$ according to the Dirac equation. However, the field $\psi(x)$ in Eq. (2.18) is not a solution of Eq. (2.1) when used in the variation principle

$$\delta \int \mathcal{L}\, dx = 0 \tag{2.19}$$

The particular $\psi(x)$ that makes Eq. (2.19) stationary is a solution of the Dirac equation (2.1). For this $\psi(x)$, it happens that $\mathcal{L}$ is zero, but that is irrelevant for the variational argument.

The canonical moments are

$$\Pi_\psi = \frac{\partial \mathcal{L}}{\partial \dot{\psi}} = i\psi^* \qquad \Pi_{\bar{\psi}} = \frac{\partial \mathcal{L}}{\partial \dot{\bar{\psi}}} = 0 \tag{2.20}$$

The canonical momentum conjugate to $\bar{\psi}(x)$ is zero, which is a serious obstacle when we want to quantize the formalism. But the $\mathcal{L}$ given by Eq. (2.18) is not the only one which gives the Dirac equation when used in Eq. (2.19). We can also use, for example,

$$\mathcal{L} = -\frac{1}{2}\left[\bar{\psi}\left(\gamma \frac{\partial \psi}{\partial x} + m\psi\right) + \left(-\frac{\partial \bar{\psi}}{\partial x}\gamma + m\bar{\psi}\right)\psi\right] \tag{2.21}$$

and we still get Eq. (2.1). Now, both canonical momenta are different from zero and given by

$$\Pi_\psi(x) = \frac{\partial \mathcal{L}}{\partial \dot{\psi}} = \frac{i}{2}\psi^* \; ; \; \Pi_{\bar{\psi}} = \frac{\partial \mathcal{L}}{\partial \dot{\bar{\psi}}} = \frac{-i}{2}\gamma_4 \psi \tag{2.22}$$

The Hamilton density becomes

$$\mathcal{H} = \frac{1}{2}\left[\bar{\psi}\left(\gamma_k \frac{\partial}{\partial x_k} + m\right)\psi + \left(-\frac{\partial \bar{\psi}}{\partial x_k}\gamma_k + m\bar{\psi}\right)\psi\right] \tag{2.23}$$

where the summation over k goes from 1 to 3. The total Hamiltonian is

$$H = \int d^3x\, \mathcal{H} \tag{2.24}$$

Further, we define a current $j_\mu(x)$ as

$$j_\mu(x) = ie\, \bar{\psi}(x)\, \gamma_\mu\, \psi(x) \tag{2.25}$$

which satisfies the conservation law $\partial j_\mu / \partial x_\mu = 0$. The total charge is

$$Q = -i \int d^3x\, j_4(x) \tag{2.26}$$

and is a constant of motion, that is, $dQ/dt = 0$.

2-2. Second Quantization

We treat $\psi(x)$ as a dynamical variable (operator), not as a state vector. To interpret what that means, we expand $\psi(x)$ in plane waves:

$$\psi_\alpha(x) = \frac{1}{\sqrt{V}} \sum_{\bar{p}} \left\{ \sum_{r=1,2} e^{ipx}\, u_\alpha^{(r)}(\bar{p})\, a^{(r)}(\bar{p}) + \sum_{r=3,4} e^{-ipx}\, u_\alpha^{(r)}(-\bar{p})\, a^{(r)}(\bar{p}) \right\} \tag{2.27}$$

where V is the volume of quantization. Since the last term corresponds to negative-energy solutions, we had exp [i $(\bar{p}\bar{x} + Ex_o)$] from the beginning in this term. However, we changed the variable of summation from $\bar{p}$ to $-\bar{p}$ and thereby got Eq. (2.27). Whether we call the operator $a^{(r)}(-\bar{p})$ or $a^{(r)}(\bar{p})$ is only a matter of definition.

The canonical quantization rules would here mean that

$$\left[a^{(r)}(\bar{p}), a^{*(r')}(\bar{p}') \right] = \delta_{rr'} \delta_{\bar{p}\bar{p}'} \tag{2.28}$$

$$\left[a^{(r)}(\bar{p}), a^{(r')}(\bar{p}') \right] = \left[a^{*(r)}(\bar{p}), a^{*(r')}(\bar{p}') \right] = 0 \tag{2.29}$$

These relations are equivalent to

$$\left[\Pi_{\psi}(x), \psi(x') \right]_{x_o = x_o'} = -i\delta(\bar{x} - \bar{x}') \tag{2.30}$$

and a similar relation between $\Pi_{\bar{\psi}}(x)$ and $\bar{\psi}(x)$.

The state vectors are now

$$|0\rangle$$

$$|\bar{p}, r\rangle = a^{*(r)}(\bar{p})|0\rangle \quad \text{etc.} \tag{2.31}$$

We introduce the particle-number operators

$$N^{(r)}(\bar{p}) = a^{*(r)}(\bar{p})\, a^{(r)}(\bar{p}) \tag{2.32}$$

Disregarding the zero-point energy (charge), the total Hamiltonian and the charge operator can then be written

$$H = \sum_{\bar{p}} E(\bar{p})\left(N^{(1)}(\bar{p}) + N^{(2)}(\bar{p}) - N^{(3)}(\bar{p}) - N^{(4)}(\bar{p})\right) \tag{2.33}$$

$$Q = e \sum_{\bar{p}} \sum_{r=1}^{4} N^{(r)}(\bar{p}) \tag{2.34}$$

We have still exactly the same problem as before, namely, that H does not have a positive definite spectrum, while the eigenvalues of Q are only positive.

From Eqs. (2.28) and (2.29) it follows that

$$\dot{\psi}(x) = i\left[H, \psi(x)\right] \tag{2.35}$$

This is a fundamental relation in "ordinary quantum mechanics," and we want that it shall also be fulfilled in a theory with second quantization. This equation implies

$$\left[a^{(r)}(\bar{p}), N^{(r')}(\bar{p}')\right] = a^{(r)}(\bar{p})\, \delta_{rr'}\, \delta_{\bar{p}\bar{p}'}$$

$$\left[a^{*(r)}(\bar{p}), N^{(r')}(\bar{p}')\right] = -a^{*(r)}(\bar{p})\, \delta_{rr'}\, \delta_{\bar{p}\bar{p}'} \tag{2.36}$$

One solution of these equations is obtained if one requires a and a* to satisfy the commutation relations given by Eqs. (2.28) and (2.29); but this is not the only solution. Another possible solution is obtained if we assume that they satisfy the anticommutation relations

$$\{a^{*(r)}(\bar{p}), a^{(r')}(\bar{p}')\} = \delta_{rr'}\delta_{\bar{p}\bar{p}'} \tag{2.37}$$

$$\{a^{(r)}(\bar{p}), a^{(r')}(\bar{p}')\} = \{a^{*(r)}(\bar{p}), a^{*(r')}(\bar{p}')\} = 0 \tag{2.38}$$

The total Hamiltonian and the charge operator Q now become

$$H = \sum_{\bar{p}} E(\bar{p}) \sum_{r=1}^{4} N^{(r)}(\bar{p}) \tag{2.39}$$

$$Q = e\sum_{\bar{p}} \left(N^{(1)}(\bar{p}) + N^{(2)}(\bar{p}) - N^{(3)}(\bar{p}) - N^{(4)}(\bar{p})\right) \tag{2.40}$$

Equation (2.38) implies that $a^{(r)}(\bar{p})\ a^{(r)}(\bar{p}) = a^{*(r)}(\bar{p})\ a^{*(r)}(\bar{p}) = 0$. After this observation it is easily shown that

$$N(1-N) = 0 \tag{2.41}$$

which means that the eigenvalues of N are only 0 or 1. (If commutation relations are used instead of anticommutation relations the eigenvalues of N are 0, 1, 2, 3, . . .).

These three equations, Eqs. (2.39) through (2.41), are exactly what we want, since Eq. (2.39) implies that the eigenvalues of H are positive definite; Eq. (2.40) implies that the eigenvalues of Q can be both positive (r = 1, 2) and negative (r = 3, 4). To every particle with charge e corresponds an antiparticle with charge -e; and Eq. (2.41) implies that the Pauli exclusion principle holds.

To get more symmetric expressions, we introduce the following new quantities:

$$b^{(1)}_{(\bar{p})} = a^{*(4)}_{(\bar{p})} \quad , \quad b^{(2)}_{(\bar{p})} = a^{*(3)}_{(\bar{p})} \tag{2.42a}$$

$$N^{(+)(r)}_{(\bar{p})} = N^{(r)}_{(\bar{p})} \qquad \text{For } r = 1, 2 \quad , \tag{2.42b}$$

$$N^{(-)(1)}_{(\bar{p})} = N^{(4)}_{(\bar{p})} \quad , \quad N^{(-)(2)}_{(\bar{p})} = N^{(3)}_{(\bar{p})} , \tag{2.42c}$$

$$U^{(+)(r)}_{(\bar{p})} = U^{(r)}_{(\bar{p})} \qquad \text{For } r = 1, 2 \ , \tag{2.42d}$$

$$U^{(-)(1)}_{(\bar{p})} = U^{(4)}_{(\bar{p})} \quad , \quad U^{(-)(2)}_{(\bar{p})} = U^{(3)}_{(\bar{p})} \tag{2.42e}$$

With these notations we get

$$H = \sum_{\bar{p}} E(\bar{p}) \sum_{r=1,2} \left(N^{(+)(r)}_{(\bar{p})} + N^{(-)(r)}_{(\bar{p})} \right) \tag{2.43}$$

$$Q = e \sum_{\bar{p}} \sum_{r=1,2} \left(N^{(+)(r)}_{(\bar{p})} - N^{(-)(r)}_{(\bar{p})} \right) \tag{2.44}$$

The Fourier representation of ψ (x) becomes

$$\psi(x) = \frac{1}{\sqrt{V}} \sum_{\bar{p}, r=1,2} \left[e^{ipx}\, U^{(+)(r)}_{(\bar{p})}\, a^{(r)}_{(\bar{p})} + e^{-ipx}\, U^{(-)(r)}_{(\bar{p})}\, b^{*(r)}_{(\bar{p})} \right] \tag{2.45}$$

where $a^{(r)}(\bar{p})$ absorbs an electron with momentum $\bar{p}$ and spin r, while $b^{*(r)}(\bar{p})$ emits a positron with momentum $\bar{p}$ and spin r.

The commutation relations between $\bar{\psi}$ and ψ are no longer simple objects, while the anticommutators become simple. It is easy to verify that the relation

$$\left\{ \bar{\psi}(x), \psi(x') \right\}_{x_0 = x_0'} = \gamma_4 \; \delta(\bar{x} - \bar{x}') \tag{2.46a}$$

is true for equal times, while

$$\left\{ \bar{\psi}(x), \bar{\psi}(x') \right\} = \left\{ \psi(x), \psi(x') \right\} = 0 \tag{2.46b}$$

hold for all points x and x'.

If $x_0 \neq x'_0$, the relation (2.46a) becomes more complicated. By means of the Fourier representation of ψ and $\bar{\psi}$ in Eq. (2.45), we get

$$\begin{aligned}\left\{\bar{\psi}_\alpha(x), \psi_\beta(x')\right\} = \frac{1}{V} \sum_{\bar{p},\bar{p}'} \sum_{r,r'=1,2} \Big[& e^{-i(px-p'x')} \bar{U}_\alpha^{(+)(r)}(\bar{p}) U_\beta^{(+)(r')}(\bar{p}') \left\{ a^{*(r)}(\bar{p}), a^{(r')}(\bar{p}') \right\} \\ & + (\cdots) \left\{ a^{*(r)}(\bar{p}), b^{*(r')}(\bar{p}') \right\} + (\cdots) \left\{ a^{(r')}(\bar{p}'), b^{(r)}(\bar{p}) \right\} \\ & + e^{i(px-p'x')} \bar{U}_\alpha^{(-)(r)}(-\bar{p}) \; U_\beta^{(-)(r')}(-\bar{p}') \left\{ b^{(r)}(\bar{p}), b^{*(r')}(\bar{p}') \right\} \Big]\end{aligned} \tag{2.47}$$

According to Eqs. (2.37) and (2.38), the first and last anticommutators are $\delta_{rr'}\delta_{\bar{p}\bar{p}'}$, and the summation over r' and $\bar{p}'$ can be performed. Afterward the summation over $\bar{p}$ can be carried out with the aid of Eqs. (2.13) and (2.14). The two other anticommutators are zero. We get

$$\left\{\bar{\Psi}_\alpha(x), \Psi_\beta(x')\right\} = \frac{-1}{V}\sum_{\bar{p}} \frac{1}{2E}\left[e^{ip(x'-x)}(i\gamma p - m)_{\beta\alpha} + e^{-ip(x'-x)}(i\gamma p + m)_{\beta\alpha}\right]$$

$$\rightarrow \frac{-1}{(2\pi)^3}\int \frac{d^3p}{2E}\left[e^{ip(x'-x)}(i\gamma p - m)_{\beta\alpha} + e^{-ip(x'-x)}(i\gamma p + m)_{\beta\alpha}\right]$$

(2.48)

In the last step we let $V \rightarrow \infty$, and the sum goes over to an integral. The transition rule is

$$\frac{1}{V}\sum_{\bar{p}} f(\bar{p}) \rightarrow \frac{1}{(2\pi)^3}\int d^3p\, f(\bar{p}) \tag{2.49}$$

By introducing a δ function, we can write the three-dimensional integral in Eq. (2.48) as a four-dimensional integral, and we get

$$\left\{\bar{\Psi}_\alpha(x), \Psi_\beta(x')\right\} = -iS_{\beta\alpha}(x'-x) \tag{2.50}$$

where

$$S(x) = \frac{-i}{(2\pi)^3} \int dp\, e^{ipx} (i\gamma p - m)\delta(p^2+m^2)\epsilon(p)$$

$$= (\gamma \frac{\partial}{\partial x} - m)\, \Delta(x) \tag{2.51}$$

and

$$\epsilon(p) = \epsilon(p_0) = \frac{p_0}{|p_0|} \tag{2.52}$$

The function $\Delta(x)$ is defined by the integral

$$\Delta(x) = \frac{-i}{(2\pi)^3} \int dp\, e^{ipx}\, \delta(p^2+m^2)\, \epsilon(p) \tag{2.53}$$

and has the following properties:

1. It is Lorentz invariant under all ordinary Lorentz transformations (without time reflection).
2. $\Delta(x) = 0$ for $x^2 > 0$ (spacelike distances) (2.54)
3. $$\frac{\partial \Delta(x)}{\partial x_0}\Big|_{x_0=0} = -\delta(\bar{x}) \tag{2.55}$$
4. $(\square - m^2)\, \Delta(x) = 0$, and hence

$$(\gamma \frac{\partial}{\partial x} + m)\, S(x) = 0 \tag{2.56}$$

5. $$\Delta(x) = \frac{-\epsilon(x)}{2\pi}\left[\delta(x^2) - \frac{m}{2}\, \frac{J_1(\sqrt{-m^2x^2})}{\sqrt{-x^2}}\, \theta(-x^2)\right. \tag{2.57}$$

where

$$\theta(a) = \frac{1+\varepsilon(a)}{2} = \begin{cases} 1 & \text{FOR } a>0 \\ 0 & \text{FOR } a<0 \end{cases} \tag{2.57a}$$

and J_1 is the Bessel function of first order.

These properties are easily shown from the integral representation of Eq. (2.53). The explicit expression (2.57) shows that Δ (x) has a δ singularity on the light cone and is oscillating for $x^2 < 0$, while it vanishes for $x^2 > 0$. Figures 2.1 and 2.2 show the properties of Δ (x).

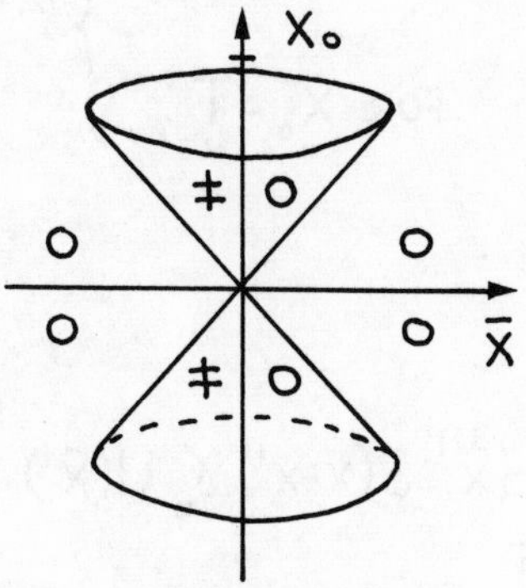

Fig. 2.1

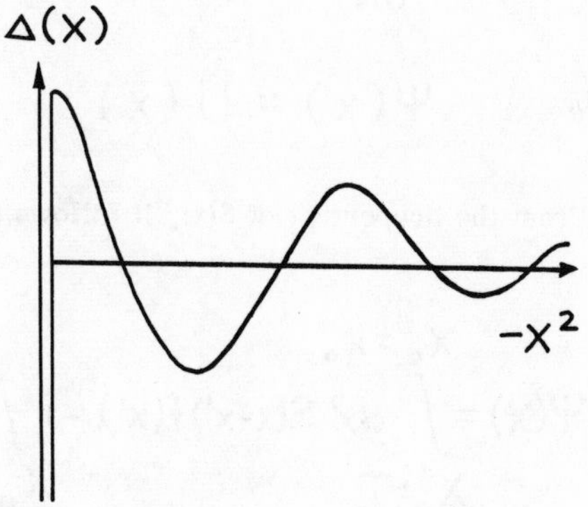

Fig. 2.2

2-3. Solution of a Generalized Cauchy Problem

The two functions Δ (x) and S (x) can be used to solve some (generalized) Cauchy problems.

1. Find a function ψ (x) such that

$$\left.\begin{aligned} &\text{a.} \quad \left(\gamma \frac{\partial}{\partial x} + m\right)\psi(x) = 0 && \text{FOR } x_0 > T \\ &\text{b.} \quad \psi(x) = u(\bar{x}) && \text{FOR } x_0 = T \end{aligned}\right\} \tag{2.58}$$

This is a well-defined problem, since the Dirac equation only contains a time derivative of first order. The solution is

$$\psi(x) = -i \int_{x_0'=T} d^3x' \, S(x-x') \gamma_4 U(\bar{x}') \tag{2.59}$$

This is immediately clear from the properties of Δ (x) and S (x) listed above.

2. A more general problem is to find a function ψ (x) such that

$$\left.\begin{array}{ll} \text{a.} \quad \left(\gamma \frac{\partial}{\partial x} + m\right) \psi(x) = f(x) & \text{FOR } x_0 > T, \\ \text{b.} \quad \psi(x) = U(\bar{x}) & \text{FOR } x_0 = T. \end{array}\right\} \tag{2.60}$$

From the properties of S(x), it follows that

$$\psi(x) = \int_{x_0'=T}^{x_0'=x_0} dx' \, S(x-x') f(x') - i \int_{x_0'=T} d^3x' \, S(x-x') \gamma_4 U(\bar{x}') \tag{2.61}$$

is the solution. Note that there is one term coming from the upper limit of the first integral when the differential operator $\partial/\partial x_0$ is applied to the first term.

Since S(x) vanishes outside the light cone, and since the first integral in Eq. (2.61) has x_0 as its upper limit, we integrate over the backward light cone indicated in Fig. 2.3. The second integral is evaluated over the "circle" in the "plane" $x_0' = T$. To take care of the upper limit, $x_0' = x_0$, it is customary to introduce a new singular function $S_R(x)$ by the equation

$$S_R(x) = -\Theta(x) \, S(x) \quad , \quad \Theta(x) \equiv \Theta(x_0) \tag{2.62}$$

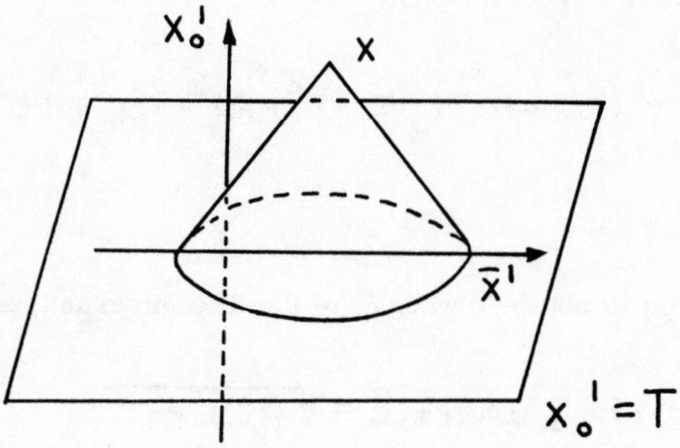

Fig. 2. 3

which satisfies the inhomogenous Dirac equation

$$(\gamma \frac{\partial}{\partial x} + m) \; S_R(x) = -\delta(x) \tag{2.63}$$

Now, the solution ψ (x) can be written

$$\psi(x) = -\int_{x_0'=T}^{\infty} dx' \, S_R(x-x') f(x') - i\int_{x_0'=T} d^3x' \, S(x-x') \gamma_4 U(\bar{x}') \tag{2.64}$$

Since the Fourier transform of δ(x) is a constant, it follows that the Fourier representation of S_R(x) must be of the form

$$S_R(x) = \frac{1}{(2\pi)^4} \int dp \; e^{ipx} \frac{(i\gamma p - m)}{p^2 + m^2} \tag{2.65}$$

This integral is not well defined, since the denominator vanishes on the mass shell. The correct way of interpreting the denominator is to give p_o a small positive imaginary part,

$$(p^2+m^2) \to (p^2+m^2)_R \equiv \bar{p}^2+m^2-(p_o+i\varepsilon)^2; \; \varepsilon > 0 \tag{2.66}$$

and say that $S_R(x)$ is obtained when $\varepsilon \to 0$. The integrand has two poles

$$p_o = \pm E - i\varepsilon \quad , \text{ where } E = \sqrt{\bar{p}^2 + m^2}$$

in the complex p_o plane. Because of the factor exp $(-i\, p_o x_o)$ the path of integration can be closed by a big half circle in the upper (lower) half plane if $x_o < 0$ $(x_o > 0)$. Therefore, the p_o integral is zero if $x_o < 0$, but is given by the sum of the residues if $x_o > 0$. This is just the factor Θ (x) in $S_R(x)$.

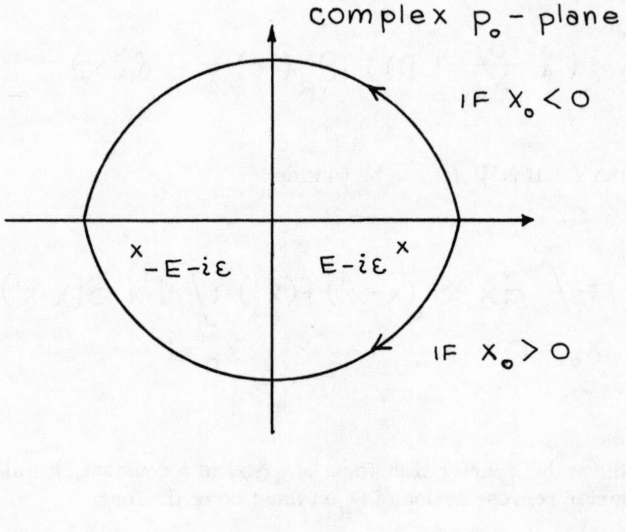

Fig. 2.4

If we interpret the denominator in other ways, we get other solutions of the inhomogeneous Dirac equation (2.63). If, for example,

$$p^2 + m^2 \rightarrow (p^2+m^2)_A \equiv \bar{p}^2 + m^2 - (p_0 - i\varepsilon)^2;\ \varepsilon > 0 \tag{2.67}$$

we get the advanced singular function $S_A(x)$, which vanishes in the forward light cone.

We summarize the discussion above in the following formulas:

$$S_R(x) = \frac{1}{(2\pi)^4}\int dp\, e^{ipx} \frac{i\gamma p - m}{(p^2+m^2)_R} = \left(\gamma\frac{\partial}{\partial x} - m\right)\Delta_R(x) \tag{2.68}$$

$$S_a(x) = \frac{1}{(2\pi)^4}\int dp\, e^{ipx} \frac{i\gamma p - m}{(p^2+m^2)_A} = \left(\gamma\frac{\partial}{\partial x} - m\right)\Delta_A(x) \tag{2.69}$$

$$S_R(x) = \begin{cases} -S(x) & x_0 > 0 \\ 0 & x_0 < 0 \end{cases} \qquad S_A(x) = \begin{cases} 0 & x_0 > 0 \\ S(x) & x_0 < 0 \end{cases} \tag{2.70}$$

$$\frac{1}{(p^2+m^2)_{R,A}} = \frac{1}{(p^2+m^2)_P} \pm i\pi\,\varepsilon(p)\,\delta(p^2+m^2) \tag{2.71}$$

where + belongs to R and − to A.

3. Find a function $\varphi(x)$ such that

$$\begin{aligned}
&\text{a.}\quad (\Box - m^2)\,\varphi(x) = -j(x) && \text{FOR } x_0 > T \\
&\text{b.}\quad \varphi(x) = u(\bar{x}) && \text{FOR } x_0 = T \\
&\text{c.}\quad \frac{\partial \varphi(x)}{\partial x_0} = v(\bar{x}) && \text{FOR } x_0 = T
\end{aligned} \tag{2.72}$$

Since the Klein-Gordon equation contains a second-order derivative with respect to x_0, we must know both $u(\bar{x})$ and $v(\bar{x})$ to get a well-defined mathematical problem. The solution to this problem is

$$\varphi(x) = -\int_{x_0'=T}^{x_0'=x_0} dx' \Delta(x-x') j(x') - \int_{x_0'=T} d^3x' \Big[\Delta(x-x') \times v(\bar{x}') + \frac{\partial \Delta(x-x')}{\partial x_0} u(\bar{x}') \Big] \tag{2.73}$$

2-4. Remark about the Physical Interpretation of the Formalism

The quantization scheme is now complete; however, we are also interested in the value of the commutator between $\bar{\psi}(x)$ and $\psi(x')$ for general points x and x'. One finds that this is not a c-number, as is the anticommutator of Eq. (2.50), but that it is a matrix. The vacuum expectation value of this matrix is

$$\langle 0 | [\bar{\psi}_\alpha(x), \psi_\beta(x')] | 0 \rangle = S^{(1)}_{\beta\alpha}(x'-x) \tag{2.74}$$

$$S^{(1)}(x) = \left(\gamma \frac{\partial}{\partial x} - m\right) \Delta^{(1)}(x) \tag{2.75}$$

$$\Delta^{(1)}(x) = \frac{1}{(2\pi)^3} \int dp\, e^{ipx} \delta(p^2 + m^2) \tag{2.76}$$

The function $\Delta^{(1)}(x)$ can be explicitly computed, and one finds that $\Delta^{(1)}(x) \neq 0$ also for $x^2 > 0$, in contradistinction to $\Delta(x)$. This means that the commutator, Eq. (2.74), does not vanish for spacelike distances between x and x'. If the field ψ (x) could be measured, two such measurements at points separated by a spacelike distance could then influence each other. This would violate causality, and we must conclude that ψ (x) itself is unobservable in principle.

Next let us look at the operator, $j_\mu(x) = ie\,\bar{\psi}(x)\gamma_\mu\psi(x)$ Before second quantization we should call this a probability current (if the factor e is disregarded). Now, we want to interpret j_μ (x) as the electric current, and this is a measurable quantity. One finds after some computation that

$$\left[j_\mu(x), j_\nu(x')\right] = ie^2\left[\bar{\psi}(x)\gamma_\mu S(x-x')\gamma_\nu \times \psi(x') - \bar{\psi}(x')\gamma_\nu S(x'-x)\gamma_\mu\psi(x)\right] \tag{2.77}$$

This commutator vanishes for $(x' - x)^2 > 0$, since it contains S functions and not $S^{(1)}$ functions. Therefore, we do not run into difficulties of the kind discussed above if we assume j_μ (x) to be observable.

3. FREE ELECTROMAGNETIC FIELD

3-1. Equations of Motion; Lagrangian

The electromagnetic fields can be described by the tensor

$$F_{\mu\nu} = \frac{\partial A_\nu(x)}{\partial x_\mu} - \frac{\partial A_\mu(x)}{\partial x_\nu} \tag{3.1}$$

where the vectorpotentials A_μ (x) have to satisfy the relations

$$\Box A_\mu(x) - \frac{\partial}{\partial x_\mu}\left(\frac{\partial A_\nu(x)}{\partial x_\nu}\right) = 0 \tag{3.2}$$

which can be summarized in a variational principle using the Lagrangian

$$\mathcal{L} = -\frac{1}{4} F_{\mu\nu} F_{\mu\nu} \tag{3.3}$$

This theory is invariant under Lorentz and gauge transformations. The last statement means that $F_{\mu\nu}$ and $\mathcal{L}$ do not change if

$$A_\mu(x) \longrightarrow A_\mu(x) + \frac{\partial \Lambda(x)}{\partial x_\mu} \tag{3.4}$$

The function Λ (x) also drops out from the equations of motion, Eq. (3.2). It is customary not to work with the somewhat complicated equations of motion [Eq. (3.2)] but to require $A_\mu(x)$ also to satisfy the Lorentz condition,

$$\frac{\partial A_\nu(x)}{\partial x_\nu} = 0 \tag{3.5}$$

The equations of motion then become

$$\Box A_\mu(x) = 0 \tag{3.6}$$

One can still perform gauge transformations, but only with Λ (x) such that

$$\Box \Lambda(x) = 0 \tag{3.7}$$

The canonical conjugate momenta become

$$\Pi_\mu = \frac{\partial \mathcal{L}}{\partial \dot{A}_\mu} = i F_{4\mu} \tag{3.8}$$

One of the momenta, namely, Π_4 , is zero. We can overcome this difficulty by choosing

$$\mathcal{L} = -\frac{1}{4} F_{\mu\nu} F_{\mu\nu} - \frac{1}{2}\left(\frac{\partial A_\nu}{\partial x_\nu}\right)^2 \tag{3.9}$$

This gives

$$\Pi_k = i F_{4k} \quad , \quad \Pi_4 = i \frac{\partial A_\nu}{\partial x_\nu} \tag{3.10}$$

That is, all canonical momenta are different from zero.

Now, the variational principle gives

$$\Box A_\mu(x) = 0 \tag{3.11}$$

directly, and not Eq. (3.2). From here follows

$$\Box \frac{\partial A_\nu(x)}{\partial x_\nu} = 0 \tag{3.12}$$

which is a weaker condition than the Lorentz condition of Eq. (3.5). We get the Lorentz condition back if we impose the extra boundary conditions

$$\frac{\partial A_\nu(x)}{\partial x_\nu} = 0 \quad \text{and} \quad \frac{\partial}{\partial x_0}\left(\frac{\partial A_\nu(x)}{\partial x_\nu}\right) = 0 \tag{3.12a}$$

for one given time $x_0 = T$. Equations (3.12) and 3.12a) imply that $\partial A_\nu(x)/\partial x_\nu = 0$ for all times.

3-2. Second Quantization

We consider $A_\mu(x)$ and $\Pi_\mu(x)$ as field operators, which have to satisfy the canonical commutation relations

$$\left[\Pi_\mu(x),\ A_\nu(x')\right]_{x_0=x_0'} = -i\,\delta_{\mu\nu}\,\delta(\bar{x}-\bar{x}') \tag{3.13}$$

$$\left[A_\mu(x),\ A_\nu(x')\right]_{x_0=x_0'} = \left[\Pi_\mu(x), \Pi_\nu(x')\right]_{x_0=x_0'} = 0 \tag{3.14}$$

From these relations we can derive the following results:

$$\left[\frac{\partial A_\mu(x)}{\partial x_0},\ A_\nu(x')\right]_{x_0=x_0'} = -i\delta_{\mu\nu}\ \delta(\bar{x}-\bar{x}') \tag{3.15}$$

$$\left[\frac{\partial A_\mu(x)}{\partial x_0},\ \frac{\partial A_\nu(x')}{\partial x_0'}\right]_{x_0=x_0'} = 0 \tag{3.16}$$

However, the relations (3. 13) and (3. 14) with $\Pi_\mu(x)$ and $A_\nu(x)$ are the fundamental ones, which are true also when the fields $A_\nu(x)$ and $\psi(x)$ are coupled. The relations (3. 15) and (3. 16) are not true for the interacting, renormalized fields.

We want to expand the electromagnetic field in plane waves. Since $A_\mu(x)$ is a vector, we have four independent polarization possibilities. To handle this situation, we introduce an orthonormal set of unit vectors $e_\mu^{(\lambda)}$, $\lambda = 1, \ldots, 4$. If we for a moment forget the Lorentz condition of Eq. (3. 5), the most general solution of Eq. (3. 6) can be written

$$A_\mu(x) = \frac{1}{\sqrt{V}} \sum_{\bar{k}} \sum_{\lambda=1}^{4} \frac{e_\mu^{(\lambda)}(\bar{k})}{\sqrt{2\omega}} \left[e^{ikx} a^{(\lambda)}(\bar{k}) + e^{-ikx} a^{+(\lambda)}(\bar{k}) \right] \tag{3.17}$$

where

$$e_\mu^{(\lambda)} e_\mu^{(\lambda')} = \delta_{\lambda\lambda'} \tag{3.18}$$

and

$$\omega = |\bar{k}| \quad , \quad k = (\bar{k}, \omega) \tag{3.19}$$

The factor $\sqrt{2w}$ is introduced to get simple commutation relations for $a^{(\lambda)}(\bar{k})$. The connection between $a^{+(\lambda)}(\bar{k})$ and $a^{(\lambda)}(\bar{k})$ is discussed below.

It is possible to choose the vectors $e_\mu^{(\lambda)}(\bar{k})$ in the following way

$$\bar{e}^{(1)} \cdot \bar{k} = 0 \qquad e_4^{(1)} = 0 \tag{3.20a}$$

$$\bar{e}^{(2)} \cdot \bar{k} = 0 \qquad e_4^{(2)} = 0 \tag{3.20b}$$

$$\bar{e}^{(3)} = \frac{\bar{k}}{\omega} \qquad e_4^{(3)} = 0 \tag{3.20c}$$

$$\bar{e}^{(4)} = 0 \qquad e_4^{(4)} = 1 \tag{3.20d}$$

Note that we do not put $e_4^{(4)} = i$. If we did, the right-hand side of Eq. (3.18) would be equal to -1 instead of +1 for $\lambda = \lambda' = 4$.

We refer to waves with $\lambda = 1, 2$ as light with transversal polarization; waves with $\lambda = 3$, as light with longitudinal polarization; and waves with $\lambda = 4$, as light with scalar polarization. It can be remarked that waves with $\lambda = 3$ and 4 are excluded if the Lorentz condition of Eq. (3.5) holds.

From Eq. (3.20) it follows that $e_\mu^{(\lambda)}$ must satisfy the completeness relation

$$e_\mu^{(\lambda)} e_\nu^{(\lambda)} = \delta_{\mu\nu} \tag{3.21}$$

The fields $A_k(x)$ are Hermitian fields, while $A_4(x)$ is a pure imaginary field. Therefore, we must put

$$a^{+(\lambda)}(\bar{k}) = a^{*(\lambda)}(\bar{k}) \quad ; \lambda \neq 4 \tag{3.22}$$

$$a^{+(4)}(\bar{k}) = -a^{*(4)}(\bar{k}) \tag{3.23}$$

where the asterisk means Hermitian conjugation. From Eqs. (3.13) and (3.14), one can derive the commutator relations:

$$\left[a^{(\lambda)}(\bar{k}), a^{*(\lambda')}(\bar{k}')\right] = \delta_{\lambda\lambda'} \delta_{\bar{k}\bar{k}'} \; ; \lambda \neq 4 \tag{3.24}$$

$$\left[a^{*(4)}(\bar{k}), a^{(4)}(\bar{k}')\right] = \delta_{\bar{k}\bar{k}'} \tag{3.25}$$

These relations imply that $a^{*(\lambda)}(\bar{k})$, $\lambda \neq 4$, is the creation operator of a photon with momentum $\bar{k}$ and polarization λ, while $a^{(4)}(\bar{k})$ [without the asterisk] is a creation operator of a scalar photon with momentum $\bar{k}$. The corresponding annihilation operators are $a^{(\lambda)}(\bar{k})$ and $a^{*(4)}(\bar{k})$.

From the expressions of $\mathcal{L}$ and Π_μ one obtains the total

Hamiltonian, which after some partial integrations can be written

$$H = \frac{1}{2}\int d^3x \left[\frac{\partial A_\mu(x)}{\partial x_0} \frac{\partial A_\mu(x)}{\partial x_0} + \frac{\partial A_\mu(x)}{\partial x_k} \frac{\partial A_\mu(x)}{\partial x_k} \right]$$

$$= \frac{1}{2}\sum_{\bar{k}} \omega \left[\sum_{\lambda=1}^{3} N^{(\lambda)}(\bar{k}) - N^{(4)}(\bar{k}) \right] \tag{3. 26}$$

The number operators $N^{(\lambda)}(\bar{k})$ are defined by the equations

$$N^{(\lambda)}(\bar{k}) = a^{*(\lambda)}(\bar{k})\, a^{(\lambda)}(\bar{k}), \quad \lambda \neq 4 \tag{3. 27}$$

$$N^{(4)}(\bar{k}) = a^{(4)}(\bar{k})\, a^{*(4)}(\bar{k}) \tag{3. 28}$$

These operators have the eigenvalues 0, 1, 2, . . . ; hence, the total Hamiltonian does not have positive definite eigenvalues. This is because so far we have left out the Lorentz condition of Eq. (3. 5). Therefore, we have all kinds of photons in our theory, and not only transversal as we have in classical electromagnetism. But if we try to impose $\partial A_\nu / \partial x_\nu = 0$ as an operator equation, we immediately get a contradiction to the canonical quantization rules. To see this, we compute the commutator between $A_\mu(x)$ and $A_\nu(x')$. Some calculations similar to those for the anticommutator of the Dirac field yield†

$$\left[A_\mu(x),\, A_\nu(x') \right] = -i\,\delta_{\mu\nu}\, D(x' - x) \tag{3. 29}$$

---

†In the future we shall use the functions $D(x)$, $D_R(x)$, $D_A(x)$, and $D^{(1)}(x)$. The integral representations of these functions are obtained by putting m = 0 in the representations of the corresponding Δ functions.

$$D(x) = \Delta(x)\Big|_{m=0} = \frac{-i}{(2\pi)^3}\int dk\, e^{ikx}\,\delta(k^2)\,\varepsilon(k) = -\frac{\varepsilon(x)}{2\pi}\,\delta(x^2) \tag{3.30}$$

If both sides of Eq. (3.29) are differentiated with respect to x_μ, we get

$$\left[\frac{\partial A_\mu(x)}{\partial x_\mu}, A_\nu(x')\right] = -i\,\frac{\partial D(x'-x)}{\partial x_\nu} \tag{3.31}$$

The contradiction is obtained when we note that the left-hand side is zero for all points x and x', but not the right-hand side.

We shall very briefly discuss two methods of incorporating the Lorentz condition into electrodynamics with second quantization. The first one was given by Fermi (1932) and the second one by Gupta and Bleuler (1950). In reality, the second method is only a modification of Fermi's original argument.

3-3. Lorentz Condition

a. <u>Fermi method</u>. To get the classical theory as a limit of the quantized theory, it is not necessary that $\partial A_\nu / \partial x_\nu$ vanishes as an operator; it is enough that the expectation values between physical states of this quantity vanish. This is fulfilled, for example, if we restrict ourselves to considering states $|\Psi\rangle$ such that

$$\frac{\partial A_\nu(x)}{\partial x_\nu}\,|\Psi\rangle = 0 \tag{3.32}$$

But this "auxiliary condition" leads to a contradiction, namely,

$$\langle\Psi|\left[\frac{\partial A_\mu(x)}{\partial x_\mu}, A_\nu(x')\right]|\Psi\rangle = \begin{cases} 0 & \text{According to (3.32)} \\ -i\,\dfrac{\partial D(x'-x)}{\partial x_\nu}\langle\Psi|\Psi\rangle \neq 0 & \text{According to (3.31)} \end{cases} \tag{3.33}$$

If one goes through all the details, the difficulties are found to arise from the fact that $\partial A_\nu / \partial x_\nu$ contains both creation and annihilation operators. This leads to an infinite number of coupled equations to determine the physical states $|\psi\rangle$, and one finds that every state $|\psi\rangle$ which satisfies Eq. (3.32) contains an infinite number of longitudinal and scalar photons. It also follows that the norm of every physical state $|\psi\rangle$ is infinite, and that Eq. (3.33) must be handled with great care and must be defined by some kind of limiting procedure. This can be done, for instance, by giving the photon a small mass μ, and then the physical states get finite norms.

But there are still difficulties. Calculating the expectation value of the anticommutator between $A_\lambda(x)$ and $A_\nu(x')$, one finds the expression

$$\langle 0|\{A_\lambda(x), A_\nu(x')\}|0\rangle = \lim_{\mu\to 0}\left[\delta_{\nu\lambda} - \frac{2}{\mu^2}\frac{\partial^2}{\partial x_\lambda \partial x_\nu}\right]\Delta^{(1)}(x'-x) \tag{3.34}$$

Obviously, the last term tends to infinity when μ tends to zero. However, this term is a kind of gauge function and disappears when gauge-invariant quantities are computed. We can then carry through our calculations as if

$$\langle 0|\{A_\lambda(x), A_\nu(x')\}|0\rangle = \delta_{\nu\lambda} D^{(1)}(x'-x) \tag{3.35}$$

This formula has the same structure as the corresponding relation for scalar fields.

b. Gupta-Bleuler method. If we could formulate the auxiliary condition in such a manner that it contains only annihilation operators, we should avoid the difficulties with infinite norms and infinite gauge functions. Let us therefore replace the Fermi condition with the condition

$$\frac{\partial A_\mu^{(+)}}{\partial x_\mu}|\psi\rangle = 0 \tag{3.36}$$

$$A_\mu^{(+)}(x) = \frac{1}{\sqrt{V}}\sum_{\bar{k}}\sum_{\lambda=1}^{4}\frac{e_\mu^{(\lambda)}}{\sqrt{2\omega}}e^{ikx}a^{(\lambda)}(\bar{k}) \tag{3.37}$$

and require that all $a^{(\lambda)}(\bar{k})$, $\lambda = 1, 2, 3, 4$ are annihilation operators. This last statement is equivalent to putting

$$a^{\dagger(\lambda)}(\bar{k}) = a^{*(\lambda)}(\bar{k}) \quad , \quad \lambda = 1, \ldots, 4 \tag{3.38}$$

instead of Eqs. (3.22) and (3.23). This means that $A_4(x)$ becomes a Hermitian operator instead of a purely imaginary one. However, this is not so serious if only the expectation value of $A_4(x)$ has the correct reality properties. To achieve this, we introduce a metric operator η and define the expectation value of an operator F by the equation

$$\langle F \rangle \equiv \text{exp. value of } F = \langle \psi | \eta F | \psi \rangle \tag{3.39}$$

Since the norm $\langle \psi | \eta | \psi \rangle$ must be real it follows that

$$\eta^* = \eta \tag{3.40}$$

We can also impose a "normalization" condition on η :

$$\eta^2 = 1$$

The requirements

$$\langle A_k(x) \rangle^* = \langle A_k(x) \rangle \text{ and } \langle A_4(x) \rangle^* = -\langle A_4(x) \rangle \tag{3.41}$$

are satisfied if

$$\left[A_k(x), \eta \right] = 0 \quad , \quad \left\{ A_4(x), \eta \right\} = 0 \tag{3.42}$$

In momentum space, these relations become

$$\left[a^{(\lambda)}(\bar{k}), \eta\right] = 0 \quad \lambda \neq 4, \quad \left\{a^{(4)}(\bar{k}), \eta\right\} = 0 \tag{3.43}$$

One finds that an operator η with these properties is diagonal in the representation we use:

$$\langle a|\eta|b\rangle = \delta_{ab}(-1)^{n_a^{(4)}} \tag{3.44}$$

where $n_a^{(4)}$ is the sum of all scalar photons in the state $|a\rangle$. One might think the factor $(-1)^{n_a^{(4)}}$ implies that a physical state could get a negative norm; however, it can be shown that all states which satisfy Eq. (3.36) have positive or zero norm.

The total Hamiltonian now becomes

$$H = \sum_{\bar{k}} \omega \sum_{\lambda=1}^{4} N^{(\lambda)}(\bar{k}) \tag{3.45}$$

where

$$N^{(\lambda)}(\bar{k}) = a^{*(\lambda)}(\bar{k})\, a^{(\lambda)}(\bar{k}) \text{ for \underline{\underline{all}} } \lambda$$

The eigenvalues of this Hamiltonian are positive definite. Further, the expectation value of H is given by

$$\langle\psi|\eta H|\psi\rangle = \sum_{\bar{k}} \omega \sum_{\lambda=1,2} n^{(\lambda)}(\bar{k}) \tag{3.46}$$

where $n^{(\lambda)}(\bar{k})$ means the number of photons with polarization λ and momentum $\bar{k}$ in the state $|\Psi\rangle$. Note that this expectation value only contains transversal photons.

Finally, one finds that

$$\langle 0|\eta\{A_\mu(x), A_\nu(x')\}|0\rangle = \langle 0|\{A_\mu(x), A_\nu(x')\}|0\rangle$$
$$= \delta_{\mu\nu} D^{(1)}(x'-x) \tag{3.47}$$

and we do not encounter the difficulties we had in connection with Eq. (3.34).

In the future we shall use the Gupta-Bleuler method to handle the Lorentz condition, and even if it is not explicitly written out, this method always lies behind the computations.

4. INTERACTING FIELDS

4-1. Equations of Motion. Lagrangian

We are now going to study the interaction between the quantized electron field and the quantized electromagnetic field. The total Lagrangian for this interacting system can be written as follows:

$$\mathcal{L} = \mathcal{L}_\Psi + \mathcal{L}_A + \mathcal{L}^{int} \tag{4.1}$$

$$\mathcal{L}_\Psi = -\frac{1}{2}\left[\bar{\Psi}\left(\gamma\frac{\partial}{\partial x} + m\right)\Psi + \left(-\frac{\partial\bar{\Psi}}{\partial x}\gamma + m\bar{\Psi}\right)\Psi\right] \tag{4.2}$$

$$\mathcal{L}_A = -\frac{1}{4}F_{\mu\nu}F_{\mu\nu} - \frac{1}{2}\left(\frac{\partial A_\nu}{\partial x_\nu}\right)^2 \tag{4.3}$$

$$\mathcal{L}^{int} = A_\mu(x)\, j_\mu(x) \tag{4.4}$$

The terms $\mathcal{L}_\psi$ and $\mathcal{L}_A$ are formally the same as the expressions (2.21) and (3.9), but ψ (x) and A_μ(x) are now the coupled fields and not the free fields. The last term $\mathcal{L}^{int}$ describes the interaction between the fields and is chosen in such a way that the variational principle yields equations of motion similar to those in the nonquantized theory, namely,

$$\left(\gamma\frac{\partial}{\partial x}+m\right)\psi(x) = ie\gamma A(x)\psi(x) \equiv f(x) \tag{4.5}$$

$$\Box A_\mu(x) = \frac{-ie}{2}\left[\bar{\psi}(x),\ \gamma_\mu\ \psi(x)\right] \equiv -j_\mu(x) \tag{4.6}$$

We have made a small change in our definition of the current operator compared with Eq. (2.25). This new definition of j_μ (x) has the advantage that it is more symmetric and that the vacuum eigenvalue of $Q = -i\int d^3x\, j_4(x)$ becomes zero.

Since $\mathcal{L}^{int}$ does not contain any time derivatives of A_μ(x) or ψ (x), the canonical momenta become the same functions of the field operators as for the free fields [Eqs. (2.22) and (3.10)]. We can therefore write the following commutators <u>for equal times</u>:

$$\left[\frac{\partial A_\mu(x)}{\partial x_0},\ A_\nu(x')\right]_{x_0=x_0'} = -i\delta_{\mu\nu}\,\delta(\bar{x}-\bar{x}') \tag{4.7}$$

$$\left\{\bar{\psi}(x),\ \psi(x')\right\}_{x_0=x_0'} = \gamma_4\,\delta(\bar{x}-\bar{x}') \tag{4.8}$$

All other "commutators" are zero for equal times. For free fields it was possible to compute the commutator relations for general points x and x' when these relations were known for equal times. They turned out to be c numbers also for $x_0 \neq x_0'$. This is <u>not</u> true for the coupled fields, since the equations of motion are much more complicated.

By means of the technique described in Sec. 2-3, we can rewrite the differential equation (4.5) as an integral equation in the following way:

$$\psi(x) = \int_T^{x_0} dx' \; S(x-x') \; f(x') - i \int_{x_0'=T} d^3x' \; S(x-x') \gamma_4 \psi(x')$$

$$= \psi_T^{(0)}(x) - \int_T^{\infty} dx' \; S_R(x-x') \; f(x') \tag{4. 9}$$

where

$$\psi_T^{(0)}(x) = -i \int_{x_0'=T} d^3x' \; S(x-x') \; \gamma_4 \; \psi(x') \tag{4. 10}$$

[The shorthand notation in the first integral of Eq. (4. 9), for example, means that the limits in time are T and x_0, while the integration shall be carried through over the whole three-dimentional space.] The formula (4. 9) is no explicit solution to our differential equation since ψ (x) itself also appears inside the integrals. From Eq. (2. 56) it follows that $\psi_T^{(0)}$(x) is a free field since it satisfies the homogenous Dirac equation

$$(\gamma \frac{\partial}{\partial x} + m) \psi_T^{(0)}(x) = 0 \tag{4. 11}$$

This explains why we have put an index (0) on this field.

The integral equation (4. 9) contains more information than the differential equation (4. 5) since in the first one we have also incorporated the boundary-value condition,

$$\psi(x) = \psi_T^{(0)}(x) \qquad \text{for } x_0 = T \tag{4. 12}$$

This equation means that the interacting field $\psi(x)$ is equal to the free field $\psi_T^{(0)}(x)$ at the time $x_0 = T$.

In the same way, we can rewrite Eq. (4.6) as an integral equation

$$A_\mu(x) = A_{\mu T}^{(0)}(x) - \int_T^{x_0} dx' \; D(x-x') \; j_\mu(x') = A_{\mu T}^{(0)}(x)$$

$$+ \int_T^{\infty} dx' \; D_R(x-x') \; j_\mu(x') \tag{4.13}$$

$$A_{\mu T}^{(0)}(x) = -\int_{x_0'=T} d^3x' \left[D(x-x') \frac{\partial A_\mu(x')}{\partial x_0'} + \frac{\partial D(x-x')}{\partial x_0} A_\mu(x') \right] \tag{4.14}$$

where $A_{\mu T}^{(0)}(x)$ is a free field.

We now come to the question of how to choose the boundary values $\psi_T^{(0)}(x)$ and $A_{\mu T}^{(0)}(x)$. Let us discuss the physical situation indicated in Fig. 4.1.

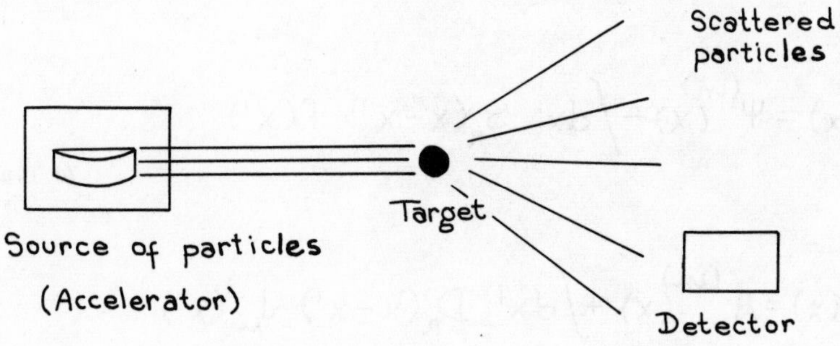

Fig. 4.1

We are not interested in what happens inside the accelerator or inside the detector. Our attention is concentrated on the scattering process, which takes place during a short time, when the particles are near the target. When the particles leave the accelerator, they are so far from the target that we can neglect the interaction and regard them as free particles, that is, as being described by a free field. If we then choose T to be that time when the particles leave the accelerator, it is a good approximation to say that $\psi_T^{(0)}(x)$ describes the beam of particles moving toward the target, the "incoming" particles. Further, we can say that the time it takes for the particles to go from the accelerator to the target is so large compared with the time for the scattering that we can put $T = -\infty$. It is therefore reasonable to choose $T = -\infty$ and to write

$$\lim_{T \to -\infty} \psi_T^{(0)}(x) = \psi^{(in)}(x) \tag{4.15}$$

where $\psi^{in}(x)$ is called the "incoming" field. We assume that the limit of Eq. (4.10) as T goes to $-\infty$ exists in some way or other.

By the same argument we choose

$$\lim_{T \to -\infty} A_{\mu T}^{(0)}(x) = A_\mu^{(in)}(x) \tag{4.16}$$

When these boundary values are given, the integral equations (4.9) and (4.13) read

$$\psi(x) = \psi^{(in)}(x) - \int dx' \; S_R(x-x') \; f(x') \tag{4.17a}$$

$$A_\mu(x) = A_\mu^{(in)}(x) + \int dx' \; D_R(x-x') \; j_\mu(x') \tag{4.17b}$$

They give us (in principle) the fields $\psi(x)$ and $A_\mu(x)$ at any time x_0 as functionals of $\psi^{in}(x)$ and $A_\mu^{in}(x)$. This appears to be a formulation of our problem, which is quite different from standard quantum theory, where one tries to find state vectors that diagonalize the total Hamiltonian. However, these two formulations are really equivalent. When the first problem is solved, we also have the solution of the second one. To make this probable, we shall discuss a simplified problem.

4-2. Electromagnetic Field in Interaction with an External c-Number Current

The equations of motion are the same as Eq. (4.6), but the current $j_\mu(x)$ is now a given c-number function of x, not a functional of the quantized fields. Equation (4.17b) now gives a solution to our problem, not merely an integral equation. Thus, the interacting field $A_\mu(x)$ is the incoming field $A^{in}(x)$ plus a c number.

The total Hamiltonian can be written

$$H(A) = H^{(0)}(A) - \int d^3x \; j_\mu(x) \; A_\mu(x) \tag{4.18}$$

where $H^{(0)}(A)$ is the same functional of the interacting field $A_\mu(x)$ as the free-field Hamiltonian in Eq. (3.26) of the free field. If the solution $A_\mu(x)$ given by Eq. (4.17b) is substituted into the expression for H, one gets

$$H(A) = H^{(0)}(A^{(in)}) + L(A^{(in)}) + E(x_0) \tag{4.19}$$

where $H^{(0)}(A^{in})$ is quadratic [see Eq. (3.26)] and $L(A^{in})$ is linear in A^{in}, while $E(x_0)$ is independent of A^{in}. The linear term turns out to be

$$L(A^{(in)}) = \int d^3x \int dx' \frac{\partial j_\mu(x')}{\partial x_0'} \left[\frac{\partial A_\mu^{(in)}(x)}{\partial x_0} D_R(x-x') \right.$$

$$\left. - A_\mu^{(in)}(x) \frac{\partial D_R(x-x')}{\partial x_0} \right] \tag{4.20}$$

The first term $H^{(o)}(A^{in})$ of the total Hamiltonian is diagonal in the free-particle states, according to our discussion in Sec. 3. Note the difference between $H^{(o)}(A)$, which is not diagonal in this representation, and $H^{(o)}(A^{in})$. The last term E is also diagonal, since it is a c number. But the second term, $L(A^{in})$, is not diagonal. However, from the explicit expression of $L(A^{in})$, it follows that $L(A^{in}) = 0$ if $\partial j_\mu(x) / \partial x_0$, that is, for static currents. If the current $j_\mu(x)$ is static, the total Hamiltonian is diagonal in the free-particle states. If the current depends on time, we do not expect stationary states, and it is meaningless to talk about diagonalizing the Hamiltonian.

However, when the current is static, the integral in Eq. (4.17) does not exist properly. We can overcome this difficulty by replacing the static current $j_\mu(\bar{x})$ by a current $j_\mu(x) = j_\mu(\bar{x})\, g(x_0)$, where $g(x_0) \approx$ constant for finite times and $g(x_0) \rightarrow 0$, when $|x_0| \rightarrow oo$. One possible function is exp $(-\alpha |x_0|)$, where α is a small positive number, which we let tend to zero, when all calculations are finished. The integral in Eq. (4.17b) is then well defined, and one finds that $L(A^{in}) = 0(\alpha)$; that is, $L(A^{in}) \rightarrow 0$ when $\alpha \rightarrow 0$.

4-3. Perturbation Theory

We turn back to the problem of solving Eqs. (4.17a) and (4.17b). The interaction between the fields is described by the charge e. When $x_0 \longrightarrow \pm \infty$, the particles are far from each other (compare the discussion of the scattering problem in Fig. 4.1) and the interaction between them is negligible. It is therefore reasonable to replace the constant charge e by

$$e \longrightarrow e(x_0) = e \ \exp(-\alpha|x_0|) \qquad \alpha \text{ small, positive} \tag{4.21}$$

in order to make all oscillating integrals convergent. This means that the charge is nearly constant for finite times and tends to zero, when $|x_0| \longrightarrow \infty$. In other words, when the particles are far away from each other, they can be regarded as free particles; and when they come closer together, the charge (interaction) has been "adiabatically switched on."

The integral equations for $\psi(x)$ and $A_\mu(x)$ now become

$$\psi(x,\alpha) = \psi^{(in)}(x) - ie\int dx' \ S_R(x-x') e^{-\alpha|x_0'|} \times \gamma A(x',\alpha) \ \psi(x',\alpha) \tag{4.22}$$

$$A_\mu(x,\alpha) = A_\mu^{(in)}(x) + \frac{ie}{2}\int dx' \ D_R(x-x') \times e^{-\alpha|x_0'|}\left[\bar{\psi}(x',\alpha), \gamma_\mu \ \psi(x',\alpha)\right] \tag{4.23}$$

The integrands that were oscillating have now become exponentially damped, and the integrals are therefore well defined. When all computations are finished, we let $\alpha \rightarrow 0$. We can say that the oscillating integrals are interpreted with the aid of an Abelian limit.

If the limits

$$\psi(x) = \lim_{\alpha \to 0} \ \psi(x,\alpha) \tag{4.24}$$

$$A_\mu(x) = \lim_{\alpha \to 0} \ A_\mu(x,\alpha) \tag{4.25}$$

exist, they are the physically interesting quantities, and we hope that these fields also diagonalize the total Hamiltonian (as was the case in our simplified model).

The integral equations (4.22) and (4.23) cannot be solved exactly; we must use some kind of perturbation theory. Since the coupling constant is small, $e^2/4\pi \approx 1/137$, it is probable that we get a good approximation method if we expand the fields in powers of e. Therefore, we write

$$\psi(x) = \sum_{n=0}^{\infty} e^n \psi^{(n)}(x) \tag{4.26}$$

$$A_\mu(x) = \sum_{n=0}^{\infty} e^n A_\mu^{(n)}(x) \tag{4.27}$$

$$j_\mu(x) = \sum_{n=0}^{\infty} e^{n+1} j_\mu^{(n)}(x) \tag{4.28}$$

If these expansions are substituted into Eqs. (4.22) and (4.23) and the expression for $j_\mu(x)$ defined in Eq. (4.6), we get

$$\psi^{(0)}(x) = \psi^{(in)}(x), \tag{4.29}$$

$$\psi^{(1)}(x) = -i \int dx' \, S_R(x-x') \, \gamma A^{(0)}(x') \, \psi^{(0)}(x'), \tag{4.30}$$

$$\bar{\psi}^{(1)}(x) = -i \int dx' \, \bar{\psi}^{(0)}(x') \, \gamma A^{(0)}(x') \, S_A(x'-x), \tag{4.31}$$

$$A_\mu^{(0)}(x) = A_\mu^{(in)}(x), \tag{4.32}$$

$$A_\mu^{(1)}(x) = \frac{i}{2}\int dx'\, D_R(x-x')\left[\overline{\Psi}^{(0)}(x'),\, \gamma_\mu \Psi^{(0)}(x')\right], \tag{4.33}$$

$$j_\mu^{(0)}(x) = \frac{i}{2}\left[\overline{\Psi}^{(0)}(x),\, \gamma_\mu \quad \Psi^{(0)}(x)\right] \tag{4.34}$$

$$\begin{aligned} j_\mu^{(1)}(x) = {} & \frac{1}{2}\int dx'\left[\overline{\Psi}^{(0)}(x),\, \gamma_\mu \; S_R(x-x') \right. \\ & \left. \times \gamma_\nu \Psi^{(0)}(x')\right] A_\nu^{(0)}(x') \\ & + \frac{1}{2}\int dx'\left[\overline{\Psi}^{(0)}(x')\; \gamma_\nu S_A(x'-x),\, \gamma_\mu \Psi^{(0)}(x)\right] A_\nu^{(0)}(x'), \end{aligned} \tag{4.35}$$

$$\begin{aligned} j_\mu^{(2)}(x) = {} & \frac{i}{8}\iint dx'\,dx''\left[\overline{\Psi}^{(0)}(x),\, \gamma_\mu\, S_R(x-x') \right. \\ & \left. \times \gamma_\nu \left\{\Psi^{(0)}(x'),\left[\overline{\Psi}^{(0)}(x''),\, \gamma_\nu \Psi^{(0)}(x'')\right]\right\}\right] D_R(x'-x'') \\ & - \frac{i}{4}\iint dx'\,dx''\left[\overline{\Psi}^{(0)}(x),\, \gamma_\mu\, S_R(x-x')\, \gamma_\nu\, S_R(x'-x'') \right. \\ & \left. \times \gamma_\lambda \Psi^{(0)}(x'')\right]\left\{A_\nu^{(0)}(x'),\, A_\lambda^{(0)}(x'')\right\} - \end{aligned}$$

$$- \frac{i}{2} \iint dx' dx'' \left[\bar{\psi}^{(0)}(x') \gamma A^{(0)}(x') S_A(x'-x), \right.$$

$$\left. \times \gamma_\mu S_R(x-x'') \gamma A^{(0)}(x'') \psi^{(0)}(x'') \right]$$

$$+ \frac{i}{8} \iint dx' dx'' \left[\left\{ \left[\bar{\psi}^{(0)}(x''), \gamma_\nu \psi^{(0)}(x'') \right], \right. \right.$$

$$\left. \left. \times \bar{\psi}^{(0)}(x') \right\} \gamma_\nu S_A(x'-x) \gamma_\mu, \psi^{(0)}(x) \right] D_R(x'-x'')$$

$$- \frac{i}{4} \iint dx' dx'' \left[\bar{\psi}^{(0)}(x'') \gamma_\nu S_A(x''-x') \gamma_\lambda \right.$$

$$\left. \times S_A(x'-x), \gamma_\mu \psi^{(0)}(x) \right] \left\{ A_\nu^{(0)}(x''), A_\lambda^{(0)}(x') \right\}.$$

(4. 36)

Note that we have a kind of causality here. For instance, the field $\psi^{(1)}(x)$ depends only on the value of the incoming field $\psi^{(0)}(x)$ inside the backward light cone, owing to the factor $S_R(x - x')$.

We now return to the question of whether or not this solution of the equations of motion (4. 22) and (4. 23) really diagonalizes the total Hamiltonian H. Basically this Hamiltonian is independent of time, but the replacement $e \rightarrow e \exp(-\alpha|x_0|)$ has made it time-dependent. Therefore, we get

$$\frac{dH}{dx_0} = \frac{\partial H}{\partial x_0} = \frac{\partial H}{\partial e(x_0)} \frac{de(x_0)}{dx_0} = -\int d^3x \frac{\partial \mathcal{L}}{\partial e(x_0)} \frac{de(x_0)}{dx_0}$$

(4. 37)

$$\frac{\partial \mathcal{L}}{\partial e(x_0)} = \frac{i}{2} A_\mu(x)\left[\bar{\Psi}(x), \gamma_\mu \Psi(x)\right] \tag{4.37a}$$

$$\frac{de(x_0)}{dx_0} = \alpha e \; e^{-\alpha|x_0|} \quad (\text{FOR } x_0 < 0) \tag{4.37b}$$

Equation (4.37) can be integrated, for example, between $x_0 = -\infty$ and $x_0 = x_0$, which gives

$$H(A(x), \Psi(x)) = H^{(0)}(A^{(in)}(x), \Psi^{(in)}(x)) - \alpha \frac{ie}{2}$$

$$\times \int_{-\infty}^{x_0} dx' \, e^{-\alpha|x'_0|} A_\mu(x')\left[\bar{\Psi}(x'), \gamma_\mu \Psi(x')\right] \tag{4.38}$$

From this we cannot conclude that $H(A, \Psi) = H^{(0)}(A^{in}, \Psi^{in})$ when $\alpha \to 0$. We must first investigate how the integral in Eq. (4.38) depends on α.

If one computes a matrix element of H between states with different energy momenta, with the aid of the expansions (4.26) and (4.27), it is found that the second term in Eq. (4.38) is proportional to $\alpha/(\alpha + i\,\Delta p_0)$, which tends to zero when $\alpha \to 0$. However, if the states are equal, this term is proportional to $\alpha/\alpha \to 1$ when $\alpha \to 0$. Therefore, the Abelian limit interpretation diagonalizes the total Hamiltonian.

So far, we have only talked about the incoming fields, which are obtained when $T \to -\infty$ in Eqs. (4.10) and (4.14). If we want, the solutions of the equations of motion can also be written:

$$\Psi(x) = \Psi_T^{(0)}(x) - \int_{-\infty}^{T} dx' \; S_A(x - x')\, f(x') \tag{4.39}$$

$$A_\mu(x) = A_{\mu\,T}^{(0)}(x) + \int_{-\infty}^{T} dx'\, D_A(x-x')\, j_\mu(x') \tag{4.40}$$

instead of Eqs. (4.9) and (4.13). If we let $T \to +\infty$, we obtain

$$\psi(x) = \psi^{(out)}(x) - \int dx'\, S_A(x-x')\, f(x') \tag{4.41}$$

$$A_\mu(x) = A_\mu^{(out)}(x) + \int dx'\, D_A(x-x')\, j_\mu(x') \tag{4.42}$$

The fields $\psi^{out}(x)$ and $A_\mu^{out}(x)$ are free fields, which describe the asymptotic properties of the particles present after the scattering.

Here, and in the following, it is always understood that the integrals are interpreted as Abelian limits; that is, we introduce a damping factor $\exp(-\alpha|x_0|)$ in the integrals.

4-4. S Matrix

If we denote the states which describe the particles generated by the accelerator by $|n, in\rangle$ and the states which describe the particles which have been scattered by $|n, out\rangle$, we have

$$H^{(0)}(A^{(in)}, \psi^{(in)})\,|n, in\rangle = E_n\,|n, in\rangle \tag{4.43}$$

$$H^{(0)}(A^{(out)}, \psi^{(out)})\,|n, out\rangle = E_n\,|n, out\rangle \tag{4.44}$$

Physically, it is reasonable to assume that $|n, in\rangle$ and $|n, out\rangle$ form a complete set of states—at least in electrodynamics, where we do not expect bound states. Hence, there must exist a unitary transformation which connects these two sets of states. It is customary to write this connection as

$$|n, out\rangle = S^{-1}|n, in\rangle \tag{4.45}$$

where S is called the S matrix. This matrix gives a complete description of the scattering process. But, there are many problems (involving finite times) which are more conveniently handled without the S matrix: vacuum polarization, Lamb shift, etc. The current operator $j_\mu(x)$ can be used for these cases, while the S matrix only connects $x_o = -\infty$ and $x_o = +\infty$.

From Eqs. (4.43) to (4.45), it follows immediately that

$$H^{(o)}(A^{(out)}, \psi^{(out)}) = S^{-1} H(A^{(in)}, \psi^{(in)}) S \tag{4.46}$$

One can also show that

$$\psi^{out}(x) = S^{-1}\psi^{(in)}(x) S \tag{4.47}$$

$$A_\mu^{(out)}(x) = S^{-1} A_\mu^{(in)}(x) S \tag{4.48}$$

The transition probability from a state $|n\rangle$ to a state $|n'\rangle$ is then given by

$$w_{n,n'} = |\langle n'|S|n\rangle|^2 \tag{4.49}$$

We can expect that

$$\langle n'|S|n\rangle = \delta_{nn'} + \langle m'|R|n\rangle \delta(p'-p) \tag{4.50}$$

where p and p' are the energy-momentum vectors for the states $|n\rangle$ and $|n'\rangle$. We now have to square a δ function; but δ^2 is a meaningless symbol. However, in practical calculations, the δ function comes from an integral,

$$\delta(p-p') = \frac{1}{(2\pi)^4}\int dx\, e^{ix(p-p')} \tag{4.51}$$

This expression can be formally squared, and one gets

$$[\delta(p-p')]^2 = \delta(p-p')\frac{1}{(2\pi)^4}\int dx = \delta(p-p')\frac{VT}{(2\pi)^4} \tag{4.52}$$

where V is the volume of periodicity and T an effective time of interaction. This really means that the transition probability per unit time is given by

$$\frac{\omega_{nn'}}{T} = \frac{V}{(2\pi)^4}|\langle n'|R|n\rangle|^2\delta(p'-p) \tag{4.53}$$

Of course, the rigor of this argument is negligible; nonetheless, in effect, it gives a convenient rule for computing transition probabilities from the S matrix. The result is correct and can be proved more rigorously.

The S matrix can be computed in the following way: From Eqs. (4.47), (4.41), and (4.17a) it follows that (without writing out the adiabatic damping factors explicitly)

$$S^{-1}\psi^{(in)}(x)S = \psi^{(out)}(x) = \psi(x) + \int dx'\; S_A(x-x')f(x')$$

$$= \psi^{(in)}(x) + \int dx'[S_A(x-x') - S_R(x-x')]\,f(x')$$

$$= \psi^{(in)}(x) + \int dx'\; S(x-x')\;f(x') \tag{4.54}$$

Multiplying by S from the left, we get

$$\left[S, \psi^{(in)}(x)\right] = -S\int dx'\ S(x-x')\ f(x') \tag{4.55}$$

In the same way, we can show that

$$\left[S, A_\mu^{(in)}(x)\right] = S\int dx'\ D(x-x')\ j_\mu(x') \tag{4.56}$$

Since the operators $\psi^{in}(x)$ and $A_\mu^{in}(x)$ form a complete set of dynamic variables, these equations determine the S matrix (up to an arbitrary phase factor). The solution (in perturbation theory and with a particular choice of the arbitrary phase) is given by

$$S = 1 - i\int dx_0'\ H_{int}^{(0)}(x_0') - \frac{1}{2}\iint dx_0'\ dx_0'' \times T\left(H_{int}^{(0)}(x_0')\ H_{int}^{(0)}(x_0'')\right) + \cdots \tag{4.57}$$

$$H_{int}^{(0)}(x_0) = -e\int d^3x\ A_\mu^{(in)}(x)\ j_\mu^{(in)}(x) \tag{4.58}$$

The symbol T means the time-ordered product,

$$T(F(x)G(x')) = \begin{cases} F(x)\ G(x') & \text{if } x_0 > x_0' \\ G(x')\ F(x) & \text{if } x_0' > x_0 \end{cases} \tag{4.59}$$

(If the operators F(x) and G(x') anticommute, we have a minus sign in front of G(x') F(x) for $x_0' > x_0$.)

We shall use the S matrix only in the final major section, where we shall study electron-proton scattering. In the next two sections, we shall work with the field operators themselves, not with the S matrix.

5. VACUUM POLARIZATION

5-1. External Field; Charge Renormalization

Suppose a high-frequency generator is producing a field $A_\mu^{ext}(x)$ between two plates of a condenser. This field can be computed with the aid of classical electromagnetic theory. It can also be measured with the aid of a test body (Fig. 5.1). If the accuracy of the measurement were

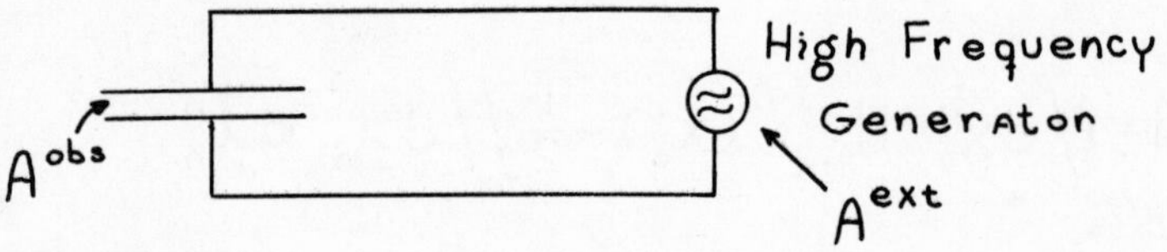

Fig. 5.1

high enough, we would find that $A^{obs}(x) \neq A^{ext}(x)$. This can be explained as an effect caused by the virtual and real particles created by the external field. This is a situation similar to that in a dielectric medium, where the applied and measured field are not equal because the medium becomes polarized.

We shall try to calculate this polarization of the vacuum. We start from the equations of motion

$$\left(\gamma \frac{\partial}{\partial x} + m\right)\psi(x) = f'(x) \equiv ie\gamma\left(A(x) + A^{ext}(x)\right)\psi(x) \tag{5.1}$$

$$\Box A_\mu(x) = -j_\mu(x) \equiv -\frac{ie}{2}\left[\bar{\Psi}(x), \gamma_\mu \Psi(x)\right] \tag{5.2}$$

where $A_\mu(x)$ stands for the radiation field and $A_\mu^{ext}(x)$ for the external field, which is a c number. The "solution" to these equations is given by Eqs. (4.17a and b) if f(x') is replaced by f'(x'). The fields $A_\mu(x)$ and $\Psi(x)$ are expanded in powers of e as in Eqs. (4.26) to (4.28), and the external field is treated as "weak." This yields

$$\Psi^{(1)}(x) = -i\int dx'\, S_R(x-x')\,\gamma\left(A^{(0)}(x') + A^{ext}(x')\right)\Psi^{(0)}(x'), \tag{5.3}$$

$$j_\mu^{(0)}(x) = \frac{i}{2}\left[\bar{\Psi}^{(0)}(x), \gamma_\mu \Psi^{(0)}(x)\right], \tag{5.4}$$

$$j_\mu^{(1)}(x) = \frac{1}{2}\int dx'\Big(\left[\bar{\Psi}^{(0)}(x), \gamma_\mu S_R(x-x')\gamma_\nu \Psi^{(0)}(x')\right]$$

$$+\left[\bar{\Psi}^{(0)}(x')\gamma_\nu S_A(x'-x), \gamma_\mu \Psi^{(0)}(x)\right]\Big)\left(A_\nu^{(0)}(x') + A_\nu^{ext}(x')\right) \tag{5.5}$$

We assume that there are no particles present in our system at $t = -\infty$. Therefore, the incoming state is $|0\rangle$, and we must compute

$$\delta j_\mu(x) = \langle 0|\, j_\mu(x)\,|0\rangle = e\langle 0|\, j_\mu^{(0)}(x)\,|0\rangle +$$

$$+e^2\langle 0|j_\mu^{(1)}(x)|0\rangle+\cdots=\frac{e^2}{2}\int dx'\,A_\nu^{ext}(x')$$

$$\times\Big(\langle 0|\left[\overline{\Psi}^{(0)}(x),\ \gamma_\mu\,S_R(x-x')\,\gamma_\nu\Psi^{(0)}(x')\right]|0\rangle$$

$$+\langle 0|\left[\overline{\Psi}^{(0)}(x')\ \gamma_\nu\ S_A(x'-x),\ \gamma_\mu\right.$$

$$\left.\times\Psi^{(0)}(x)\ \right]|0\rangle\Big)+\cdots. \tag{5.6}$$

[Note that $\langle 0|\,j_\mu^{(0)}(x)\,|0\rangle = 0$ and $\langle 0\,|\,A_\mu^{(0)}(x)\,|0\rangle = 0.$] The vacuum expectation values in Eq. (5.6) are easily calculated, and the first approximation of $\delta\, j_\mu(x)$ becomes

$$\delta j_\mu(x)=\int dx'\quad K_{\mu\nu}(x-x')\,A_\nu^{ext}(x') \tag{5.7}$$

$$K_{\mu\nu}(x-x')=\frac{e^2}{2}\Big(\mathrm{Tr}\left[\gamma_\mu\ S_R(x-x')\ \gamma_\nu\ S^{(1)}(x'-x)\right]$$

$$+\mathrm{Tr}\left[\gamma_\mu\ S^{(1)}(x-x')\ \gamma_\nu\ S_A(x'-x)\right]\Big) \tag{5.8}$$

These equations show that, as soon as we have an external field, we get an induced current $\delta\, j_\mu(x)$.

To handle the kernel $K_{\mu\nu}(x - x')$, we introduce its Fourier representation

$$K_{\mu\nu}(x-x')=\frac{1}{(2\pi)^4}\int dp\,e^{ip(x-x')}K_{\mu\nu}(p) \tag{5.9}$$

$$K_{\mu\nu}(p) = \frac{e^2}{16\pi^3} \iint d\underset{\sim}{q}\, d\underset{\sim}{q}'\, \delta(\underset{\sim}{p}-\underset{\sim}{q}+\underset{\sim}{q}')$$

$$\times \left(\frac{\delta(\underset{\sim}{q}'^2+m^2)}{(\underset{\sim}{q}^2+m^2)_R} + \frac{\delta(\underset{\sim}{q}^2+m^2)}{(\underset{\sim}{q}'^2+m^2)_A} \right) \times \mathrm{Tr}\Big[\gamma_\mu (i\gamma \underset{\sim}{q} - m)$$

$$\times \gamma_\nu (i\gamma \underset{\sim}{q}' - m) \Big] \tag{5.10}$$

where $K_{\mu\nu}(p)$ is obtained by using the Fourier representations of $S_R(x)$ and $S_A(x)$, Eqs. (2.68) and (2.69). The quantity $K_{\mu\nu}(p)$ transforms as a tensor (under Lorentz transformations) and depends only on the vector p. The most general form of $K_{\mu\nu}(p)$ must therefore be

$$K_{\mu\nu}(p) = p_\mu p_\nu G(p) + \delta_{\mu\nu} H(p) \tag{5.11}$$

where G(p) and H(p) are invariant functions. (They are not necessarily functions of p^2 only, since they can also depend on the sign of p_o.) Consequently, we have only two functions to compute instead of the sixteen elements of $K_{\mu\nu}(p)$.

The Dirac equation implies that

$$\frac{\partial}{\partial x_\mu} \langle 0 | j_\mu(x) | 0 \rangle = 0 \tag{5.12}$$

which means that the current is conserved. In p space, this becomes

$$p_\mu \delta j_\mu(p) = 0 \tag{5.13}$$

The convolution integral of Eq. (5.7) becomes a product in p space; that is,

$$\delta j_\mu(p) = K_{\mu\nu}(p) A_\nu^{\mathrm{ext}}(p) \tag{5.14}$$

Since this is true for all $A^{ext}(p)$, Eqs. (5.13) and (5.14) imply that

$$P_\mu K_{\mu\nu}(p) = 0 \tag{5.15}$$

or, according to Eq. (5.11),

$$P_\nu \left(p^2 G(p) + H(p)\right) = 0 \tag{5.16}$$

Hence,

$$K_{\mu\nu}(p) = (P_\mu P_\nu - \delta_{\mu\nu} P^2)\, G(P) \tag{5.17}$$

and we have only one function to compute. Put $\nu = \mu$ and summing over μ in Eq. (5.17) gives

$$G(p) = \frac{K_{\mu\mu}(p)}{-3p^2} = \frac{-e^2}{6p^2(2\pi)^3} \iint dq\, dq'\, \delta(p - q + q')$$

$$\times \mathrm{Tr}\left[\gamma_\mu (i\gamma q - m)\, \gamma_\mu (i\gamma q' - m\right] \times \left\{ \frac{\delta(q'^2 + m^2)}{(q^2 + m^2)_P} \right.$$

$$+ \frac{\delta(q^2 + m^2)}{(q'^2 + m^2)_P} + i\pi\, \delta(q^2 + m^2)\, \delta(q'^2 + m^2)$$

$$\left. \times \left[\varepsilon(q) - \varepsilon(q')\right] \right\} \tag{5.18}$$

where we have used Eq. (2.71). The imaginary part of G(p) becomes

$$\mathcal{J}m\, G(p) = \frac{-e^2\pi}{6p^2(2\pi)^3}\iint dq\, dq'\, \delta(p-q+q')$$

$$\times\, \delta(q^2+m^2)\, \delta(q'^2+m^2) \times \left[\varepsilon(q) - \varepsilon(q')\right]$$

$$\times\, \mathrm{Tr}\left[\gamma_\mu (i\gamma q - m)\, \gamma_\mu\, (i\gamma q' - m)\right] \tag{5.19}$$

We now summarize some formulas that are convenient for trace calculations:

$$\gamma_\mu \gamma_\mu = 4 \quad , \quad \gamma_\mu \gamma_\nu \gamma_\lambda \gamma_\mu = 4\delta_{\nu\lambda} \tag{5.20}$$

$$\gamma_\mu \gamma_\lambda \gamma_\mu = -2\gamma_\mu \quad , \quad \gamma_\mu \gamma_\nu \gamma_\lambda \gamma_\sigma \gamma_\mu = -2\gamma_\sigma \gamma_\lambda \gamma_\nu \tag{5.21}$$

$$\mathrm{Tr}\left[\gamma_\mu \gamma_\nu\right] = 4\delta_{\mu\nu} \tag{5.22}$$

$$\mathrm{Tr}\left[\text{odd number of } \gamma\text{'s}\right] = 0 \tag{5.23}$$

By means of these formulas, we get

$$\mathrm{Tr}\left[\gamma_\mu (i\gamma q - m)\gamma_\mu (i\gamma q' - m)\right] = -2\,\mathrm{Tr}\left[(i\gamma q + 2m)\right.$$

$$\left.\times (i\gamma q' - m)\right] = 2\,\mathrm{Tr}\left[\gamma q\, \gamma q'\right] + 4m^2\, \mathrm{Tr}\left[1\right]$$

$$= 8(qq' + 2m^2) \tag{5.24}$$

If this expression is substituted in Eq. (5.19) and the q' integration is performed, with the aid of the first δ function, we get

$$\mathrm{Im}\, G(p) = \frac{-e^2}{6p^2\pi^2} \int dq\, \delta(q^2+m^2)\, \delta((q-p)^2+m^2)$$

$$\times (q^2 - qp + 2m^2)[\epsilon(q) - \epsilon(q-p)] \tag{5.25}$$

The integral is Lorentz invariant and can be computed in a special coordinate system. It is easily seen that Im G(p) = 0 if $p^2 \geq 0$. (For example, if $p^2 > 0$, we can choose a coordinate system such that $p_o = 0$. The factor involving the ϵ functions then becomes $[\epsilon(q) - \epsilon(q)] = 0$.) It is therefore enough to compute Im G(p) for $p^2 < 0$, and we can choose a coordinate system such that $\bar{p} = 0$. In this system we get

$$\mathrm{Im}\, G(p) = \frac{-e^2}{6p^2\pi^2} \int dq\, \delta(q^2+m^2)\, \delta(2q_o p_o - p_o^2)$$

$$\times \left(m^2 + \frac{1}{2} p_o^2\right)[\epsilon(q_o) - \epsilon(q_o - p_o)] \tag{5.26}$$

(Note that $\delta[(q-p)^2 + m^2] = \delta(p^2 - 2qp)$ because of the first δ function.) The relation $qp = p^2/2$ has then been used to simplify the algebraic factor outside the δ functions. The q_o integration is performed by means of $\delta(2p_o q_o - p_o^2)$, yielding

$$\mathrm{Im}\, G(p) = \frac{-e^2}{12p^2\pi^2|p_o|}\left(m^2 + \frac{p_o^2}{2}\right)\int d^3q$$

$$\times \delta\left(\bar{q}^2 + m^2 - \frac{1}{4}p_o^2\right)\left[\epsilon\left(\frac{p_o}{2}\right) - \epsilon\left(-\frac{p_o}{2}\right)\right] \tag{5.27}$$

The integration over the angles gives 4π, and by means of the δ function we can carry out the $|\bar{q}|$ integration. We then get

$$\mathcal{I}m\, G(p) = \frac{e^2}{12\pi}\sqrt{1+\frac{4m^2}{p^2}}\left(1-\frac{2m^2}{p^2}\right)\theta(-p^2-4m^2)\varepsilon(p) \tag{5.28}$$

where we have replaced $-p_0^2$ by p^2 to get an invariant expression.

The external field satisfies the equation

$$\Box A_\mu^{ext}(x) - \frac{\partial^2 A_\nu^{ext}(x)}{\partial x_\mu \partial x_\nu} = - j_\mu^{ext}(x) \tag{5.29}$$

which in p space reads

$$(p_\mu p_\nu - \delta_{\mu\nu} p^2) A_\nu^{ext}(p) = - j_\mu^{ext}(p) \tag{5.30}$$

From Eqs. (5.14), (5.17), and (5.30) it follows that

$$\delta j_\mu(p) = - G(p)\, j_\mu^{ext}(p) \tag{5.31}$$

This product in p space can be written as a convolution integral in x space:

$$\delta j_\mu(x) = -\int dx'\, G(x-x')\, j_\mu^{ext}(x') \tag{5.32}$$

where

$$G(x) = \frac{1}{(2\pi)^4} \int dp\, e^{ipx} G(p) \tag{5.33}$$

and

$$K_{\mu\nu}(x) = \left(\Box \delta_{\mu\nu} - \frac{\partial^2}{\partial x_\mu \partial x_\nu} \right) G(x) \tag{5.34}$$

The function $K_{\mu\nu}(x)$, and therefore also G(x), has a causal property—that is,

$$G(x) = 0 \qquad \text{FOR} \qquad x_0 < 0 \tag{5.35}$$

Eq. (5.32) has the physical meaning that we get no induced current before the external field is switched on.

We shall now show that the causal property of G(x) (plus a boundary condition) gives a relationship between Re G(p) and Im G(p). Consider the Fourier transform of G(x):

$$G(p) = \int dx\, e^{-ipx} G(x) = \lim_{\varepsilon \to 0+} \int d^3x\, e^{-i\bar{p}\bar{x}} \times \int_0^\infty dx_0\, e^{ix_0(p_0 + i\varepsilon)} G(\bar{x}, x_0) \tag{5.36}$$

Since the x_0 integral only goes from 0 to ∞, we can put in the factor $\exp(-\varepsilon x_0)$, $(\varepsilon > 0)$, thereby improving the convergence of the integral. This means that

$$G(\bar{p}, p_0) = \text{B.V.} \quad G(\bar{p}, z) \quad ; \; z = p_0 + i\varepsilon \tag{5.37}$$

where $G(\bar{p}, z)$ is an analytic function, regular in the upper half plane (B. V. stands for "boundary value of"). Using the Cauchy theorem, we write

$$G(\bar{p}, z) = \frac{1}{2\pi i} \int_C \frac{dt\, G(\bar{p}, t)}{t - z} \tag{5.38}$$

where C is the path indicated in Fig. 5.2. If we assume that $|G(\bar{p}, z)| \to 0$

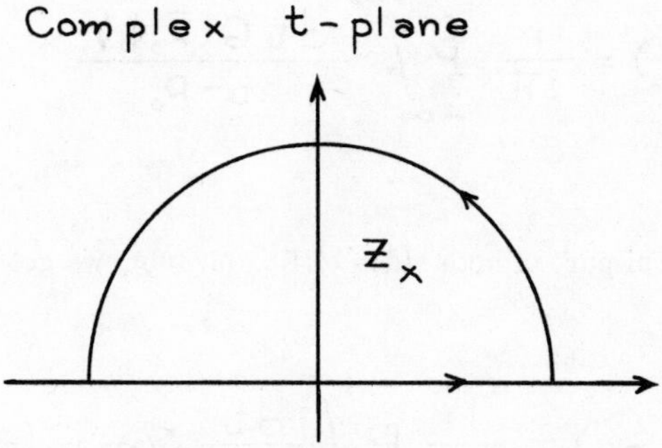

Fig. 5.2

sufficiently fast when $|z| \to \infty$, we can neglect the contribution from the large semicircle and get

$$G(\bar{p}, z) = \frac{1}{2\pi i} \int_{-\infty}^{+\infty} \frac{dt\, G(\bar{p}, t)}{t - z} \tag{5.39}$$

If we take the limit of $G(\bar{p}, z)$, with $z = p_o + i\varepsilon$, as $\varepsilon \to 0$, using Eq. (2.71) we obtain

$$G(\bar{p}, p_o) = \frac{1}{2\pi i} \lim_{\varepsilon \to 0} \int_{-\infty}^{+\infty} \frac{dt\, G(\bar{p},t)}{t - p_o - i\varepsilon}$$

$$= \frac{1}{2\pi i} P \int_{-\infty}^{\infty} \frac{dt\, G(\bar{p},t)}{t - p_o} + \frac{1}{2} G(\bar{p}, p_o) \tag{5.40a}$$

or

$$G(\bar{p}, p_o) = \frac{1}{i\pi} P \int_{-\infty}^{+\infty} \frac{dt\, G(\bar{p},t)}{t - p_o} \tag{5.40b}$$

If we take the real part of both sides of Eq. (5.40b), we get

$$\mathrm{Re}\, G(\bar{p}, p_o) = \frac{1}{\pi} P \int_{-\infty}^{+\infty} \frac{dt}{t - p_o} \mathcal{I}m\, G(\bar{p},t) \tag{5.41}$$

which is the relation we want.

In passing, we remark that the relation (5.41) is very general and always appears when we have an external agent acting on a system with a causal linear response. It has nothing to do with perturbation theory, nor with quantum theory or electrodynamics as such. Equations such as (5.41) are usually referred to as "dispersion relations."

We write

$$\mathcal{I}m\, G(p) = \pi \varepsilon(p) \Pi^{(o)}(p^2) \tag{5.42}$$

where $\Pi^{(0)}(p^2)$ is called the "polarization function." The index (0) indicates that it is the first nontrivial approximation in perturbation theory. The real part of G(p) is then given by

$$\operatorname{Re} G(p) = P\int_0^\infty \frac{dt}{t-p_0}\,\Pi^{(0)}(\bar{p}^2-t^2) - P\int_0^\infty \frac{dt}{-t-p_0}$$

$$\times\,\Pi^{(0)}(\bar{p}^2-t^2) = P\int_0^\infty \frac{dt\;2t}{t^2-p_0^2}\,\Pi^{(0)}(\bar{p}^2-t^2)$$

$$= P\int_{-\bar{p}^2}^\infty \frac{da\,\Pi^{(0)}(-a)}{a+\bar{p}^2-p_0^2} = P\int_{4m^2}^\infty \frac{da\,\Pi^{(0)}(-a)}{a+p^2} \tag{5.43}$$

The lower limit $-\bar{p}^2$ can be replaced by $4m^2$, since $\Pi^{(0)}(-a) = 0$ for $a < 4m^2$ [Eq. (5.28)]. We now have the whole function G(p):

$$G(p) = \int_{4m^2}^\infty \frac{da\,\Pi^{(0)}(-a)}{(a+p^2)_P} + i\pi\,\varepsilon(p)\,\Pi^{(0)}(p^2)$$

$$= \int_{4m^2}^\infty \frac{da\,\Pi^{(0)}(-a)}{(a+p^2)_R} \tag{5.44}$$

The observed quantity must be the sum of the external current and the induced current; that is,

$$j_\mu^{ext}(x) + \delta j_\mu(x) = \frac{1}{(2\pi)^4}\int dp\, e^{ipx}\, j_\mu^{ext}(p)\left(1 - G(p)\right) \tag{5.45}$$

In agreement with the discussion in the beginning of this section, we call d(p) = 1 - G(p) the "dielectric constant of the vacuum."

The existence of the polarization of the vacuum influences, in principle, all external fields. In particular, when one defines the unit of charge in classical electrostatics, one considers a certain geometric arrangement of static charges (the unit charge repels an identical charge at unit distance by unit force). We have now learned that the charge unit defined in this way is not the "true" charge but, rather, is the true charge slightly modified by virtual pairs. Instead of taking this explicitly into account when defining the charge unit, we can include this effect in the definition of d and say that our charge definition implies that d = 1 in the geometrical configuration used. As all macroscopic distances are large compared with the distance over which the Fourier transform of d varies appreciatively (the Compton wavelength of the electron), we can say that d should be normalized to one for fields constant in space and time, that is, $j_\mu^{ext} = C$. Such fields have a Fourier transform, which is $(2\pi)^4 C\,\delta(p)$. The right-hand side of Eq. (5.45) becomes C d(o), and we require d(0) = 1. To obtain this we define d(p) = 1 - G(p) + G(o). What can be observed is not the value of d(o) but the variation of d(p) with "frequency" p.

The measurable quantity is then given by

$$j_\mu^{obs}(x) = \frac{1}{(2\pi)^4}\int dp\, e^{ipx}\, j_\mu^{ext}(p)\left[1 - G(p) + G(o)\right]$$

$$= \frac{1}{(2\pi)^4}\int dp\, e^{ipx}\, j_\mu^{ext}(p)\left[1 - \int_{4m^2}^{\infty} \frac{da\, \Pi^{(o)}(-a)}{(a+p^2)_R} + \right.$$

$$+\int_{4m^2}^{\infty}\frac{da\,\Pi^{(0)}(-a)}{a}\Bigg] = \frac{1}{(2\pi)^4}\int dp\, e^{ipx}\, j_{\mu}^{ext}(p)$$

$$\times\left[1+p^2\int_{4m^2}^{\infty}\frac{da\,\Pi^{(0)}(-a)}{a(a+p^2)_R}\right] \tag{5.46}$$

and the dielectric constant of the vacuum is

$$d(p) = 1 - G(p) + G(0) = 1 + p^2\int_{4m^2}^{\infty}\frac{da\,\Pi^{(0)}(-a)}{a(a+p^2)_R} \tag{5.47}$$

$$\mathrm{Re}\,(1-d(p)) = -p^2\int_{4m^2}^{\infty}\frac{da\,\Pi^{(0)}(-a)}{a(a+p^2)\,P} \tag{5.47a}$$

The normalization of d(p) performed above to get d(0) = 1 is usually referred to as "charge renormalization."

The integral in Eq. (5.47a) can be calculated by straightforward methods and becomes

$$\mathrm{Re}\,(1-d(p)) = \frac{e^2}{12\pi^2}\left[\frac{5}{3} - \frac{4m^2}{p^2} - \left(1-\frac{2m^2}{p^2}\right)\times\right.$$

$$\times \sqrt{1+\frac{4m^2}{p^2}}\, \log \frac{1+\sqrt{1+\frac{4m^2}{p^2}}}{1-\sqrt{1+\frac{4m^2}{p^2}}}\Bigg]$$

(5.48)

if $(1 + 4m^2/p^2) > 0$; otherwise, the logarithm has to be replaced by an arctan function. For small values of $|p^2/m^2|$ we get

$$\mathrm{Re}\,(1-d(p)) = -\frac{p^2}{m^2}\,\frac{e^2}{60\pi^2} + \cdots \tag{5.48a}$$

The function $\Pi^{(0)}(p^2)$, which is essentially Im d(p), and Re [1 - d(p)] are plotted in Fig. (5.3).

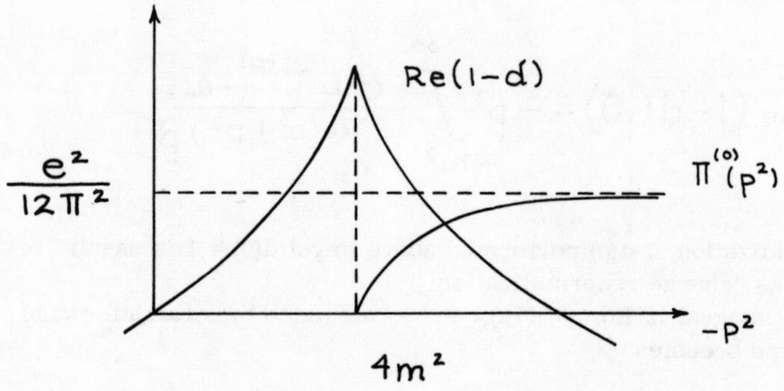

Fig. 5.3

Note that d(p) is a complex number, which means that there is a phase difference between $j_\mu^{ext}(x)$ and $j_\mu^{obs}(x)$. One can show that the imaginary part corresponds to the creation of real pairs, and these take energy away from the external source. Note that Im d(p) $\neq$ 0 only for $-p^2 > 4m^2$. This limit corresponds to the threshold for the creation of an electron-positron pair.

So far, we have not worried about the convergence of the integrals

$$G(p) = \int_{4m^2}^{\infty} \frac{da\, \Pi^{(0)}(-a)}{(a+p^2)_R} \quad \text{AND} \quad G(0) = \int_{4m^2}^{\infty} \frac{da\, \Pi^{(0)}(-a)}{a} \tag{5.49}$$

From Eqs. (5.42) and (5.28), it follows that $\Pi^{(0)}(-a) \rightarrow$ const, when $a \rightarrow \infty$ and both G(p) and G(0) are logarithmically divergent. However, the difference G(p) - G(0) in Eq. (5.47) is a convergent integral. The renormalization procedure has thus improved the convergence of the theory. Even if this is of great practical importance, we emphasize that it is not the main purpose of the renormalization. Also, if the integrals of Eq. (5.49) had been finite, we should have performed the charge renormalization in the same way.

We also wish to point out that the technique described in this section, using invariance and causality properties, has not only saved us some work of calculation but is also very essential to give a sharp definition of the divergent integrals involved. If one tries to calculate Re G(p) by straightforward methods, difficulties are met. To be able to handle the many-valued integral in Eq. (5.18), one must introduce some kind of cutoff procedure, and this must be done in a relativistic invariant way. By the method described above, we have avoided these difficulties.

5-2. Application to Hydrogenlike Atoms

If we try to confirm the existence of the vacuum polarization with an experimental arrangement like that in Fig. (5.1), in practice it is very difficult to build such an apparatus. The external field created by the generator must have a very high frequency corresponding to an energy of roughly the electron mass. Furthermore, the distance between the plates must be of the order of the Compton wavelength of the electron. In other circumstances, the effect we are looking for is very small.

But, nature itself has provided us with a useful "apparatus," namely, the atom. If the vacuum has a frequency-dependent dielectric constant, the energy levels are slightly changed from the values one gets with the aid of the nonquantized Dirac equation.

Let us consider a hydrogenlike atom: by this we mean an atom with only one particle of mass M (electron or μ meson) bounded to a central nucleus (e. g., a proton) with charge +Ze. The "proton" can be regarded as one of the plates of the condenser and the "electron" as the other plate. Our external current can be taken to be $ie\bar{u}_n(\bar{x})\gamma_\mu u_n(\bar{x})$, where $u_n(\bar{x})$ are the solutions of the Dirac equation in a Coulomb field.

To start with, we neglect any change of the electron current (μ-meson current) itself, when the virtual electron-positron pairs are created. The change in the energy levels is then given by

$$\delta E = -\int d^3x\, A_\mu^{coul}(\bar{x})\, \delta j_\mu(x) \tag{5.50}$$

where $\delta j_\mu(x)$ is the change in the current because of the polarization of the vacuum. According to Eq. (5. 46), $\delta j_\mu(x)$ is given by

$$\delta j_\mu(x) = \frac{1}{(2\pi)^4}\int dp\, e^{ipx}\, j_\mu^{ext}(p)\, p^2 \times$$

$$\int_{4m^2}^{\infty} \frac{da\, \Pi^{(0)}(-a)}{a(a+p^2)_R} = \frac{ie}{(2\pi)^4}\int dp\, e^{ipx}\int dx'$$

$$\times e^{-ipx'}\,\bar{u}_n(\bar{x}')\,\gamma_\mu\, u_n(\bar{x}')\, p^2 \int_{4m^2}^{\infty} \frac{da\, \Pi^{(0)}(-a)}{a(a+p^2)_R} \tag{5.51}$$

The symbol m denotes the mass of these particles, which are (virtually) created and which cause the polarization of the vacuum.

The x'_0 integration can be performed. The result is

$$\delta j_\mu(x) = \frac{ie}{(2\pi)^3} \iint d^3p\, d^3x'\, e^{i\bar{p}(\bar{x}-\bar{x}')}$$

$$\times \bar{U}_n(\bar{x}')\, \gamma_\mu U_n(\bar{x}')\, \bar{p}^2 \int_{4m^2}^{\infty} \frac{da\, \Pi^{(0)}(-a)}{a(a+\bar{p}^2)} \tag{5.52}$$

Since $a + p^{-2} > 0$ for all a in the range of integration, we can drop the retarded prescription. Using

$$A_\mu^{\text{Coul}}(\bar{x}) = -i\delta_{\mu 4} \frac{Ze}{4\pi|\bar{x}|} \tag{5.53}$$

and the expression for $\delta j_\mu(x)$ given above, we find from Eq. (5.50) that

$$\delta E = \frac{-Ze^2}{2(2\pi)^4} \iiint d^3p\, d^3x\, d^3x'\, e^{i\bar{p}(\bar{x}-\bar{x}')}$$

$$\times \frac{\bar{p}^2}{|\bar{x}|} |U_n(\bar{x}')|^2 \int_{4m^2}^{\infty} \frac{da\, \Pi^{(0)}(-a)}{a(a+\bar{p}^2)} \tag{5.54}$$

The function $|u_n(\bar{x}')|^2 = \rho(\bar{x}')$ is the probability density of the electron according to the Dirac theory. If $\rho(\bar{x}')$ is replaced by its Fourier representation,

$$\rho(\bar{x}') = \frac{1}{(2\pi)^3} \int d^3p'\, e^{i\bar{p}'\bar{x}'}\, \rho(\bar{p}') \tag{5.55}$$

the $\bar{x}'$ integration and then the $\bar{p}'$ integration can be performed. Finally, the $\bar{x}$ integration becomes

$$\int \frac{d^3x \, e^{i\bar{p}\bar{x}}}{|\bar{x}|} = \frac{4\pi}{\bar{p}^2} \tag{5.56}$$

and we get

$$\delta E = \frac{-ze^2}{(2\pi)^3} \int d^3p \, \rho(\bar{p}) \int_{4m^2}^{\infty} \frac{da \, \Pi^{(0)}(-a)}{a(a+\bar{p}^2)} \tag{5.57}$$

The integral over a is given by Eq. (5.48), and $\rho(\bar{p})$ is a known function; therefore it is possible to calculate δE numerically. However, we are only interested in an estimate of the value of δE, and to obtain this, we make certain approximations.

The energy levels (calculated by the Schrödinger equation) for a hydrogenlike atom are given by

$$E_n = -\frac{1}{2} \frac{M\alpha^2 z^2}{n^2} \tag{5.58}$$

where n = the principal quantum number, M = the mass of the light particle circling around the nucleus, and $\alpha = e^2/4\pi$ is the fine structure constant. The relativistic corrections are of order $\alpha^2 E_n$, and we expect that the correction δE due to vacuum polarization is still smaller. Therefore, we put $\rho(\bar{x}) = |\varphi_n(\bar{x})|^2$, where the $\varphi_n(\bar{x})$ are the solution of the Schrödinger equation. The exact behavior of $\rho(\bar{x})$ depends on the quantum numbers n and ℓ; but roughly speaking, we have $\rho(z) \approx 0$ for $|\bar{x}| > 1/\alpha M$ (the Bohr radius). This means that $\rho(\bar{p}) \approx 0$ for $|\bar{p}| > \alpha M$. If we assume that $\alpha M \ll m$, we can approximate the a integral by its value for $|\bar{p}| = 0$, which is $e^2/60\pi^2 m^2$ [compare Eq. (5.48a)]. This gives

$$\delta E = \frac{-Ze^4}{15m^2(2\pi)^5}\int d^3p\, \rho(\bar{p}) = -\frac{4}{15}\frac{Z\alpha^2}{m^2}|\varphi_n(0)|^2 \tag{5.59}$$

If the light particle is an electron, we have M = m and our assumption $\alpha M \ll m$ is fulfilled. But, if this particle is a μ meson, we have $M = \mu \approx 207$ m, and $\alpha M \ll m$ is not fulfilled.

The value of $|\varphi_n(0)|^2$ is

$$|\varphi_n(0)|^2 = \delta_{l,0}\frac{Z^3\alpha^3 M^3}{\pi n^3} \tag{5.60}$$

That is, it is only $\neq 0$ for S states, and we get

$$\delta E = -\frac{4}{15\pi}\frac{Z^4\alpha^5 M^3}{n^3 m^2}\delta_{l,0} = \frac{8Z^2\alpha^3}{15\pi}\left(\frac{M}{m}\right)^2\frac{E_n}{n}\delta_{l,0} \tag{5.61}$$

If the light particle is an electron, we have M/m = 1 and the correction is of order $\alpha^3 E_n$. This is one order of magnitude smaller than the relativistic correction mentioned above.

If the light particle is a μ meson, a careful investigation shows that $M/m \equiv \mu/m$ has to be replaced by an expression of the order of $\log(\mu/m)$.

We shall now compare with experimental data and consider, for example, the 2S 1/2 and 2 P 1/2 levels in hydrogen. According to the Dirac theory, these levels have the same energy; but according to Eq. (5.61) (with Z = 1, n = 2, M = m), the P level is unchanged while the S level is depressed by $\delta E = 4\alpha^3 |E_2| / 15\pi \approx 27$ Mc/sec, where we have expressed the energy in frequency units. The experimental result is that the S level lies $\approx$1000 Mc/sec above the P level.

If one compares theory and experiment when the light particle is a μ meson instead of an electron, the agreement is much better. Actually, there is no discrepancy inside the (rather large) experimental errors.

In the calculation above we have made the following approximations:

1. Only first-order terms in the external field have been kept.
2. Only the creation of virtual electron-positron pairs has been taken into consideration.
3. We have replaced $|u_n(\bar{x})|^2$ by $|\varphi_n(\bar{x})|^2$; that is, we have neglected relativistic corrections to the vacuum polarization itself.
4. We have neglected the change of the current from the light particle (mass M) when the virtual particles of mass m are created.

We can expect that assumptions (1), (2), and (3) are rather good approximations at least for small values of Z. In connection with (2), it can be mentioned that the mass of the virtual particles appears in the denominator of Eq. (5.61). Therefore, the effect due to virtual μ mesons or heavier particles is very small compared with the contribution from virtual electrons. In the case when $M = \mu \gg m$ the fourth assumption is justified, and the agreement of Eq. (5.61) with experiment is also rather good.

But, if M = m—that is, if the light particle is an electron—it is not reasonable to expect that we can neglect the recoil of the light particle and treat its current as an external undisturbed current. In this case we must replace the external current by $\langle q | j_\mu(x) | q' \rangle$, which we study in perturbation theory. The first term, $e \langle q | j_\mu^{(0)}(x) | q' \rangle$, is trivial. To get the first interesting contribution to the radiative corrections, it is necessary to compute $e^3 \langle q | j_\mu^{(2)}(x) | q' \rangle$. This will be done in the next section.

6. RADIATIVE CORRECTIONS TO $\langle q | j_\mu(x) | q' \rangle$

6-1. Vacuum Polarization and Other Trivial Terms; Mass Renormalization

The operator $j_\mu^{(2)}(x)$ is given by Eq. (4.36). The first and the fourth term contain the factor $[\bar{\psi}^{(0)}(x''), \gamma_\nu \psi^{(0)}(x'')]$, which can give transition from $|q'\rangle$ to $|q\rangle$. We are then left with the vacuum expectation value of the remaining factors in these terms, and (except for a D_R function) this is exactly the vacuum polarization term [compare Eq. (5.6)]. But, the first and fourth terms also give other contributions to $\langle q| j_\mu^{(2)}(x) |q'\rangle$. Collecting contributions from all terms, we write

$$e^3\langle q| j_\mu^{(2)}(x) |q'\rangle = \frac{ie}{2}\iint dx'\,dx''\; K_{\mu\nu}(x-x')$$

$$\times D_R(x'-x'')\,\langle q|\left[\bar{\Psi}^{(0)}(x''),\, \gamma_\nu\, \Psi^{(0)}(x'')\right]|q'\rangle$$

$$+\frac{ie}{2}\int dx'\,\langle q|\left[\bar{\Psi}^{(0)}(x),\, \gamma_\mu\, S_R(x-x')\,\phi(x')\right]|q'\rangle$$

$$+\frac{ie}{2}\int dx'\,\langle q|\left[\bar{\phi}(x')\,S_A(x'-x),\, \gamma_\mu\, \Psi^{(0)}(x)\right]|q'\rangle$$

$$+\frac{ie}{2}\iint dx'\,dx''\,\langle q|\left[\bar{\Psi}^{(0)}(x'),\, K_\mu(x'-x,\, x-x'')\,\Psi^{(0)}(x'')\right]|q'\rangle$$

(6. 1)

The function $K_{\mu\nu}(x - x')$ is given by Eq. (5. 8) and has been studied in detail in Sec. 5. The first term in Eq. (6. 1) is the polarization of the vacuum caused by the potential

$$\frac{ie}{2}\int dx''\, D_R(x'-x'')\left[\bar{\Psi}^{(0)}(x''),\, \gamma_\mu\, \Psi^{(0)}(x'')\right]$$

(6. 2)

from the electron. The second and third terms in Eq. (6. 1) take care of the corrections of the operator $\Psi(x)$ itself, and the fourth term contains the rest of the radiative corrections. As we shall see later, this is really the main term as far as observable effects are concerned.

The operator ϕ (x) and the matrix $K_\mu(x' - x,\ x - x'')$ are given by

$$\phi(x) = -\frac{e^2}{2}\int dx'\, \gamma_\lambda \Big[S^{(1)}(x-x')\, D_A(x'-x) + S_R(x-x')$$

$$\times D^{(1)}(x-x)\Big]\, \gamma_\lambda\, \psi^{(0)}(x') \tag{6. 3}$$

$$K_\mu(x'-x,\ x-x'') = -\frac{e^2}{2}\,\gamma_\lambda\Big[S^{(1)}(x'-x)\,\gamma_\mu\, S_R(x-x'')$$

$$\times D_R(x''-x') + S_A(x'-x)\,\gamma_\mu\, S^{(1)}(x-x'')\, D_R(x'-x'')$$

$$+ S_A(x'-x)\,\gamma_\mu\, S_R(x-x'')\, D^{(1)}(x'-x'')\Big]\,\gamma_\lambda \tag{6. 4}$$

From the expansions of ψ (x) and $A_\mu(x)$, Eqs. (4. 29) through (4. 33), it is easily seen that

$$\langle 0|\, f^{(1)}(x)\, |q\rangle = ie\langle 0|\, \gamma A^{(0)}(x)\, \psi^{(1)}(x)\, |q\rangle$$

$$+ie\langle 0|\, \gamma A^{(1)}(x)\, \psi^{(0)}(x)\, |q\rangle = -\langle 0|\, \phi(x)\, |q\rangle \tag{6. 5}$$

and

$$\langle 0|\, \psi(x)\, |q\rangle = \langle 0|\, \psi^{(0)}(x)\, |q\rangle + \int dx'\, S_R(x-x') \times$$

$$\langle 0 | \phi(x') | q \rangle \quad + \cdots \tag{6.6}$$

Hence, the operator ϕ (x) appears in the first radiative correction to $\langle 0 | \psi(x) | q \rangle$. We shall see that this is important for the physical interpretation of the divergent integrals appearing in the calculation of ϕ (x).

We write ϕ(x) in the following way:

$$\phi(x) = \int dx' \, F(x-x') \, \psi^{(0)}(x') \tag{6.7}$$

$$F(x-x') = -\frac{e^2}{2} \gamma_\lambda \left[S^{(1)}(x-x') \, D_A(x'-x) + S_R(x-x') \, D^{(1)}(x'-x) \right] \gamma_\lambda = \frac{1}{(2\pi)^4} \int dq \, e^{iq(x-x')} F(q), \tag{6.8}$$

$$F(q) = -\frac{e^2}{2(2\pi)^3} \iint dp \, dk \, \delta(q-p+k) \, \gamma_\lambda \times (i\gamma p - m) \, \gamma_\lambda \left[\frac{\delta(p^2+m^2)}{(k^2)_A} + \frac{\delta(k^2)}{(p^2+m^2)_R} \right] \tag{6.9}$$

The function F(x) has a causal structure; that is, F(x) = 0 for $x_0 < 0$. From the discussion in Sec. 5.1, it follows that it is enough to compute Im F(q). The real part is then obtained from

$$\mathrm{Re}\, F(q) = \frac{1}{\pi} P \int_{-\infty}^{+\infty} \frac{dt}{t - q_0} \, \mathcal{I}m\, F(\bar{q}, t) \tag{6.10}$$

The imaginary part of F(q) is given by

$$\mathcal{I}m\, F(q) = -\frac{\pi e^2}{2(2\pi)^3} \int dk\, \delta(k^2)\, \delta((q+k)^2 + m^2)$$
$$\times \gamma_\lambda \left[i\gamma(q+k) - m \right] \gamma_\lambda \left[\epsilon(q+k) - \epsilon(k) \right] \tag{6.11}$$

[Note that $i\gamma p - m$ can be treated as a real number since it can be written as $\gamma \frac{\partial}{\partial x} - m$ is x space. Therefore, it does not influence the causal structure of the expression.] Using Eqs. (5.20) and (5.21), we get

$$\gamma_\lambda \left[i\gamma(q+k) - m \right] \gamma_\lambda = -2\left[i\gamma(q+k) + 2m \right] \tag{6.12}$$

Hence, we have to evaluate the following two typical integrals:

$$I(q) = \int dk\, \delta(k^2)\, \delta((q+k)^2 + m^2) \left[\epsilon(q+k) - \epsilon(k) \right] \tag{6.13}$$

$$I_\mu(q) = \int dk\, k_\mu\, \delta(k^2)\, \delta((q+k)^2 + m^2) \left[\epsilon(q+k) - \epsilon(k) \right] \tag{6.14}$$

The first integral, I(q), is zero when $q^2 \geq 0$ and is easily evaluated in a system where $\bar{q} = 0$. The result is

$$I(q) = \pi\left(1 + \frac{m^2}{q^2}\right)\theta(-q^2 - m^2)\,\mathcal{E}(q) \tag{6.15}$$

Since $I_\mu(q)$ transforms like a vector under Lorentz transformations and only depends on the vector q_μ, its most general form must be

$$I_\mu(q) = q_\mu A(q) \tag{6.16}$$

where A(q) is a scalar function of q. Hence,

$$q^2 A(q) = q_\mu I_\mu(q) = \int dk\; qk\; \delta(k^2)\,\delta((q+k)^2 + m^2)$$

$$\left[\mathcal{E}(q+k) - \mathcal{E}(k)\right] = -\frac{q^2 + m^2}{2}\, I(q) \tag{6.17}$$

and we get the result

$$I_\mu(q) = -\frac{\pi}{2}\left(1 + \frac{m^2}{q^2}\right)^2 q_\mu\, \theta(-q^2 - m^2)\,\mathcal{E}(q) \tag{6.18}$$

The function Im F(q) can then be written

$$\begin{aligned} \mathcal{I}m\, F(q) &= \frac{\pi e^2}{(2\pi)^3}\left[i\gamma q + 2m - \frac{1}{2}\left(1 + \frac{m^2}{q^2}\right) i\gamma q\right] I(q) \\ &= \pi\,\mathcal{E}(q)\left[\Sigma_1^{(0)}(q^2) + (i\gamma q + m)\,\Sigma_2^{(0)}(q^2)\right] \end{aligned} \tag{6.19}$$

with

$$\Sigma_1^{(o)}(q^2) = \frac{me^2}{16\pi^2}\left(3+\frac{m^2}{q^2}\right)\left(1+\frac{m^2}{q^2}\right)\theta(-q^2-m^2)$$

$$\Sigma_2^{(o)}(q^2) = \frac{e^2}{16\pi^2}\left[1-\left(\frac{m^2}{q^2}\right)^2\right]\theta(-q^2-m^2) \tag{6.21}$$

The index (o) on $\Sigma_j^{(o)}(q^2)$ indicates that the calculations are carried through in first order of perturbation theory. However, the causality and invariance arguments are more general, and we expect functions $\Sigma_j(q^2)$ also in higher orders and in an "exact" solution, if such a solution exists.

As mentioned before, the real part of F(q) is given by the "dispersion relation" of Eq. (6.10), and using the same rewritten versions as in Eqs. (5.41) to (5.44), the whole function F(q) can be written

$$F(q) = \int_0^\infty \frac{da\,\Sigma_1^{(o)}(-a)}{(a+q^2)_R} + (i\gamma q + m)\int_0^\infty \frac{da\,\Sigma_2^{(o)}(-a)}{(a+q^2)_R} \tag{6.22}$$

(The lower limit can be replaced by m^2, since $\Sigma_j^{(o)}(-a) = 0$ for $a \leq m^2$.) From Eqs. (6.20) and (6.21), it follows that $\Sigma_j^{(o)}(-a) \rightarrow$ const when $a \rightarrow \infty$; hence, the integrals in Eq. (6.22) are logarithmically divergent.

We can understand the physical meaning of the terms in Eq. (6.22) by using Eqs. (6.5) and (6.6). The first of these equations can be written

$$\left(\gamma\frac{\partial}{\partial x} + m\right)\langle 0|\,\psi(x)\,|q\rangle = -\langle 0|\,\phi(x)\,|q\rangle \tag{6.23}$$

According to Eqs. (6.7), (6.8), and (6.22), we have

$$\langle 0|\phi(x)|q\rangle = \int dx' F(x-x') \langle 0|\psi^{(0)}(x')|q\rangle$$

$$= \int dx' F(x-x') \frac{1}{\sqrt{V}} u(\bar{q})\, e^{iqx'}$$

$$= \frac{1}{\sqrt{V}} \left[\int_0^\infty \frac{da\, \Sigma_1^{(0)}(-a)}{a-m^2} + (i\gamma q + m) \right.$$

$$\left. \times \int_0^\infty \frac{da\, \Sigma_2^{(0)}(-a)}{a-m^2} \right] u(\bar{q})\, e^{iqx} \tag{6.24}$$

The denominators $(a + q^2)$ in Eq. (6.22) have been replaced by $a - m^2$, as the energy-momentum vector in Eq. (6.24) belongs to an electron and fulfills $q^2 + m^2 = 0$. Further, the retarded prescription can be deleted as $\Sigma_i^{(0)}(-a) = 0$ for $a \leq m^2$.

Since $(i\gamma q + m)\, u(\bar{q}) = 0$, we get

$$\langle 0|\phi(x)|q\rangle = \int_0^\infty \frac{da\, \Sigma_1^{(0)}(-a)}{a-m^2} \langle 0|\psi^{(0)}(x)|q\rangle \tag{6.25}$$

In the approximation used here, Eq. (6.25) can be replaced by

$$\langle 0|\phi(x)|q\rangle = \int_0^\infty \frac{da\, \Sigma_1^{(0)}(-a)}{a-m^2} \langle 0|\psi(x)|q\rangle \tag{6.26}$$

and Eq. (6.23) reads

$$\left[\gamma\frac{\partial}{\partial x}+m+\int_0^\infty\frac{da\,\Sigma_1^{(0)}(-a)}{a-m^2}\right]\langle 0|\psi(x)|q\rangle=0 \tag{6.27}$$

This equation shows that the interacting field $\psi(x)$ satisfies the same equation as a free electron with mass $(m+\delta m)$, where

$$\delta m=\int_0^\infty\frac{da\,\Sigma_1^{(0)}(-a)}{a-m^2} \tag{6.28}$$

Since, the physical electron is interacting with the electromagnetic field, it is surrounded by a cloud of virtual photons. The quantity δm is the difference between the mass of this physical electron and the free electron. If we want to measure the mass of the electron, however, we normally include also the cloud of the virtual photons. Therefore, what we measure, m_{exp}, is not m but $(m+\delta m)$. We rewrite the Dirac equation of the interacting field $\psi(x)$ so that the left-hand side contains the experimental mass, and not the free electron mass:

$$\left(\gamma\frac{\partial}{\partial x}+m_{exp}\right)\psi(x)=ie\gamma A(x)\psi(x)+\delta m\,\psi(x) \tag{6.29}$$

After this "mass renormalization," we have to interpret f(x) in Eq. (4.17a) as $ie\,\gamma A(x)\psi(x)+\delta m\,\psi(x)$, and the expansions of $\psi(x)$, $A_\mu(x)$, and $j_\mu(x)$ are slightly changed. Further, all the singular functions — S(x), $S_R(x)$, etc. — are from now on constructed with the experimental mass. In the future, we shall drop the index "exp" and only write **m** for the experimental mass.

It follows that we have to do the replacement

$$\phi(x)\longrightarrow\phi(x)-\delta m\,\psi^{(0)}(x) \tag{6.30}$$

in Eqs. (6. 1), (6. 5), and (6. 6). The last of these equations now reads

$$\langle 0|\psi(x)|q\rangle = \langle 0|\psi^{(0)}(x)|q\rangle + \int dx'$$

$$S_R(x-x')\langle 0|\phi(x') - \delta m\,\psi^{(0)}(x')|q\rangle \tag{6.31}$$

According to Eqs. (6. 25) and (6. 28), the integrand seems to be zero and hence $\langle 0|\psi(x)|q\rangle = \langle 0|\psi^{(0)}(x)|q$; however, the integral in Eq. (6. 31) is not well defined. The S_R function gives a factor $1/(q^2 + m^2) = 1/0$, and the whole integral is therefore of the form $0/0$. To handle this integral, one can introduce the adiabatic factor $\exp(-\alpha|x_0|)$ and calculate very carefully. The result of such a calculation is

$$\langle 0|\psi(x)|q\rangle = \left\{1 - \frac{1}{2}\int_0^\infty \frac{da}{a-m^2}\left[\Sigma_2^{(0)}(-a)\right.\right.$$

$$\left.\left. - \frac{2m}{a-m^2}\,\Sigma_1^{(0)}(-a)\right]\right\}\langle 0|\psi^{(0)}(x)|q\rangle \tag{6.32}$$

The factor 1/2 comes from the Abelian limiting procedure.

The second term in Eq. (6. 1) becomes

$$\frac{ie}{2}\int dx'\langle q|\left[\bar{\psi}^{(0)}(x),\, \gamma_\mu S_R(x-x')\big(\phi(x') - \right.$$

$$\delta m\, \psi^{(0)}(x')\big)\big]|q'\rangle = ie\langle q|\bar{\psi}^{(0)}(x)|0\rangle\gamma_\mu$$

$$\times\int dx'\, S_R(x-x')\langle 0|\big(\phi(x')-\delta m\,\psi^{(0)}(x')\big)|q'\rangle$$

$$= -\frac{ie}{2V}\,\bar{u}(\bar{q})\,\gamma_\mu u(q')\,e^{iQx}\int_0^\infty \frac{da}{a-m^2}$$

$$\times\left[\Sigma_2^{(0)}(-a) - \frac{2m}{a-m^2}\Sigma_1^{(0)}(-a)\right] \tag{6.33}$$

where

$$Q = q'-q \;;\quad Q^2>0 \tag{6.34}$$

The third term in Eq. (6.1) also gives the contribution (6.33), and the first term is the vacuum polarization term. We can then summarize our results so far in the following expression:

$$e^3\langle q|j_\mu^{(2)}(x)|q'\rangle = \Big\{Q^2\int_0^\infty \frac{da\,\Pi^{(0)}(-a)}{a(a+Q^2)}$$

$$-\int_0^\infty \frac{da}{a-m^2}\left[\Sigma_2^{(0)}(-a) - \frac{2m}{a-m^2}\,\Sigma_1^{(0)}(-a)\right]\Big\}$$

$$\times\frac{ie}{V}\,\bar{u}(\bar{q})\,\gamma_\mu\, u(\bar{q}')\,e^{iQx} + \frac{ie}{V}\iint dx'\,dx''$$

$$\times\,\bar{u}(\bar{q})K_\mu(x'-x,\,x-x'')\,u(\bar{q}')\,e^{iq'x''-iqx'} \tag{6.35}$$

where $K_\mu(x' - x, x - x'')$ is given by Eq. (6.4). (Since $Q^2 > 0$, and hence $a + Q^2 > 0$, for all a in the interval of integration, we can drop the retarded prescription.) The first term in Eq. (6.35) shows that we have performed the same charge renormalization for the one-electron states as for an external field. We shall return to this point later.

6-2. The Main Radiative Correction to $\langle q | j_\mu(x) | q' \rangle$

We now consider the last term in Eq. (6.35) and introduce the notation $\mathfrak{X}_\mu$ for this term. If we write $K_\mu(x' - x, x - x'')$ as a Fourier integral,

$$K_\mu(x' - x, x - x'') = \frac{1}{(2\pi)^8} \iint dq\, dq'\, K_\mu(q, q') \times e^{iq(x'-x) + iq'(x - x'')} \tag{6.36}$$

we get

$$\mathfrak{X}_\mu \equiv \frac{ie}{V} e^{iQx}\, \bar{u}(\bar{q})\, K_\mu(q, q')\, u(\bar{q}') \tag{6.37}$$

$$K_\mu(q, q') = -\frac{e^2}{2} \frac{1}{(2\pi)^3} \int dk\, \gamma_\lambda [i\gamma(q - k) - m] \times \gamma_\mu [i\gamma(q' - k) - m] \gamma_\lambda \times \left\{ \frac{\delta(k^2)}{((q-k)^2 + m^2)_A ((q'-k)^2 + m^2)_R} + \frac{\delta((q'-k)^2 + m^2)}{(k^2)_R ((q-k)^2 + m^2)_A} + \frac{\delta((q-k)^2 + m^2)}{(k^2)_A ((q'-k)^2 + m^2)_R} \right\} \tag{6.38}$$

From expression (6.38) it follows that $K_\mu(q, q')$ transforms like a γ_μ matrix under all Lorentz transformations. [Note that it does not transform as a 4-vector, since $(K_\mu)_{\alpha\beta}$ has two free Dirac spin indices, which couple the u's together.] Further, $(K_\mu)_{\alpha\beta}$ depends on two vectors q and q'. It must be built up of factors such as $(\gamma_\mu)_{\alpha\beta} F$, $q_\mu \delta_{\alpha\beta} F$, and $q'_\mu \delta_{\alpha\beta} F$, where F stands for some scalar function of q and q'. But, one can also get terms such as $i\gamma q(\gamma_\mu)_{\alpha\beta} F$ and $(i\gamma q)(i\gamma q')(\gamma_\mu)_{\alpha\beta}$. Higher powers are not needed, since they can be reduced to a linear combination of the expressions above. We can also leave out γ_5, since if we also took terms containing γ_5, they should not have correct transformation properties under reflections. Therefore, the most general form of $K_\mu(q, q')$ is

$$K_\mu(q, q') = \sum_{r,r'=0}^{1} (i\gamma q + m)^r \Big[\gamma_\mu F_1^{rr'}(q, q') + iq_\mu F_2^{rr'}(q, q') + iq'_\mu F_3^{rr'}(q, q')\Big] \times (i\gamma q' + m)^{r'} \tag{6.39}$$

where $F_i^{rr'}$ are 12 scalar functions of q and q' to compute. [Note that there are 64 terms in $(K_\mu)_{\alpha\beta}$.] Fortunately, we do not need the most general, $K_\mu(q, q')$. From Eq. (6.37) it follows that $K_\mu(q, q')$ stands between $\bar{u}(\bar{q})$ and $u(\bar{q}')$; hence, those terms in $K_\mu(q, q')$ which contain $(i\gamma q + m)$ or $(i\gamma q' + m)$ vanish. We get

$$\bar{u}(\bar{q}) K_\mu(q, q') u(\bar{q}') = \bar{u}(\bar{q}) \Big[\gamma_\mu F_1^{00}(q, q') + iq_\mu F_2^{00}(q, q') + iq'_\mu F_3^{00}(q, q')\Big] u(\bar{q}') \tag{6.40}$$

and have only three functions $F_i(q, q')$ to compute (we drop the upper index).

We shall now show that the invariance of the theory under charge conjugation yields $F_2(-q', -q) = F_3(q, q')$.

Charge conjugation is a unitary transformation which, applied to a state with a given number of electrons and positrons, interchanges the roles of electrons and positrons. It can be described by an operator $\mathcal{C}$ such that

$$\mathcal{C}|q, el\rangle = |q, pos\rangle \quad , \tag{6.41}$$

$$\mathcal{C}|q, pos\rangle = |q, el\rangle \quad etc. \tag{6.42}$$

If this unitary transformation is applied to the Dirac field, we get

$$\mathcal{C}^{-1}\psi_\alpha(x)\mathcal{C} = C_{\alpha\beta}\bar{\psi}_\beta(x) \tag{6.43}$$

Note that $\mathcal{C}$ is an infinite matrix in the space of state vectors, while C is a 4 x 4 matrix in the space of Dirac matrices.

The matrix C has the following properties:

$$C = -C^T \quad , \qquad T = \text{transposed} \tag{6.44}$$

$$C^{-1} = C^* \quad , \qquad * = \text{Hermitian conj.} \tag{6.45}$$

$$C^{-1}\gamma_\mu C = -\gamma_\mu^T \quad , \tag{6.46}$$

$$C\bar{u}^{(+)(r)}(\bar{q}) = u^{(-)(r)}(-q) , \; C\bar{u}^{(-)(r)}(-\bar{q}) = u^{(+)(r)}(q) \tag{6.47}$$

[With our conventions of Eq. (2.42), the index r is the same on both sides of Eq. (6.47).] In the particular representation given by Eqs. (2.4) and (2.5), one can show that $C = \gamma_4 \gamma_2$ satisfies these requirements.

The current operator $j_\mu(x)$ transforms in the following way:

$$\mathcal{C}^{-1} j_\mu(x) \mathcal{C} = -j_\mu(x) , \tag{6.48}$$

which is physically reasonable. We consider a particular matrix element of $j_\mu(x)$, namely,

$$\langle q, pos | j_\mu(x) | q', pos \rangle = - \langle q, pos | \mathcal{C}^{-1} \times j_\mu(x) \mathcal{C} | q', pos \rangle = - \langle q, el | j_\mu(x) | q', el \rangle \tag{6.49}$$

To see how the minus sign results, we can verify this relation for the free field current $e\, j_\mu^{(o)}(x)$. We get

$$e \langle q, pos | j_\mu^{(o)}(x) | q', pos \rangle = \frac{ie}{2} \langle q, pos | \times \left[\bar{\Psi}^{(o)}(x), \gamma_\mu \Psi^{(o)}(x) \right] | q', pos \rangle = -ie \langle q, pos | \times \Psi^{(o)}(x) | 0 \rangle \gamma_\mu^T \langle 0 | \bar{\Psi}^{(o)}(x) | q', pos \rangle = -\frac{ie}{V} \times \bar{u}^{(-)}(-q') \gamma_\mu u^{(-)}(-q) e^{iQx} \tag{6.50}$$

The minus sign results because we have to change the order of $\bar{\psi}^{(o)}(x)$ and $\psi^{(o)}(x)$ in the first term of the commutator and these fields anticommute. Using Eqs. (6.44) to (6.47), the expression (6.50) can be written

$$-\frac{ie}{V} C^{-1} u^{(+)}(\bar{q}') \gamma_\mu C \bar{u}^{(+)}(\bar{q}) e^{iQx} = \frac{ie}{V}$$

$$\times u^{(+)}(\bar{q}') C^{-1} \gamma_\mu C \bar{u}^{(+)}(\bar{q}) e^{iQx} = -\frac{ie}{V} u^{(+)}(\bar{q}')$$

$$\times \gamma_\mu^T \bar{u}^{(+)}(\bar{q}) e^{iQx} = -\langle q\, el | j_\mu^{(0)}(x) | q'\, el \rangle \tag{6.51}$$

and the verification is completed.

Since the theory is invariant under charge conjugation, and since the first term in Eq. (6.35) has the correct transformation properties, we must require also that the last term, containing $K_\mu(q, q')$, must transform in accordance with Eq. (6.49). This means something for $K_\mu(q, q')$ itself. In the calculation above, if we replace γ_μ by a more complicated expression, as by $K_\mu(q, q')$ in Eq. (6.38), the main part of the calculation goes through without any important change. This means that $K_\mu(q, q')$ must have similar transformation properties under charge conjugation as γ_μ has. In detail, we get

$$C^{-1} K_\mu(q, q') C = -K_\mu^T(-q', -q) \tag{6.52}$$

Actually, we have only shown this relation for that part of $K_\mu(q, q')$ which is given by Eq. (6.40), but one can show that the relation is true for the whole matrix $K_\mu(q, q')$.

We substitute the value for $K_\mu(q, q')$ given by Eq. (6.39) into Eq. (6.52). If we interchange the summation indices r and r', this last equation can be written

$$-C^{-1} K_\mu(-q', -q) C = -\sum_{r, r'=0}^{1} C^{-1} (-i\gamma q' + m)^{r'} C C^{-1} \times$$

$$\times\left[\gamma_\mu F_1^{r'r}(-q',-q)-iq'_\mu F_2^{r'r}(-q',-q)\right.$$

$$\left.-iq_\mu F_3^{r'r}(-q',-q)\right]CC^{-1}(-i\gamma q+m)^r C$$

$$\equiv K_\mu^T(q,q') \tag{6.53}$$

From Eq. (6.46), it follows that

$$C^{-1}(-i\gamma q+m)^r C=\left[(i\gamma q+m)^r\right]^T \tag{6.54}$$

and Eq. (6.53) reads

$$\sum_{r,r'=0}^{1}\left[(i\gamma q'+m)^{r'}\right]^T\left[\gamma_\mu^T F_1^{r'r}(-q',-q)+iq_\mu'\right.$$

$$\left.\times F_2^{r'r}(-q',-q)+iq_\mu F_3^{r'r}(-q',-q)\right]\left[(i\gamma q+m)^r\right]^T$$

$$\equiv K_\mu^T(q,q') \tag{6.55}$$

Transposing both sides, we get

$$\sum_{r,r'=0}^{1}(i\gamma q+m)^r\left[\gamma_\mu F_1^{r'r}(-q',-q)+\right.$$

$$+iq_\mu F_3^{r'r}(-q',-q)+iq'_\mu F_2^{r'r}(-q',-q)\Big] (i\gamma q'+m)^{r'} \equiv$$

$$\equiv K_\mu(q,q') \tag{6.56}$$

A comparison with Eq. (6.39) gives the relations

$$F_1^{r'r}(-q',-q)=F_1^{rr'}(q,q') \tag{6.57}$$

$$F_2^{r'r}(-q',-q)=F_3^{rr'}(q,q') \tag{6.58}$$

between the amplitudes $F_j^{rr'}(q,q')$. Especially for the $F_j^{oo}(q,q')$ amplitudes, which are the only ones appearing in Eq. (6.40), we get

$$F_2^{oo}(-q',-q)=F_3^{oo}(q,q') \tag{6.59}$$

We are only interested in $F_j^{oo}(q,q')$ on the mass shell, $q^2+m^2=q'^2+m^2=0$. These functions can then only depend on one vector, for example, the difference between the two vectors q' and q. Further, we note that the vector $Q=q'-q$ is invariant under the transformation $q' \rightleftarrows -q$, and we get

$$F_2^{oo}(Q)=F_3^{oo}(Q) \tag{6.60}$$

Equation (6.40) now becomes

$$\bar{u}(\bar{q})\, K_\mu(q,q')\, u(\bar{q}') = \bar{u}(\bar{q}) \Big[\gamma_\mu F_1(Q) + $$
$$+ i \frac{q_\mu + q_\mu'}{2m} F_2(Q) \Big] u(\bar{q}') \tag{6.61}$$

where

$$F_1(Q) = F_1^{oo}(Q) \tag{6.61a}$$

$$\frac{1}{2m} F_2(Q) = F_2^{oo}(Q) \tag{6.61b}$$

(Introducing the factor 2m allows $F_1(Q)$ and $F_2(Q)$ to have the same dimensions.) Consequently, we have only two functions, $F_1(Q)$ and $F_2(Q)$, to compute. We want to point out that, in the calculations above, we have never used the explicit form of $K_\mu(q, q')$ but only very general invariance arguments. This means also that in higher approximations and in an exact solution, if such a solution exists, the matrix element $\langle q | j_\mu(x) | q' \rangle$ must have the same structure as the right-hand side of Eq. (6.61). Further, the result is not dependent on the particular interaction we are studying here. Also, for example, in a meson theory the matrix element of the proton current operator between two proton states must have the same structure. The problem in meson theory is that we cannot compute $F_i(Q)$, since we have no reliable perturbation theory. But, in electron-proton scattering experiments, it is just the functions $F_i(Q)$, called "form factors," which are investigated to analyze the structure of the proton. We shall return to this in Sec. 7.

We shall now indicate how to calculate $F_1(Q)$ and $F_2(Q)$ by means of Eqs. (6.38) and (6.39). It is convenient to calculate the two traces:

$$T_1 = \mathrm{Tr}\left[(i\gamma q - m)\, K_\mu(q, q')(i\gamma q' - m) \right] \tag{6.62}$$

$$T_2 = \mathrm{Tr}\left[\gamma_\mu(i\gamma q - m)\, K_\mu(q, q')(i\gamma q' - m)\right] \tag{6.63}$$

Because of the factors ($i\gamma q - m$) and ($i\gamma q' - m$), we get factors ($q^2 + m^2$) or ($q'^2 + m^2$) in front of all functions $F_i^{r'r}(Q)$ with r' or r $\neq$ 0 when we substitute $K_\mu(q, q')$, as given by Eq. (6.39), into Eqs. (6.62) and (6.63). Since $q^2 + m^2 = q'^2 + m^2 = 0$, the only nonvanishing terms contain the functions $F_1^{00}(Q)$. We get

$$T_1 = \mathrm{Tr}\left[(i\gamma q - m)\,\gamma_\mu\,(i\gamma q' - m)\right] F_1(Q)$$

$$+\, i\,\frac{q_\mu + q'_\mu}{2m}\,\mathrm{Tr}\left[(i\gamma q - m)(i\gamma q' - m)\right] F_2(Q)$$

$$= 4i(q_\mu + q_\mu')\left[-mF_1(Q) + \frac{Q^2 + 4m^2}{4m}F_2(Q)\right] \tag{6.64}$$

$$T_2 = -4\left[(Q^2 - 2m^2)F_1(Q) + \frac{1}{2}(Q^2 + 4m^2)F_2(Q)\right] \tag{6.65}$$

where we have used that $Q^2 = (q' - q)^2 = -2q'q - 2m^2$. If we substitute $K_\mu(q, q')$, as given by Eq. (6.38), into Eqs. (6.62) and (6.63), we get two other expressions for T_1 and T_2, which we can compare with Eqs. (6.64) and (6.65). This gives the following relations:

$$-mF_1(Q) + \frac{1}{4m}(Q^2 + 4m^2)F_2(Q) = \frac{-e^2}{8(2\pi)^3}$$

$$\frac{1}{Q^2 + 4m^2}\int dk \left\{\qquad\right\} S_1 \equiv X_1 \tag{6.66}$$

$$(Q^2-2m^2)F_1(Q)+\frac{1}{2}(Q^2+4m^2)F_2(Q)$$

$$=\frac{+e^2}{8(2\pi)^3}\int dk\left\{\quad\right\}S_2 \equiv X_2 \tag{6.67}$$

where { } stands for the value in curly brackets in Eq. (6.38). Furthermore,

$$S_1=\mathrm{Tr}\Big[(i\gamma q-m)\,\gamma_\lambda\,(i\gamma(q-k)-m)\,i\gamma(q+q')$$

$$\times(i\gamma(q'-k)-m)\,\gamma_\lambda\,(i\gamma q'-m)\Big] \tag{6.68}$$

$$S_2=\mathrm{Tr}\Big[\gamma_\mu\,(i\gamma q-m)\,\gamma_\lambda\,(i\gamma(q-k)-m)$$

$$\times\gamma_\mu\,(i\gamma(q'-k)-m)\,\gamma_\lambda\,(i\gamma q'-m)\Big] \tag{6.69}$$

We have multiplied both sides in Eq. (6.64) by $i\,(q_\mu + q_\mu')$ and divided by $-4(q+q')^2 = 4(Q^2+4m^2)$. Calculations give the following result for the two traces S_1 and S_2:

$$S_1 = 8m(Q^2+4m^2)\Big[\frac{2k^2(q+q')^2}{Q^2+4m^2}+k^2$$

$$-k(q+q')-Q^2-2m^2\Big] \tag{6.70}$$

$$S_2 = -8\left[4qk\,q'k + 2m^2k^2 + 2(Q^2 - m^2)\right.$$

$$\left.\times k(q+q') + (Q^2 + 2m^2)(Q^2 - 2m^2)\right] \tag{6.71}$$

The imaginary part of X_1 is given by

$$\operatorname{Im} X_1 = \frac{-e^2}{16(2\pi)^2}\,\frac{1}{Q^2+4m^2}\,P\!\int dk$$

$$\times\left\{\frac{\delta(k^2)\,\delta((q-k)^2+m^2)}{(q'-k)^2+m^2}\left[-\varepsilon(q-k)-\varepsilon(k)\right]\right.$$

$$+\frac{\delta(k^2)\,\delta((q'-k)^2+m^2)}{(q-k)^2+m^2}\left[\varepsilon(q'-k)+\varepsilon(k)\right]$$

$$+\frac{\delta((q-k)^2+m^2)\,\delta((q'-k)^2+m^2)}{k^2}$$

$$\left.\times\left[\varepsilon(q'-k)-\varepsilon(q-k)\right]\right\}S_1 \tag{6.72}$$

The second δ function of the first term in the curly brackets becomes $\delta\,[(q-k)^2 + m^2] = \delta(q^2 + k^2 - 2\,qk + m^2) = \delta(-2\,qk)$. However, the product of the timelike vector q and the lightlike vector k is different from zero, except for the case that k vanishes identically. But this is only a point in the space of integration and yields no important contribution to the integral.

Therefore, the first term in Eq. (6.72) does not give any

contribution to Im X_1. In the same manner, we can show that the second term also gives no contribution, and we are left with only the third term.

From the two remaining δ functions, it follows that $qk = q'k = 1/2\, k^2$. This can be used to simplify S_1 somewhat. Afterward it is a straightforward calculation to compute Im X_1. In the same way, we can compute Im X_2. Solving Eqs. (6.66) and (6.67) for Im F_1 (Q) and Im F_2(Q) we get

$$\operatorname{Im} F_1^{(0)}(Q) = \frac{-e^2}{8\pi^2}\left[\frac{3}{2}\left(1+\frac{4m^2}{Q^2}\right)-\left(1+\frac{2m^2}{Q^2}\right)\right.$$

$$\left.\times \log\left(1-\frac{Q^2+4m^2}{\mu^2}\right)\right]\frac{\theta(-Q^2-4m^2)}{\sqrt{1+\frac{4m^2}{Q^2}}}\,\pi\varepsilon(Q) \tag{6.73}$$

$$\operatorname{Im} F_2^{(0)}(Q) = \frac{-e^2}{4\pi^2}\,\frac{m^2}{Q^2}\,\frac{\theta(-Q^2-4m^2)}{\sqrt{1+\frac{4m^2}{Q^2}}}\,\pi\varepsilon(Q) \tag{6.74}$$

We have put index (o) on F_j(Q) to indicate that these functions are calculated in the first order. The logarithm in Im $F_1^{(0)}$(Q) comes from the denominator $(k^2)_P$ in Eq. (6.72). A corresponding term does not appear in Im $F_2^{(0)}$(Q) because of some spurious cancellations.

If one performs the k_0 and $|\bar{k}|$ integration in Eq. (6.72) by means of the δ functions, one finds that the integral over the angles is not well defined, since the denominator vanishes at the end points of the interval of integration. To make the integral well defined, one can formally give the photon a small mass μ, that is, replace $(k^2)_P$ by $(k^2 + \mu^2)_P$. It is this photon mass μ which appears in Eq. (6.73).

We write

$$\operatorname{Im} F_j^{(0)}(Q) = \pi \mathcal{E}(Q)\, f_j^{(0)}(Q^2) \tag{6.75}$$

Because the function $K_\mu(x' - x,\ x - x'')$ has a causal structure, we can hope that the real part of $F_j^{(0)}(Q)$ is given by the dispersion relation

$$\operatorname{Re} F_j^{(0)}(Q) = P \int_0^\infty \frac{da\, f_j^{(0)}(-a)}{a + Q^2} \tag{6.76}$$

In fact, these relations are true, but, they do not follow from general arguments using only causality. One must use the explicit expansions of $F_j^{(0)}(Q)$ in this first approximation of perturbation theory to verify Eq. (6.76). In the same way as for the vacuum polarization function, Eq. (5.44), the whole function $F_j^{(0)}(Q)$ can be written as a retarded integral, and $K_\mu(q, q')$ becomes [compare Eq. (6.61)]

$$K_\mu(q, q') = \gamma_\mu \int_0^\infty \frac{da\, f_1^{(0)}(-a)}{(a + Q^2)_R} + \frac{i(q_\mu + q'_\mu)}{2m} \int_0^\infty \frac{da\, f_2^{(0)}(-a)}{(a + Q^2)_R} \tag{6.77}$$

Since $Q^2 = (q' - q)^2 > 0$, the denominators never vanish in the interval of integration and the retarded prescription can be deleted.

We have now handled all terms in the first radiative correction to $j_\mu(x)$. If we use the identity

$$\int_0^\infty \frac{da\, f_1^{(0)}(-a)}{a + Q^2} = -Q^2 \int_0^\infty \frac{da\, f_1^{(0)}(-a)}{a(a + Q^2)} + \int_0^\infty \frac{da\, f_1^{(0)}(-a)}{a} \tag{6.78a}$$

we can summarize our results in the following expression:

$$e^3\langle q|j_\mu^{(2)}(x)|q'\rangle = \Big\{Q^2\int_0^\infty \frac{da}{a(a+Q^2)}$$

$$\times\Big[\Pi^{(0)}(-a)-f_1^{(0)}(-a)\Big]-\int_0^\infty \frac{da}{a-m^2}\Big[\Sigma_2^{(0)}(-a)-\frac{2m}{a-m^2}$$

$$\times\Sigma_1^{(0)}(-a)\Big]+\int_0^\infty \frac{da\,f_1^{(0)}(-a)}{a}\Big\}\frac{ie}{V}\bar{u}(\bar{q})\gamma_\mu$$

$$\times u(\bar{q}')e^{iQx}-\frac{e}{V}\,\frac{q_\mu+q_\mu'}{2m}\,\bar{u}(\bar{q})u(\bar{q}')$$

$$\times e^{iQx}\int_0^\infty \frac{da\,f_2^{(0)}(-a)}{a+Q^2} \tag{6.78}$$

If we compare this with Eq. (6.35), we find that the term containing $K_\mu(x'-x,\ x-x'')$ has given a contribution of the same general structure as the contribution from the vacuum polarization but also a new term proportional to $(q_\mu + q_\mu')$. We shall investigate this term in the next section.

6-3. Anomalous Magnetic Moment of the Electron and the μ Meson

The last term in Eq. (6.78) can be rewritten by using the identity

$$ie\,\bar{u}(\bar{q})\gamma_\mu u(\bar{q}') = \frac{e(q_\mu+q_\mu')}{2m}\bar{u}(\bar{q})u(\bar{q}')+$$

$$+ \frac{ie}{2m} Q_\nu \bar{u}(\bar{q}) \sigma_{\mu\nu} u(\bar{q}') \tag{6.79}$$

$$\sigma_{\mu\nu} = \frac{i}{2} (\gamma_\nu \gamma_\mu - \gamma_\mu \gamma_\nu) \tag{6.80}$$

This relation is easily proved by means of the Dirac equation. Physically, it means that we have split the total current in one translational part and one spin part.

Equation (6.78) can now be written

$$e^3 \langle q | j_\mu^{(2)}(x) | q' \rangle = e \langle q | j_\mu^{(0)}(x) | q' \rangle$$

$$\times \left\{ Q^2 \int_0^\infty \frac{da}{a(a+Q^2)} \left[\Pi^{(0)}(-a) - f_1^{(0)}(-a) + f_2(-a) \right] + C \right\}$$

$$+ e \frac{\partial}{\partial x_\nu} \langle q | m_{\mu\nu}^{(0)}(x) | q' \rangle \int_0^\infty \frac{da\, f_2^{(0)}(-a)}{a+Q^2} \tag{6.81}$$

$$m_{\mu\nu}^{(0)}(x) = \frac{1}{4m} \left[\bar{\psi}^{(0)}(x), \sigma_{\mu\nu} \psi^{(0)}(x) \right] \tag{6.82}$$

The constant C stands for the integrals over $\sum_i^{(0)}(-a)$ and $f_i^{(0)}(-a)$, which do not involve Q, and is discussed later in this section.

From the Dirac theory, it follows that the magnetic moment density of a free electron is

$$e\langle q|\, m_{\mu\nu}^{(0)}(x)\,|q\rangle \tag{6.83}$$

corresponding to a static magnetic moment $\mu^{(0)} = e/2m$. The last term in Eq. (6.81) shows that the electron has an anomalous magnetic moment. If we put $q \approx q'$, that is, $Q^2 \approx 0$, we find that the static anomalous magnetic moment is

$$\mu^{(0)} \int_0^\infty \frac{da}{a}\, f_2^{(0)}(-a) = \mu^{(0)} \frac{\alpha}{2\pi} \tag{6.84}$$

This means that the g factor is not exactly 2 but is

$$g_e = 2\left(1 + \frac{\alpha}{2\pi}\right) = 2 \times 1.0011614 \tag{6.85}$$

To obtain the numerical value we have used

$$\alpha^{-1} = 137.0392 \tag{6.86}$$

We shall discuss the origin of this value of the fine structure constant later. The experimental value for the g factor is *

$$(g_e)_{exp.} = 2\,(1.00115963 \pm 0.00000002) \tag{6.87}$$

The first-order expression (6.85) lies outside the errors of the experimental value. Perhaps, the disagreement will be removed if the next order of perturbation theory is also taken into account. To check this

---

*This very accurate value of $(g_e)_{exp}$ became available in February 1963 and has been incorporated in these notes during the proof-reading.

one must calculate the contribution to the anomalous magnetic moment from $\langle q | j_\mu^{(4)}(x) | q' \rangle$. This has been done, and the result is

$$g_e = 2\left(1 + \frac{\alpha}{2\pi} - 0{,}328\frac{\alpha^2}{\pi^2}\right) = 2 \cdot 1.0011596 \tag{6.88}$$

This value lies within the errors of the experimental value. The fourth order term is rather well checked by experiment, because the error in the experimental value is only one percent of the fourth order correction. However, the influence of the α^3 term is unknown.

The general shape of $\langle q | j_\mu^{(2)}(x) | q' \rangle$, Eq. (6. 81), is mainly given by invariance arguments. The predictions of quantum electrodynamics lie in the detailed shape of the functions $f_1^{(0)}$, $f_2^{(0)}$, etc. For the magnetic moment, it is only the function $f_2^{(0)}$ which enters. One can ask what the agreement between experiment and theory means for the function $f_2^{(0)}(Q^2)$. Let us assume that $f_2^{(0)}(Q^2)$, sketched in Fig. 6. 1, is correct for small values of $|Q^2|$. It is possible that electrodynamics goes wrong for

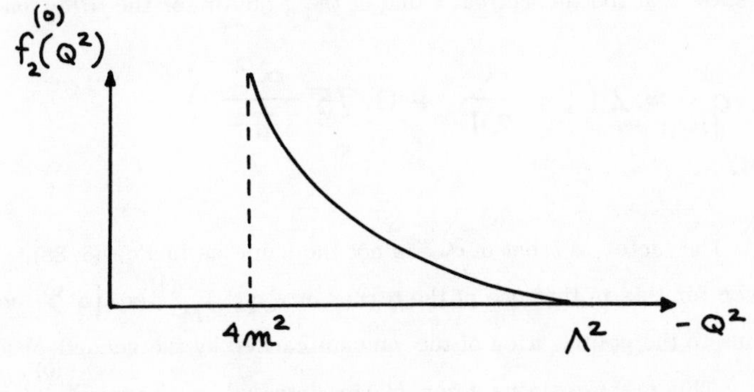

Fig. 6. 1

high energies and that the function $f_2^{(0)}(Q^2)$ must be modified in some way for large values of $|Q^2|$. We introduce a cutoff energy Λ^2 in such a way that the difference between $\alpha/2\pi$ and the integral

$$\int_{4m^2}^{\Lambda^2} \frac{da}{a} f_2^{(0)}(-a) = \frac{\alpha}{2\pi}\left[1 - \frac{2}{1+\left(\frac{\Lambda}{m}\right)^2}\right] \approx \frac{\alpha}{2\pi} - \frac{\alpha}{\pi}\left(\frac{m}{\Lambda}\right)^2$$

(6.89)

lies within the experimental errors for the g_e factor. We can then say that electrodynamics is checked up to this energy.

From Eq. (6.89) it follows that the correction to $\alpha/2\pi$ is proportional to $(m/\Lambda)^2$, where m is mass of the particle under consideration—so far, the electron mass. However, the theory developed here is good also for other particles with spin 1/2 and no strong interaction. We can get a higher value of Λ^2, that is, a better insight into electrodynamics, if we study the g factor of a heavier spin 1/2 particle instead of the electron. If we consider a μ meson, the magnetic-moment term in Eq. (6.81) must be exactly the same, but the m appearing in $f_2^{(0)}(-a)$ is now the μ meson mass. The vacuum polarization term becomes changed, because we cannot only consider creation of virtual μ meson pairs. The contribution from the creation of virtual electron-positron pairs is also important. One can show that the theoretical value of the g factor for the μ meson becomes

$$g_\mu = 2\left(1 + \frac{\alpha}{2\pi} + 0.75\frac{\alpha^2}{\pi^2}\right)$$

(6.90)

The factor in front of α^2 is not the same as in Eq. (6.88). The reason for this is that one of the terms in $\langle q| j_\mu^{(4)}(x) |q'\rangle$ corresponds to the polarization of the vacuum caused by the second-order current. This term contains a convolution integral involving $\Pi^{(0)}(-a)$ and $f_2^{(0)}(-a)$. Since the vacuum polarization is not the same for the electron and for the μ meson, we get different contributions to the anomalous magnetic moment from this approximation.

The experimental datum is

$$(g_\mu)_{exp} = 2\left(1 + \frac{\alpha}{2\pi} + x \cdot 0.75\frac{\alpha^2}{\pi^2}\right)$$

(6.91)

where

$$x = 0.2 \pm 1.2$$

This means that the first term, $\alpha/2\pi$, is checked, but not the second one. However, we are more interested in getting an estimate of Λ^2. Let us assume that $\Lambda = M_p$ (the proton mass). According to Eq. (6.89), we get

$$\frac{1}{2}\delta g_\mu = -\frac{\alpha}{2\pi}\left(\frac{m_\mu}{M_p}\right)^2 \approx -\frac{\alpha^2}{\pi} \tag{6.92}$$

where δg_μ is the correction to g_μ caused by the cutoff procedure. This correction lies within the experimental error; consequently, the energy above which electrodynamics could possibly be modified is larger than something of the order M_p.

The correction to g_e caused by introducing this cutoff energy is

$$\frac{1}{2}\delta g_e = -\frac{\alpha}{2\pi}\left(\frac{m_e}{M_p}\right)^2 \approx -\frac{\alpha^4}{4\pi} \tag{6.93}$$

We can therefore expect that the α^3 term in the theoretical value of g_e is also correct.

We return to the expression for $\langle q | j_\mu^{(2)}(x) | q' \rangle$ given by Eq. (6.81). It contains a constant, which can be written

$$C = \int_0^\infty \frac{da}{a}\left[f_1^{(0)}(-a) - f_2^{(0)}(-a)\right] - \int_0^\infty \frac{da}{a-m^2}$$

$$\times\left[\Sigma_2^{(0)}(-a) - \frac{2m}{a-m^2}\Sigma_1^{(0)}(-a)\right] \tag{6.94}$$

This constant is not well defined since the integrals are divergent. We can give a physical interpretation to this constant by computing the expectation value of the charge operator. The result is

$$e_{exp} = \langle q|Q|q\rangle = -i\int d^3x \langle q|j_4(x)|q\rangle$$

$$= -ie\int d^3x \langle q|j_4^{(0)}(x)|q\rangle - ie^3\int d^3x \langle q|$$

$$\times j_4^{(2)}(x)|q'\rangle = e(1+C) \tag{6.95}$$

[Note that q = q' is equivalent to Q = 0, and all terms in Eq. (6.81) except the contribution proportional to C drop out.]

To obtain Eq. (6.81), we have made the same charge renormalization for the electron as for the external field. This has lead to a charge of the one-electron state, which is e(1 + C) and not e. Therefore, we must perform one more charge renormalization for the one-electron states. To get the observable quantity $\langle q|j_\mu^{obs}(x)|q'\rangle$, we must divide $\langle q|j_\mu(x)|q'\rangle$ by (1 + C), which in this approximation is equivalent to subtracting $Ce\langle q|j_\mu^{(0)}(x)|q'\rangle$ from Eq. (6.81). We get

$$\langle q|j_\mu^{obs}(x)|q'\rangle = e\langle q|j_\mu^{(0)}(x)|q'\rangle\Big[1+Q^2$$

$$\int_0^\infty \frac{da\, g^{(0)}(-a)}{a(a+Q^2)} + e\frac{\partial}{\partial x_\nu}\langle q|m_{\mu\nu}^{(0)}(x)|q'\rangle\int_0^\infty \frac{da\, f_2^{(0)}(-a)}{a+Q^2}\Big] \tag{6.96}$$

where e now is the experimental charge, and

$$g^{(0)}(-a) = \Pi^{(0)}(-a) - f_1^{(0)}(-a) + f_2^{(0)}(-a) \qquad (6.97)$$

The first charge renormalization (in vacuum polarization) was an adjustment of the unit of our external charge (current). The second charge renormalization is an adjustment of the charge of the one-electron states.

Finally, we want to say a few words about the "value of C." Since C is defined as the difference between two divergent integrals, the value of C can only be defined as the result of some limiting procedure. If one defines the integrals by means of the regularization procedure, for instance, it is possible to show that the two integrals cancel and C = 0. This means that no second-charge renormalization is needed. The fact that the two integrals in Eq. (6.94) are equal is known as the "Ward Identity." It is true not only in first-order perturbation theory but quite generally.

6-4. Application to the Hydrogen Atom; Lamb shift

We can now use Eq. (6.96) to calculate the change in the energy levels due to radiative corrections. We take the solution of the Dirac equation in the Coulomb field as zero-order approximation. Further, we assume the electron is in a bound state $|n\rangle$. The displacement of the energy levels is, in first approximation, given by

$$\delta E = -\int d^3x \, A_\mu^{\text{coul}}(\bar{x}) \langle n|\delta j_\mu(x)|n\rangle \qquad (6.98)$$

$$\delta j_\mu(x) = j_\mu(x) - e j_\mu^{(0)}(x) \qquad (6.99)$$

We expand the bound state $|n\rangle$ in free-particle states $|q, r\rangle$

$$|n\rangle = \frac{1}{\sqrt{V}} \sum_{\bar{q}, r} f_n^{(r)}(\bar{q}) \, |q, r\rangle \qquad (6.100)$$

Since $|n\rangle$ is a normalized state, we get

$$\langle n|n\rangle = \frac{1}{V}\sum_{\bar{q},r} |f_n^{(r)}(\bar{q})|^2 = \frac{1}{(2\pi)^3}$$

$$\times\int d^3q \sum_r |f_n^{(r)}(\bar{q})|^2 = 1 \tag{6.101}$$

The amplitude $f_n^{(r)}(q)$ is chosen to be the Fourier transform of the solution $u_n(\bar{x})$ of the Dirac equation in a Coulomb field; that is,

$$u_n(\bar{x}) = \frac{1}{V}\sum_{\bar{q},r} f_n^{(r)}(\bar{q})\, u^{(+)(r)}(\bar{q})\, e^{i\bar{q}\bar{x}} \tag{6.102}$$

This corresponds to taking

$$\langle 0|\psi^{(0)}(x)|n\rangle = u_n(\bar{x})\, e^{-iE_n x_0} \tag{6.102a}$$

If we suppress the spin index (r), Eq. (6.98) becomes

$$\delta E = -\frac{1}{V}\sum_{\bar{q},q'} f_n^*(\bar{q})\, f_n(\bar{q}')\int d^3x\, A_\mu^{Coul}(\bar{x})\langle q|\delta j_\mu(x)|q'\rangle \tag{6.103}$$

We can now expand $\langle q|\delta j_\mu(x)|q'\rangle$ in powers of e, and the first approximation is given by Eq. (6.96). It is convenient to split δE into two parts

$$\delta E = \delta E^{(1)} + \delta E^{(2)} \tag{6.104}$$

$$\delta E^{(1)} = \frac{-e}{V} \sum_{\bar{q},\bar{q}'} f_n^*(\bar{q})\, f_n(\bar{q}')\, Q^2 \int_0^\infty \frac{da\, g^{(0)}(-a)}{a(a+Q^2)}$$

$$\times \int d^3x\, A_\mu^{\text{Coul}}(\bar{x}) \langle q | j_\mu^{(0)}(x) | q' \rangle \tag{6.105}$$

$$\delta E^{(2)} = \frac{-e}{V} \sum_{\bar{q},\bar{q}'} f_n^*(\bar{q})\, f_n(\bar{q}') \int_0^\infty \frac{da\, f_2^{(0)}(-a)}{a+Q^2}$$

$$\times \int d^3x\, A_\mu^{\text{Coul}}(\bar{x}) \frac{\partial}{\partial x_\nu} \langle q | m_{\mu\nu}^{(0)}(x) | q' \rangle \tag{6.106}$$

The first term $\delta E^{(1)}$ is of exactly the same form as the δE we calculated in Sec. 5-2 in connection with vacuum polarization. We have only to replace $\Pi^{(0)}(-a)$ by $g^{(0)}(-a)$ in Eq. (5.57) to get $\delta E^{(1)}$. Hence,

$$\delta E^{(1)} = \frac{-Ze^2}{(2\pi)^3} \int d^3p\, \rho(\bar{p}) \int_0^\infty \frac{da\, g^{(0)}(-a)}{a(a+\bar{p}^2)} \tag{6.107}$$

$$\rho(\bar{p}) = \int d^3x\, |\varphi_n(\bar{x})|^2 e^{-i\bar{p}\bar{x}} \tag{6.107a}$$

We have made the same approximation as in Sec. 5-2, that is, replaced $u_n(\bar{x})$ by $\varphi_n(\bar{x})$, the solution of the Schrödinger equation in a Coulomb field. Since $g^{(0)}(-a) = 0$ for $a \leq m^2$ and since $\rho(\bar{p}) \approx 0$ for $|\bar{p}| > \alpha m$, we can put $a + \bar{p}^2 \approx a$ and get

$$\delta E^{(1)} = -Ze^{(2)} |\varphi_n(0)|^2 \int_0^\infty \frac{da\, g^{(0)}(-a)}{a^2} \tag{6.108}$$

The integral over a can be performed, and the value of $|\varphi_n(0)|^2$ is given by Eq. (5.60). We obtain

$$\delta E^{(1)} = \frac{4}{3\pi} \frac{m Z^4 \alpha^5}{n^3} \left[\log \frac{m}{\mu} - \frac{23}{40}\right] \delta_{l,0} \tag{6.109}$$

Unfortunately, we get an infrared divergence (when $\mu \to 0$) in this final result. Before discussing this problem, we calculate $\delta E^{(2)}$.

Since $A_\mu^{\text{Coul}}(\bar{x}) = 0$ for $\mu \neq 4$ and since $m_{4\nu}^{(0)}(x) = 0$ for $\nu = 4$, we are left with only the three terms $m_{4k}^{(0)}(x)$. If we use Eqs. (6.82) and (6.102) and make the approximation $a + \bar{Q}^2 \approx a$, we get

$$\delta E^{(2)} = \frac{\alpha}{2\pi} \frac{e}{2m} \frac{Ze}{4\pi} \int \frac{d^3x}{r} \frac{\partial}{\partial x_k} \left[\bar{u}_n(\bar{x}) \gamma_4 \gamma_k u_n(\bar{x})\right] \tag{6.110}$$

The integrand can be handled in the following way:

$$X \equiv \frac{\partial}{\partial x_k} \left[\bar{u}_n(\bar{x}) \gamma_4 \gamma_k u_n(\bar{x})\right] =$$

$$=u_n^*(\bar{x})\,\gamma_k\,\frac{\partial u_n(\bar{x})}{\partial x_k}+\frac{\partial u_n^*(\bar{x})}{\partial x_k}\,\gamma_k\,u_n(\bar{x}) \tag{6.111}$$

The Dirac equation in a Coulomb field reads

$$\left(\gamma_k\frac{\partial}{\partial x_k}+m\right)u_n(\bar{x})=\gamma_4\,u_n(\bar{x})\left[E_n+\frac{Z\alpha}{r}\right] \tag{6.112}$$

Using this, we get

$$X=2\left(E_n+\frac{Z\alpha}{r}\right)\bar{u}_n(\bar{x})u_n(\bar{x})-2m|u_n(\bar{x})|^2 \tag{6.113}$$

The solutions $u_n(\bar{x})$ of the Dirac equation can be approximated by

$$u_{big}(\bar{x})=\varphi_n(\bar{x})\,\xi \tag{6.114}$$

$$u_{small}(\bar{x})=-\frac{i}{2m}\,\bar{\sigma}\,\mathrm{grad}\,u_{big}(\bar{x}) \tag{6.115}$$

where ξ is the nonrelativistic spin function $\binom{1}{0}$ or $\binom{0}{1}$. Introducing this in Eq. (6.113) and using the well-known formula

$$(\bar{\sigma}\bar{A})(\bar{\sigma}\bar{B})=\bar{A}\bar{B}+i\bar{\sigma}(\bar{A}\times\bar{B}) \tag{6.116}$$

we get

$$X=2\left[E_n-m+\frac{Z\alpha}{r}\right]|\varphi_n(\bar{x})|^2-$$

$$-\frac{1}{m}\,\mathrm{grad}\,\varphi_n^*(\bar{x})\cdot\mathrm{grad}\,\varphi_n(\bar{x})-\frac{2i}{m}$$

$$\times\,\bar{S}\left[\mathrm{grad}\,\varphi_n^*(\bar{x})\times\mathrm{grad}\,\varphi_n(\bar{x})\right] \tag{6.117}$$

with

$$\bar{S}=\frac{1}{2}<\xi\,|\,\bar{\sigma}\,|\,\xi> \tag{6.118}$$

The functions $\varphi_n(\bar{x})$ satisfy the Schrödinger equation

$$\left(E_n-m+\frac{Z\alpha}{r}\right)\varphi_n(\bar{x})=-\frac{\Delta}{2m}\varphi_n(\bar{x}) \tag{6.119}$$

If we use this equation, the two first terms in Eq. (6.117) become $-1/2m\,\Delta|\varphi_n(\bar{x})|^2$, and this shall be integrated over $\bar{x}$. Partial integration and the formula

$$\Delta\frac{1}{r}=-4\pi\delta(\bar{x}) \tag{6.120}$$

gives

$$-\frac{1}{2m}\int\frac{d^3x}{r}\,\Delta|\varphi_n(\bar{x})|^2=\frac{2\pi}{m}|\varphi_n(0)|^2 \tag{6.121}$$

The last term in Eq. (6.117), integrated over $\bar{x}$, becomes

$$-\frac{2i}{m}\,\bar{S}\int\frac{d^3x}{r}\left[\operatorname{grad}\varphi_n^*(\bar{x})\times\operatorname{grad}\varphi_n(\bar{x})\right]$$

$$=\frac{2}{m}<\bar{S}\cdot\bar{L}><\frac{1}{r^3}>$$

(6.122)

Using

$$<\bar{S}\cdot\bar{L}>=\frac{1}{2}\left[j(j+1)-\ell(\ell+1)-\frac{3}{4}\right]$$

(6.123)

we can summarize $\delta E^{(2)}$ in the following expression:

$$\delta E^{(2)}=\frac{Z\alpha^2}{4\pi m^2}\left[2\pi|\varphi_n(0)|^2+(j(j+1)-\ell(\ell+1)\right.$$

$$\left.-\frac{3}{4})<\frac{1}{r^3}>\right]$$

(6.124)

The function $|\varphi_n(0)|^2$ is defined in Eq. (5.60), and the nonrelativistic expectation value of $1/r^3$ is (for $\ell\neq 0$)

$$<\frac{1}{r^3}>=\frac{Z^3m^3\alpha^3}{n^3\ell(\ell+\frac{1}{2})(\ell+1)}$$

(6.125)

For $\ell = 0$ this expectation value is zero. We get

$$\delta E^{(2)} = \frac{m Z^4 \alpha^5}{2\pi n^3} \quad \frac{C_{\ell, j}}{2\ell + 1} \tag{6.126}$$

$$C_{\ell, j} = \begin{cases} \dfrac{1}{\ell + 1} & j = \ell + \frac{1}{2} \\ -\dfrac{1}{\ell} & j = \ell - \frac{1}{2} \end{cases} \tag{6.127}$$

Hence, we have calculated both $\delta E^{(1)}$ and $\delta E^{(2)}$, and we have found that $\delta E^{(1)} = 0$ for $\ell \neq 0$, while $\delta E^{(2)} \neq 0$ for all ℓ.

To compare with experiment, we can consider the 2P 3/2 and 2P 1/2 levels in the hydrogen atom. According to the Dirac theory, the difference between these two levels is

$$\delta E^{(0)} = \frac{m \alpha^4}{32} \left[1 + \frac{5}{8} \alpha^2 + \cdots \right] \tag{6.128}$$

The splitting, caused by the radiative corrections in first approximation, is

$$\delta E^{(2)} = \delta E^{(2)}(2P\tfrac{3}{2}) - \delta E^{(2)}(2P\tfrac{1}{2}) = \frac{m\alpha^5}{32\pi} \tag{6.129}$$

If the next radiative correction to the magnetic moment is also taken into account, one gets

$$\delta E^{(2)} = \frac{m\alpha^4}{32}\left[\frac{\alpha}{\pi} - 0{,}656\,\frac{\alpha^2}{\pi^2}\right] \tag{6.130}$$

The total difference is

$$\Delta E = \delta E^{(0)} + \delta E^{(2)} = \frac{m\alpha^4}{32}\left[1 + \frac{\alpha}{\pi} + \frac{5}{8}\alpha^2 - 0{,}656\,\frac{\alpha^2}{\pi^2}\right] \tag{6.131}$$

The experimental result is

$$(\Delta E)_{exp} = 10971.6 \pm 0.2 \quad \text{Mc/sec.} \tag{6.132}$$

We want to check quantum electrodynamics by comparing these two results; but the accuracy of the measurements is so high that the value of α, given by other experiments, is not good enough. Therefore, one uses Eqs. (6.131) and (6.132), the Rydberg constant $R_y = m\alpha^2/2 = 109737.309$ cm^{-1}, and the velocity of light $c = 2.997931 \cdot 10^{10}$ cm/sec (the latter two known with very high precision) to compute α and obtains

$$\alpha^{-1} = 137.0392 \pm 0.0012$$

Now, we have a good α value and can compute the energy difference between, for example, the 2S 1/2 and 2P 1/2 levels in the hydrogen atom (a value known as the "Lamb shift"). The experimental value is

$$(\Delta E)_{exp} = 1057.77 \pm 0.10 \quad \text{Mc/sec.} \tag{6.133}$$

The theoretical value involves $\delta E^{(1)}$, and we must view the problem with the photon mass μ appearing in $\delta E^{(1)}$. In the calculations above we have regarded the electron as free in all intermediate states. We have used bound electron states only in the initial and final states in Eq. (6.98). As long as the virtual photons have energy which is large compared with the binding energy of the electron to the proton ($\sim m\alpha^2$), this is a rather good approximation. But when the virtual photons have very low energy, the recoil of the electron is also small, and we must treat the electron as bound also in the intermediate states. The energy of the photons up to which we cannot regard the electron as free must be of the order of magnitude $m\alpha^2$. Therefore, we can expect that $\log (m/\mu)$ has to be replaced by something like $\log (m/m\alpha^2) = 2 \log (1/\alpha)$. Of course, this is only a rough estimate, and one has to go through all the details to get the correct replacement. This has been done, and the theoretical value of the energy difference turns out to be

$$(\Delta E)_{theor} = 1052.1 \quad Mc/sec. \tag{6.134}$$

If the radiative correction of the next order is calculated, and if other small small terms such as the motion of the proton and its finite extension are included, one gets

$$(\Delta E)_{theor} = 1057.95 \pm 0.15 \ Mc/sec. \tag{6.135}$$

Finally, we can mention that the correction due to the finite extension of the proton, though difficult to calculate, is of the order of magnitude 0.1 Mc/sec. This is of the same order of magnitude as the second-order radiative correction to ΔE, the α^6 term in Eq. (6.131). If, in the future, it is possible to attain higher accuracy in the measurement of ΔE, this cannot be used to check quantum electrodynamics but should give an insight into the extension of the proton.

7. SCATTERING OF ELECTRONS BY PROTONS

7-1. Elastic Cross Section; the Proton Treated as a Point Charge

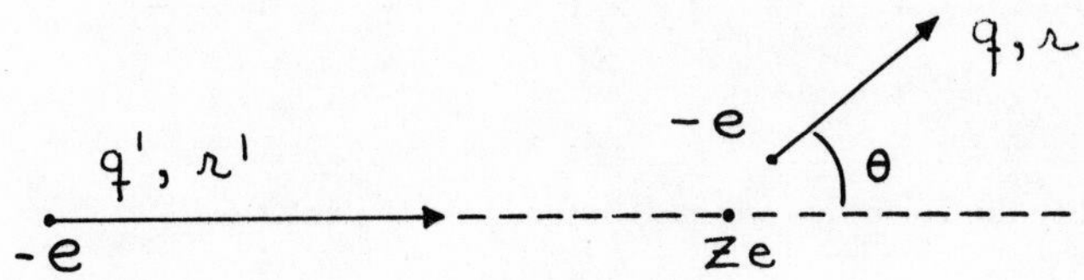

Fig. 7.1

We want to calculate the cross section for scattering of electrons by protons. As a first approximation, we treat the proton as a point charge, and the field from the proton as a weak perturbation. The S matrix can then be expanded in this external field and reads

$$S = 1 + i \int dx \; j_\mu(x) \, A_\mu^{ext}(x) \tag{7.1}$$

The operator $j_\mu(x)$ is the current, including its radiative interactions. We are interested in the matrix element

$$\langle q | S | q' \rangle = i \int dx \, \langle q | j_\mu(x) | q' \rangle A_\mu^{ext}(x) \tag{7.2}$$

(We suppress spin indices and assume that $|q\rangle \neq |q'\rangle$.) We can now perform an expansion of $\langle q | j_\mu(x) | q' \rangle$ in powers of the radiative field. If we take only the first two approximations into account, as given by Eq. (6.96), we get

$$\langle q | S | q' \rangle = ie \int dx \, A_\mu^{ext}(x) \left\{ \langle q | j_\mu^{(0)}(x) | q' \rangle \text{cont.} \right.$$

$$\times\left[1+\bar{g}^{(0)}(Q^2)\right]+iQ_\nu \langle q|m_{\mu\nu}^{(0)}(x)|q'\rangle \bar{f}_2^{(0)}(Q^2)\Big\} \tag{7.3}$$

To simplify the formulas we have introduced the notations

$$\bar{g}^{(0)}(Q^2) = Q^2\int_0^\infty \frac{da\, g^{(0)}(-a)}{a(a+Q^2)} \tag{7.4}$$

$$\bar{f}_2^{(0)}(Q^2) = \int_0^\infty \frac{da\, f_2^{(0)}(-a)}{a+Q^2} \tag{7.5}$$

[The functions $g^{(0)}(-a)$ and $f_2^{(0)}(-a)$ are given by Eqs. (6.97) and (6.73) to (6.75), and $\Pi^{(0)}(-a)$ by Eqs. (5.42) and (5.28).] Since both terms in Eq. (7.3) contain a factor 1/V exp (iQx), we can write

$$\langle q|S|q'\rangle = \frac{i}{V}\,\mathcal{J}_\mu(q,q')\int dx\, e^{iQx} A_\mu^{ext}(x) \tag{7.6}$$

$$\mathcal{J}_\mu(q,q') = ie\,\bar{u}(\bar{q})\gamma_\mu u(\bar{q}')\left[1+\bar{g}^{(0)}(Q^2)\right]$$

$$+\frac{Q_\lambda}{2m}\, ie\,\bar{u}(\bar{q})\sigma_{\mu\lambda}u(\bar{q}')\,\bar{f}_2^{(0)}(Q^2) \tag{7.7}$$

where $u(\bar{q}') = u^{(+)(r')}(\bar{q}')$, etc.

Assuming that the external field is independent of time, we get

$$\int dx\, A_\mu^{ext}(\bar{x})\, e^{iQx} = 2\pi\, \delta(Q_0)\, A_\mu^{ext}(\bar{Q}) \tag{7.8}$$

$$A_\mu^{ext}(\bar{Q}) = \int d^3x\, e^{i\bar{Q}\bar{x}}\, A_\mu^{ext}(\bar{x}) \tag{7.9}$$

Equation (7.6) now becomes

$$\langle q|S|q'\rangle = \frac{1}{V}\, 2\pi i\, \delta(Q_0)\, \mathcal{J}_\mu(q, q')\, A_\mu^{ext}(\bar{Q}) \tag{7.10}$$

The δ function indicates that the electron has the same energy after scattering as before. This comes because we have treated the proton as infinitely heavy. If we use Eq. (4.49) and square the δ function in the way described in connection with Eqs. (4.51) and (4.52), the transition probability per unit time becomes

$$\frac{\delta w}{\delta t} = \frac{2\pi\,\delta(Q_0)}{V^2} \left| \mathcal{J}_\mu(q, q')\, A_\mu^{ext}(\bar{Q}) \right|^2 \tag{7.11}$$

The flux of incoming electrons is v_{in}/V, where $v_{in} = |\bar{q}'|/q_0'$ is the velocity of the incoming electrons. If we divide by this flux and sum over all final states and also average over the two spin states of the incoming electrons, the elastic cross section becomes

$$\sigma^{el} = \frac{1}{2} \sum_{\bar{q}, r, r'} \frac{\delta w}{\delta t}\, \frac{V}{v_{in}} \tag{7.12}$$

Introducing Eq. (7.11) and writing the sum over $\bar{q}$ as an integral, we get

$$\sigma^{el} = \frac{q_0'}{8\pi^2|\bar{q}'|} \sum_{r,r'} \int d^3q\, \delta(Q_0) \left| \mathcal{J}_\mu(q,q') A_\mu^{ext}(\bar{Q}) \right|^2 \tag{7.13}$$

We write $d^3q = |\bar{q}|^2 d|\bar{q}| d\Omega = |\bar{q}| q_0 dq_0 d\Omega$ and perform the q_0 integration by means of the δ function. This gives

$$\sigma^{el} = \frac{q_0^2}{8\pi^2} \sum_{r,r'} \int d\Omega \left| \mathcal{J}_\mu(q,q') A_\mu^{ext}(\bar{Q}) \right|^2 \tag{7.14}$$

From Eqs. (7.7) and (7.10) it follows that

$$A_\mu^{ext\,*}(\bar{Q}) = \begin{cases} A_\mu^{ext}(-\bar{Q}) & \mu \neq 4 \\ -A_4^{ext}(-\bar{Q}) & \end{cases} \tag{7.15}$$

$$\mathcal{J}_\mu^*(q,q') \begin{cases} \mathcal{J}_\mu(q',q) & \mu \neq 4 \\ -\mathcal{J}_4(q',q) & \end{cases} \tag{7.16}$$

The differential cross section then becomes

$$\frac{d\sigma^{el}}{d\Omega} = \frac{q_0^2}{8\pi^2} A_\mu^{ext}(\bar{Q}) A_\nu^{ext}(-\bar{Q}) \sum_{r,r'} \mathcal{J}_\mu(q,q') \mathcal{J}_\nu(q',q) \tag{7.17}$$

Note that this formula is obtained by neglecting the recoil of the proton and treating the proton as an external field. But so far we have not used the exact shape of this field, only that it is time-independent. Further, the formula is also valid for higher radiative approximations, but $J_\mu(q, q')$ is then given by an expression different from Eq. (7.7). However, expression (7.17) is changed if we also take higher approximations in the external field into account.

We are only interested in the first radiative correction to the differential cross section. Therefore, when we multiply $J_\mu(q, q')$ and $J_\nu(q', q)$, we drop all terms which are proportional to higher powers than e^4. [Note that $g^{(0)}(-a)$ and $f_2^{(0)}(-a)$ are proportional to e^2.] We get

$$\begin{aligned}\sum_{r,r'} J_\mu J_\nu = -e^2 \sum_{r,r'} \Big\{ & \bar{u}(\bar{q})\gamma_\mu u(\bar{q}')\bar{u}(\bar{q}')\gamma_\nu u(\bar{q})\left[1+2\bar{g}^{(0)}(Q^2)\right] \\ & - \bar{u}(\bar{q})\gamma_\mu u(\bar{q}')\bar{u}(\bar{q}')\sigma_{\nu\lambda} u(\bar{q})\frac{Q_\lambda}{2m}\bar{f}_2^{(0)}(Q^2) \\ & + \bar{u}(\bar{q})\sigma_{\mu\lambda} u(\bar{q}')\bar{u}(\bar{q}')\gamma_\nu u(\bar{q})\frac{Q_\lambda}{2m}\bar{f}_2^{(0)}(Q^2)\Big\}\end{aligned} \tag{7.18}$$

The summation over the spin indices can be carried through by means of Eq. (2.13), and we obtain

$$\sum_{r,r'} J_\mu J_\nu = \frac{-e^2}{4q_0^2}\Big\{\mathrm{Tr}\left[\gamma_\mu(i\gamma q'-m)\gamma_\nu(i\gamma q-m)\right]\left(1+2\bar{g}^{(0)}\right) -$$

$$-\frac{Q_\lambda}{2m}\mathrm{Tr}\left[\gamma_\mu(i\gamma q'-m)\sigma_{\nu\lambda}(i\gamma q-m)\right]\bar{f}_2^{(0)}$$

$$+\frac{Q_\lambda}{2m}\mathrm{Tr}\left[\gamma_\nu(i\gamma q-m)\sigma_{\mu\lambda}(i\gamma q'-m)\right]\bar{f}_2^{(0)}\Big\}$$

(7.19)

The traces are easily calculated, giving

$$\mathrm{Tr}\left[\gamma_\mu(i\gamma q'-m)\,\gamma_\nu(i\gamma q-m)\right]=-4\Big[q'_\mu q_\nu$$
$$+q'_\nu q_\mu-\delta_{\mu\nu}(qq'+m^2)\Big] \tag{7.20}$$

$$\mathrm{Tr}\left[\gamma_\mu(i\gamma q'-m)\,\sigma_{\nu\lambda}(i\gamma q-m)\right]=4m\Big[Q_\lambda\delta_{\nu\mu}$$
$$-Q_\nu\delta_{\mu\lambda}\Big] \tag{7.21}$$

Substituting this into Eq. (7.19), we get

$$\sum_{r,r'}\mathcal{J}_\mu\mathcal{J}_\nu=\frac{e^2}{q_0^2}\Big\{\Big[q'_\mu q_\nu+q'_\nu q_\mu-\delta_{\mu\nu}$$
$$\times(qq'+m^2)\Big](1+2\bar{g}^{(0)})+(Q^2\delta_{\nu\mu}-Q_\mu Q_\nu)\bar{f}_2^{(0)}\Big\} \tag{7.22}$$

Now, we assume that the external field fulfills the Lorentz condition

$$Q_\mu A_\mu^{ext}(\bar{Q}) = 0 \tag{7.23}$$

This is no restriction on the external field but is merely a special choice of gauge function. Equation (7.23) can be written

$$q_\mu A_\mu^{ext}(\bar{Q}) = q'_\mu A_\mu^{ext}(\bar{Q}) \tag{7.24}$$

which means that it is not necessary to make a distinction between q and q_μ' in Eq. (7.22).

After substituting Eqs. (7.22) and (7.24) into Eq. (7.17), we get the following differential cross section:

$$\frac{d\sigma^{el}}{d\Omega} = \frac{e^2}{4\pi^2}\left\{\left(q_\mu q_\nu + \delta_{\mu\nu}\frac{Q^2}{4}\right)\left(1+2\bar{g}^{(0)}(Q^2)\right) + \delta_{\mu\nu}\frac{Q^2}{2}\bar{f}_2^{(0)}(Q^2)\right\} A_\mu^{ext}(\bar{Q}) A_\nu^{ext}(-\bar{Q}) \tag{7.25}$$

In the simplified calculation in this section, we assume that the potential from the proton is a Coulomb field; that is,

$$A_\mu^{ext}(\bar{Q}) = -i\delta_{\mu 4}\frac{Ze}{\bar{Q}^2} \tag{7.26}$$

Since $q_o = q_o'$ and $|\bar{q}| = |\bar{q}'|$, we get

$$Q^2 = \bar{Q}^2 = 4\bar{q}^2 \sin^2 \frac{\theta}{2} \tag{7.27}$$

With this external field the differential cross section, without any radiative corrections at all, becomes

$$\frac{d\sigma^{(0)}}{d\Omega} = \frac{e^2}{4\pi^2}\left(q_\mu q_\nu + \delta_{\mu\nu}\frac{Q^2}{4}\right) A_\mu^{ext}(\bar{Q}) A_\nu^{ext}$$

$$\times(-\bar{Q}) = \left(\frac{Z\alpha m}{2\bar{q}^2 \sin^2 \frac{\theta}{2}}\right)^2 \left(1 + \frac{\bar{q}^2}{m^2}\cos^2\frac{\theta}{2}\right) \tag{7.28}$$

The first squared factor is the Rutherford cross section, and the second factor is the relativistic correction to the same.

It is now easy to see, comparing Eqs. (7.25) and (7.28), that the cross section with first-order radiative corrections becomes

$$\frac{d\sigma^{el}}{d\Omega} = \frac{d\sigma^{(0)}}{d\Omega}\left[1 - \delta^{el}\right] \tag{7.29}$$

$$\delta^{el} = -2\bar{g}^{(0)}(Q^2) + \frac{Q^2}{2\left(m^2 + \bar{q}^2\cos^2\frac{\theta}{2}\right)}\bar{f}_2^{(0)}(Q^2) \tag{7.30}$$

$$Q^2 = \bar{Q}^2 = 4\bar{q}^2 \sin^2\frac{\theta}{2} \tag{7.31}$$

The functions $f_2^{(o)}(-a)$ and $g^{(o)}(-a)$ are explicitly given by Eqs. (6.97) and (6.73 to (6.75); and the integrals over a, Eqs. (7.4) and (7.5) can be performed, yielding $\bar{g}^{(o)}(Q^2)$ and $\bar{f}_2^{(o)}(Q^2)$. The result is some lengthy expressions containing more than elementary functions, which we shall not give in detail here. Since the function $f_1^{(o)}(-a)$ contains the photon mass μ, the function $\bar{g}^{(o)}(Q^2)$, but not $\bar{f}_2^{(o)}(Q^2)$, contains μ. One finds

$$\bar{g}^{(o)}(Q^2) = \frac{e^2}{4\pi^2}\left[1 - \frac{2m^2+Q^2}{Q^2\sqrt{1+\frac{4m^2}{Q^2}}}\log\frac{\sqrt{1+\frac{4m^2}{Q^2}}+1}{\sqrt{1+\frac{4m^2}{Q^2}}-1}\right]\log\frac{m}{\mu}$$

$$+ \text{(terms not containing } \mu) \tag{7.32}$$

Again we have the problem with μ appearing in a final answer in such a way that a physically measurable quantity tends to infinity when μ tends to zero. When we calculated the Lamb shift in Sec. 6-4, we also had problems when $\mu \rightarrow 0$. We found that these problems disappeared when we took the binding of the electron to the proton into account. This cannot be the solution here. The electrons are coming from "infinity," are scattered by the proton, and go to "infinity" again. But it can happen that, at the same time as an electron becomes scattered, it also emits a photon with energy w. This means that the energy q_o of the scattered electron is not exactly the same as the energy q_o' of the incoming electron but that $q_o = q_o' - w$. If the detector has the energy resolution ΔE, it also accepts this electron as long as $w \leq \Delta E$. Therefore, the cross section one measures, $d\sigma^{obs}/d\Omega$, is <u>not</u> the elastic cross section, $d\sigma^{el}/d\Omega$, but is

$$\frac{d\sigma^{obs}}{d\Omega} = \frac{d\sigma^{el}}{d\Omega} + \frac{d\sigma^{rad}}{d\Omega} \tag{7.33}$$

Here, $d\sigma^{rad}/d\Omega$ is the cross section for an electron to be scattered into the solid angle element $d\Omega$, at the same time emitting a photon with an energy w such that $w \leq \Delta E$. This cross section is calculated in the next section.

7-2. Cross Section for Emission of Photons with $w \leq \Delta E$

The S matrix is defined by Eq. (4.57); but now, $H_{int}^{(o)}$ is given by

$$H_{int}^{(o)}(x_o) = -\int d^3x \; j_\mu^{(o)}(x)\left[A_\mu^{ext.}(x) + A_\mu^{(o)}(x)\right] \tag{7.34}$$

instead of the expression (4.58). This means that we have expanded the S matrix in <u>both</u> the external and the radiative field and have assumed that it is enough to take only the first order of these fields into account.

We are interested in the matrix element $\langle q, k|S|q'\rangle$. The second term of the S matrix contains the correct number of $A_\mu^{(o)}(x)$ and $\psi^{(o)}(x)$ but it cannot perform the transition since energy is then not conserved. We must go to the third term of the S matrix and obtain

$$\langle q, k|S|q'\rangle = \frac{-e^2}{2}\iint dx'dx''\langle q|\bar{\psi}^{(o)}(x'')|0\rangle$$

$$\times\gamma_\nu S_F(x''-x')\,\gamma_\lambda\langle 0|\psi^{(o)}(x')|q'\rangle\;\left[\langle k|A_\nu^{(o)}(x'')\right.$$

$$\left.\times|0\rangle A_\lambda^{ext}(x') + \langle k|A_\lambda^{(o)}(x')|0\rangle A_\nu^{ext}(x'')\right] \tag{7.35}$$

where

$$\langle 0|T\left(\bar{\Psi}^{(0)}(x)\ \psi^{(0)}(x')\right)|0\rangle = \frac{1}{2} S_F(x'-x) \qquad (7.36)$$

$$S_F(x) = \frac{2}{i}\ \frac{1}{(2\pi)^4} \int dp\ e^{ipx} \frac{i\gamma p - m}{p^2 + m^2 - i\epsilon} \qquad (7.37)$$

As in Sec. 7-1, we assume that the external field is independent of time and get

$$\langle q, k|S|q'\rangle = \frac{ie^2}{\sqrt{V^3}} \frac{1}{\sqrt{2\omega}}\ \bar{u}(\bar{q})$$

$$\times\left[\gamma_\nu \frac{i\gamma(q'-k) - m}{(q'-k)^2 + m^2}\ \gamma e + \gamma e \frac{i\gamma(q+k) - m}{(q+k)^2 + m^2} \gamma_\nu\right]$$

$$\times u(\bar{q}')\ A_\nu^{ext}(\bar{q}' - \bar{q} - \bar{k})\ 2\pi\ \delta(q_0' - q_0 - k_0) \qquad (7.38)$$

Here, we have suppressed spin indices, and e stands for the polarization vector of the emitted photon. Since $q^2 + m^2 = 0$ and $k^2 = 0$, the denominators become $-2q'k$ and $2qk$, and the imaginary part $i\epsilon$ coming from $S_F(x)$ can be omitted. We sum over the polarizations of the photon and the scattered electron and average over the polarizations of the incoming electron. The differential cross section for an electron to be scattered in the solid angle $d\Omega$, and at the same time emit a photon with an energy $w \le \Delta E$, becomes

$$\frac{d\sigma^{rad}}{d\Omega} = \frac{e^4}{(2\pi)^5} \frac{|\bar{q}|}{8|\bar{q}'|} \int_{\omega \leq \Delta E} \frac{d^3k}{2\omega} A_\mu^{ext}(\bar{q}' - \bar{q} - \bar{k})$$

$$\times A_\nu^{ext}(\bar{k} + \bar{q} - \bar{q}')\, T_{\mu\nu} \tag{7.39}$$

$$T_{\mu\nu} = \mathrm{Tr}\Big[(i\gamma q - m)\Big\{\gamma_\mu \frac{i\gamma(q'-k)-m}{-2q'k}\gamma_\lambda$$

$$+\gamma_\lambda \frac{i\gamma(q+k)-m}{2qk}\gamma_\mu\Big\}\quad(i\gamma q' - m)\Big\{\gamma_\lambda$$

$$\times \frac{i\gamma(q'-k)-m}{-2q'k}\gamma_\nu + \gamma_\nu \frac{i\gamma(q+k)-m}{2qk}\gamma_\lambda\Big\}\Big] \tag{7.40}$$

Note that the summation over the transversal photons ($\lambda = 1, 2$) yields a Lorentz covariant summation over γ_λ ($\lambda = 1, \ldots, 4$). We use that ΔE is small compared with m and neglect k compared with q and q' in the numerators. The tensor $T_{\mu\nu}$ can then be written

$$T_{\mu\nu} = \frac{A_{\mu\nu}}{(-2q'k)^2} + \frac{B_{\mu\nu}}{(2qk)^2} - \frac{C_{\mu\nu}}{4qk\, q'k} \tag{7.41}$$

where, for example,

$$A_{\mu\nu} = \mathrm{Tr}\Big[(i\gamma q - m)\,\gamma_\mu\,(i\gamma q' - m)\,\gamma_\lambda\,(i\gamma q' - m)$$

$$\times \gamma_\lambda\,(i\gamma q' - m)\,\gamma_\nu\Big] \tag{7.42}$$

and similar expressions for $B_{\mu\nu}$ and $C_{\mu\nu}$.

The summation over λ can then be performed, yielding $-2(i\gamma q' + 2m)$. Since $q'^2 + m^2 = 0$, we get

$$(i\gamma q' + 2m)(i\gamma q' - m) = (i\gamma q' + m)(i\gamma q' - m)$$

$$+ m(i\gamma q' - m) = m\,(i\gamma q' - m) \tag{7.43}$$

$$(i\gamma q' - m)(i\gamma q' - m) = -2m(i\gamma q' - m) \tag{7.44}$$

Using this expression, $A_{\mu\nu}$ can be written

$$A_{\mu\nu} = 4m^2\,\mathrm{Tr}\Big[(i\gamma q - m)\,\gamma_\mu\,(i\gamma q' - m)\,\gamma_\nu\Big] \tag{7.45}$$

This is the same trace which appears in $d\sigma^{el}/d\Omega$ and $d\sigma^{(0)}/d\Omega$ [Eqs. (7.17), (7.19), and (7.20)]. Since we neglect k in comparison to q and q', we have $|\bar{q}|/|\bar{q}'| \approx 1$, and A_μ^{ext} is only a function of $(\bar{q}' - \bar{q})$ and can be taken outside the integral in Eq. (7.39). We can then immediately write down the following result:

$$\frac{d\sigma^{rad}}{d\Omega} = \frac{d\sigma^{(0)}}{d\Omega}\,\frac{4e^2}{(2\pi)^3}\int_{\omega \leq \Delta E} \frac{d^3k}{2\omega}\Big[-\frac{m^2}{(-2q'k)^2} - \frac{m^2}{(2qk)^2}$$

$$-\frac{2m^2 + Q^2}{(2qk)(-2q'k)}\Big] \tag{7.46}$$

The w integral is $\sim \int_0^{\Delta E} \frac{d\omega}{\omega}$, which is logarithimically divergent at the lower limit. We introduce a small photon mass μ and make the following replacements:

$$2qk = (q+k)^2 + m^2 \longrightarrow 2qk - \mu^2$$

$$-2q'k = (q'-k)^2 + m^2 \longrightarrow -2q'k - \mu^2 \qquad (7.47)$$

Introducing a δ function, we can write Eq. (7.46) as

$$\frac{d\sigma^{rad}}{d\Omega} = \frac{d\sigma^{(0)}}{d\Omega} \frac{4e^2}{(2\pi)^3} \int dk\, \delta(k^2+\mu^2)$$

$$\times \theta(\Delta E - k_0) \left\{ \frac{2m^2 + Q^2}{(2qk-\mu^2)(2q'k+\mu^2)} - \frac{m^2}{(2qk-\mu^2)^2} - \frac{m^2}{(2q'k+m^2)^2} \right\}$$

(7.48)

We choose the cutoff mass μ smaller than all other quantities in the theory and have $\mu \ll \Delta E \ll m \approx q_0 \approx |\vec{q}|$. Then, neglecting μ^2 in the denominators, we have to calculate an integral of the form

$$I = \int dk\, \delta(k^2+\mu^2)\, \theta(\Delta E - k_0) \frac{1}{qk\, q'k}$$

$$= \frac{1}{2} \int d\Omega \int_0^{\sqrt{(\Delta E)^2 - \mu^2}} \frac{x^2 dx}{\sqrt{x^2+\mu^2}} \frac{1}{\left[q_0\sqrt{x^2+\mu^2} - \vec{q}\vec{k}\right]\left[q_0'\sqrt{x^2+\mu^2} - \vec{q}'\vec{k}\right]}$$

(7.49)

with $x = |\bar{k}|$. We are only interested in I for the case that $q^2 = -m^2$, $q'^2 = -m^2$, $q_o > 0$, and $q_o' > 0$. It is convenient to calculate I in that coordinate system where $\bar{q} + \bar{q}' = 0$. In this system we have $q_o = q_o' = 1/2(Q^2 + 4m^2)^{1/2}$ and $|\bar{q}| = |\bar{q}'| = 1/2(Q^2)^{1/2}$. We get

$$I = \pi \int_{-1}^{+1} du \int_0^{\Delta E} \frac{x^2 dx}{\sqrt{x^2+\mu^2}} \frac{1}{\left(q_o\sqrt{x^2+\mu^2} - |\bar{q}|xu\right)\left(q_o\sqrt{x^2+\mu^2} + |\bar{q}|xu\right)} =$$

$$= \frac{\pi}{|\bar{q}|\, q_o} \int_0^{\Delta E} \frac{x\,dx}{x^2+\mu^2} \log \frac{q_o\sqrt{x^2+\mu^2} + x|\bar{q}|}{q_o\sqrt{x^2+\mu^2} - x|\bar{q}|} \tag{7.50}$$

It is possible to evaluate this last integral exactly, but the result is somewhat lengthy; however, we are only interested in its μ dependence. We put $x = \mu y$ and obtain

$$I = \frac{\pi}{|\bar{q}|\, q_o} \left\{ \int_0^{\Delta E/\mu} \frac{y\,dy}{y^2+1} \log \frac{q_o + |\bar{q}|}{q_o - |\bar{q}|} + \right.$$

$$\left. + \int_0^{\Delta E/\mu} \frac{y\,dy}{y^2+1} \log \left[\frac{q_o\sqrt{y^2+1} + y|\bar{q}|}{q_o\sqrt{y^2+1} - y|\bar{q}|} \cdot \frac{q_o - |\bar{q}|}{q_o + |\bar{q}|} \right] \right\} \tag{7.51}$$

The logarithm in the second integral is of the order $1/y^2$ (for large values of y); hence, the integrand is of the order $1/y^3$. Therefore, we can let $\mu \to 0$ in the upper limit of this integral and get an integral that is independent of μ.

The first integral is easily performed. The result, written in an invariant form, is

$$I(Q^2) = \frac{4\pi}{Q^2\sqrt{1+\frac{4m^2}{Q^2}}} \log\frac{\Delta E}{\mu} \log\frac{\sqrt{1+\frac{4m^2}{Q^2}}+1}{\sqrt{1+\frac{4m^2}{Q^2}}-1}$$

$$+ \text{(terms indep. of } \mu \text{ and } \Delta E)$$

(7.52)

If we put $\mathbf{q} = \mathbf{q}'$, that is, $Q = 0$, we get the other two integrals involved in Eq. (7.48). For $Q^2 = 0$, Eq. (7.52) becomes

$$I(0) = \frac{2\pi}{m^2} \log\frac{\Delta E}{\mu} + \text{(terms indep. of } \mu \text{ and } \Delta E) \qquad (7.52a)$$

If these expressions are substituted into Eq. (7.48), we get

$$\frac{d\sigma^{rad}}{d\Omega} = \frac{d\sigma^{(0)}}{d\Omega} \frac{e^2}{2\pi^2} \log\frac{\Delta E}{\mu} \left[\frac{2m^2+Q^2}{Q^2\sqrt{1+\frac{4m^2}{Q^2}}}\right.$$

$$\left. \times \log\frac{\sqrt{1+\frac{4m^2}{Q^2}}+1}{\sqrt{1+\frac{4m^2}{Q^2}}-1} - 1\right] + \text{(terms indep. of } \mu \text{ and } \Delta E)$$

(7.53)

This cross section shall be added to $d\sigma^{el}/d\Omega$, as given by Eqs.

(7.29) to (7.32). One finds that the sum, which is the observable cross section, is independent of μ, or

$$\frac{d\sigma^{obs}}{d\Omega} = \frac{d\sigma^{(0)}}{d\Omega}(1-\delta) \tag{7.54}$$

$$\delta = \frac{e^2}{2\pi^2}\log\frac{\Delta E}{m}\left[1 - \frac{Q^2+2m^2}{Q^2\sqrt{1+\frac{4m^2}{Q^2}}} \times \log\frac{\sqrt{1+\frac{4m^2}{Q^2}}+1}{\sqrt{1+\frac{4m^2}{Q^2}}-1}\right] + (\text{terms indep. of } \Delta E) \tag{7.55}$$

The observable cross section depends on the energy resolution ΔE of the detector, but in every experimental situation this is a known quantity.

We now come to the question of whether it is possible to check the theory, that is, whether it is possible to measure the radiative correction to the cross section. We shall discuss two cases: $|\bar{q}'|^2 \ll m^2$ and $|\bar{q}'|^2 \gg m^2$.

$|\bar{q}'|^2 \ll m^2$. In this case, the incoming electron has a low energy, and we can expect that our approximation of neglecting the recoil of the proton is rather good. However, the correction δ is very small (it is proportional to $|\bar{q}'|^2/m^2$), and we have

$$\frac{d\sigma^{obs}}{d\Omega} \approx \frac{d\sigma^{(0)}}{d\Omega} \approx \frac{d\sigma^{Rutherford}}{d\Omega} \tag{7.56}$$

To be able to see the radiative corrections, we must take high energies.

$|\bar{q}'|^2 \gg m^2$. We also assume that $|\bar{q}'|^2 \sin^2(\theta/2) \gg m^2$; that is, we are not studying forward scattering. Further, we assume that $E \gg \Delta E > m$, where E is the energy of the incoming electron. With these assumptions, we obtain

$$\delta \approx \frac{e^2}{\pi^2}\left\{\frac{1}{2}\left[\log\left(\frac{4E^2}{m^2}y\right)-1\right]\left(\log\frac{E}{\Delta E}-\frac{13}{12}\right)+\frac{17}{72}-X(y)\right\} \tag{7.57}$$

$$X(y)=\frac{1}{4}\left[\phi(-y)+\frac{\pi^2}{12}-\log y \log(1-y)\right] \tag{7.58}$$

$$y=\sin^2\frac{\theta}{2} \tag{7.59}$$

$$\phi(y)=\int_1^y \frac{dt}{t}\log(1+t) \tag{7.60}$$

For those values of θ for which the estimates of Eq. (7.57) is true, we have $X \approx 1$ and get

$$\delta \approx \alpha \log\frac{E}{m}\log\frac{E}{\Delta E} \approx \alpha \log\frac{E}{m} \tag{7.61}$$

In the last step, we have supposed that $\Delta E \approx E/10$, and hence $\log(E/\Delta E) \approx 2 \approx 1$.

To be able to measure δ, it is reasonable to require that $\delta \approx 1/10$.

Equation (7.61) then tells us that $E \approx 10M$ (M = proton mass). For such electrons, the recoil of the proton is very large, and our approximation of treating the proton as fixed is very bad.

For reasonable energies we must take the recoil of the proton into account. At the same time, we also drop the assumption that the proton is a point charge.

7-3. Consideration of the Recoil and the Extension of the Proton

We shall now consider the scattering situation indicated in Fig. 7.2

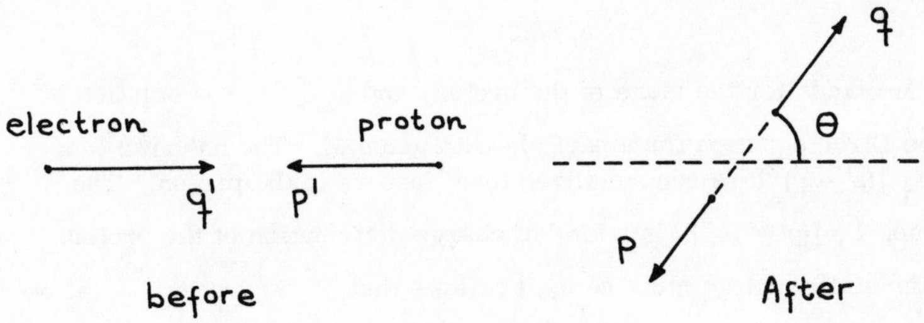

Fig. 7.2

The matrix element $\langle q | S | q' \rangle$ of the S matrix is given by Eqs. (7.2) to (7.5); however, the "external field" $A_\mu^{ext}(x)$ is now the potential

$$A_\mu^{ext}(x) = \int dx' \; D_R(x - x') \langle p | j_\mu(x') | p' \rangle \qquad (7.62)$$

from the current of the proton.

Physically, we know that the proton interacts with essentially everything in nature. It is hopeless to try to calculate in detail the matrix element $\langle p | j_\mu(x) | p' \rangle$. But we know—or at least assume—two things about the interaction between the proton and other elementary particles:

1. The interaction is Lorentz invariant.
2. The main interaction of the proton responsible for the shape of the particle is invariant under charge conjugation.

According to our discussion in Sec. 6-2, we conclude that $\langle p | j_\mu(x) | p' \rangle$ must have the same general shape as the matrix element of the electron current; that is,

$$\langle p | j_\mu(x) | p' \rangle = e^{i(p'-p)x} \frac{ie}{V} \bar{u}_M(\bar{p}) \Big[\gamma_\mu F_1((p'-p)^2)$$

$$+ (p'-p)_\lambda \frac{\sigma_{\mu\lambda}}{2M} \mu_p F_2((p'-p)^2) \Big] u_M(\bar{p}') \tag{7.63}$$

Here, M stands for the mass of the proton, and $u_M(\bar{p})$ is the solution of the free Dirac equation for a particle with mass M. The unknown functions $F_i\,[(p'-p)^2]$ are renormalized form factors of the proton. The first one, $F_1\,[(p'-p)^2]$, is a kind of charge distribution of the proton. Since the static charge must be e, it follows that

$$F_1(0) = 1 \tag{7.64}$$

The second term in Eq. (7.63) gives the contribution to the proton current caused by the anomalous magnetic moment of the proton (μ_p), and we have

$$F_2(0) = 1 \tag{7.65}$$

In the calculations in Sec. 7-1 we did not use the exact shape of the external field until Eq. (7.25). Most of the calculations of this section can therefore be taken over unchanged; however, the integral in Eq. (7.8) must be replaced by

$$2\pi \delta(Q_0) A_\mu^{ext}(\bar{Q}) = \int dx\, A_\mu^{ext}(\bar{x}) e^{iQx} \longrightarrow \text{cont.}$$

$$\iint dx\, dx'\, e^{iQx}\, D_R(x-x') \langle p | j_\mu(x') | p' \rangle$$

$$= \int dx' \frac{1}{Q^2}\, e^{iQx'} \langle p | j_\mu(x') | p' \rangle = \frac{ie}{V}(2\pi)^4$$

$$\times \frac{\delta(p'-p+q'-q)}{Q^2}\quad \bar{u}_M(\bar{p}) \Big[\gamma_\mu F_1(Q^2)$$

$$-\mu_p \frac{Q_\lambda}{2M}\quad \sigma_{\mu\lambda} F_2(Q^2) \Big] u_M(\bar{p}') \tag{7.66}$$

$$Q = q' - q = -(p'-p) \tag{7.67}$$

If we substitute this into Eq. (7.6), square, and sum over all polarization indices, we get

$$\frac{\delta w}{\delta t} = \frac{(2\pi)^4 \delta(p'-p+q'-q)}{V^4 (Q^2)^2} \frac{V}{4} \sum_{pol} \Big| \mathcal{J}_\mu(q, q')$$

$$\times \bar{u}_M(\bar{p}) \Big(\gamma_\mu F_1 - \mu_p \frac{Q_\lambda}{2M}\quad \sigma_{\mu\lambda} F_2 \Big) u_M(\bar{p}') \Big|^2 \tag{7.68}$$

(The factor 1/4 comes from the averaging over the polarizations of the electron and proton before the scattering.) From this we obtain the total cross section:

$$\sigma = \frac{1}{v_{in}} \frac{e^2}{16\pi^2} \iint d^3p\, d^3q \frac{\delta(p'-p+q'-q)}{(Q^2)^2} \sum_{pol} \left| \quad \right|^2 \tag{7.69}$$

If we compare this with Eq. (7.13), we notice that we get this new cross section from the old one by performing the replacement

$$A_\mu^{ext}(\bar{Q})\, A_\nu^{ext}(-\bar{Q}) \rightarrow \frac{-e^2}{8p_0p_0'} \frac{1}{(Q^2)^2} \mathrm{Tr}\Big[(i\gamma p - M)$$

$$\times\Big(\gamma_\mu F_1 - \mu_p \frac{Q_\lambda}{2M} \sigma_{\mu\lambda} F_2\Big) \times (i\gamma p' - M)\Big(\gamma_\nu F_1 - \mu_p$$

$$\times \frac{Q_\rho}{2M} \sigma_{\nu\rho} F_2\Big)\Big] = \frac{e^2}{2p_0p_0'} \frac{1}{(Q^2)^2} \Big\{(F_1 + \mu_p F_2)^2$$

$$\times\Big[p_\mu p_\nu' + p_\nu p_\mu' - \delta_{\mu\nu}(pp' + M^2)\Big] - \mu_p F_2 \Big[F_1$$

$$+ \mu_p F_2 \Big(1 + \frac{pp' - M^2}{4M^2}\Big)\Big](p_\mu + p_\mu')(p_\nu + p_\nu')\Big\} \tag{7.70}$$

If one neglects all radiative corrections, that is, puts $\bar{g}^{(0)} = \bar{f}^{(0)} = 0$

in the expression (7.7) for J_μ, some calculations give

$$\sigma^{(0)} = \frac{\alpha^2}{v_{in}} \iint d^3p\, d^3q \frac{\delta(p'-p+q'-q)}{(Q^2)^2 p_0 p_0'}$$

$$\times \Big\{ (F_1 + \mu_p F_2)^2 \left[p_\mu p_\nu' + p_\nu p_\mu' - \delta_{\mu\nu}(pp' + M^2) \right]$$

$$- \mu_p F_2 \left[F_1 + \mu_p F_2 \left(1 + \frac{pp' - M^2}{4M^2}\right) \right] (p_\mu + p_\mu')$$

$$\times (p_\nu + p_\nu') \Big] \Big\} \quad \frac{1}{q_0 q_0'} \Big\{ q_\mu q_\nu' + q_\nu q_\mu'$$

$$- \delta_{\mu\nu}(qq' + m^2) \Big\} \tag{7.71}$$

Since $\partial j_\mu(x)/\partial x_\mu = 0$, a partial integration in Eq. (7.62) gives $\partial A_\mu^{ext}(x)/\partial x_\mu = 0$ or $Q_\mu A_\mu^{ext}(Q) = 0$. Therefore, the last factor in Eq. (7.71) becomes $2q_\mu q_\nu - \delta_{\mu\nu}(qq' + m^2) \approx 2q_\mu q_\nu - \delta_{\mu\nu} qq'$. We have dropped m^2 in comparison to qq', because we are only interested in high energies.

We now introduce two invariant quantities s and t:

$$s = -(p' + q')^2 = (E_{C.M.}^{tot})^2 \tag{7.72}$$

$$t = -Q^2 = -(p' - p)^2 = -(q' - q)^2 \tag{7.73}$$

When we multiply the bracketed terms in Eq. (7.71), we get products such as pq, pq', etc., and these products can be expressed in s and t:

$$pq = p'q' = -\frac{1}{2}(s - m^2 - M^2) \approx -\frac{1}{2}(s - M^2) \tag{7.74}$$

$$pp' = \frac{1}{2}(t - 2M^2) \quad , \quad qq' = \frac{1}{2}(t - 2m^2) \approx \frac{1}{2}t \tag{7.75}$$

$$pq' = p'q = -\frac{1}{2}(s + t - m^2 - M^2) \approx -\frac{1}{2}(s + t - M^2) \tag{7.76}$$

With these relations the product of the two braces in Eq. (7.71) can be expressed in terms of s and t:

$$\{\ \} \cdot \{\ \} = \Bigg\{ \left[(s - M^2)^2 + st\right] \Bigg[F_1^2(t) + \frac{t^2\left[F_1(t) + \mu_p F_2(t)\right]^2}{2\left[(s - M^2)^2 + st\right]} - \frac{t}{4M^2}\,\mu_p^2 F_2^2(t) \Bigg] \Bigg\} \tag{7.77}$$

Since the solid angle varies from one coordinate system to another, we are more interested in the invariant cross section $d\sigma^{(0)}/dt$. When we know this cross section, we can afterward obtain $d\sigma^{(0)}/d\Omega$ in any coordinate system we wish. Using Eqs. (7.72) to (7.77), we get

$$\sigma^{(0)} = \frac{\alpha^2}{v_{in}} \frac{1}{p_0' q_0'} \iiint dt\, d^3p\, d^3q\, \frac{1}{t^2 p_0 q_0} \times \delta(t + Q^2)\, \delta(p' - p + q' - q) \{\qquad\} \tag{7.78}$$

where the empty braces represent the right-hand side of Eq. (7.77).

Since p is on the mass shell for the proton and q is on the mass shell for the electron, $\sigma^{(0)}$ can be written

$$\sigma^{(0)} = \frac{\alpha^2}{v_{in}} \frac{4}{q'_0 p'_0} \int \frac{\alpha t}{t^2} \{ \quad \} \iint dp\, dq\, \delta(p'-p+q-q)$$

$$\times \delta(t+(q'-q)^2) \quad \delta(p^2+M^2)\,\delta(q^2)\,\theta(p)\,\theta(q)$$

(7.79)

[We have put $\delta(q^2+m^2) \approx \delta(q^2)$, since $m \approx 0$ in this high-energy approximation.] In the laboratory system, we have

$$v_{in}\, p'_0 q'_0 = \frac{|\bar{q}'|}{q'_0} M q'_0 = \sqrt{(p'q')^2 - m^2M^2} \approx -p'q' = \frac{1}{2}(s-M^2)$$

(7.80)

By means of the δ functions, the p and q integrations can be performed, yielding

$$\iint dp\, dq\, \delta(p'-p+q'-q)\,\delta(t+(q'-q)^2)$$

$$\times \delta(p^2+M^2)\,\delta(q^2)\,\theta(p)\,\theta(q) = \frac{\pi}{2}\,\frac{1}{s-M^2} \qquad (7.81)$$

Substituting Eqs. (7.80) and (7.81) into Eq. (7.79), we get the so-called "Rosenbluth formula":

$$\frac{d\sigma^{(0)}}{d\Omega} = \frac{4\pi\alpha^2}{t^2}\left[1+\frac{st}{(s-M^2)^2}\right]\left\{F_1^2(t)+\frac{t^2}{2[(s-M^2)^2+st]}\right.$$

$$\left.\times\left[F_1(t)+\mu_p F_2(t)\right]^2-\frac{t}{4M^2}\mu_p^2 F_2^2(t)\right\}$$

(7. 82)

This formula takes care of the recoil and the extension of the proton but involves no radiative corrections.

Normally, the experimental arrangements are such that the proton is at rest from the beginning, and we want to express the cross section of Eq. (7. 82) in this system. Since $m \approx 0$, compared with M, the connection between $\bar{q}$ and $|\bar{q}'|$ is the same as between w and w' in Compton scattering. We have

$$\frac{1}{|\bar{q}|} = \frac{1}{|\bar{q}'|}\left(1+\frac{E}{M}(1-\cos\Theta)\right) = \frac{1}{E}\left(1+\frac{2E}{M}\sin^2\frac{\Theta}{2}\right) \tag{7. 83}$$

where $E = q_o'$ (the energy of the incoming electron in the laboratory system) and Θ is the scattering angle. This relation gives

$$s = M^2 + 2EM \tag{7. 84}$$

$$t = -\frac{4E^2\sin^2\frac{\Theta}{2}}{1+\frac{2E}{M}\sin^2\frac{\Theta}{2}}$$

(7. 85)

$$\frac{dt}{d(\cos\theta)} = \frac{2E^2}{\left(1 + \frac{2E}{M}\sin^2\frac{\theta}{2}\right)^2} \tag{7.86}$$

where we have put $m \approx 0$ compared with other energies. If these expressions are substituted into Eq. (7.82), the cross section in the laboratory system becomes

$$\frac{d\sigma^{(0)}}{d\Omega_{lab}} = \frac{\alpha^2\cos^2\frac{\theta}{2}}{4E^2\sin^4\frac{\theta}{2}} \frac{1}{1 + \frac{2E}{M}\sin^2\frac{\theta}{2}} \left\{F_1^2(t) - \frac{t}{4M^2}\left[2(F_1(t) + \mu_p F_2)^2 \operatorname{tg}^2\frac{\theta}{2} + \mu_p^2 F_2^2(t)\right]\right\} = \frac{d\sigma^{Ros}}{d\Omega} \tag{7.87}$$

The first factor is the Rutherford cross section with relativistic corrections; the second factor, recoil corrections; and the third factor, (within the braces), the corrections due to the extension of the proton.

The next problem is to incorporate the radiative corrections. We must go back to Eq. (7.69). From this expression, we get Eq. (7.71) by taking

$$J_\mu(q, q') = ie\, \bar{u}(\bar{q})\, \gamma_\mu\, u(\bar{q}') \tag{7.88}$$

But if we include the first radiative correction, $J_\mu(q, q')$ is given by Eq.

(7.7). The first term in this expression must give $d\sigma^{\mathrm{Ros}}/d\Omega$ multiplied by $[1 + \bar{g}(Q^2)]$. The second term is of another structure than Eq. (7.88) and therefore cannot be so easily incorporated. However, one finds that

$$\bar{f}_2^{(0)}(Q^2) \approx \frac{\alpha}{\pi} \frac{m^2}{-t} \log\left(\frac{-t}{m^2}\right) \approx 0 \tag{7.89}$$

Since $-t \gg m^2$, we can neglect the contribution from the second term in $J_\mu(q, q')$; consequently, we get (after adding $d\sigma^{\mathrm{rad}}/d\Omega$)

$$\frac{d\sigma}{d\Omega} = \frac{d\sigma^{\mathrm{Ros}}}{d\Omega}(1 - \delta) \tag{7.90}$$

with the same δ as in Eq. (7.55).

This final expression, which we can compare with experiment, contains two unknown functions $F_i(t)$, while we have a theory for δ. We can now take two different points of view or approaches: (1) Try to check quantum electrodynamics by checking δ with experiment; (2) Believe in quantum electrodynamics and try to find $F_i(t)$ by measuring $d\sigma/d\Omega$ at different energies and angles.

1. Since the functions $F_i(t)$ describe the extension of the proton caused by virtual π mesons, etc., we do not expect $F_i(t)$ to change very much before an energy transfer $\approx m_\pi$. Therefore, if we choose a scattering energy which is $< m_\pi$ (but $\gg m$), it is reasonable to replace the $F_i(t)$ by their values at the origin. For such energies, δ is quite small. However, the experiment has been done by Tautfest and Panofsky (1957), who found

$$\frac{\sigma_{\mathrm{exp}}}{\sigma_{\mathrm{teor}}} = 0.988 \pm 0.021 \tag{7.91}$$

Hence there is no discrepancy between experiment and theory. Nevertheless, quantum electron dynamics is much better checked by the measurements of the g factors of the electron and of the μ meson.

2. It is more interesting to try to find out from experiment what $F_i(t)$ really are. One way is to check whether the term in braces in Eq. (7.87) only depends on t and not on s. This is a nontrivial statement. Up to the highest t values ($\approx 40 \times 10^{26}$ cm^{-2}) attained, no discrepancy between theory and experiment has been found on this point.

Measurements* have shown that the behavior of $F_i(t)$ is something like that indicated in Fig. 73.

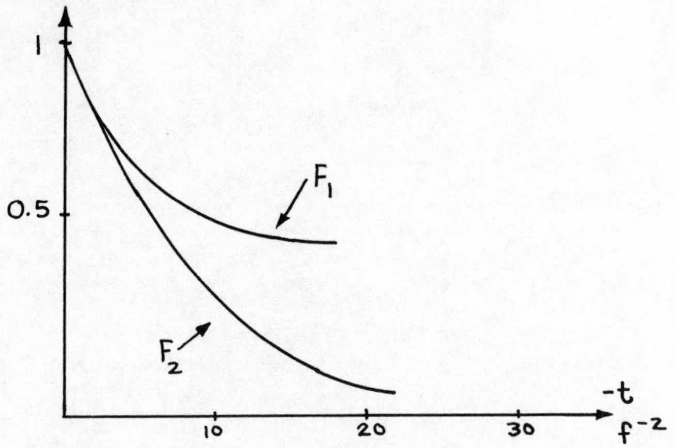

Fig. 7.3

In electrodynamics it is possible to write the form factors of the electron as integrals over certain weight functions. In analogy with this, one writes

$$F_i(t) = \int_0^\infty \frac{dt' \; f_i(t')}{t - t'} \tag{7.92}$$

---

*R. Hofstadter, F. Bumiller, and M. Croissiaux, Phys. Rev. Letters, 5, 263 (1960).

The weight functions $f_i(t)$ can be expected to have a kind of "resonance" at the energies of the ρ, w, ζ, ..., particles. One approximates these resonances by δ functions and tries to fit the experimental data in this way.* The agreement is reasonable up to $-t = 20\ f^{-2}$ but not satisfactory for larger values of $|t|$.

---

*Cf. S. Fubini, Phys. Rev. Letters, 6, 367 (1961).

WEAK INTERACTIONS

J. D. Jackson
University of Illinois

Notes by the lecturer
Assisted by E. Sarachik

Note: *There is a trivial, but crucial, error in sign in the "very simple calculation" with Eq. (5.1), p. 330, on lambda decay. Correction of this mistake changes the sign of the right-hand side of Eq. (5.5), and leads to a theoretical prediction of large positive* α *(Okubo, Marshak, and Sudarshan, 1959), in complete contradiction with experiment. Thus the simple application of the (V - A) theory to lambda decay fails badly.*

CONTENTS

CONTENTS (continued)

CONTENTS (continued)

INTRODUCTORY REMARKS

The current status of weak interactions is in some respects not very different from nearly 30 years ago, when Fermi first proposed his theory. While it is true that there are much more experimental data available and a corresponding complexity in the theoretical description, in essence we are still dealing with a phenomenological theory created in analogy with electromagnetism. That the 4-fermion, point-interaction theory, whose general structure was written down by Fermi, cannot be exact is clear. Apart from problems of renormalization, such a theory predicts cross sections which violate conservation of probability (or, as it is popular to say, violate "unitarity") at very high energies. The introduction of vector bosons to mediate (another popular word) weak interactions avoids this last problem; but such bosons have not been seen. Furthermore, they present renormalization problems of their own. The nonexistence of such bosons and the renormalization difficulties may be remedied soon. At the moment, however, weak interaction theories—whether local or nonlocal in the fermions—must be considered as phenomenological.

While the theory may be less than definitive, weak interactions do exist and play an important role in high-energy physics. Their role is enhanced appreciably by the lack of parity conservation in decays. This leads, as we shall see in greater detail below, to polarization phenomena and angular asymmetries which are useful tools in the interpretation of strong interaction processes.

This series of lectures will not pretend to be a comprehensive treatise on weak interactions, nor will it be a survey of the whole field. I believe that the first aim is not possible in a short period and that the second is out of place at a summer school. My aim is to treat certain aspects of weak interactions in some detail, using those topics as a means to teach concepts and techniques and to prepare the reader for the assimilation of research papers in the field. Some of what I have to say will be rather elementary, while some will not be on such a rudimentary level. But I will try to do some calculations before your eyes, or at least carry them to the point where the results really will follow from a few "trivial but tedious" steps.

There are a number of review articles and summaries on our subject, some of which are listed below. I shall attempt to refer the reader to one or more of these related readings when I think that a point has been adequately treated there.

Review Articles and Summaries on Weak Interactions and Related Topics

Symmetries and invariances:

G. Lüders, Rend. Scuola Intern. Fis. "Enrico Fermi," Varenna, Corso XI, Interazioni Deboli, p. 9 (1959).

R. E. Marshak and E. C. G. Sudarshan, Introduction to Elementary Particle Physics, Interscience, New York, 1961.

G. C. Wick, Ann. Rev. Nuclear Sci., 8, 1 (1958).

General weak interactions:

R. Gatto, Nuovo Cimento Suppl., 14, 340 (1959).

________, Rend. Scuola Intern. Fis. "Enrico Fermi," Varenna, Corso XI, Interazioni Deboli, p. 336 (1959).

________, Fortschr. Physik, 7, 147 (1959).

M. Gell-Mann, Rev. Mod. Phys., 31, 834 (1959).

S. B. Treiman, in C. de Witt and R. Omnes (eds.) Dispersion Relations and Elementary Particles (Les Houches, 1960), Wiley, New York, 1960, pp. 515-598.

Beta decay and neutrinos:

J. S. Allen, Revs. Modern Phys., 31, 791 (1959).

O. Kofoed-Hansen, Rend. Scuola Intern. Fis. "Enrico Fermi," Varenna, Corso XI, Interazioni Deboli, p. 251 (1959).

E. J. Konopinski, Ann. Rev. Nuclear Sci., 9, 99 (1959).

C. S. Wu, Revs. Modern Phys., 31, 783 (1959).

________, in V. F. Weisskopf and M. Fierz (eds.), Theoretical Physics in the Twentieth Century, Interscience, New York, 1960, p. 249.

Strange particle decays:

R. H. Dalitz, Revs. Modern Phys., 31, 823 (1959).

________, Rend. Scuola Intern. Fis. "Enrico Fermi," Varenna, Corso XI, Interazioni Deboli, p. 299 (1959).

M. Gell-Mann and A. H. Rosenfeld, "Hyperons and Heavy Mesons," Ann. Rev. Nuclear Sci., 7, 407 (1957).

L. Okun', "Strange Particles: Decays," Ann. Rev. Nuclear Sci., 9, 61 (1959).

Miscellaneous:

J. Rainwater, "Mu-Meson Physics," Ann. Rev. Nuclear Sci., 7, 1 (1957).

Proceedings of the International Conference on High Energy Physics, Geneva, 1958; Kiev, 1959; Rochester, 1960; Geneva, 1962.

1. SIMPLE PHENOMENOLOGICAL DISCUSSION OF DECAYS

1.1 Isospin and Strangeness Changes

Until 25 years ago the only decay processes known were alpha, beta, and gamma emission. In the early 1900's Rutherford and Soddy established that in alpha decay the charge and the baryon number of the decaying system changed, while in beta decay only the charge changed, and in gamma decay neither changed. As everyone knows, only beta decay belongs in the category of weak interactions; but now there are weak interactions where other quantum numbers, such as strangeness, change as well as the charge. Furthermore, it is not always useful to try to isolate the "decaying system." For example, in the beta decay of the free neutron,

$$n \rightarrow p + e^- + \nu$$

we can say, in analogy with heavier nuclei, that the nucleon is the decaying system whose charge changes. But in pion decay,

$$\pi^+ \rightarrow \mu^+ + \nu$$

the decaying system cannot be usefully defined.

To replace the concept of charge change in weak interactions, we use the z-component of isotopic spin, T_z. Those particles with strong interaction (Okun' calls them "adrons") have definite assignments of (T, T_z). By convention we assign $T = 0 = T_z$ to all leptons. Then we find that <u>all</u> weak interaction processes involve $\Delta T_z = \pm 1$ or $\Delta T_z = \pm 1/2$, except for mu decay which involves only leptons.

Similarly, we can assign the strangeness quantum number S to the adrons. Again by convention, the leptons are assigned S = 0. Then the known decay processes divide into those with $\Delta S = 0$ and $\Delta S = \pm 1$. No decays are known with $|\Delta S| > 1$. Some examples are as follows:

$\underline{\Delta S = 0}$

$$n \to p + e^- + \nu$$
$$\pi^\pm \to \mu^\pm + \nu$$
$$\pi^\pm \to e^\pm + \nu$$
$$\pi^\pm \to \pi^0 + e^\pm + \nu$$
$$\mu^\pm \to e^\pm + \nu + \nu$$

$\underline{\Delta S = \pm 1}$

$$\Lambda \to N + \pi$$
$$\Sigma \to N + \pi$$
$$\Xi \to \Lambda + \pi$$
$$K^\pm \to \mu^\pm + \nu$$
$$K^\pm \to e^\pm + \pi^0 + \nu$$
$$K^\pm \to \mu^\pm + \pi^0 + \nu$$
$$K^\pm \to \pi^\pm + \pi^0$$
$$K^\pm \to \pi^\pm + \pi^+ + \pi^-$$
$$K^0 \to \pi^+ + \pi^-$$

Examination of these decay modes shows that, for the $\Delta S = 0$ decays, $\Delta T_z = \pm 1$; while for $\Delta S = \pm 1$ decays, $\Delta T_z = \pm 1/2$. (This transition between integral and half-integral change in T_z is nothing mysterious. It is merely a consequence of charge and baryon conservation via the relation $Q = T_z + B/2 + S/2$.)

The bewildering array of different decays, some involving leptons and some only adrons, cries out for ordering. The empirical facts about ΔT_z suggest general principles concerning the isotopic spin nature of the weak interactions. But before proceeding to such details, we shall discuss the decay rates in a very phenomenological way, patterned after the treatment by Jauch (1959).

1.2 Decay Rates

In Appendix A data are presented on the decay properties of all particles (apart from the new pionic resonances) which are stable in the absence of weak and electromagnetic interactions. From this we see that, in the list of decay processes above, the lifetimes range from ~1000 sec for the neutron decay, through 2.2×10^{-6} sec for mu-meson decay, down to $\sim 10^{-10}$ sec for Λ, Σ, and K_o decays. We are accustomed to wide variations in lifetimes of decaying systems because of variations in the energy release. But variations can occur because of different intrinsic strengths of interaction and selection rules. To see to what extent the interaction strengths vary and/or selection rules might be operating, we shall make a phenomenological analysis of the decay rates. Appendix B contains a summary of rules about the S matrix and its connection to a transition rate. From Eq. (B. 7) we see that the differential rate of transition of a single system A to a final state B is

$$d\omega_{B\leftarrow A} = (2\pi)^4 |\mathcal{M}|^2 \prod_i \left(\frac{m_i}{E_i}\right) \prod_j \left(\frac{1}{2E_j}\right) \delta^4(P_A - P_B) \tag{1.1}$$

where $\mathcal{M}$ is the Lorentz-invariant Feynman amplitude (spinor products, etc.), and there is one factor (m_i/E_i) or $(2E_j)^{-1}$ for each fermion or boson, respectively, in the initial or final state. For each final-state particle, there will be a density-of-states factor $d^3p_i/(2\pi)^3$.

In order to compare different decay processes, we need to exhibit the general structure of the matrix element $\mathcal{M}$ and define a dimensionless coupling constant. The interaction Hamiltonian or Lagrangian density for a process involving a total of x bosons and 2y fermions in the initial and final states can be written symbolically

$$\mathcal{H}_{int} = \lambda \phi^x (\bar{\psi}\psi)^y \tag{1.2}$$

where ϕ is a boson field and ψ a fermion spinor field. In natural units the dimensions of the various quantities in Eq. (1.2) are

$$[\mathcal{H}_{int}] = M^4, \quad [\phi] = M, \quad [\bar{\psi}\psi] = M^3 \tag{1.3}$$

This means that the coefficient λ in Eq. (1.2) has dimensions

$[\lambda] = M^{4-x-3y}$. In order to have a dimensionless measure of the interaction strength, we arbitrarily define $\lambda = g\ M^{4-x-3y}$, where now M is the mass of the decaying particle and g is dimensionless. Other masses could be used, but for our phenomenological discussion the least arbitrary choice has been made.

Furthermore, in using Eq. (1.1) we shall absorb the dimensionless Fermion factors (m/E) into the matrix element. This has some justification because of the presence of projection operators for the spinors in the traces and for other reasons. Hence, in the present application of Eq. (1.1) we shall assume that the combined quantity is constant and write

$$|m|^2 \prod_{i=1}^{2y} \left(\frac{m_i}{E_i}\right) \simeq g^2 M^{8-2x-6y} \tag{1.4}$$

Then the transition rate formula is

$$dw_{B\leftarrow A} = (2\pi)^4 g_{BA}^2 M^{8-2x-6y} \prod_{j=1}^{x} \left(\frac{1}{2E_j}\right) \delta^4(P_A - P_B) \prod_{\text{final}} \frac{d^3p_i}{(2\pi)^3} \tag{1.5}$$

In Eq. (1.5) x and 2y are the total number of bosons and fermions in states A and B; M_A is the mass of the initial state; the first product is over bosons only, while the second product is over the particles in the final state B. The differential rate formula (1.5) contains phase space distributions of particles. These are of some interest in their own right, but here we are primarily interested in the total transition rate. Therefore we define a dimensionless phase space integral:

$$F_{BA} = (2\pi)^4 M_A^{7-2x-6y} \prod_{\text{final}} \int \frac{d^3p_i}{(2\pi)^3} \prod_{j=1}^{x} \left(\frac{1}{2E_j}\right) \delta^4(P_A - P_B) \tag{1.6}$$

The total transition rate formula then is

$$\Gamma_{BA} = g^2_{BA} F_{BA} M_A \tag{1.7}$$

The phase space integral F_{BA} is a function of M_A and the masses of the particles in the final state. For two- and three-body final states, various results for F_{BA} are derived in Appendix C.

1.3 Two-Body Decays

The simplest decay modes to deal with are the two-body modes. These are shown in Table 1 with Q values and decay rate from Appendix A, the numerical values of F_{BA} found from the formulas of Appendix C, and g^2_{BA} from Eq. (1.7). A useful transition rate unit is $m_p = (m_p c^2/\hbar) = 1.426 \times 10^{24}\ \text{sec}^{-1}$.

The number in parentheses in the columns for Γ, M_A, and g^2 is the power of 10 by which the accompanying number is to be multiplied. It should be noted that in some cases the transition rate given is a partial rate because of a charge multiplicity in the final state.

For five out of the seven weak decay processes, the table shows a remarkable constancy in g^2 despite a factor of 10 variation in Q value. This strongly implies a common mechanism for all these decays, even though some involve leptons and some do not; some, baryons and others not.

The two exceptions which seem to have decay couplings of the order of 1/50 of the others are the two-body decay modes of the charged K meson ($K^+ \rightarrow \mu^+ + \nu$; $K^+ \rightarrow \pi^+ + \pi^0$). Comparison of the first with ordinary pion decay suggests that the $\Delta S \neq 0$ leptonic decay interactions are weaker than the $\Delta S = 0$ leptonic couplings. We shall see more evidence for that below. For the 2π mode of decay of the K^+, comparison with the K_o decay into 2π's indicates that some sort of selection rule or inhibition involving charge or isospin is operating.

The possibility of approximate selection rules is emphasized by the electronic decay of the pion (not included in the table). The decay mode $\pi \rightarrow e + \nu$, would be expected from Eq. (1.7) to occur at about four times the rate of $\pi \rightarrow \mu + \nu$ since $16\pi F_{BA} \simeq 1.0$ for this mode. In contrast, the rate for electronic decay is observed to be 1.2×10^{-4} relative to the muonic

Table 1

Two-Body Decay Modes

Q, Mev	Process	Γ, sec^{-1}	M_A, sec^{-1}	$16\pi F_{BA}$	g^2	Remarks
36	$\Lambda \rightarrow N + \pi$	2.0 (9)	1.70 (24)	0.570	1.0(-13)	Rate is 0.5 total rate
116	$\Sigma^- \rightarrow n + \pi^-$	6.3 (9)	1.82 (24)	1.03	1.7(-13)	
66	$\Xi \rightarrow \Lambda + \pi$	8.7 (9)	2.02 (24)	1.56	1.4(-13)	
34	$\pi^+ \rightarrow \mu^+ + \nu$	3.9 (7)	2.14 (23)	0.289	0.32(-13)	
388	$K^+ \rightarrow \mu^+ + \nu$	4.7 (7)	7.54 (23)	0.952	0.033(-13)	
218	$K^0 \rightarrow \pi^+ + \pi^-$	3.3 (9)	7.60 (23)	0.830	2.6(-13)	Rate is 0.33 total rate
219	$K^+ \rightarrow \pi^+ + \pi^0$	2.0 (7)	7.54 (23)	0.828	0.016(-13)	
135	$\pi^0 \rightarrow \gamma + \gamma$	5 (15)	2.06 (23)	1.000	1.2(-6)	Electromagnetic decay

decay. This means that there is an inhibition factor of roughly 3×10^{-5} operating. Such a factor can emerge from a particular theory; indeed, it is one of the striking successes of the universal (V-A) coupling that just the right factor is found.

The last example in the table does not belong in the present discussion. It has been included only to illustrate the powers and limitations of a phenomenological approach. The decay $\pi^0 \rightarrow \gamma + \gamma$ involves two electromagnetic couplings; hence the decay rate will contain two powers of $\alpha = 1/137$. Numerically, $\alpha^2 = 5.3 \times 10^{-5}$. This can be compared with the phenomenological $g^2 = 1.2 \times 10^{-6}$. They differ by a factor of 44. If one feels that this is too large a discrepancy, one has at least two ways of "doctoring" the result. One is to remark that the electromagnetic coupling is not really α , but rather $\alpha/2\pi$ (e.g., the correction to the electron's magnetic moment). This gives a revised estimate for g^2 of $(\alpha/2\pi)^2 = 1.35 \times 10^{-6}$. The other way is to say that we really know a little about pions and their interactions. In fact, we know that the decay of π^0 proceeds via diagrams such as Fig. 1.

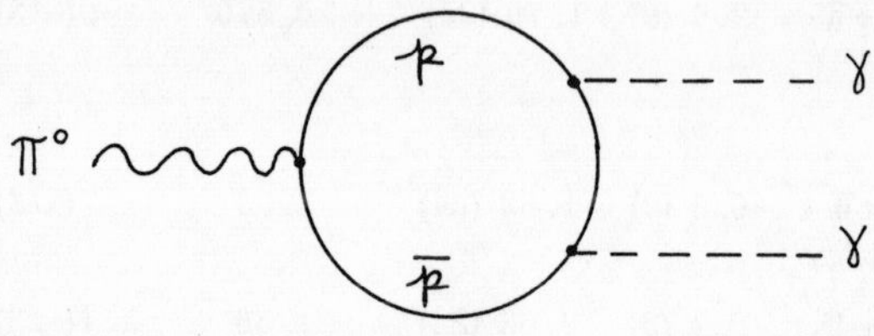

Fig. 1

Because of the odd parity of the pion, the nucleon coupling vertex will involve (in the static limit) a factor of $(\mu/m) = 0.144$, where μ and m are the pion and nucleon masses. This factor appears squared in the rate; consequently, another "improved" estimate of g^2 is $(\mu\alpha/m)^2 \simeq 1.1 \times 10^{-6}$. Both revised estimates are very close to the empirical value of g^2. But what would happen if we combined the two "improvements"?

1.4 Three-Body Decays

The various three-body decays in Appendix A can be discussed just as the two-body modes. The appropriate phase space factors are presented in Appendix C. Because of the complexity of the general result for arbitrary masses, only special cases are given—for example, all particles nonrelativistic, two relativistic fermions, etc. These restricted results are all that we need. Table 2 contains six of the three-body decay modes. The relevant phase space formula number is tabulated, as well as the values of the correction factors R_i and the numerical values of F_{BA}. The effective coupling constants have been computed from Eq. (1.7).

The first observation we make is that there is not quite as much regularity in the values of g^2 as for the two-body modes. In particular,

Table 2

Three-Body Decay Modes

Process	Q, Mev	Γ, sec^{-1}	M_A, sec^{-1}	Phase space formula	R	F_{BA}	g^2	Remarks
$\mu \rightarrow e\nu\nu$	105.	4.5 (5)	1.62 (23)	C.7	--	2.9 (-5)	0.95 (-13)	
$\pi^+ \rightarrow \pi^0 e\nu$	4.1	6 (-1)	2.14 (23)	C.11	0.94	5.0(-12)	6. (-13)	
$K \rightarrow \pi\pi\pi$	75.	2 (6)	7.54 (23)	C.5	--	3.5 (-6)	7.6 (-13)	Rate is 1/3 of $\tau + \tau'$ rate
$K \rightarrow \pi^0 e\nu$	358.	4 (6)	7.54 (23)	C.17	0.78	1.7 (-6)	30. (-13)	
$n \rightarrow pe\nu$	0.783	0.95(-3)	1.43 (24)	C.11	0.471	1.24(-18)	5.4 (-10)	
$\Lambda \rightarrow pe\nu$	177.	4 (6)	1.70 (24)	C.15	1.25	4.6 (-8)	5.1 (-11)	

the coupling constants for the two baryon decays differ by a large factor from the leptonic and mesonic couplings. When we examine the various pieces that go into the calculation of g^2, we find that the phase space integral is a very sensitive function of the masses and mass differences involved. This can be seen from the tabulated values of F_{BA}, where the extreme values differ by a factor of 10^{13}. In fact, for all but the τ decay mode ($K \rightarrow 3\pi$), the phase space integral has the form

$$F_{BA} = \frac{1}{60\pi^3}\left(\frac{\Delta}{M_A}\right)^5 R \tag{1.8}$$

where Δ is the maximum charged lepton energy, M_A is the mass of the decaying particle, and R is a relatively slowly varying function. The dependence of F_{BA} on $(\Delta/M)^5$ implies that the results for g^2 will reflect our arbitrary use of the initial particle's mass in the definition of g^2 below Eq. (1. 3) to a much greater extent than for the two-body modes. For example, if we had used the pion mass, instead of the neutron mass, in the definition of g^2 for neutron decay, we would have obtained $g^2 = 4 \times 10^{-14}$ instead of 5×10^{-10}.

This sensitivity on the mass parameters used to define g^2 prevents comparison of decay modes of very different character. But similar processes may profitably be compared. Thus we see from the table that the coupling strength for Λ beta decay is an order of magnitude smaller than that of ordinary beta decay.

1. 5 Mu-Meson Capture

The capture of mu-mesons by nuclei, in particular hydrogen,

$$\mu^- + p \rightarrow n + \nu$$

is not a decay process as we have defined it by our formulas of Sec. 1. 2. But we can estimate the rate in terms of a dimensionless coupling strength by a few simple changes. Starting with the decay of a fermion into three fermions, according to Eq. (1. 5), we replace one of the density-of-states factors $d^3p/(2\pi)^3$ by $(1/\pi a^3)$, where a is the Bohr radius of a mu-meson around a proton. This factor gives the probability of finding the mu-meson at the proton and is the appropriate factor for the bound (μ p) system. Then from the definitions of Sec. (1. 2) and Appendix C we find the rate of capture to be

$$\Gamma \simeq \frac{2}{\pi} g^2 M_A \frac{F_{BA}}{(M_A a)^3} \tag{1. 9}$$

where F_{BA} is given by Eq. (C. 2) with $m_1 = m_n$, $m_2 = 0$, and $M_A = m_p + m_\mu$. The factor $M_A a \simeq (M_A/\mu e^2) = 1.35 \times 10^3$, while $F_{BA} \simeq 1.33 \times 10^{-3}$.

With the recently observed capture rate in hydrogen of $\Gamma \simeq 600 \text{ sec}^{-1}$, we find $g^2 \simeq 11. \times 10^{-10}$. This value may be compared with the effective coupling of 5×10^{-10} for neutron beta decay. We see that mu-meson capture exhibits a coupling strength very similar to ordinary beta decay.

The over-all qualitative conclusion on the three-body modes and mu capture is that, for widely different Q values and correspondingly different phase space volumes, the effective coupling strengths are remarkably similar. Just as for the two-body decays, this points to a common interaction responsible for all decay processes. We now turn to the problem of the detailed structure of this interaction.

2. FOUR-FERMION COUPLING; MU-MESON DECAY

To begin the detailed study of weak interactions, we consider the prototype decay process:

$$F_1 \rightarrow F_2 + F_3 + F_4$$

where F_i is the ith fermion. Ordinary beta decay and mu-meson decay are two classic examples. It was for beta decay that Fermi first wrote down a phenomenological interaction in analogy with the electromagnetic coupling to charged particles.

2.1 Four-Fermion Coupling

Fermi's beta-decay interaction had the form

$$\mathcal{H}_{int} = G(\bar{\psi}_1 \gamma_\alpha \psi_2)(\bar{\psi}_3 \gamma_\alpha \psi_4) + h.c. \tag{2.1}$$

in analogy with the electromagnetic coupling

$$\mathcal{H}_{int}^{(em)} = ie(\bar{\psi}\gamma_\alpha \psi)A_\alpha \tag{2.2}$$

The notation for the spinors and gamma matrices is not Fermi's notation but Pauli's. A summary of this notation is found in Appendix B.

We know that the most general bilinear form involving Dirac spinors is a linear combination of 16 different terms which are conveniently sorted out into five sets with different transformation properties under Lorentz transformations and spatial inversions. These five groups will be denoted by O_i (i = 1, 2, 3, 4, 5) and will sometimes be designated by letters (S, V, T, A, P). Their explicit forms are given in Table 3.

Table 3

Bilinear Forms $(\overline{\Psi}_1 O_i \Psi_2)$

i	Name	O_i
1	Scalar	1
2	Vector	γ_α
3	Tensor	$\frac{1}{\sqrt{2}}\sigma_{\alpha\beta} = \frac{1}{2\sqrt{2}\,i}(\gamma_\alpha\gamma_\beta - \gamma_\beta\gamma_\alpha)$
4	Axial vector	$i\gamma_\alpha\gamma_5$
5	Pseudoscalar	γ_5

The names of the operators denote their Lorentz and space transformation properties. [See Appendix E, especially Eq. (E. 16).]

In creating a Hamiltonian or Lagrangian density, one must be careful to make a Lorentz scalar quantity. For a four-fermion interaction, such as Eq. (2. 1), this means that two bilinear forms with the same Lorentz transformation characteristics must be combined into a suitable scalar product. For the dual reasons of simplicity and hindsight, we shall exclude the possibility of derivative couplings. Consequently, the generalization of Eq. (2. 1) is

$$\mathcal{H}_{int} = \sum_{i=1}^{5} C_i (\overline{\Psi}_1 O_i \Psi_2)(\overline{\Psi}_3 O_i \Psi_4) + h.c. \tag{2.3}$$

where the C_i are coupling constants with dimensions M^{-2}. The meaning of $(\bar{\psi}_1 O_i \psi_2)(\bar{\psi}_3 O_i \psi_4)$ is that all appropriate indices are to be summed over; for example,

$$(\bar{\psi}_1 O_3 \psi_2)(\bar{\psi}_3 O_3 \psi_4) = \frac{1}{2} \sum_{\mu,\nu} (\bar{\psi}_1 \sigma_{\mu\nu} \psi_2)(\bar{\psi}_3 \sigma_{\mu\nu} \psi_4) \tag{2.4}$$

The general interaction density, Eq. (2.3), was constructed to be a Lorentz scalar and also a scalar under spatial inversions. The latter choice is quite natural if parity is a good quantum number, but is not necessary. An interaction which is a pseudoscalar under spatial inversion could not be distinguished in any way from a scalar one. Thus, we can mix vector and axial vector terms, scalar and pseudoscalar terms, etc. The most general Lorentz-invariant, pseudoscalar, four-fermion interaction density can be shown to be

$$\mathcal{H}'_{int} = \sum_{i=1}^{5} C'_i (\bar{\psi}_1 O_i \psi_2)(\bar{\psi}_3 O_i \gamma_5 \psi_4) + \text{h.c.} \tag{2.5}$$

The formula (2.5), in itself, cannot be distinguished physically from Eq. (2.3). But a linear combination of the two gives rise to new physical effects, as you all know from the famous work of Lee and Yang. Thus, the most general four-fermion interaction density without derivative couplings is

$$\mathcal{H}_{int} = \sum_{i=1}^{5} (\bar{\psi}_1 O_i \psi_2)(\bar{\psi}_3 O_i (C_i + C'_i \gamma_5) \psi_4) + \text{h.c.} \tag{2.6}$$

2.2 Fierz-Michel Reordering Theorem

Before proceeding to calculate with Eq. (2.6), we note an important theorem due to Fierz, and later elaborated by Michel, on the reordering of the spinors in the quadrilinear forms. Let us define

$$J_i(1234) = (\overline{\psi}_1 O_i \psi_2)(\overline{\psi}_3 O_i \psi_4) \tag{2.7}$$

If the spinors in Eq. (2.7) are reordered to form, say, $J_i(3214)$, we can ask how the new object is related to the old ones. Since the five Lorentz scalars of Eq. (2.7) are all such quadrilinear forms there are, it is clear that the reordered object must be a linear combination of the old objects:

$$J_i(3214) = \sum_{j=1}^{5} \lambda_{ij} J_j(1234) \tag{2.8}$$

The coefficients λ_{ij} form a matrix array which can be calculated in a straightforward way to be

$$\lambda_{ij} = -\frac{1}{4}\begin{pmatrix} 1 & 1 & 1 & 1 & 1 \\ 4 & -2 & 0 & 2 & -4 \\ 6 & 0 & -2 & 0 & 6 \\ 4 & 2 & 0 & -2 & -4 \\ 1 & -1 & 1 & -1 & 1 \end{pmatrix} \tag{2.9}$$

In writing λ_{ij} it has been assumed that <u>the different ψ's anticommute</u>. If they are taken to commute, there is an over-all minus sign which should be included.

The result of Eq. (2.8), which applies to the interchange 1 ↔ 3, holds also for the exchange 2 ↔ 4 since it is obvious that $J_i(3214) = J_i(1432)$.

The reordering of spinors within the <u>bilinear</u> forms is closely related to charge conjugation. Again with the assumption that the spinor fields anticommute, the interchange 1 ↔ 2 yields

$$(\overline{\psi}_2 O_i \psi_1) = N_i (\overline{\psi}_1^c O_i \psi_2^c) \tag{2.10}$$

where $N_i = 1, -1, -1, 1, 1$ for $i = 1, 2, 3, 4, 5$, and ψ^c is the field charge conjugate to ψ (see Appendix E).

The two results, Eqs. (2.8) and (2.10), allow one to rearrange the spinor fields in the quadrilinear forms into any desired combination. If there happen to be additional factors present, as in Eq. (2.6), these can be adjoined to the neighboring spinor for purposes of manipulation and then displayed explicitly afterwards, if desired.

2.3 Two-Component Neutrino

In beta decay, one of the bilinear forms involves nucleons and the other leptons, namely, electron and neutrino. In Eq. (2.6) we can identify $(\bar{3}4)$ as $(\bar{e}\,\nu)$. Then the leptonic bilinear form is

$$\left(\bar{\psi}_e O_i \left(1 + \frac{C_i'}{C_i}\gamma_5\right)\psi_\nu\right) \tag{2.11}$$

It is now a well-known story that the neutrinos which emerge in beta decay are completely left-handed, corresponding to $C_i' = C_i$. We refer the reader to the detailed articles on beta decay: Konopinski (1959) and Wu (1959, 1960) for the experimental evidence; Treiman (1960) for the associated theory of the two-component neutrino.

We shall accept as a working hypothesis that whenever a neutrino field appears in an interaction Lagrangian, there is multiplying it a factor $(1 + \gamma_5)$. Furthermore, we shall not at present distinguish between beta-decay neutrinos and pion-decay neutrinos, since all neutrinos are apparently left-handed.

2.4 Mu-Meson Decay

As our prototype calculation, we shall choose mu-meson decay. There are several reasons for this: It is a pure decay process, uncomplicated by strong interactions; it is a decay with ultrarelativistic particles, necessitating covariant calculational procedures; the calculation is straightforward once the interaction is specified.

In writing down the appropriate interaction, Eq. (2.6), there is arbitrariness in the ordering. If we take over the beta decay bilinear form $(\bar{e}\,\nu)$, it is natural to combine it with $(\bar{\nu}\mu)$. But for reasons that will be immediately obvious it is more convenient to take the ordering $(\bar{e}\mu)(\bar{\nu}\nu)$. Thus we write the interaction as

$$\mathcal{H}_{int} = \frac{1}{2}\sum_{i=1}^{5} C_i\left(\bar{\Psi}_e O_i \psi_\mu\right)\left(\bar{\Psi}_\nu(1-\gamma_5)O_i(1+\gamma_5)\psi_\nu\right) + h.c. \tag{2.12}$$

The factors $(1-\gamma_5)$ and $(1+\gamma_5)$ come from the assumption of the last section. In writing Eq. (2.12), we have assumed that the decay is $\mu \to e + \nu + \bar{\nu}$, and not $\mu \to e + \nu + \nu$ or $e + \bar{\nu} + \bar{\nu}$. All three possibilities should be explored, but the last two are excluded experimentally by the electron spectrum (see below). The sum over all five invariants is actually restricted to two terms because the operators S, T, and P all commute with γ_5 and give a neutrino bracket which is identically zero. The operators V and A anticommute with γ_5 and so give a nonvanishing result. Thus Eq. (2.12) becomes

$$\mathcal{H}_{int} = \left(\bar{\Psi}_e \gamma_\alpha (C_V - C_A\gamma_5)\psi_\mu\right)\left(\bar{\Psi}_\nu \gamma_\alpha(1+\gamma_5)\psi_\nu\right) + h.c. \tag{2.13}$$

It is of mild interest at this stage to apply the Fierz-Michel reordering theorem to Eq. (2.13) in order to exhibit it in a form more closely equivalent to ordinary beta decay. Therefore we apply Eqs. (2.8) and (2.9) to obtain

$$\begin{aligned}\mathcal{H}_{int} = {} & \frac{1}{2}(C_V - C_A)\left(\bar{\Psi}_\nu \gamma_\alpha(1+\gamma_5)\psi_\mu\right)\left(\bar{\Psi}_e\gamma_\alpha(1+\gamma_5)\psi_\nu\right) \\ & -(C_V+C_A)\left(\bar{\Psi}_\nu(1-\gamma_5)\psi_\mu\right)\left(\bar{\Psi}_e(1+\gamma_5)\psi_\nu\right) + h.c.\end{aligned} \tag{2.14}$$

The expression (2.13) started out with only V and A couplings but now

Eq. (2.14) has V, A and S, P couplings whose relative amounts depend on the ratio C_A/C_V. From the work on neutrino recoil spectra, notably by Allen and coworkers (Allen, 1959), it is known that in beta decay the dominant interactions are V and A. By analogy, we might expect that in mu-meson decay, written in the beta decay form of Eq. (2.14), a similar dominance would occur. This implies that $C_A \simeq - C_V$, a conclusion we shall show is verified experimentally.

Starting with the interaction of Eq. (2.13), we can write down the S matrix element $\langle e\nu\bar{\nu}|\mu\rangle$ according to the rules summarized in Appendix B. The result for the Feynman amplitude $\mathfrak{M}$ is

$$\mathfrak{M} = \left(\bar{u}_e(\vec{p})\gamma_\alpha(C_V - C_A\gamma_5)u_\mu(\vec{P})\right)\left(\bar{u}_\nu(\vec{q}_1)\gamma_\alpha(1+\gamma_5)v_\nu(\vec{q}_2)\right) \tag{2.15}$$

In Eq. (2.15) the electron and neutrino momenta are $\vec{p}$, $\vec{q}_1$, and $\vec{q}_2$, respectively, while the mu-meson momentum is $\vec{P}$.

The absolute square of Eq. (2.15), inserted in the transition-rate formula (1.1), will give the differential probability for mu-meson decay. But since neutrino spins are not observable directly, the useful quantity is $|\mathfrak{M}|^2$, summed over neutrino spin states. To perform this sum, let us define the vector A_α :

$$A_\alpha = \bar{u}_e(\vec{p})\gamma_\alpha(C_V - \gamma_5 C_A)u_\mu(\vec{P}) \tag{2.16}$$

Then

$$\sum_{\nu\text{ spins}} |\mathfrak{M}|^2 = \sum_{\text{spins}} \left(\bar{u}_1 \gamma\cdot A(1+\gamma_5)v_2\right)\left(\bar{v}_2\beta(1+\gamma_5)\gamma\cdot A^*\beta u_1\right)$$

We now make use of the standard projection operators,

$$\Lambda_\pm = \frac{1}{2m}\left(\pm m - i\gamma\cdot p\right) \tag{2.17}$$

for positive and negative energy states. Here the neutrino mass in the numerator can be dropped, but the mass in the denominator is retained to cancel with the mass in the factor (m/E), which has been factored out. Thus we obtain

$$\sum_{\text{spins}} |\mathfrak{M}|^2 = \frac{1}{4m_\nu^2} \mathrm{Tr}\left[(-i\gamma\cdot q_1)\,\gamma\cdot A(1+\gamma_5)(-i\gamma\cdot q_2)\beta(1+\gamma_5)\gamma\cdot A^*\beta\right]$$

$$= -\frac{1}{2m_\nu^2}\mathrm{Tr}\left[\gamma\cdot q_1\,\gamma\cdot A\,\gamma\cdot q_2(1-\gamma_5)\beta\gamma\cdot A^*\beta\right]$$

If we define a 4-vector $A' \equiv (\mathbf{A}^*, iA_0^*)$, then $\beta\gamma\cdot A^*\beta = -\gamma\cdot A'$ and the matrix element squared becomes

$$\sum_{\text{spins}} |\mathfrak{M}|^2 = \frac{1}{2m_\nu^2}\mathrm{Tr}\left[\gamma\cdot q_1\,\gamma\cdot A\,\gamma\cdot q_2\,\gamma\cdot A'(1+\gamma_5)\right] \tag{2.18}$$

The trace can be evaluated by standard methods to yield

$$\sum_{\text{spins}} |\mathfrak{M}|^2 = \frac{2}{m_\nu^2}\Big[(q_1\cdot A)(q_2\cdot A') + (q_2\cdot A)(q_1\cdot A') - (q_1\cdot q_2)(A\cdot A') + \det(q_1 A q_2 A')\Big] \tag{2.19}$$

The next step in the calculation is to integrate over the momenta of the two neutrinos, subject to the conservation laws, leaving a differential spectrum in the electron variables. According to Eq. (1. 1) the desired transition rate is

$$dw = \frac{m_e}{(2\pi)^5}\frac{d^3p}{E}\iint \frac{d^3q_1}{q_1}\frac{d^3q_2}{q_2}\, m_\nu^2 \sum_{\text{spins}} |\mathcal{M}|^2\, \delta^4(p+q_1+q_2-P) \tag{2.20}$$

The necessary integrals over phase space are discussed in Appendix D, especially in Eq. (D. 20). It is first necessary to change variables in Eq. (2. 19) according to Eq. (D. 5). This yields

$$m_\nu^2 \sum_{\text{spins}} |\mathcal{M}|^2 = \Big[(K\cdot A)(K\cdot A') - (Q\cdot A)(Q\cdot A') - \tfrac{1}{2}(A\cdot A')(K^2-Q^2) + 2\det(q_1 A q_2 A')\Big] \tag{2.21}$$

The last term in Eq. (2. 21) integrates to zero, because the determinant is odd under interchange of q_1 and q_2 while the integration treats them symmetrically. The integrals over the other terms can be easily read off from Eq. (D. 20); hence Eq. (2. 20) becomes

$$dw = \frac{m_e}{(2\pi)^4}\cdot\frac{d^3p}{E}\cdot\frac{2}{3}\Big[(K\cdot A)(K\cdot A') - K^2(A\cdot A')\Big] \tag{2.22}$$

where $K = P - p$.

From the definition of A in Eq. (2. 16) and from the free-particle equations of motion, Eq. (2. 22) can be written

$$dw = \frac{2}{3}\frac{m_e}{(2\pi)^4}\frac{d^3p}{E}\Big[m^2(\bar{u}_\mu(C_V^* - C_A^*\gamma_5)u_e)(\bar{u}_e(C_V + C_A\gamma_5)u_\mu)$$

$$+ (P-p)^2(\bar{u}_\mu\gamma_\alpha(C_V^* - C_A^*\gamma_5)u_e)(\bar{u}_e\gamma_\alpha(C_V - C_A\gamma_5)u_\mu)\Big] \qquad (2.23)$$

Inside the square bracket we have omitted terms proportional to the electron mass; m is the mass of the mu meson.

2.5 Longitudinal Polarization of the Decay Electrons

The first observation to be made about Eq. (2.23) is that the electron spinor can always be written multiplied by a factor $(C_V^* - C_A^*\gamma_5)$. Thus the effective electron spinor is

$$u_{eff} = (C_V^* - C_A^*\gamma_5)u$$

$$= \left[(C_V^* - C_A^*)\left(\frac{1+\gamma_5}{2}\right) + (C_V^* + C_A^*)\left(\frac{1-\gamma_5}{2}\right)\right]u \qquad (2.24)$$

For a relativistic particle the operators $1/2\,(1 \pm \gamma_5)$ project out states with longitudinal polarization ∓ 1. Furthermore, the projected states are orthogonal; thus we expect the electrons from negative mu-meson decay to have a longitudinal polarization

$$P_{long} = \frac{|C_V + C_A|^2 - |C_V - C_A|^2}{|C_V + C_A|^2 + |C_V - C_A|^2} = \frac{C_V C_A^* + C_A C_V^*}{|C_V|^2 + |C_A|^2} \equiv \xi \qquad (2.25)$$

For μ^+ decay, the positrons will have polarization $-\xi$. This argument makes no reference to other than electron properties; hence it can be expected to hold only if all other observables (e.g., the direction of the mu-meson spin) are ignored. As a matter of fact, the first term in Eq. (2.23) always yields the result in Eq. (2.25), but the second term does so only if we sum over the mu-meson spin states.

Observation of the longitudinal polarization of the electrons and positrons from μ^- and μ^+ decay shows that the particles are appreciably polarized, with the electrons (positrons) having negative (positive) helicity (Macq, Crowe, and Haddock, 1958). This corresponds to ξ negative and large, implying that C_A/C_V has a magnitude near unity and a phase near 180°.

2.6 Directional Asymmetry of Electrons from Polarized Mu Mesons

If we sum over the spin states of the electron in Eq. (2.23), we shall obtain the angular and energy distribution of the electrons relative to the direction of the mu-meson spin. This calculation involves a projection operator, Eq. (2.17), and evaluation of a trace in the same way as for the neutrinos. For a mu meson at rest, we find

$$dw = \frac{m^5}{24(2\pi)^3}\left(|C_V|^2 + |C_A|^2\right) \cdot$$
$$\cdot \left\{ \frac{x^2}{2\pi}\left[(3-2x) + \xi(2x-1)\langle\vec{\sigma}\rangle\cdot\vec{n}\right] dx\, d\Omega \right\} \tag{2.26}$$

where x = 2p/m is the electron energy or momentum in units of the maximum, $\langle\vec{\sigma}\rangle$ is the expectation value of the mu-meson spin, ξ is defined by Eq. (2.25), and $\vec{n}$ is a unit vector in the direction of the electron momentum. The curly bracketed factor integrates over angle and energy to unity. Thus the factor in front is the total decay rate. Equation (2.26) shows an energy-dependent directional asymmetry which has been verified in some detail.

In comparing theory and experiment, it is customary to write the most general theoretical result. Neglecting the electron mass, this formula (Bouchiat and Michel, 1957) is

$$dw = \lambda x^2 \left\{ 3(1-x) + 2\rho\left(\tfrac{4}{3}x - 1\right) + \xi\langle\vec{\sigma}\rangle\cdot\vec{n}\left[(1-x) + 2\delta\left(\tfrac{4}{3}x-1\right)\right]\right\} dx\, d\Omega \tag{2.27}$$

The parameters λ, ρ, ξ and δ are functions of the various coupling constants; ρ is called the Michel parameter (Michel, 1950). Comparison of Eqs. (2. 27) and (2. 26) shows that the two-component neutrino hypothesis restricts ρ and δ to be $\rho = \delta = 3/4$. The most recent experimental results for μ^+ decay in a hydrogen bubble chamber (Plano, 1960) yield

$$\rho = 0.780 \pm 0.025$$

$$\delta = 0.78 \pm 0.05$$

$$|\xi| = 0.94 \pm 0.07$$

For negative mu mesons, a recent determination of the Michel parameter (Block et al, 1962) gave

$$\rho = 0.751 \pm 0.034$$

Recent Russian work on emulsions (Vaisenberg, Smirnit-skii, and Kolganova, 1961) yielded values for ρ, δ and $|\xi|$ about 10 per cent smaller than those quoted above; but the experimental method was such as to bias the results in that direction.

2. 7 Interaction Form and Coupling Constant

We can conclude from the experimental data on longitudinal polarization, spectrum shape, and directional asymmetry that mu-meson decay involves two-component neutrinos and equal amounts of vector and axial-vector coupling with opposite signs. Thus the interaction Eq. (2. 13) can be written in the form

$$\mathcal{H}_{int} = \frac{G}{\sqrt{2}} \left(\bar{\psi}_e \gamma_\alpha (1+\gamma_5) \psi_\mu \right) \left(\bar{\psi}_\nu \gamma_\alpha (1+\gamma_5) \psi_\nu \right) + h.c. \tag{2.28}$$

In this expression we have written $C_V = - C_A = G/\sqrt{2}$ for later convenience. Note that the reordered form of Eq. (2. 14), with the grouping $(\bar{\nu}\mu)(\bar{e}\nu)$, will have exactly the same structure as Eq. (2. 28).

In terms of the newly defined coupling constant G in Eq. (2. 28), the total decay rate is

$$\Gamma_\mu = \frac{G^2 m^5}{24 (2\pi)^3} (0.9956) \tag{2.29}$$

The factor 0.9956 is an electromagnetic radiative correction (Berman, 1958). Comparison with Eq. (1.7) shows that G has the dimensions of M^{-2}. It is customary to express G in units of m_p^{-2}. Recent values of the positive mu-meson lifetime (Fischer et al, 1959; Reiter et al., 1960) yield $\tau_\mu = (2.211 \pm 0.003) \times 10^{-6}$ sec. With a mu-meson mass of 105.65 $\pm$ 0.01 Mev and a proton mass of 938.21 $\pm$ 0.01 Mev, the calculated value of G is

$$G = (1.023 \pm 0.002) \times 10^{-5} \; m_p^{-2} \tag{2.30}$$

As a final remark about mu-meson decay we note that, if we had assumed that the two neutrinos which are emitted were $(\nu\nu)$ or $(\bar{\nu}\bar{\nu})$, we would have obtained a Michel parameter $\rho = 0$. The experimental result of $\rho \simeq 0.75$ excludes these alternatives.

3. INVARIANCE AND SYMMETRY ARGUMENTS, PION DECAY, BETA DECAY, AND GENERAL STRUCTURE OF THE MATRIX ELEMENTS

The "pure" decay of a mu meson, unencumbered by strong interactions, is a useful starting point for the exploration of the structure of weak interactions. From it we extract the suggestive idea that lepton pairs always occur in the bilinear combination, $[\bar{\psi}_1 \gamma_\alpha (1+\gamma_5) \psi_2]$. But to proceed further and study decay processes involving adrons (bosons and baryons), we must invoke invariance and symmetry arguments about both the weak and strong interactions. In this way we can examine the general structure and understand what limits it. The only alternative is to postulate a weak interaction such as Eq. (2.6) and commence calculating in perturbation theory in the strong couplings. This is a notoriously poor way to proceed.

As a first, simple example of invariance arguments we shall treat charged pion decay. Then we shall summarize the various symmetry arguments about parity, charge conjugation, time reversal, and G parity and discuss their experimental status. These results will be used to establish the general form of the matrix elements involving strongly interacting particles.

3.1 Pion Decay

The decay of the charged pion is overwhelmingly via the two-body mode, $\pi \to \mu + \nu$.* As was mentioned in Sec. 1.3, the alternative decay mode $\pi \to e + \nu$ occurs very weakly (relative rate $\sim 10^{-4}$), even though the available phase space is larger than for the muon mode. This is the key point which any theory must explain. If it is assumed that the leptons are coupled locally, then the most general Feynman amplitude for pion decay is

$$\mathfrak{M} = \sum_{i=1}^{5} F_i \left(\bar{u}_\ell(p) O_i (1+\gamma_5) u_\nu(q)\right) \tag{3.1}$$

where the operators O_i are as given in Table 3 and the F_i are constants (actually 4-tensors of appropriate rank for the operators O_i). The lepton (muon or electron) 4-momentum is p, the neutrino value is q, and that of the pion is Q = p + q. In Eq. (3.1) we have assumed, as usual, that the neutrino appears with a factor $(1 + \gamma_5)$. This is important for the polarization of the emitted lepton but is irrelevant as far as the total rate is concerned.

In writing Eq. (3.1), we have exploited the Lorentz invariance of $\mathfrak{M}$ and the fact that the pion has zero spin. The factors F_i are determined by both weak and strong interactions and can be functions of the available dynamic variables. The assumption of local leptonic coupling implies that only the sum, p + q, of the leptonic 4-momenta enters. By conservation of energy and momentum, the sum is equal to Q; consequently the F_i can be tensors formed from Q, times functions of the scalar product, $Q^2 = -m_\pi^2$, which is a constant. The possible forms are [we list only S, V, and T because of the presence of the factor $(1 + \gamma_5)$]:

Scalar $$F_1 O_1 = \frac{G}{\sqrt{2}} m_\pi^2 f_S$$

*There is a three-body decay mode, $\pi^\pm \to \pi^0 + e^\pm + \nu$, as listed in Table 2, with a relative probability of $\sim 10^{-8}$. This mode is discussed below, in Sec. 4.4, p. 318.

Vector $$F_2 O_2 = \frac{G}{\sqrt{2}} m_\pi f_V \, i Q_\alpha \gamma_\alpha$$

Tensor $$F_3 O_3 = \frac{G}{\sqrt{2}} f_T \, i Q_\alpha Q_\beta \sigma_{\alpha\beta} = 0 . \qquad (3.2)$$

The factors $G/\sqrt{2}$ have been inserted in analogy with Eq. (2.28) to exhibit the weak coupling strength explicitly; f_S, f_V, and f_T are dimensionless constants; the various factors of m_π assure this. We note that the tensor coupling vanishes identically because the only tensor which can be formed from Q is symmetric, while $\sigma_{\alpha\beta}$ is antisymmetric. Only scalar and vector couplings are present.*

The Feynman amplitude of Eq. (3.1) is then

$$\mathfrak{M} = \frac{G}{\sqrt{2}} m_\pi^2 \, \bar{u}_\ell(p) \left[f_S + i f_V \frac{\gamma \cdot Q}{m_\pi} \right] (1+\gamma_5) u_\nu(q) \qquad (3.3)$$

Using $Q = p + q$, and the equations of motion $[(i\gamma \cdot p + m)\, u(p) = 0]$, this can be written

$$\mathfrak{M} = \frac{G}{\sqrt{2}} m_\pi^2 \left(f_S - \frac{m_\ell}{m_\pi} f_V \right) \left(\bar{u}_\ell(p)(1+\gamma_5) u_\nu(q) \right) \qquad (3.4)$$

where m_ℓ is the leptonic mass. Equation (3.4) has two interesting features. One is the confirmation from the spinor product that the emission of a right-handed antineutrino (left-handed neutrino) is

---

*To be precise, perhaps we should say pseudoscalar and axial vector couplings, because the pion is pseudoscalar. But the presence of $(1 + \gamma_5)$ destroys the distinction. We shall therefore use the simpler terminology.

accompanied by a right-handed lepton (left-handed antilepton), as is required by conservation of angular momentum for the two-body decay of a zero-spin system. Experiment shows that the muons from pion decay do have these helicities: negative helicity from π^+ decay and positive from π^- decay (Alikhanov et al., 1960; Backenstoss et al., 1961; Bardon, Franzini, and Lee, 1961). Hence, the presence of a factor $(1 + \gamma_5)$ is confirmed here, as well as in muon and beta decay.

The other feature of Eq. (3.4) is that the vector coupling is proportional to the leptonic mass. Consequently the probability of electron emission relative to muon emission would be of the order of $(m_e/m_\mu)^2 \simeq (1/200)^2$ _if_ the coupling were pure vector _and_ the constants $f_V^{(e)}$ and $f_V^{(\mu)}$ were the same order of magnitude. We saw in Sec. 1.5 that the $(\mu\nu)$ coupling to nucleons in mu-meson capture was of roughly the same strength as the $(e\nu)$ coupling in beta decay. Thus it is extremely attractive to suppose that the $(e\nu)$ and $(\mu\nu)$ coupling strengths are identical, and that the small branching ratio for $\pi \rightarrow e + \nu$ is caused by the dominance of the vector coupling. The quantitative results given below are in complete agreement with this assumption.

Granting for the moment this idea of a universal vector coupling for leptons, we can ask for the "physical explanation" of the proportionality to the leptonic mass. The explanation is that the bilinear form $(\psi_\ell \gamma_\alpha (1+\gamma_5)\psi_\nu)$ causes both lepton and neutrino spinor to be effectively multiplied by $1/2\ (1 + \gamma_5)$. If both particles were ultrarelativistic, they would be created only as a left-handed lepton and a right-handed antineutrino (for π^- decay). But since their momenta are oppositely directed and the pion spin is zero, such a final state is forbidden by conservation of angular momentum. Hence it is only the finite mass of the lepton which allows the decay to occur via vector coupling. The more massive the lepton, the more nonrelativistic its motion, and the more of the required state of angular momentum is left after operation with $(1 + \gamma_5)$.*

The decay rate of Eq. (1.1) for a pion at rest can be written from Eq. (3.4) as

---

*The argument does not, in fact, depend on the emission of a neutrino of definite helicity. The amplitudes for each helicity can be discussed separately with the same conclusion.

$$d\omega = \frac{G^2}{16\pi^2} m_\pi^3 m_\ell m_\nu \left| f_S - \frac{m_\ell}{m_\pi} f_V \right|^2 \cdot \left| \bar{u}_\ell (1+\gamma_5) u_\nu \right|^2 \frac{d^3p}{p_0} \frac{d^3q}{q_0} \delta^4(p+q-Q) \tag{3.5}$$

The two-body phase space integral,

$$\iint \frac{d^3p}{p_0} \frac{d^3q}{q_0} \delta^4(p+q-Q)$$

can be seen from Eq. (C. 1) to be equal to 32 π^2 times Eq. (C. 3); or from Eq. (D. 3), to be equal to Eq. (D. 15) with $\mu^2 = \rho^2 = m_\ell^{\ 2}$ and $K^2 = - m_\pi^{\ 2}$. Therefore the decay rate is

$$d\omega = \frac{G^2}{8\pi} m_\pi^3 m_\ell m_\nu \left(1 - \frac{m_\ell^2}{m_\pi^2}\right) \left| f_S - \frac{m_\ell}{m_\pi} f_V \right|^2 \cdot \left| \bar{u}_\ell (1+\gamma_5) u_\nu \right|^2 \tag{3.6}$$

The sum over spins of the neutrino and lepton is easily found to be

$$\sum_{\text{spins}} \left| \bar{u}_\ell(p)(1+\gamma_5) u_\nu(q) \right|^2 = - \frac{2p\cdot q}{m_\ell m_\nu} = \frac{m_\pi^2}{m_\ell m_\nu}\left(1 - \frac{m_\ell^2}{m_\pi^2}\right)$$

Thus the pion decay rate is finally

$$\Gamma = \frac{G^2}{8\pi} m_\pi^5 \left(1 - \frac{m_\ell^2}{m_\pi^2}\right)^2 \left| f_S - \frac{m_\ell}{m_\pi} f_V \right|^2 \tag{3.7}$$

The decay rate formula, Eq. (3.7), can be applied to both the muonic and electronic modes. A priori there is no connection between the constants f_S and f_V for the two modes. But from our discussion above, it is attractive to suppose that the constants f_S and f_V (which are determined mainly from the strong interactions) are the same for both leptonic couplings. Then Eq. (3.7) makes very different predictions about the relative rates for $\pi \to e + \nu$ and $\pi \to \mu + \nu$, depending on whether the scalar or vector coupling dominates. In the two extremes the branching ratio is

$$\frac{\pi \to e + \nu}{\pi \to \mu + \nu} \simeq \frac{1}{\left(1 - \frac{m_\mu^2}{m_\pi^2}\right)^2} \begin{Bmatrix} 1 \\ \left(\frac{m_e}{m_\mu}\right)^2 \end{Bmatrix} \simeq \begin{cases} 5.49 \\ 1.29 \times 10^{-4} \end{cases} \tag{3.8}$$

where the upper (lower) number is for scalar (vector) coupling. Radiative corrections (Berman, 1958; Smorodinskii and Hu Shih-k'e, 1962) which depend on the experimental energy resolution reduce the vector value to about 1.20×10^{-4}. The experimental results (e.g., Anderson et al., 1959; Budagov et al., 1959-60) for both positive and negative pions agree with this numerical value to within error of about 10 per cent. Thus the hypothesis of a universal vector coupling for leptons is in striking agreement with experiments on pion decay.

For K-meson decay, similar considerations apply for the $K_{\mu 2}$ and K_{e2} decay modes. So far, the K_{e2} mode has not been observed. Only an upper limit of less than 1 per cent has been set on its relative abundance. This is completely consistent with the estimate of 2.6×10^{-5} from Eq. (3.7) with universal vector coupling. Furthermore, the 1 per cent limit shows that only a very small amount of scalar coupling could be present.

Assuming only vector coupling in Eq. (3.7), we can use the observed pion lifetime of 2.55×10^{-8} sec and the value of G from mu-meson decay in Eq. (2.30) to determine the numerical value of the empirical constant f_V. The result is

$$|(f_V)_\pi| = 0.935 \tag{3.9}$$

This is a very reasonable number, bearing out in a somewhat more sophisticated manner the conclusions about the phenomenological coupling strengths for pion and muon decays in Tables 1 and 2.

From the rate of $K_{\mu 2}$ decay (see Appendix A) a number corresponding to Eq. (3.9) can be calculated by replacing m_π with m_K in Eq. (3.7). The result is that

$$|(Gf_V)_K| \simeq 0.075\,|(Gf_V)_\pi| \tag{3.10}$$

The effective K-meson-lepton coupling is thus seen to be ~ 13 times weaker than the effective pion-lepton coupling, as was already pointed out in the discussion of Table 1 in Sec. 1.3.

3.2 P, C, and T Symmetries

We have seen in pion decay how the structure of the matrix elements was limited by Lorentz invariance. We now turn to other invariance properties to see their effects. The symmetry operations of space inversion, charge conjugation, and time reversal are treated in many books and are summarized in Appendix E. The articles by Wick (1958) and Lüders (1959) and the book by Marshak and Sudarshan (1961) have extensive discussions of most aspects, including the evidence for their conservation in strong interactions. Treiman (1960) examines in some detail the question of time-reversal invariance and its effect on the relative phases of amplitudes when final-state interactions are present (e.g., $\Lambda \rightarrow N + \pi$). Consequently, we shall only touch on a few points.

The general 4-fermion interaction of Eq. (2.6),

$$\mathcal{H}_{int} = \sum_{i=1}^{5} (\overline{\psi}_1 O_i \psi_2)(\overline{\psi}_3 O_i (C_i + C_i' \gamma_5)\psi_4) + \text{h.c.} \tag{3.11}$$

depends on the ten complex coupling constants C_i and C_i'. It is of interest to examine the behavior of H_{int} under the different operations P, C, and T. The relevant formulas concerning the bilinear forms are Eqs. (E. 16), (E. 26), and (E. 42). The results of the transformation can be expressed as changes in the coupling constants. Table 4 summarizes the transformations and lists the requirement for invariance with respect to a given symmetry operation.

Table 4

Transformation	C	C'	Requirement for invariance
Space inversion	C	$-C'$	$C' = 0$
Charge conjugation	C*	$-C'^*$	C real, C' pure imaginary
Time reversal	C*	C'^*	C real, C' real

From Table 4 it is evident that by suitable choice of the constants (in magnitude and phase) one can construct a 4-fermion interaction which conserves P, C, and T separately, which lacks conservation of any pair of them, or lacks invariance under all three operations simultaneously.

The lack of invariance under a symmetry operation is reflected in the probability distributions for physical processes. Consider, for example, a decay process in which a system at rest with angular momentum $\vec{J}$ decays into several particles with momenta $\vec{p}_i$ and spins $\vec{s}_i$. The differential probability distribution for observation of these particles must be rotationally invariant (conservation of angular momentum); hence the distribution must be made up of a linear combination of scalar products of the various observables ($\vec{J}$, $\vec{p}_i$, $\vec{s}_i$). Furthermore, if space inversion invariance holds, these scalar products must be scalars, not pseudoscalars. Thus $(\vec{p}_i \cdot \vec{p}_j)$ and $(\vec{J} \cdot \vec{s}_i)$ are permitted, but $(\vec{J} \cdot \vec{p}_i)$ is not allowed. Similarly, if time-reversal invariance holds, scalar products, such as $\vec{J} \cdot (\vec{p}_i \times \vec{p}_j)$, which are odd under time reversal, must not occur.* On the other hand, experimental observation of these "forbidden" terms would prove the violation of the appropriate symmetry principle.

In mu-meson decay the observation of longitudinal polarization (a term of the form $\vec{s}_i \cdot \vec{p}_i$) and a directional asymmetry ($\vec{J} \cdot \vec{p}_i$) shows conclusively that parity is not conserved in mu decay. The PCT theorem implies that, since these terms are allowed by time-reversal invariance, charge-conjugation invariance is also violated. The numerical values of the various quantities are such that the interaction takes the form of Eq. (2.28), which is equivalent to Eq. (3.11) with $C_A = C_A' = -C_V = -C_V'$. From Table 4, we see that such an interaction is T-invariant (or PC-invariant).

3.3 Beta Decay

The interaction of Eq. (3.11) can be treated as a phenomenological form describing ordinary beta decay. Then the general distribution function for allowed beta decay can be calculated in a straightforward way (e.g., Jackson, Treiman, and Wyld, 1957). The comparison of these results with experiment is described in detail by Konopinski (1959) and Kofoed-Hansen (1959). Of particular importance are the electron-neutrino correlation experiments described by Allen (1959) and the fine series of experiments on polarized neutron decay (Burgy et al., 1958, 1958a). The combined conclusions from all these careful experiments are that the beta interaction is predominantly V and A with $C_V = C_V'$, $C_A = C_A'$, and $C_A \simeq -1.2\, C_V$. The relative phase is established to within $\pm 8^\circ$ of 180°. Thus the beta interaction is T or CP-invariant.

To illustrate how these conclusions were reached from experiment, we state the probability distribution for the decay of polarized neutrons with average spin $\langle\vec{\sigma}\rangle$ into an electron of momentum $\vec{p}$ and energy E, a neutrino of momentum $\vec{q}$, and a recoil proton:

$$dw = \frac{F(Z,E)}{(2\pi)^5} p^2 (E_0 - E)^2 \xi \left\{ 1 + a \frac{\vec{p} \cdot \vec{q}}{E q} + \right.$$

*This statement must be qualified because of the possibility of final-state interactions which destroy the simple connection between a state and its time-reversed partner. Remember that time reversal turns "in" states into "out" states!

$$+ \langle \vec{\sigma} \rangle \cdot \left[A \frac{\vec{p}}{E} + B \frac{\vec{q}}{q} + D \frac{\vec{p} \times \vec{q}}{E q} \right] \Big\} dp \, d\Omega_e \, d\Omega_\nu \tag{3.12}$$

The factors in front of the curly bracket represent the usual allowed beta spectrum, with F(Z, E) being the Fermi function which contains the effects of the Coulomb field in the final state. The parameter a is the electron-neutrino directional correlation coefficient. The parameters A and B are different from zero if parity is not conserved, while D is non-vanishing if time-reversal invariance fails.

From the work of Allen (1959) and others on the (e, ν) correlation for various nuclei, the interaction is known to be predominantly V and A. Many experiments have been done on the longitudinal polarization of beta rays (e. g., Spivak et al., 1961; Lipnik et al., 1962). These all give polarizations near the maximum ($\pm$ v/c for $e^{\pm}$) and imply the presence of $(1 + \gamma_5)$ in the leptonic bilinear form, that is, $C_i = C_i'$ in Eq. (3.11).

With the assumption that $C_i' = C_i$ and the dominance of V and A, the coefficients in Eq. (3.12) take on the following values:

$$\begin{aligned}
\xi &= 2\left[|C_V|^2 + 3|C_A|^2 \right] \\
\xi a &= 2\left[|C_V|^2 - |C_A|^2 \right] \\
\xi A &= -2\left[2|C_A|^2 + 2\,\mathrm{Re}(C_V C_A^*) \right] \\
\xi B &= 2\left[2|C_A|^2 - 2\,\mathrm{Re}(C_V C_A^*) \right] \\
\xi D &= -2\left[2\,\mathrm{Im}(C_V C_A^*) \right]
\end{aligned} \tag{3.13}$$

The experimental observations on unpolarized neutron decay yield an (e, ν) directional correlation coefficient of

$$a = \begin{cases} +0.07 \pm 0.12 \\ -0.06 \pm 0.13 \end{cases}$$

where the upper value is that of Robson (1958) and the lower that of Trebukhovskii et al. (1959). The measurements (Burgy et al., 1958, 1958a) of the other asymmetry parameters in Eq. (3.12) with polarized neutrons yield

$$A = -0.09 \pm 0.03$$

$$B = 0.88 \pm 0.15$$

$$D = -0.04 \pm 0.07$$

Inspection of expressions (3.13) shows that the experimental data on a imply $|C_V| \simeq |C_A|$, while the small values of A and D, plus the large value of B, indicate that C_V and C_A are real and of opposite sign. When use is made of the observed value of the neutron lifetime and that of O^{14}, the ratio of the magnitudes of C_V and C_A is found to be

$$\left|\frac{C_A}{C_V}\right| = 1.19 \pm 0.04 \tag{3.14}$$

With the assumption of opposite phase for C_V and C_A, the calculated values of the parameters in Eq. (3.12) are $a = -0.08 \pm 0.01$, $A = -0.09 \pm 0.01$, $B = +0.99 \pm 0.01$, $D = 0$. These are in quite reasonable accord with the data.

We shall defer discussion of the absolute magnitude of C_V for beta decay until Sec. (4.1). On the question of the possible presence of scalar and tensor couplings, the (e, ν) correlation experiments limit such contributions to less than ~ 10 per cent (in the square of the coupling constants). Similar limits have been set in other experiments (Mann, Miskel, and Bloom, 1958; Lauritsen et al., 1958; Barnes, Greenstein, and Nordberg, 1958).

3.4 Limitations on Structure of Matrix Elements because of Time-Reversal Invariance; Form Factors

In mu-meson and beta decay, the observations are consistent with the assumption of time-reversal invariance for the weak interaction; hence we shall accept this as a general requirement for all weak interaction processes. The imposition of T invariance enforces certain reality conditions, as we shall now demonstrate. Because of the likelihood of V-A coupling, we shall concentrate on matrix elements with 4-vector structure. The general amplitude to be considered is shown diagrammatically in Fig. 2.

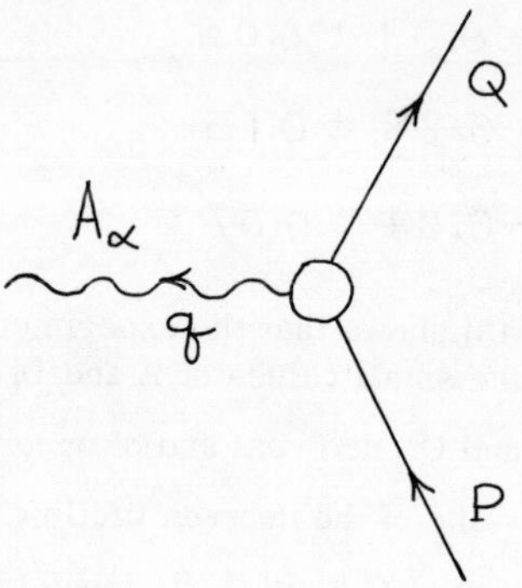

Fig. 2

An initial particle of momentum P transforms into a final particle of momentum Q by a vector interaction at the vertex where momentum q = P - Q is carried off. We wish to discuss the structure of the matrix element with respect to the initial and final particles. The vector associated with q (e. g., photon, lepton pair, etc.) will be described only by a 4-vector, A_α, which will be assumed to behave like a current under time reversal; that is, if $A_\alpha = (\vec{A}, iA_0)$, then $A_{T\alpha} = (-\vec{A}, iA_0) = -A_\alpha{}^*$.

First we consider that the initial and final particles are spinless. By arguments on Lorentz invariance similar to those used in Sec. 3.1 on pion decay, we can conclude that the Feynman amplitude $\mathcal{M}$ will have the general form

$$\mathcal{M} = \left[g_1(q^2)P_\alpha + g_2(q^2)Q_\alpha\right]A_\alpha \tag{3.15}$$

where $g_i(q^2)$ is a Lorentz invariant function of the square of the 4-momenta transfer q.* Any alternative expression involving, for example, P_α and q_α as the 4-vectors can always be cast in the form of Eq. (3.15).

We now ask for the restrictions on $\mathfrak{M}$ because of time-reversal invariance. The time-reversed matrix element is

$$\mathfrak{M}_T = \left[g_1(q^2)P_{T\alpha} + g_2(q^2)Q_{T\alpha}\right]A_{T\alpha} \tag{3.16}$$

where $P_{T\alpha} = -P_\alpha^*$, etc., are the time-reversed 4-momenta and current. Note that q^2 is unchanged by time reversal. Thus,

$$\mathfrak{M}_T = \left[g_1(q^2)P_\alpha^* + g_2(q^2)Q_\alpha^*\right]A_\alpha^* \tag{3.17}$$

From Eq. (E.28) of Appendix E, it is seen that time-reversal invariance requires

$$\mathfrak{M}_T^* = \mathfrak{M} \tag{3.18}$$

Therefore, we find

$$g_1 = g_1^* \qquad g_2 = g_2^* \tag{3.19}$$

The Lorentz invariant functions g_i must be real.

If the initial and final particles are fermions then the Feynman

---

*We choose q^2 rather than some other equivalent scalar product such as $P \cdot Q$ because of the use of the point $q^2 = 0$ for the definition of coupling constants.

amplitude for a vector transition has the general structure*

$$\mathcal{M} = \bar{u}(Q)\left[g_V \gamma_\alpha + g_T \sigma_{\alpha\beta} q_\beta + g_S q_\alpha\right] u(P)\, A_\alpha \tag{3.20}$$

The functions g_V, g_T, and g_S are Lorentz invariant functions of q^2.

The time-reversal matrix element is

$$\begin{aligned}\mathcal{M}_T &= \bar{u}_T(Q)\left[g_V \gamma_\alpha + g_T \sigma_{\alpha\beta} q_{T\beta} + g_S q_{T\alpha}\right] u_T(P)\, A_{T\alpha} \\ &= \bar{u}_T(Q)\left[-g_V \gamma_\alpha + g_T \sigma_{\alpha\beta} q_\beta^* + g_S q_\alpha^*\right] u_T(P)\, A_\alpha^*\end{aligned} \tag{3.21}$$

---

*The reader may wonder what happened to the other possible 4-vectors such as $(P + Q)_\alpha$ and $\sigma_{\alpha\beta}(P + Q)_\beta$. We leave it as an exercise for the reader to show that, when use is made of the equations of motion of the particles, these operators can be transformed into the effective forms

$$(P+Q)_\alpha = i(m_1+m_2)\gamma_\alpha - i\sigma_{\alpha\beta} q_\beta$$

$$\sigma_{\alpha\beta}(P+Q)_\beta = (m_1-m_2)\gamma_\alpha + i q_\alpha$$

where m_1 and m_2 are the masses of the initial and final fermions. Similarly, the axial vector counterparts can be transformed by

$$\gamma_5(P+Q)_\alpha = -i(m_1-m_2)\gamma_\alpha\gamma_5 - i\sigma_{\alpha\beta} q_\beta \gamma_5$$

$$\sigma_{\alpha\beta}(P+Q)_\beta\gamma_5 = -(m_1+m_2)\gamma_\alpha\gamma_5 + i q_\alpha \gamma_5$$

The condition of time-reversal invariance, Eq. (3.18), combined with the result of Eq. (E.44) for time-reversed bilinear forms leads to the requirements

$$g_V^* = -g_V, \quad g_T^* = -g_T, \quad g_S^* = g_S \tag{3.22}$$

Thus g_V and g_T are purely imaginary, while g_S is real. For convenience it is worthwhile to exhibit explicitly a factor of i for the purely imaginary functions. Consequently we write $g_V = if_V$, $g_T = if_T$, and $g_S = f_S$. This gives the general structure,

$$\mathcal{M}_V = \bar{u}(Q)\left[if_V(q^2)\gamma_\alpha + if_T(q^2)\sigma_{\alpha\beta}q_\beta + f_S q_\alpha\right]u(P)A_\alpha \tag{3.23}$$

where the f's are all real if time-reversal invariance holds.

For an axial-vector matrix element, similar considerations show that the form is

$$\mathcal{M}_A = \bar{u}(Q)\left[if_A(q^2)\gamma_\alpha\gamma_5 + if_T'(q^2)\sigma_{\alpha\beta}q_\beta\gamma_5 + f_P(q^2)q_\alpha\gamma_5\right]u(P)A_\alpha \tag{3.24}$$

where all the f's are real if time-reversal invariance holds.

If the 4-vector current A_α is produced by a lepton pair, it takes the form

$$A_\alpha = -i\,\bar{u}_\ell(p_1)\gamma_\alpha(1+\gamma_5)u_\nu(p_2) \tag{3.25}$$

where $p_1 + p_2 = q$. The presence of the factor $-i$ is necessary to make A reverse its spatial components under time reversal, as can be seen from the first term in Eq. (3. 23). The presence of both vector and axial-vector parts in Eq. (3. 25) means that the general fermion matrix element will be a sum of Eqs. (3. 23) and (3. 24). Parity conservation for the strong interactions will, of course, limit the generality, perhaps selecting only the vector or only the axial-vector part.

The original example of these arguments is the coupling of the nucleons to the electromagnetic field. The interaction is of the form

$$\mathcal{H}_{int} = -j_\alpha A_\alpha \tag{3. 26}$$

where A_α is now the vector potential and j_α is the electromagnetic current 4-vector. For a vertex such as we have been considering, the general form of the matrix element $\langle Q | j_\alpha | P \rangle$ can be read from Eq. (3. 23) to be

$$\sqrt{\frac{Q_0 P_0}{m^2}} \langle Q | j_\alpha | P \rangle = e\, \bar{u}(Q) \left[i F_1(q^2) \gamma_\alpha + \frac{i\lambda}{2m} F_2(q^2) \sigma_{\alpha\beta} q_\beta \right] u(P) \tag{3. 27}$$

Here e is the proton charge, λ is the anomalous magnetic moment of the nucleon, and $F_1(q^2)$ and $F_2(q^2)$ are two Lorentz invariant functions of q^2. The scalar term in Eq. (3. 23) is absent because of the conservation law $\partial j_\alpha / \partial x_\alpha = 0$. The functions F_1 and F_2 are called form factors (they can be related nonrelativistically to spatial Fourier transforms of the charge and magnetic moment densities). The normalization has been chosen so that $F_1(0) = F_2(0) = 1$ for the proton, and $F_1(0) = 0$ and $F_2(0) = 1$ for the neutron.

This corresponds to the proton having charge e and magnetic moment $(1 + \lambda_p)\, e\hbar/2mc$, and the neutron having no charge and magnetic moment $\lambda_n\, e\hbar/2mc$. The form factors $F_i(q^2)$ are studied experimentally for spacelike q^2 $(q^2 > 0)$ in high-energy electron scattering.

When the conserved vector coupling is discussed (Sec. 4.1), we shall return to the question of whether the weak interaction form factors (f_V, f_T, f_S, f_A, f_T', f_P) in Eqs. (3.23) and (3.24) have any connection to the nucleon electromagnetic form factors.

3.5 Current-Current Form of the Interaction; Restrictions Imposed by G-Conjugation Invariance

The four-fermion interaction of Eq. (2.28) for mu-meson decay can be written as

$$\mathcal{H}_{int} = -\frac{G}{\sqrt{2}} J_\alpha^{(\ell)} J_\alpha^{(\ell)\dagger} \tag{3.28}$$

where

$$J_\alpha^{(\ell)} = i\left(\bar{\psi}_\nu \gamma_\alpha (1+\gamma_5)\psi_e\right) + i\left(\bar{\psi}_\nu \gamma_\alpha (1+\gamma_5)\psi_\mu\right) \tag{3.29}$$

is the leptonic "current." This interaction also includes terms which describe the processes $\mu + \nu \rightarrow \mu + \nu$, $e^+ + e^- \rightarrow \nu + \bar{\nu}$, etc. But it does not contain such unwanted couplings as ($\bar{e}e$), ($\bar{\mu}e$), which would lead to unobserved processes such as $\mu \rightarrow e + e + e$.

The leptonic current of Eq. (3.29) is characterized by $\Delta Q = +1$, where ΔQ is the change in charge produced by the bilinear form. This requirement also applies to the nucleonic "current" which enters in beta decay and mu-meson capture. Thus, these processes can be described by an interaction of the form

$$\mathcal{H}_{int} = -\frac{G'}{\sqrt{2}} J_\alpha^{(N)} J_\alpha^{(\ell)\dagger} \tag{3.30}$$

where the nucleonic current is

$$J_\alpha^{(N)} = i(\overline{\psi}_p \gamma_\alpha (1+\gamma_5)\psi_n) \tag{3.31}$$

and the constant G' for beta decay is related to C_V and C_A in Eq. (3.11). The factor $\sqrt{2}$ is present, so that G' is effectively the Fermi coupling constant g_F of conventional beta-decay theory.

The reader may object that Eq. (3.30) is only qualitatively correct in that the evidence on beta decay (Sec. 3.3) implied a neutron decay matrix element of the form

$$\mathcal{M} \sim (\overline{u}_p \gamma_\alpha (1+1.19\gamma_5) u_n)(\overline{u}_e \gamma_\alpha (1+\gamma_5) u_\nu) \tag{3.32}$$

where the coefficient 1.19 is the ratio [Eq. (3.14)] of axial-vector to vector couplings. But if the currents in Eq. (3.30) are interpreted as Heisenberg operators containing the exact nucleon fields, then the difference between Eqs. (3.31) and (3.32) can be understood in terms of renormalization effects of the strong interactions. The leptonic-current matrix element has the same form as the current itself, because the renormalization effects are only electromagnetic and are neglected.

When the possibility of appreciable renormalization effects is allowed for, the matrix elements of the nucleon current of Eq. (3.31) can have the general structure discussed in the previous section. Thus, if we write $J_\alpha^{(N)} = V_\alpha + A_\alpha$, where V_α and A_α are the vector and axial-vector parts, the matrix elements of V_α and A_α can be written from Eqs. (3.23) and (3.24), as follows:

$$\sqrt{\frac{P_0 Q_0}{m^2}} \langle p | V_\alpha | n \rangle =$$

$$\overline{u}(Q)[i f_V \gamma_\alpha + i f_T \sigma_{\alpha\beta} q_\beta + f_S q_\alpha] u(P)$$

$$\sqrt{\frac{P_0 Q_0}{m^2}}\langle p|A_\alpha|n\rangle =$$

$$\bar{u}(Q)\left[i f_A \gamma_\alpha \gamma_5 + i f_T' \sigma_{\alpha\beta} q_\beta \gamma_5 + f_P q_\alpha \gamma_5 \right] u(P) \tag{3.33}$$

where the neutron (proton) has 4-momenta P(Q), q = P - Q, and the f's are Lorentz invariant form factors which are functions of q^2.

The general results of Eq. (3.33) will be valid even if the particular form of the nucleonic current, Eq. (3.31), is augmented by terms involving other adrons (e.g., $\pi^- \partial_\alpha \pi^0$, $\bar{\Sigma}^+\Lambda$). Furthermore, if the adronic currents are restricted to those which behave under G-conjugation (see Appendix E) in the same way as ($\bar{p}$n), then the number of form factors in Eq. (3.33) can be reduced from six to four. Thus, we suppose that all "currents" formed from adrons transform under G conjugation as

$$G^{-1} V_\alpha G = +V_\alpha$$

$$G^{-1} A_\alpha G = -A_\alpha \tag{3.34}$$

This is the behavior of the ($\bar{p}$n) bilinear form* in the first line of Eq. (E.55). Then inspection of both sides of Eq. (3.33), making use of Eq. (E.55) for the different covariants, shows that the scalar term in the matrix element of V_α and the tensor term in the matrix element of A_α must be absent. Consequently, if the current satisfies Eq. (3.34), then the matrix elements of V_α and A_α are

---

*The reader may verify that some other allowable combinations are $[(\bar{\Sigma}^+\Lambda) + (\bar{\Lambda}\Sigma^-)]$ and $[(\bar{\Sigma}^+\Sigma^0) - (\bar{\Sigma}^0\Sigma^-)]$.

$$\sqrt{\frac{P_0 Q_0}{m^2}}\langle p|V_\alpha|n\rangle = i\,\bar{u}(Q)\left[f_V\gamma_\alpha + f_T\sigma_{\alpha\beta}q_\beta\right]u(P)$$

$$\sqrt{\frac{P_0 Q_0}{m^2}}\langle p|A_\alpha|n\rangle = \bar{u}(Q)\left[i f_A\gamma_\alpha\gamma_5 + f_P q_\alpha\gamma_5\right]u(P) \tag{3.35}$$

General expressions for strong-interaction matrix elements of (S, V, T, A, P) interactions, which transform under G conjugation either as the $(\bar{p}n)$ bilinear form or in the opposite manner, were first derived by Weinberg (1958) and are summarized by Treiman (1960, p. 541). We shall require only the expressions given above.

4. CONSERVED AND PARTIALLY CONSERVED CURRENTS; BETA AND PION DECAY AND MU-MESON CAPTURE

In Chapters 2 and 3 we have explored the structure of weak interactions through the examples of mu-meson decay and beta decay. We have also considered the restrictions imposed by invariance and symmetry requirements. Now we turn to the question of the universality of the 4-fermion coupling and the behavior of the form factors appearing because of the strong interactions.

4.1 Conserved Vector Current

In beta decays which are $(0 \rightarrow 0$, no) transitions, only the vector part of the nucleonic current of Eq. (3.31) is operative. Furthermore, the energy release is generally so small that $q^2 \simeq 0$ (in units of m_π^2 or m_p^2). Thus we see from Eqs. (3.30) and (3.35) that the effective coupling constant C_V of Sec. (3.3) is

$$C_V = \frac{G'}{\sqrt{2}} f_V(0) \tag{4.1}$$

The decay rate is given by a known function of energy times the square of this coupling constant times a nuclear matrix element. For light nuclei, where isotopic spin is a good quantum number, the nuclear matrix element can be computed accurately because it is an overlap integral of the wave functions of two members of the same isotopic multiplet. If the nuclear matrix element is known, the magnitude of the coupling constant can be obtained. The nucleus 0^{14} is the best known example of a $(0 \rightarrow 0$, no) transition. The experimental data (Bardin et al., 1960) on end-point energy and half-life allow one to calculate the value of $G' f_V(0)$:

$$G' f_V(0) = (1.015 \pm 0.002) \times 10^{-5} \, m_p^{-2} \tag{4.2}$$

This number can be compared with the coupling constant G of mu-meson decay, Eq. (2.30). The numbers agree within 1 per cent. With this sort of accuracy under consideration, various fine effects such as electromagnetic radiative corrections must be included (Berman, 1958; Durand, Landovitz, and Marr, 1960; Berman and Sirlin, 1962). While there is some disagreement on the proper radiative corrections for beta decay, the final conclusion is that G and $G' f_V(0)$ differ by less than 3 per cent.

The remarkable agreement between Eqs. (4.2) and (2.30) implies a universality of weak-interaction couplings. But a more daring and productive interpretation (Feynman and Gell-Mann, 1958) is found by assuming $G' = G$ in Eqs. (3.28) and (3.30), and focusing on the result $f_V(0) = 1$. The factor $f_V(0)$ represents renormalization effects of the strong interactions. A priori, it might be expected to have a value very different from unity. But the result $f_V(0) = 1$ implies an absence of renormalization effects.* There is another place in physics where renormalization effects are absent, namely, for the electric charge. The universality of electric charge can be traced to the existence of a conserved electromagnetic current (which is intimately connected with restricted gauge invariance). It is natural to seek a similar explanation for the vector part of the weak-interaction current.

The Feynman—Gell-Mann hypothesis is that the vector part of the nucleonic current, Eq. (3.31), is augmented by just those terms which will make the total current be conserved. Then renormalization effects will be absent, and the equality of Eqs. (4.2) and (2.30) will have a

---

*The use of the phrase "absence of renormalization effects" is somewhat imprecise. What is meant is the absence of detectable renormalization effects.

natural explanation. For simplicity we shall consider nucleons and pions to be the only strongly interacting particles. The addition ot the K mesons and hyperons is straightforward. The electromagnetic current of nucleons and pions (in units of e) is

$$j_\alpha = i\left(\overline{\psi}_p \gamma_\alpha \psi_p\right) + i\left(\frac{\partial \phi}{\partial x_\alpha}\phi^\dagger - \phi\frac{\partial \phi^\dagger}{\partial x_\alpha}\right) \tag{4.3}$$

where $\phi = \frac{1}{\sqrt{2}}(\phi_1 + i\phi_2)$ is the field which destroys negative pions (and creates positive pions). Using isotopic spin notation, this current can be written as

$$j_\alpha = j_\alpha^{(B)} + j_\alpha^{(3)} \tag{4.4}$$

where

$$j_\alpha^{(B)} = \frac{i}{2}\left(\overline{N}\gamma_\alpha N\right)$$

is the baryon isoscalar current, and $j_\alpha^{(3)}$ is the third component of the isovector current,

$$\underset{\sim}{j}_\alpha = \frac{i}{2}\left(\overline{N}\gamma_\alpha \underset{\sim}{\tau} N\right) - \underset{\sim}{\phi} \times \frac{\partial}{\partial x_\alpha}\underset{\sim}{\phi} \tag{4.5}$$

The electromagnetic current of Eq. (4.3) is therefore seen to be made up of two parts, each of which is divergenceless. The isoscalar current $j_\alpha^{(B)}$ is conserved because of conservation of baryon number, while the isovector current $j_\alpha^{(3)}$ has zero divergence because of conservation of the third component of isotopic spin. Now because of conservation of total isotopic spin in strong interactions, <u>all</u> components of the isovector current of Eq. (4.5) are conserved:

$$\frac{\partial}{\partial x_\alpha}\underset{\sim}{j}_\alpha = 0 \tag{4.6}$$

Inspection shows that the vector part of the nucleonic weak-interaction current of Eq. (3.31) is the first term of $(j_\alpha^{(1)} + i j_\alpha^{(2)})$ in Eq. (4.5). Hence the appropriate conserved vector weak-interaction current to replace Eq. (3.31) is

$$V_\alpha = j_\alpha^{(1)} + i\, j_\alpha^{(2)}$$

$$= i(\overline{\Psi}_p \gamma_\alpha \Psi_n) + i\sqrt{2}\left(\frac{\partial \phi_0}{\partial x_\alpha}\phi - \phi_0 \frac{\partial \phi}{\partial x_\alpha}\right) + \cdots \tag{4.7}$$

with conservation expressed by

$$\frac{\partial V_\alpha}{\partial x_\alpha} = 0 \tag{4.8}$$

We remark here that the dots in Eq. (4.7) represent the contributions from K mesons and hyperons. These terms will give rise to $\Delta S = 0$ decay processes, such as $\Sigma^- \to \Lambda + e^- + \nu$, with known (or reasonably well-known) rates. One event of the $\Sigma^- - \Lambda$ beta decay was reported by Block at the 1962 International Conference on High Energy Physics, CERN, Geneva (July 4-11, 1962).

We are now in a position to connect the weak-interaction vector amplitude, Eq. (3.35), to the electromagnetic form factors in Eq. (3.27). We merely decompose the form factors into isoscalar and isovector parts as for the current of Eq. (4.4). Thus, we define F_{IS}, F_{IV}, F_{2S}, and F_{2V} so that

$$F_{1p} = \tfrac{1}{2}(F_{1S} + F_{1V})$$

$$F_{1n} = \tfrac{1}{2}(F_{1S} - F_{1V})$$

$$\lambda_p F_{2p} = \tfrac{1}{2}(\mu_p' + \mu_n)F_{2S} + \tfrac{1}{2}(\mu_p' - \mu_n)F_{2V}$$

$$\lambda_n F_{2n} = \tfrac{1}{2}(\mu_p' + \mu_n)F_{2S} - \tfrac{1}{2}(\mu_p' - \mu_n)F_{2V} \tag{4.9}$$

Here $\mu_p' = 1.793$ and $\mu_n = -1.913$ are the anomalous magnetic moments of the nucleons. The isovector part of the electromagnetic current of Eq. (4.4) therefore has a matrix element,

$$\sqrt{\frac{P_0 Q_0}{m^2}} \langle Q | j_\alpha^{(3)} | P \rangle = \frac{e}{2} \bar{u}(Q) \left[i F_{1V} \gamma_\alpha + i \frac{\Delta\mu}{2m} F_{2V} \sigma_{\alpha\beta} q_\beta \right] \tau_3 u(P) \tag{4.10}$$

where $\Delta\mu = \mu_p' - \mu_n = 3.706$. With the conserved vector current of Eq. (4.7), we can immediately write down the weak-interaction vector matrix element, Eq. (3.35), between neutron and proton states in terms of the isovector electromagnetic form factors:

$$\sqrt{\frac{P_0 Q_0}{m^2}} \langle Q | V_\alpha | P \rangle = i \bar{u}(Q) \left[F_{1V}(q^2) \gamma_\alpha + \frac{\Delta\mu}{2m} F_{2V}(q^2) \sigma_{\alpha\beta} q_\beta \right] u(P) \tag{4.11}$$

In beta decay we need only the values $F_{1V}(0) = F_{2V}(0) = 1$. But in mu-meson capture, $q^2 = \mu^2 m/(m + \mu) \simeq 0.9\ \mu^2$, where μ_2 is the mass of the mu meson, and in high-energy neutrino reactions, q^2 is even larger. Consequently we shall need the experimentally determined isovector form factors in Eq. (4.11).

Before discussing the experimental evidence for the conserved vector current of Eq. (4.11), we turn to the axial-vector current A_α.

4.2 Lack of Conservation of Axial-Vector Current

In view of the discussion of V_α, it is natural to inquire whether the axial-vector current A_α is also conserved. The existence of the ratio $|C_A/C_V| \simeq 1.2$ implies that it is probably not. But stronger arguments can be given.

Consider the decay of the pion ($\pi \to \ell + \nu$). The strong coupling of the pion to baryons means that the decay is caused by the adronic current. Since the pion is pseudoscalar, the axial-vector current A_α is operative. Thus the Feynman amplitude for pion decay is

$$\mathcal{M} = i \frac{G}{\sqrt{2}} \sqrt{2Q_0} \langle 0 | A_\alpha | \pi \rangle \cdot \left(\bar{u}_\ell(p_1) \gamma_\alpha (1+\gamma_5) u_\nu(p_2) \right) \tag{4.12}$$

where Q is the pion 4-momentum.

On invariance grounds (Sec. 3.1) we have already written

$$\mathcal{M} = i \frac{G}{\sqrt{2}} m_\pi f_\pi(-m_\pi^2) Q_\alpha \cdot \left(\bar{u}_\ell(p_1) \gamma_\alpha (1+\gamma_5) u_\nu(p_2) \right)$$

Thus the matrix element of A_α is (as could have been deduced directly)

$$\langle 0 | A_\alpha | \pi \rangle = \frac{m_\pi f_\pi}{\sqrt{2Q_0}} Q_\alpha \tag{4.13}$$

where $f_\pi(-m_\pi^2) \simeq 0.935$ is the constant of Eq. (3.9).

The expression (4.13) is in direct contradiction to conservation of A_α. In fact, from Eq. (4.13) we can evaluate the vacuum - one pion matrix element of $\partial A_\alpha / \partial x_\alpha$:

$$\langle 0 | \frac{\partial A_\alpha}{\partial x_\alpha} | \pi \rangle = i Q_\alpha \langle 0 | A_\alpha | \pi \rangle = -i \frac{m_\pi^3 f_\pi}{\sqrt{2Q_0}} \tag{4.14}$$

This is not zero. Consequently $\partial A_\alpha / \partial x_\alpha \neq 0$. This argument that pion decay proves the nonconservation of A_α was first given by Taylor (1958).

Another argument against the conservation of A_α can be found in the structure of the phenomenological 4-fermion beta-decay interaction (Goldberger and Treiman, 1958a). If we demand that the neutron-proton matrix element of the divergence of A_α vanish, we find from Eq. (3.35) that

$$0 = \langle p | \frac{\partial A_\alpha}{\partial x_\alpha} | n \rangle = \bar{u}(Q)\left(i f_A \gamma \cdot q \gamma_5 + f_P \gamma_5 q^2\right) u(P)$$

When use is made of the equations of motion to eliminate $i\gamma \cdot q$, the result is

$$0 = \bar{u}(Q)\left(2m f_A + f_P q^2\right)\gamma_5 u(P)$$

Therefore

$$f_P(q^2) = -\frac{2m}{q^2} f_A(q^2) \tag{4.15}$$

Then the axial-vector nucleonic matrix element reads

$$\sqrt{\frac{P_0 Q_0}{m^2}} \langle p | A_\alpha | n \rangle = f_A(q^2)\, \bar{u}(Q)\left(i\gamma_\alpha \gamma_5 - \frac{2m}{q^2} q_\alpha \gamma_5\right) u(P) \tag{4.16}$$

When the pseudoscalar term is coupled to the leptonic current and use is made of the leptonic equations of motion, there results a pseudoscalar coupling between nucleons and leptons of the form of Eq. (3.11) with effective coupling (in the limit of small q^2),

$$C_P = C'_P = \frac{2 m_\ell m_p}{q^2} C_A \simeq \frac{2 m_p}{m_\ell} C_A \tag{4.17}$$

where $C_A = - G f_A(0)/\sqrt{2}$. Thus, if A_α is conserved, there is an effective or induced pseudoscalar coupling in beta decay with $C_P \simeq 3.7 \times 10^3 C_A$. This is in gross contradiction to fact, even when the relativistic nature of the pseudoscalar coupling is allowed for.

4.3 Partially Conserved Axial-Vector Current; Goldberger-Treiman Relation; Induced Pseudoscalar Coupling

In treating the problems of pion decay and mu-meson capture by dispersion relation techniques, Goldberger and Treiman (1958; 1958b) showed that, with certain approximations, the pion-decay rate could be related to the axial-vector coupling constant. In our notation, their result (known as the Goldberger-Treiman relation) was

$$f_\pi(-m_\pi^2) \simeq \sqrt{2}\, \frac{m_p}{m_\pi} \frac{f_A(0)}{g_\pi} \tag{4.18}$$

where f_π is the pion-decay constant in Eqs. (4.13) and (3.9), $f_A(0) = 1.19$ is the ratio $-C_A/C_V$, and g_π is the pion-nucleon coupling constant ($g_\pi^2/4\pi \simeq 13.5$). Numerically, the right-hand side of Eq. (4.18) is equal to 0.873, while the experimental value of Eq. (3.9) is 0.935. Since the pion-nucleon coupling constant is uncertain to about 5 to 10 per cent and there is an error of about 4 per cent in f_A [Eq. (3.14)], the agreement is remarkable.

In addition, Goldberger and Treiman showed that for mu-meson capture the axial-vector current had a matrix element, not given by Eq. (4.16) but by

$$\sqrt{\frac{P_0 Q_0}{m^2}} \langle p | A_\alpha | n \rangle \simeq f_A(0)\, \bar{u}(Q) \left(i \gamma_\alpha \gamma_5 - 7 \frac{q_\alpha}{m_\mu} \gamma_5 \right) u(P) \tag{4.19}$$

The second term is equivalent to a pseudoscalar coupling, $C_P^{(\mu)} \simeq 7\, C_A^{(\mu)} \simeq 7\, C_A$. The numerical value 7 comes from use of the experimental value for Eq. (4.18). *

The results in Eqs. (4.18) and (4.19) can be attributed to the dominance of the one-pion pole in the dispersion relation for $\langle p \,|\, A_\alpha \,|\, n \rangle$. Various authors have tried to make this dominance plausible (1) by inventing models in which the divergence of A_α is proportional to the pion field, as is suggested by the one-pion matrix element of Eq. (4.14). Polkinghorne, 1958; Gell-Mann and Levy, 1960; Bernstein, Gell-Mann and Michel, 1960), and (2) by assuming that the divergence of A_α vanishes at high energies sufficiently rapidly (i. e., is partially conserved) that its matrix elements satisfy unsubtracted dispersion relations which are dominated by the lowest-mass singularities (Nambu, 1960; Bernstein et al., 1960; Chou, 1961).

To show the origin of Eqs. (4.18) and (4.19), we shall follow the work of Nambu (1960) since his approach exhibits all the assumptions clearly at the start. Nambu observes that, in Eq. (4.16) for the conserved axial current, the pseudoscalar term has a $1/q^2$ factor which can be thought of as the propagator for a massless pseudoscalar boson. In perturbation theory, such a contribution to beta decay or mu-meson capture would come from a diagram such as that shown in Fig. 3.

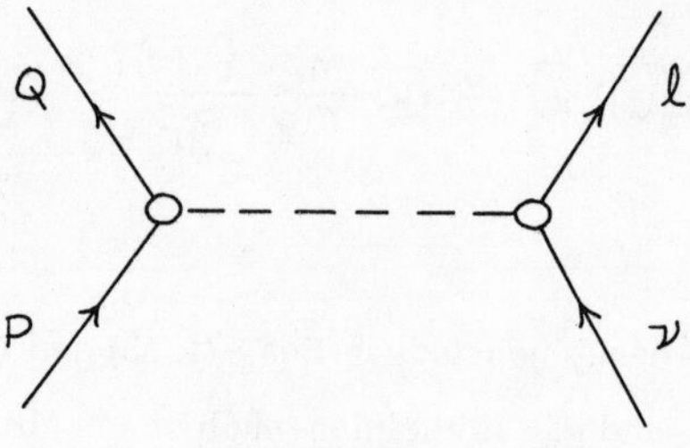

Fig. 3

Of course, there are no massless pseudoscalar bosons; furthermore, the axial-vector current is not conserved. But when we think for a moment, it is evident that (1) our knowledge of the lack of conservation is

*The original Goldberger-Treiman coefficient was 8. This value is inferred from the slightly different numbers given by Goldberger (1959).

restricted to matrix elements of small q^2, and (2) the pion is a pseudoscalar particle of relatively small mass. This suggested to Nambu that the matrix element $\langle p | A_\alpha | n \rangle$ might have the structure

$$\sqrt{\frac{P_0 Q_0}{m^2}} \langle p | A_\alpha | n \rangle =$$

$$\bar{u}(Q) \left[i \gamma_\alpha \gamma_5 F_A(q^2) - \frac{2m\, q_\alpha}{q^2 + m_\pi^2} \gamma_5 F_P(q^2) \right] u(P) \tag{4.20}$$

where $F_A(0) \simeq F_P(0) \simeq 1.19$, and $F_A(q^2) = F_P(q^2)$ for $q^2 >> m_\pi^2$. Then, if the pion mass can be neglected, the axial current is conserved [Eq. (4.16) is recovered]. The second term in Eq. (4.20) is evidently the contribution (in perturbation theory or dispersion relations) from the diagram above, in which a single pion is in the intermediate state (Goldberger and Treiman, 1958b; Wolfenstein, 1958). But the coefficient is fixed by the condition of partial conservation.

If the pseudoscalar term is evaluated at $q^2 \simeq m_\mu^2 / [(1 + (m_\mu/m)]$ for mu-meson capture, the result is the same as Eq. (4.19), with a coefficient 6.8 $F_P(m_\mu^2)$ instead of 7. Thus, the Nambu form, Eq. (4.20), yields the same result as that of Goldberger and Treiman for the induced pseudoscalar coupling in mu-meson capture, provided $F_P(m_\mu^2) \simeq F_A(0)$. Since the induced pseudoscalar coupling is proportional to the lepton mass, there is a negligible contribution in beta decay.

To obtain the Goldberger-Treiman relations, Eq. (4.18), for the pion decay amplitude we must interpret the pseudoscalar part of Eq. (4.20) in terms of the diagram above. We can certainly write

$$-\frac{2m \gamma_5 q_\alpha F_P(q^2)}{q^2 + m_\pi^2} =$$

$$i^2 (\sqrt{2}\, g_\pi \gamma_5) \frac{1}{q^2 + m_\pi^2} m_\pi f_\pi(q^2) \Phi(q^2) q_\alpha \tag{4.21}$$

where $f_\pi(q^2)$ is the pion-decay amplitude off the mass shell, and Φ is some function of q^2. But this equation is empty unless we attach meaning to its separate components. The factor $(\sqrt{2}\, g_\pi \gamma_5)$ is associated with the pion-nucleon vertex, the factor $m_\pi f_\pi(q^2)$ with the pion-lepton vertex. Now in the limit as $q^2 \rightarrow -m_\pi^2$, it is clear that $\langle p|A_\alpha|n\rangle$ has a pole. Furthermore, at that pole the $n \rightarrow p + \pi$ vertex is described exactly by the renormalized coupling constant g_π, and the $\pi \rightarrow \ell + \nu$ vertex is given by $f_\pi(-m_\pi^2)$. This means that $\Phi(q^2)$, which describes the pion-nucleon vertex, the renormalization of the pion propagator, and the effects of higher mass states, goes to unity at $q^2 = -m_\pi^2$. From Eq. (4.21), we therefore find the pion-decay amplitude,

$$f_\pi(-m_\pi^2) = \sqrt{2}\, \frac{m}{m_\pi} \frac{F_P(-m_\pi^2)}{g_\pi} \tag{4.22}$$

If $F_P(q^2)$ is assumed to be slowly varying, so that $F_P(-m_\pi^2) \simeq F_P(0) \simeq F_A(0)$, the Goldberger-Treiman relation of Eq. (4.18) follows.

4.4 Tests of the Conserved Vector Current

In the previous sections we have obtained the expressions (4.11) and (4.20) for nuclear matrix elements of V_α and A_α, with form factors near unity (or 1.19) for the momentum transfers involved in beta decay and muon capture. We now turn to the question of the experimental verification of these expressions. For the conserved vector current, there are three experiments, two of which have been performed reasonably well; however, we shall indicate the other one first.

The conserved vector current of Eq. (4.7) involves the pion fields explicitly. This means that the beta decay of the charged pion, $\pi^- \rightarrow \pi^0 + e^- + \bar{\nu}$, has a known matrix element,

$$\mathcal{M} = -i\sqrt{2}\, \frac{G}{\sqrt{2}} (P_\alpha + Q_\alpha)\left(\bar{u}_e \gamma_\alpha (1+\gamma_5) v_\nu\right) \tag{4.23}$$

where P and Q are the 4-momenta of the π^- and π^0, respectively.

Since the energy release is small (Q = 4.1 Mev), the no-recoil approximation of beta-decay can be used. Then only the time part of the matrix element survives:

$$\mathcal{M} \simeq G\left(m_{\pi^-} + m_{\pi^0}\right)\left(\bar{u}_e \gamma_4 (1+\gamma_5) v_\nu\right) \tag{4.24}$$

A straightforward calculation of the decay rate gives*

$$\Gamma_\beta = \frac{G^2}{30\pi^3} \Delta^5 R_0\left(\frac{m_e}{\Delta}\right) \tag{4.25}$$

where $\Delta = 4.52 \pm 0.10$ Mev is the maximum electron energy and R_0 is the correction factor of Eq. (C.12). With $R_0 = 0.94$ from Table 2 and G from Eq. (4.2) or (2.30), the beta-decay rate turns out to be $\Gamma_\beta = 0.39 \pm 0.04\ \text{sec}^{-1}$. This means a branching ratio, $\Gamma_\beta \tau_\pi = (1.0 \pm 0.1) \times 10^{-8}$. Very recent experimental work, reported at the 1962 International Conference on High Energy Physics, CERN, Geneva (July 4–11, 1962), indicates a branching ratio of $(1.7 \pm 0.5) \times 10^{-8}$ on the basis of ~ 16 events (De Pommier et al., 1962; Dunaitsev et al., 1962). Since the process can certainly occur, even without the explicit pion coupling in the conserved vector current of Eq. (4.7), more refined experiments are necessary to establish agreement or disagreement with the definite rate predicted by the conserved vector current hypothesis.**

One test of the conserved vector current which has been performed was first suggested by Gell-Mann (1958). In a ($\Delta J = 1$, no) transition in

---

*An alternative way to calculate the rate is to note that, since $\pi^- \to \pi^0 + e^- + \nu$ is a ($0 \to 0$, no) transition, it has the same matrix element as O^{14}. This means that the two transitions have the same ft value, and the relative rates can be calculated from the relative f values.

**It is of interest to note that the rate of Eq. (4.25) for pionic beta decay was first suggested by Gerstein and Zeldovich (1956) in a discussion of the possibility of conserved currents. But at that time it seemed of only academic interest because the beta interaction was believed to be S and T.

nuclei, the dominant matrix element is the so-called "Gamow-Teller matrix element," $\langle f | \vec{\sigma}_N | i \rangle$, coming from the spatial part of the axial-vector coupling. But there are small correction terms, called "forbidden" matrix elements, which come from higher-order parts of the vector and axial-vector couplings. These various contributions to the ($\Delta J = 1$, no) matrix element can be exhibited by making a Pauli reduction on the spinors in the nucleonic matrix elements of Eqs. (4. 11) and (4. 20) and extracting those parts proportional to the nucleon spin. The result is

$$\mathcal{M} \simeq \frac{G}{\sqrt{2}} \left\langle f \left| \frac{C_A}{C_V} \vec{\sigma}_N + i \, \frac{1+\Delta\mu}{2m} (\vec{q} \times \vec{\sigma}_N) \right| i \right\rangle \cdot \left(\bar{e} \beta \vec{\sigma} (1+\gamma_5) \nu \right) \tag{4.26}$$

In this expression the first term is the normal Gamow-Teller matrix element, while the second is a "forbidden" contribution from the vector coupling of Eq. (4. 11). There are a number of terms that have been omitted — a forbidden contribution from the axial-vector coupling (Gell-Mann b term) which is negligible for high-energy transitions, contributions from the orbital angular momentum, and mesonic exchange currents. In the transitions of interest, the neglected terms are unimportant; if they were important, the test of the conserved vector current would be less conclusive.

In Eq. (4. 26) the presence of $\Delta\mu = 3.71$ depends on the conserved vector current assumption. The original nucleonic current of Eq. (3. 31) would give Eq. (4. 26) with $\Delta\mu \simeq 0$. Thus, the experimental test must be a quantitative one which distinguishes between a coefficient of 1 and 4. 71. Since $1 + \Delta\mu = \mu_p - \mu_n$, where μ_p and μ_n are the complete magnetic moments of the nucleons, including virtual pi-mesonic effects, and since the structure of Eq. (4. 11) is obtained from the electromagnetic form factors, Gell-Mann called the effect under consideration "weak magnetism." The name is particularly appropriate for this ($\Delta J = 1$, no) transition because the correction term in Eq. (4. 26) can be obtained directly from the interaction $-\vec{\mu} \cdot \vec{B}$, which describes the corresponding M1 transition, in the same way as we went from the electromagnetic current of Eq. (4. 3) to the weak interaction current of Eq. (4. 7), with $\vec{B} = \vec{\nabla} \times \vec{A}$ changing into the curl of the leptonic current.

A calculation of the beta spectrum from Eq. (4. 26) shows that the normal allowed spectrum is multiplied by a correction factor

$$1 + \frac{8}{3} a E \tag{4.27}$$

where E is the electron energy, and

$$a = \left|\frac{C_V}{C_A}\right| \frac{1 + \Delta\mu}{2m} \simeq \frac{2.0}{m} \simeq 0.21\ \%\ \text{per Mev} \tag{4.28}$$

Equation (4.27), with positive a, holds for a β^- transition. The sign of a reverses for β^+ transitions.

The triad of nuclei, B^{12}, C^{12}, and N^{12}, afford the possibility of a test of the correction factor of Eq. (4.27). The ground states of B^{12} and N^{12}, together with an excited state in C^{12} at 15.11 Mev, form a $T = 1$, $J = 1^+$ isotopic spin multiplet. B^{12} and N^{12} beta-decay to the C^{12} ground state ($T = 0$, $J = 0^+$) with end-point energies of 13.37 and 16.43 Mev, respectively (see Fig. 4).

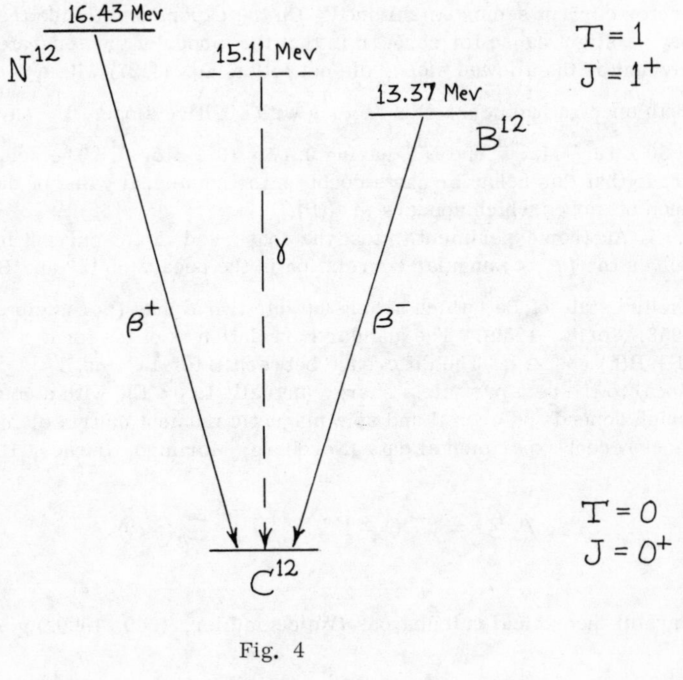

Fig. 4

The radiative M1 transition rate from the 15.11-Mev state in C^{12} to the ground state has been observed and allows one to determine a independent of any approximations such as the neglect of orbital magnetic moments. The experimental coefficient of m^{-1} in Eq. (4.28) is found to be 2.3 ± 0.2, in reasonable accord with the value 2.0.

The ratio R(E) of the beta spectrum of B^{12} to that of N^{12}, in each case divided by the allowed spectrum, should be a linear function of beta-ray energy,

$$R(E) \simeq 1 + \frac{16}{3} a E \tag{4.29}$$

where $(16/3)\, a \simeq 1.31 \times 10^{-2}$ Mev^{-1} — or 1.11×10^{-2} Mev^{-1} if we use Eq. (4.28). There is a radiative correction which lowers this value to $(1.1 \pm 0.2) \times 10^{-2}$. The experimental measurements of R(E) (Mayer-Kuckuk and Michel, 1961) gave a linear function of energy with a slope $(1.13 \pm 0.25) \times 10^{-2}$ Mev^{-1}, which is in good agreement with the predicted value. If $\Delta\mu = 0$ in Eq. (4.28), the theoretical value would be about one-fifth as large. Consequently the hypothesis of a conserved vector current seems established. On the experimental side there is perhaps a slight cause for concern in that the slopes of the separate spectra, divided by the allowed slope, did not follow Eq. (4.27) with $a = \pm 2.3/m$. Both spectra had correction factors with positive slope, B^{12} having 1.30×10^{-2} Mev^{-1} and N^{12} having 0.17×10^{-2} Mev^{-1}. The sceptic might argue that this behavior casts doubt on the numerical value of the difference of slopes which appears in R(E).

Another experiment to test the conserved vector current idea involves the (β, α) angular correlation in the decays of Li^8 and B^8 to an excited state of Be^8 which breaks up into two alphas (Bernstein and Lewis, 1958; Morita, 1959). The angular correlation is of the form $[1 + B(E) \cos^2\theta]$. The difference between B for Li^8 and B^8 is proportional to the beta particle's energy (actually to p^2/E), with a coefficient which depends on orbital and spin magnetic moment matrix elements. The most recent experimental data (Nordberg, Morinigo, Barnes, 1962) give

$$\Delta B = (7.0 \pm 1.2) \times 10^{-3}\, E_\beta(\text{Mev})$$

Careful theoretical calculations (Weidenmüller, 1960, 1960a) give a coefficient in the range 5. - 9. for the conserved vector current ($\Delta\mu = 3.71$), and 1.- 4. for the old theory ($\Delta\mu = 0$). Again we see that conservation of the vector current is confirmed, although the uncertainties in nuclear matrix elements and the smallness of the effect make the test less conclusive than the $N^{12} - B^{12}$ spectra.

The overall conclusion is that the hypothesis of a conserved vector current is in agreement with experiment. While further and more accurate tests would be desirable, we may take the structure of Eq. (4.11) as a correct representation of the nucleonic vector matrix element for all momentum transfers.

4.5 Mu-Meson Capture

Mu-meson capture is the least-known of the weak interactions involving ordinary particles ($\Delta S = 0$ processes). The reasons for our comparative ignorance—or better, our lack of very accurate information— are several. The process involves a reasonable momentum transfer ($q^2 \simeq m_\mu^2$) so that "forbidden" contributions to nuclear matrix elements are appreciable. This brings considerable uncertainty and complication into the theoretical calculation. On the experimental side, the products of muon capture are high-energy neutrinos and one or more neutrons and gamma rays from nuclear deexcitation. Consequently, the experimentalist must bring elaborate techniques to bear in order to make significant observations. In the last few years several crucial experiments have been performed and the situation is reasonably clear, although more accurate data are desirable.

The theory of muon capture has been treated in great detail by Primakoff and others (Primakoff, 1959; Fujii and Primakoff, 1959; Blokhintsev and Dolinskii, 1962). Consequently we shall only touch on some qualitative points. Treiman (1960) has a somewhat more detailed survey.

For some time it was not known whether the couplings in muon capture bore any resemblance to those in beta decay or muon decay. Such questions as whether there was a mixture of Fermi (S and V) and Gamow-Teller (T and A) lay beyond the experimental techniques available. Much work has been done on the total capture rate of negative muons in various nuclei, notably by Telegdi and coworkers at Chicago (e.g., Lathrop et al., 1961). These rates, including such things as the isotope effect (Cramer et al., 1962; Bertram et al., 1960), can be correlated in terms of a "closure-approximation" formula of Primakoff (1959). Telegdi (1962) has shown that these capture rates in complex nuclei demand the presence of Fermi and Gamow-Teller couplings with roughly equal strengths.

With the beta and muon decay couplings known to be V and A, it was natural to assume that the muon capture interaction involves the standard leptonic vector form for (μ,ν).

But the question still remained as to whether the nuclear coupling was a mixture of V and A, and if so, what mixture [e. g., (V - A) or (V + A)]? This question can be answered by looking at the spin dependence of the capture rate. Even though we know from Secs. 4. 1 and 4. 3 that strong interactions introduce extensive modifications in the matrix elements, we shall consider the simple (V - A) coupling as a phenomenological interaction for muon capture. This will give qualitatively correct conclusions. Thus we write

$$\mathcal{H}_{int} \simeq \frac{G}{\sqrt{2}}\left(\overline{\psi}_n \gamma_\alpha (1+\gamma_5)\psi_p\right)\left(\overline{\psi}_\nu \gamma_\alpha (1+\gamma_5)\psi_\mu\right) \tag{4.30}$$

for the interaction describing $\mu^- + p \rightarrow n + \nu$.

In order to exhibit the spin dependence of the capture rate, we apply the Fierz-Michel reordering theorem (Eq. 2. 8) to group the muon and the proton together. The result of this operation is

$$\mathcal{H}_{int} = \frac{2G}{\sqrt{2}}\left(\overline{\psi}_\nu (1-\gamma_5)\psi_n^c\right)\left(\overline{\psi}_p^c (1+\gamma_5)\psi_\mu\right) \tag{4.31}$$

Equation (4. 31) shows that the reordered coupling is S and P. This means that in the bound (μp) atom, capture must occur only from ^1S_o states, with $^3S_1$ capture entirely forbidden.

If the coupling of Eq. (4. 30) is changed to (V + A) by changing the sign of γ_5 in the ($\bar{n}$p) bracket, then Eq. (4. 31) is replaced by

$$\mathcal{H}'_{int} = -\frac{G}{\sqrt{2}}\left(\overline{\psi}_\nu \gamma_\alpha (1+\gamma_5)\psi_n^c\right)\left(\overline{\psi}_p^c \gamma_\alpha (1+\gamma_5)\psi_\mu\right) \tag{4.32}$$

giving (V - A) in the reordered form. Then capture in the (μp) atom occurs equally from the $^3S_1$ and ^1S_o states. *

---

*The ^1S_o capture involves the Fermi matrix element $|M_F|^2 = 1$, while the $^3S_1$ capture involves the Gamow-Teller matrix element $|M_{GT}|^2 = 3$, averaged over the initial spin.

These conclusions, based on Eqs. (4. 31) and (4. 32), have only qualitative validity. But it is clear that, if the muon capture coupling is predominantly (V - A), the capture rate should show a strong spin dependence favoring J = 0 capture. Detailed calculations, using the nuclear matrix elements of Eqs. (4. 11) and (4. 20), show that in hydrogen the ratio of $^1S_0$ to $^3S_1$ capture is about 50 [Primakoff, 1959, Eqs. (33a) and (33b)].

For heavier nuclei, the spin dependence (hyperfine effect) is diminished because all but a few of the protons which can capture the muon are in closed shells with spins paired off. For an odd Z, odd A nucleus with one proton of angular momentum L outside a spinless core, the difference in capture rates for the hyperfine states $F = I \pm 1/2$, divided by the average rate, can be shown very simply to be (Bernstein et al., 1958):

$$\frac{\Gamma_+ - \Gamma_-}{\Gamma_{av}} \simeq -\frac{1}{Z}\begin{cases} \dfrac{2I+1}{I} & \text{for } I = L + \frac{1}{2} \\ -\dfrac{2I+1}{I+1} & \text{for } I = L - \frac{1}{2} \end{cases} \tag{4.33}$$

Here I is the nuclear spin. The factor Z^{-1} takes into account the fact that only capture on the outside proton will show spin dependence. The numerical coefficient -1 comes from the assumption of exactly (V - A). Primakoff (1959) finds -0. 945 instead. The statistical factors are the differences in the expectation values of $\vec{\sigma}_p \cdot \vec{\sigma}_\mu$ in the two hyperfine states.

Telegdi and collaborators have performed an ingenious series of experiments on the time dependence of the various products which emerge upon muon capture in F^{19} (Winston and Telegdi, 1961; Culligan et al., 1961; Lundy et al., 1962). These studies show that the capture rate in F^{19} is spin-dependent, with the magnitude of the effect in agreement with Eq. (4. 33). F^{19} is a nucleus with spin I = 1/2 which can be thought of as a proton in an $s_{1/2}$ orbit outside a spinless core. Thus, this odd proton serves as an almost free proton on which to observe spin-dependent effects. The mu-meson - F^{19} system forms hyperfine states with F = 0 and F = 1, corresponding to the $^1S_0$ and $^3S_1$ states of the (μ, p) atom. These states are shown in Fig. 5. If the atom is formed in the upper F = 1 state, an Auger-type transition can occur with a rate R_C to the ground F = 0 state. This rate is found to be of the order of 3×10^6 sec^{-1} in fluorine.

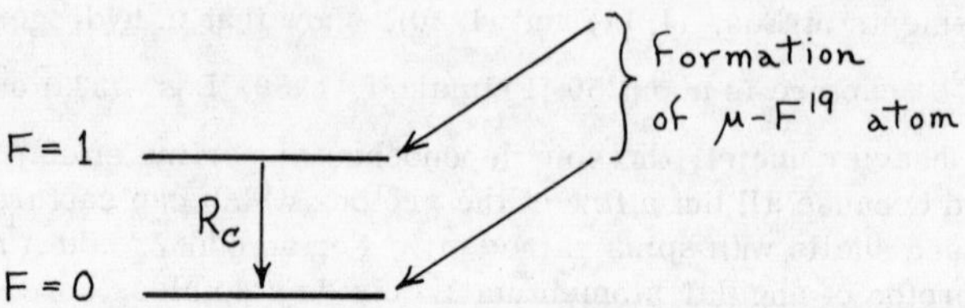

Fig. 5

Let us now make the extreme assumptions that the atoms are all formed in the F = 1 state and that all the capture occurs on the odd proton. If the interaction is (V - A), capture only occurs from the F = 0 state. This means that the temporal distribution of decay products will show a typical radioactive growth and decay curve appropriate to a "daughter" activity, as sketched in Fig. 6. The time t_o is related to the Auger conversion rate and the disappearance rate of muons. If the interaction were (V + A), no spin dependence would exist. The decay products would show a pure exponential dependence.

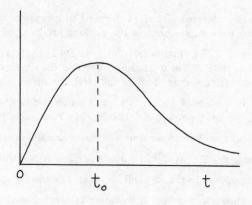

Fig. 6

In actual fact, the atoms are formed in both F states and the odd proton only contributes ~1/9 of the total rate. Consequently the growth and decay is actually only ~10 per cent of the total. But the experimental data, at times of order 0.1 to 0.6 μ sec, definitely show a growth of the decay products in time, proving the spin dependence of the capture rate, in accord with the (V - A) prediction of Eq. (4.33)—or better, with (Fermi) - (Gamow-Teller).

An experiment on the directional asymmetry of the electrons from the decay of mu mesons bound in silver and red and black phosphorus can be used, with certain assumptions, to infer a spin dependence in the capture rates of the same order as predicted by the (V - A) theory (Egorov et al., 1962; Ignatenko et al., 1962). But this experiment is less convincing than the work of the Chicago group on F^{19}.

4.6 Induced Pseudoscalar Coupling and Conserved Vector Current in Muon Capture

The data discussed in the previous section showed that the dominant coupling in muon capture can be taken as (V - A). Now the question arises as to the detailed structure, and as to whether the conserved vector current matrix element of Eq. (4.11) and the partially conserved axial-vector current matrix element, Eqs. (4.20) or (4.19), do indeed appear in muon capture.

The evidence for the presence of an induced pseudoscalar coupling of about the magnitude and sign given in Eq. (4.19) comes from the directional asymmetry of the product neutrons from the capture of polarized muons (see, for example, Blokhintsev and Dolinskii, 1962). In fact, the neutron asymmetry data, plus capture rates in complex nuclei, are consistent with (without proving) the expressions of Eqs. (4.11) and (4.19), with $f_A(0) \gtrsim 1$.

To confirm the magnitude of the couplings, accurate data on capture rates are needed. From the theoretical point of view, the lightest nuclei are best, with free protons being ideal. Unfortunately for experiment, the capture rate in hydrogen is very small relative to the decay rate, and the (μp) atom is involved in complicated atomic and molecular processes in liquid hydrogen. For heavier nuclei, the experiments are easier, but the theoretical uncertainties in the detailed nuclear physics are greater. The compromise ground involves capture in C^{12}, He^3, and H^1.

The capture rate in C^{12} for the formation of B^{12} in its ground state has been measured by various groups, the experimental values ranging from 6×10^3 sec^{-1} to 9×10^3 sec^{-1}. The most recent result seems to be $(6.31 \pm 0.24) \times 10^3$ sec^{-1} (Maier et al., 1961). The theoretical result, calculated on the basis of Eqs. (4.11) and (4.19), is 7.5×10^3 sec^{-1}. If the conserved vector current hypothesis is abandoned, the theoretical result is about 20 per cent smaller (that is, $6.0 \times 10^3\ sec^{-1}$).* The data on C^{12} therefore seem to imply absence of the conserved vector current.

Pontecorvo and coworkers have studied the capture of muons in He^3 with a diffusion chamber (Falomkin et al., 1962). The most recent result of this group (reported at the 1962 Geneva Conference) was that the rate for the process $\mu^- + He^3 \rightarrow H^3 + \nu$ is $(1.41 \pm 0.14) \times 10^3\ sec^{-1}$. Wolfenstein (at that same meeting) gave the best theoretical value for this rate as $(1.40 \pm 0.15) \times 10^3\ sec^{-1}$, although previous calculations have given values such as $1.56 \times 10^3\ sec^{-1}$ (Werntz, 1960) and $1.46 \times 10^3\ sec^{-1}$ (Fujii and Primakoff, 1959). Without the conserved vector current, the theoretical value would be roughly 15 per cent smaller. The theoretical value, based on Eqs. (4.11) and (4.19), is in embarrassingly good agreement with experiment.

The capture in hydrogen is of the greatest significance to the theorist. Three experiments have been performed with liquid hydrogen, one at Chicago (Hildebrand, 1962) and another at CERN, both with liquid hydrogen bubble chambers, and the third at Columbia (Bleser et al., 1962) with counters. The comparison of theory and experiment is given in Table 5.

Table 5

System	Theoretical rate (sec^{-1})	Observed rate (sec^{-1})
$(\mu p)_{F=0}$	636.	--
$(\mu p)_{F=1}$	13.	--
$(p\mu p)$	560.	515 ± 85 (Columbia)
$0.7\ (p\mu p) + 0.3\ (\mu p)$	583.	426 ± 60 (Chicago-CERN)

*Some theoretical estimates give the rate without the conserved vector current as $5 \times 10^3\ sec^{-1}$.

The theoretical atomic rates are calculated from Eqs. (4.11) and (4.19), with G of Eq. (4.2). The mu-mesonic molecular rate is calculated from the formula $\Gamma_{mol} = 2\gamma_0 [\eta\Gamma_0 + (1-\eta)\Gamma_1]$

where Γ_0 and Γ_1 are the F = 0 and F = 1 atomic capture rates, $2\gamma_0 = 1.17$ is the probability of finding the muon in the molecule at the site of a proton, relative to the atomic probability, and η is probability that the muon and a proton are in a singlet spin state. The value of η depends on the relative abundance of the ortho and para forms of the molecule and can be shown to be in the range $3/8 < \eta < 3/4$ (Weinberg, 1960a), with the expected value near the upper limit.

The Columbia result is in reasonable agreement with theory, while the combined Chicago-CERN value (quoted at the 1962 Geneva Conference) for the mixture of atomic and molecular captures appropriate for the bubble chamber is somewhat lower than theory. Clearly more accurate data are required to make a detailed verification of the magnitude of coupling constants. But already the sign (V - A) can be established independently here, since (V + A) can be shown to give a molecular rate less than 200. sec^{-1}.

The present status of muon capture theory and experiment is that the presence of Fermi and Gamow-Teller couplings, the strong spin dependence of the capture process, the neutron asymmetries, and the absolute capture rates are all consistent with the (V - A) theory with a conserved vector current and the induced pseudoscalar coupling. But it should be kept in mind that for the moment other interpretations are possible. For example, if additional adronic currents which transform under G conjugation oppositely to Eq. (3.34) are assumed to be present, there will be six form factors [Eqs. (3.33)], instead of four. The added contributions may be as large as the weak magnetism and induced pseudoscalar parts (Adams, 1962).

5. SOME ASPECTS OF THE DECAYS OF STRANGE PARTICLES

Apart from our phenomenological discussions in Chapter 1, we have said nothing so far about the decays of strange particles. The previous chapters have been devoted to decay processes with $\Delta S = 0$. A reasonably clear picture as to the structure of the $\Delta S = 0$ interactions has been established, at least for small momentum transfers. When we turn to the $\Delta S \neq 0$ decay processes, we find a much less satisfactory state of affairs. There are several reasons for this: On the experimental side, there are generally far fewer events of any given type observed than for the decays of ordinary particles, while from the point of view of theory, the large momentum transfers and the presence of adrons only in many decays complicates the theoretical description.

In the time available, we shall be unable to cover, even superficially, all the K-meson and hyperon decay modes. Consistent with our previous policy of discussing some topics thoroughly, rather than all topics briefly, we shall concentrate on only a few problems. It is hoped that the reader will be able to apply the attitudes and techniques he has learned to the neglected topics. A guide to some of the topics not covered appears in Chapter 6. The reviews of Dalitz (1959, 1959a), Gell-Mann and Rosenfeld (1957), and Okun' (1959) cover various aspects of the older literature.

It is natural to try to discuss the decays of K mesons and hyperons within the framework of a 4-fermion or current-current interaction. From the existence of strong directional asymmetries and longitudinal polarizations, we know that parity is not conserved in these decays. In fact, it was the $\tau - \theta$ puzzle of K-meson decay which led to the prediction of parity nonconservation by Lee and Yang. Further, decays like $K^+ \rightarrow \mu^+ + \nu$ appear in all respects the same as the corresponding decay, $\pi^+ \rightarrow \mu^+ + \nu$. We saw in Sec. 3.1 that the rates for $K_{\mu 2}$ and K_{e2} were consistent with the vector leptonic coupling of Eq. (3.25), just as for the pion. Observation of the longitudinal polarization of the muons from $K_{\mu 2}$ decay shows that it is the same as for pion decay (Coombes et al., 1957). With this type of evidence available, we shall attempt to pattern the interaction for $\Delta S \neq 0$ as closely as possible after the $\Delta S = 0$ forms of Chapters 2, 3, and 4.

5.1 Lambda Decay

To illustrate the use of our previous experience as a guide, we consider a phenomenological description of lambda decay, $\Lambda \rightarrow p + \pi^-$. Because the pion is a spinless boson, the Feynman amplitude for the decay can be written

$$\mathcal{M}_\Lambda = \bar{u}_p (a + b\gamma_5) u_\Lambda \tag{5.1}$$

The presence of $a \neq 0$ allows for nonconservation of parity in the decay.

The structure of Eq. (5.1), while completely general, does not reflect our experience from $\Delta S = 0$ decays. In an analogy with those processes, we expect a baryonic coupling of the vector form $[\bar{\psi}_p \gamma_\alpha (1 + \gamma_5) \psi_\Lambda]$. Consequently, we would write the alternative form for $\mathcal{M}$:

$$\mathcal{M}_\Lambda \simeq i\frac{G}{\sqrt{2}} m_\pi f_\Lambda Q_\alpha \left(\bar{u}_p \gamma_\alpha (1+\gamma_5) u_\Lambda\right) \tag{5.2}$$

where Q_α is the 4-momentum of the negative pion. This matrix element must be viewed as very approximate since the renormalization effects of strong interactions have been ignored completely. Note that this is exactly the same structure as the amplitude of Eq. (4.12) for $\pi \to \mu + \nu$. Equation (5.2) is equivalent to Eq. (5.1) with $b/a = -(m_\Lambda + m_p)/(m_\Lambda - m_p) \simeq -11.6$. A very simple calculation with Eq. (5.1) shows that the angular distribution of the pions relative to the spin direction of the Λ is

$$dw \sim \left(1 + \alpha \langle \vec{\sigma}_\Lambda \rangle \cdot \frac{\vec{Q}}{Q}\right) d\Omega \tag{5.3}$$

while the longitudinal polarization of the protons is

$$P_{long} = -\alpha \tag{5.4}$$

where

$$\alpha = \frac{\mathrm{Re}(b/a)}{1 + \frac{Q^2}{4m_p^2}|b/a|^2}\left(\frac{Q}{m_p}\right) \tag{5.5}$$

The asymmetry parameter α can be interpreted physically as $2\,\mathrm{Re}\,(sp^*)/(|s|^2 + |p|^2)$ where s and p are the $s_{1/2}$ and $p_{1/2}$ decay amplitudes. With the value $(b/a) = -11.6$ from Eq. (5.2) and $|\vec{Q}| \simeq 100$. Mev/c, we find $\alpha \simeq -0.90$. Thus we anticipate a large directional asymmetry in lambda decay, with the decay protons having a large positive helicity.

The large directional asymmetry was verified experimentally many years ago, but the existence and sign of the proton helicity was initially in doubt. Recent experiments all agree on positive helicity, with $\alpha = -0.67^{+0.18}_{-0.24}$ (Beall et al., 1962), $\alpha = -0.75^{+0.50}_{-0.15}$ (Leitner et al.,

1961), $\alpha = -0.67\,^{+0.36}_{-0.29}$ (Gray et al., 1962), $\alpha = -0.62 \pm 0.07$ (Cronin and Overseth, 1962 Geneva Conference). These values of α correspond to $b/a \simeq -7 \pm 1$ in Eq. (5.1), or to a factor $(1 + 0.6\,\gamma_5)$ in Eq. (5.2), instead of $(1 + \gamma_5)$. This difference indicates the magnitude of renormalization effects from the strong interactions. The observed rate of $2.5 \times 10^9\ \mathrm{sec}^{-1}$ can be used to calculate the dimensionless constant f_Λ in Eq. (5.2). The result is $f_\Lambda \simeq 1.52$, as compared with $f_\pi \simeq 0.94$ from pion decay. Again, we find reasonable renormalization effects.

For the other lambda-decay mode ($\Lambda \to n + \pi^0$) we expect similar results; in fact, a perturbation calculation would give the same asymmetry parameter α and a relative rate equal to 1/2 of the $(p\pi^-)$ mode (from the $\sqrt{2}\,g_\pi$ for $\pi^\pm$ emission and g_π for π^0 emission from nucleons). It happens that the sign and the rough magnitude of α for the neutral mode is the same as for the charged mode (1.0 ± 0.27), and the relative rate is 0.55 ± 0.04 (Humphrey and Ross, 1962).

5.2 $\Delta S \neq 0$ Currents; $\Delta Q = \Delta S$ and $\Delta Q = -\Delta S$

While we should not take these agreements too seriously because of the simplicity of our starting point, Eq. (5.2), we can use them to argue for $\Delta S \neq 0$ currents of the form

$$(p, \Lambda) \equiv \left(\overline{\psi}_p \gamma_\alpha (1 + \gamma_5) \psi_\Lambda\right) \tag{5.6}$$

In Eq. (5.6) we have introduced a convenient abbreviation. Note that a particle symbol on the left (right) of the comma creates (destroys) that particle.*

For certain models of strong interactions, such as the Sakata model, Eqs. (5.6) and (3.31) and the lepton current of Eq. (3.29) are all the currents possible (Okun', 1959). But for less restrictive models we can ask about additional $\Delta S \neq 0$ currents. Evidently, some possibilities are

---

*For bosons, the notation is

$$(a, b) = i\left(\frac{\partial a^\dagger}{\partial x_\alpha} b - a^\dagger \frac{\partial b}{\partial x_\alpha}\right)$$

$$(p,\Lambda),\ (p,\Sigma^0),\ (n,\Sigma^-),\ (\pi^0,K^-),\ (\pi^+,\overline{K}^0),\ \cdots \tag{5.7}$$

or

$$(n,\Sigma^+),\ (\Sigma^-,\Xi^0),\ (K^0,\pi^+),\ \cdots \tag{5.8}$$

or

$$(n,\Lambda),\ (\Sigma^-,\Xi^-),\ (\pi^0,\overline{K}^0),\ \cdots \tag{5.9}$$

All the currents have been written with $\Delta S = +1$ (the adjoint will give $\Delta S = -1$). But the first set, expression (5.7), has $\Delta Q = +1$, in analogy with Eq. (5.6), while the second and third sets have $\Delta Q = -1$ and $\Delta Q = 0$.

It has commonly been assumed that only currents of the type (5.7), with $\Delta Q = +\Delta S$, occur in nature. Such currents, in combination with the $\Delta S = 0$ currents and strong interactions, provide for observed processes such as

$$\begin{aligned}
\Lambda &\rightarrow p + l^- + \nu\\
\Sigma^- &\rightarrow n + l^- + \nu\\
\Lambda &\rightarrow N + \pi\\
\Sigma &\rightarrow N + \pi\\
K &\rightarrow \pi + \pi\\
K^\pm &\rightarrow \pi^0 + l^\pm + \nu\\
K^0 &\rightarrow \pi^- + l^+ + \nu
\end{aligned}$$

If only $\Delta Q = +\ \Delta S$ currents exist, $|\Delta S| > 1$ decays are forbidden. Furthermore, the following processes are forbidden:

$$\begin{aligned}
\Sigma^+ &\rightarrow n + l^+ + \nu\\
K^0 &\rightarrow \pi^+ + l^- + \nu
\end{aligned} \tag{5.10}$$

These can occur only via interactions with $\Delta Q = -\Delta S$.

Recently the assumption of only $\Delta Q = +\Delta S$ currents has apparently been contradicted by fact. One event of $\Sigma^+ \to n + \ell^+ + \nu$ has been observed (Galtieri et al., 1962). While it is quite right to regard one event as inconclusive, this particular example is extremely difficult to interpret in any other way. Further, an experiment on K^0's decaying into $(\pi^\pm + \ell^\mp + \nu)$ indicates comparable numbers of π^+ and π^-, in disagreement with the prediction that only π^- should appear (Ely et al., 1962). In addition, a similar Berkeley experiment disagrees with the predictions of the $\Delta Q = +\Delta S$ rule (Alexander, Almeida, and Crawford, 1962). Both these experiments involve limited statistics. Consequently, the prudent man will perhaps sit on the fence, being ready to accept the breakdown of the $\Delta Q = +\Delta S$ rule, but not ready to bet his life on its violation. (See Sec. 5.3 for the detailed arguments.)

The problem of $\Delta Q = \pm\Delta S$ is related to the so-called $\Delta T = 1/2$ rule. It was observed in Sec. 1.1 that, for $\Delta S = \pm 1$ decays, the z component of isotopic spin changed according to $\Delta T_z = \pm 1/2$. But this can be seen to be connected with the requirement $\Delta Q = +\Delta S$. For the processes described in the preceding paragraph, $\Delta T_z = \pm 3/2$.

It is attractive to see whether the weak-interaction currents transform in isospin space according to some definite value of ΔT (e.g., $\Delta T = 1/2$, or $\Delta T = 3/2$), as well as ΔT_z. It is clear that $\Delta T \geqslant \Delta T_z$; hence, for $\Delta Q = +\Delta S$ currents, we can have $\Delta T = 1/2, 3/2, \ldots$. But for $\Delta Q = -\Delta S$, the minimum value is $\Delta T = 3/2$. The presence of decay processes such as

$$\begin{aligned} &\Lambda \to p + e^- + \nu \\ &K^+ \to \mu^+ + \nu \end{aligned} \tag{5.11}$$

where $\Delta T = 1/2$ is the only allowed value, shows that the $\Delta Q = +\Delta S$ interactions involve some part which satisfies $\Delta T = 1/2$. The question of whether there is some part with $\Delta T = 3/2$, or higher, can be answered in principle by studying decay processes which can have $\Delta T = 1/2$ and/or $\Delta T = 3/2$. For example,

$$\begin{aligned} &K^+ \to \pi^0 + \ell^+ + \nu \\ &K^0 \to \pi^- + \ell^+ + \nu \end{aligned} \tag{5.12}$$

Before discussing this example in detail, we wish to make two points about the possible existence of both $\Delta Q = +\Delta S$ and $\Delta Q = -\Delta S$

interactions. The combination gives rise to $|\Delta S| = 2$ decay processes, such as $\Xi \rightarrow N + \pi$. So far these have not been observed. The other related point involves the $K_1^o - K_2^o$ mass difference. This mass difference is known experimentally to be $|\Delta m| \simeq 1.5\ \hbar/\tau_1 c^2$, where τ_1 is the K_1^o lifetime (10^{-10} sec). [Good et al. (1961) found 0.84 + 0.25 in units of $\hbar/\tau_1 c^2$; Fitch, Piroué, and Perkins (1961) found 1.9 ± 0.3; Camerini et al. (1962) found 1.5 ± 0.2.] The order of magnitude of the mass difference is very reasonable if $|\Delta S| = 1$ decays are all that occur, but it is much smaller than expected if $|\Delta S| = 2$ transitions are possible. The theoretical argument, originally due to Okun' and Pontecorvo, is that $\Delta m \simeq 2 \langle K^o | \text{interaction} | \bar{K}^o \rangle$, where the matrix element is the coupling between K^o and $\bar{K}^o$ produced by the weak interactions. Since K^o and $\bar{K}^o$ have $\Delta S = 2$, the matrix element will be second order in the weak couplings if only $|\Delta S| = 1$ transitions are allowed. The decay rate is also second order. Consequently, $|\Delta m| \sim \hbar/\tau_1 c^2$ is reasonable. But if $|\Delta S| = 2$ transitions occur, the mass difference will be first order in the weak couplings, while the decay rate is still second order. Then a mass splitting of the order of 10^6 times that observed would be reasonable.

Thus, the lack of evidence for $|\Delta S| = 2$ transitions and the observed $K_1^o - K_2^o$ mass difference both argue for the absence of $\Delta Q = -\Delta S$ currents in combination with $\Delta Q = +\Delta S$ interactions. One qualifying remark needs to be made. If the $|\Delta S| = 2$ transitions are only leptonic, then the mass difference will again be second order in the weak couplings. This hypothesis is consistent with the known facts, since the evidence for $\Delta Q = -\Delta S$ transitions involves leptonic modes.

5.3 Isospin and Time-Reversal Properties in $K \rightarrow \pi + \ell + \nu$

As an example of the isospin character of the weak interactions, we shall consider the three-body leptonic modes of K mesons. We first assume that only $\Delta Q = +\Delta S$ transitions occur. This means that we wish to make predictions about the relative rates of

$$K^+ \rightarrow \pi^o + \ell^+ + \nu$$
$$K^o \rightarrow \pi^- + \ell^+ + \nu$$
$$\bar{K}^o \rightarrow \pi^+ + \ell^- + \nu \qquad (5.13)$$

or the exponentially decaying states, K_1^o and K_2^o.

The possible values of ΔT are $\Delta T = 1/2,\ 3/2$. To see the consequences of assuming the dominance of one or the other of these values, we use the "spurion" trick of Wentzel. We consider the equivalent processes,

$$K^+ + \pi^o \rightarrow \ell^+ + \nu$$
$$K^o + \pi^+ \rightarrow \ell^+ + \nu$$

and write out the product wave functions of $(K\pi)$ as linear combinations of states with $T = 1/2$ and $3/2$:

$$K^+\pi^o = -\frac{1}{\sqrt{3}}\Phi\left(\tfrac{1}{2},\tfrac{1}{2}\right) + \sqrt{\frac{2}{3}}\Phi\left(\tfrac{3}{2},\tfrac{1}{2}\right)$$

$$K^o\pi^+ = \sqrt{\frac{2}{3}}\Phi\left(\tfrac{1}{2},\tfrac{1}{2}\right) + \frac{1}{\sqrt{3}}\Phi\left(\tfrac{3}{2},\tfrac{1}{2}\right) \qquad (5.14)$$

Here $\Phi(T,\ T_z)$ is the isospin state with eigenvalues T and T_z.

If the decay amplitudes for $\Delta T = 1/2,\ 3/2$ are denoted by A_1 and A_3, respectively, then the rates can be written

$$\Gamma(K^+ \rightarrow \pi^o \ell^+ \nu) = \left| -\frac{1}{\sqrt{3}}A_1 + \sqrt{\frac{2}{3}}A_3 \right|^2$$

$$\Gamma(K^o \rightarrow \pi^- \ell^+ \nu) = \left| \sqrt{\frac{2}{3}}A_1 + \frac{1}{\sqrt{3}}A_3 \right|^2 \qquad (5.15)$$

If the transition proceeds entirely via $\Delta T = 1/2$, the relative rate will be

$$\frac{\Gamma(K^o \rightarrow \pi^- \ell^+ \nu)}{\Gamma(K^+ \rightarrow \pi^o \ell^+ \nu)} = 2 \qquad (5.16)$$

For a pure $\Delta T = 3/2$ transition, the ratio is 0.5. For a mixture, any ratio is possible.

The rates for neutral K-meson decay are most profitably discussed in terms of the eigenstates of CP, namely,

$$K_1^0 = \frac{1}{\sqrt{2}}(K^0 + \overline{K}^0)$$

$$K_2^0 = \frac{1}{\sqrt{2}}(K^0 - \overline{K}^0) \tag{5.17}$$

These linear combinations have eigenvalues of CP = $\pm$ 1. The short-lived K_1^0 decays predominantly into 2 pions, with some three-body leptonic component. The long-lived K_2^0 is forbidden by CP or time-reversal invariance to decay into 2 pions and decays via 3π's or $(\pi \ell \nu)$, as indicated in Appendix A.

With the assumption of $\Delta Q = + \Delta S$ transitions, the decay of K_1^0 and K_2^0 into $(\pi^- \ell^+ \nu)$ comes only from the K^0 parts in Eq. (5.17). Thus the matrix elements are related by

$$\langle \pi^- \ell^+ \nu | K_1^0 \rangle = \langle \pi^- \ell^+ \nu | K_2^0 \rangle = \frac{1}{\sqrt{2}} \langle \pi^- \ell^+ \nu | K^0 \rangle \tag{5.18}$$

Similarly,

$$\langle \pi^+ \ell^- \nu | K_1^0 \rangle = -\langle \pi^+ \ell^- \nu | K_2^0 \rangle = \frac{1}{\sqrt{2}} \langle \pi^+ \ell^- \nu | \overline{K}^0 \rangle \tag{5.19}$$

With K_1^0 and K_2^0 being eigenstates of CP, the CP or time-reversal invariance of weak interactions can be used to show that the rates for $K_1^0 \rightarrow \pi^+ \ell^- \nu$ and $K_1^0 \rightarrow \pi^- \ell^+ \nu$ are equal, as are the rates for $K_2^0 \rightarrow \pi^+ \ell^- \nu$ and $K_2^0 \rightarrow \pi^- \ell^+ \nu$. Experimental data on the K_2^0 three-body leptonic modes yield relative rates of $\Gamma(K_2^0 \rightarrow \pi^- e^+ \nu)/\Gamma(K_2^0 \rightarrow \pi^+ e^- \nu) = 1.16 \pm 0.17$ (Luers et al., 1961) and $\Gamma(K_2^0 \rightarrow \pi^- \ell^+ \nu)/$

$\Gamma(K_2^o \rightarrow \pi^+ \ell^- \nu) = 0.90 \pm 0.18$ (Anikina et al., 1962). Hence, the data are consistent with CP invariance. A further confirmation of time-reversal invariance is the result of Anikina et al. (1962), that no 2π events were seen in 597 K_2^o decays.

If we denote the total rate for $K_i^o \rightarrow \pi^+ \ell^- \nu$ plus $K_i^o \rightarrow \pi^- \ell^+ \nu$ as $\Gamma(K_i^o \rightarrow \pi^\pm \ell^\mp \nu)$, we have the following relations from combining Eqs. (5.16), (5.18), and (5.19):

$$\Gamma(K_1^o \rightarrow \pi^\pm \ell^\mp \nu) = \Gamma(K_2^o \rightarrow \pi^\pm \ell^\mp \nu) = 2\Gamma(K^+ \rightarrow \pi^o \ell^+ \nu) \tag{5.20}$$

The first equality (from the left) depends on CP invariance and the $\Delta Q = + \Delta S$ rule. The second equality depends on the $\Delta T = 1/2$ rule.

The right-hand side of Eq. (5.20) can be compared with experiment. From Appendix A we see that $2\Gamma(K^+ \rightarrow \pi^o \ell^+ \nu) \simeq 16 \times 10^6 \text{ sec}^{-1}$, while $\Gamma(K_2^o \rightarrow \pi^\pm \ell^\mp \nu) \simeq 12 \times 10^6 \text{ sec}^{-1}$. The over-all errors amount to perhaps 20 per cent for the K^+ and 30 per cent for the K_2^o data; consequently, the data are consistent with Eq. (5.20). In detail, Neagu et al. (1961, 1961a) found $\Gamma(K_2^o \rightarrow \pi^\pm e^\mp \nu) = (6.2 \pm 2.0) \times 10^6 \text{ sec}^{-1}$, as compared to $2\Gamma(K^+ \rightarrow \pi^o e^+ \nu) = (8.4 \pm 1.2) \times 10^6 \text{ sec}^{-1}$. Similar results were found by Luers et al. (1961). These experiments are relatively inaccurate; hence it is not possible to exclude an appreciable admixture of $\Delta T = 3/2$ in the decay, although a pure $\Delta T = 3/2$ transition can be ruled out.

The experiments by Ely et al. (1962) and by Alexander, Almeida, and Crawford (1962) bear on the first equality in Eq. (5.20). These workers find the equality grossly violated; that is,

$$\frac{\Gamma(K_1^o \rightarrow \pi^\pm \ell^\mp \nu)}{\Gamma(K_2^o \rightarrow \pi^\pm \ell^\mp \nu)} = \begin{cases} 11.9\,^{+7.5}_{-5.6} & \text{(Ely et al.)} \\ 6.6\,^{+6.0}_{-4.0} & \text{(Alexander et al.)} \end{cases} \tag{5.21}$$

But their statistical accuracy is rather low. Needless to say, the agreement between K^+ and K_2^o data of the previous paragraph cannot be argued to support the $\Delta T = 1/2$ rule if these K_1^o - K_2^o data are taken into account. In terms of $(\Delta T, \Delta T_z)$ amplitudes, the result of Eq. (5.21) implies the existence of at least (1/2, 1/2) and (3/2, 3/2) amplitudes. The presence of some (3/2, 1/2) contribution cannot be excluded. In addition to a violation of the left-hand side of Eq. (5.20), Alexander, Almeida, and Crawford found that $\Gamma(K_2^o \rightarrow \pi^{\pm} \ell^{\mp} \nu) \simeq \Gamma(K^+ \rightarrow \pi^o \ell^+ \nu)$, reinforcing their argument for amplitudes other than (1/2, 1/2).

Sachs and Treiman (1962) have given a theoretical discussion of the time dependence of these three-body leptonic modes of K_1^o and K_2^o, with special attention to the question of a violation of time-reversal invariance. The present data cannot be used to argue this point.

5.4 $\Delta T = 1/2$ Rule

Apart from the recent, and not completely conclusive, evidence just discussed, the $\Delta T = 1/2$ rule has had a rather remarkable success in predicting branching ratios, especially for decays which involve only adrons. Take, as an example, the lambda decays,

$$\begin{aligned} \Lambda &\rightarrow p + \pi^- \\ \Lambda &\rightarrow n + \pi^o \end{aligned} \tag{5.22}$$

Because lambda isospin is zero, it is convenient to add the "spurion" to it. This means that we write the $(N\pi)$ systems as linear combinations of $T = 1/2$ and $T = 3/2$ states:

$$\begin{aligned} (p\pi^-) &= -\sqrt{\tfrac{2}{3}}\,\Phi(\tfrac{1}{2},-\tfrac{1}{2}) + \tfrac{1}{\sqrt{3}}\,\Phi(\tfrac{3}{2},-\tfrac{1}{2}) \\ (n\pi^o) &= \tfrac{1}{\sqrt{3}}\,\Phi(\tfrac{1}{2},-\tfrac{1}{2}) + \sqrt{\tfrac{2}{3}}\,\Phi(\tfrac{3}{2},-\tfrac{1}{2}) \end{aligned} \tag{5.23}$$

Then, with the same notation as in Eqs. (5.14) and (5.15), we find

$$\frac{\Gamma(\Lambda \to p\pi^-)}{\Gamma(\Lambda \to n\pi^0)} = \frac{|\sqrt{2}A_1 - A_3|^2}{|A_1 + \sqrt{2}A_3|^2} \tag{5.24}$$

Experimentally, the ratio is 1.80 ± 0.13 (Humphrey and Ross, 1962), $2.5^{+1.5}_{-0.7}$ (Baglin et al., 1960), in accord with the assumption that $|A_1| >> |A_3|$.

Other predictions of the $\Delta T = 1/2$ rule, such as the strong inhibition of $K^+ \to \pi^+\pi^0$ relative to $K_1^0 \to \pi\pi$, and the relative rates for $K_1^0 \to \pi^+\pi^-$ and $K_1^0 \to \pi^0\pi^0$, are well known. For $\Sigma \to N + \pi$ decays, the rule predicts the Gell-Mann—Rosenfeld triangle (Gell-Mann and Rosenfeld, 1957), with its statement that $\Gamma(\Sigma^+ \to p\pi^0) \simeq \Gamma(\Sigma^+ \to n\pi^+) \simeq \Gamma(\Sigma^- \to n\pi^-)$. Humphrey and Ross (1962) find the first two rates equal to within 5 per cent. As shown in Appendix A, the partial rates are all very nearly equal. The triangle itself is in less satisfactory condition. Recent data (Tripp, Watson, and Ferro-Luzzi, 1962) give asymmetry parameters, akin to α_Λ in Eq. (5.3),

$$\begin{aligned} \alpha(\Sigma^+ \to p\pi^0) &= 0.78 \pm 0.08 \\ \alpha(\Sigma^+ \to n\pi^+) &= 0.05 \pm 0.08 \\ \alpha(\Sigma^- \to n\pi^-) &= 0.16 \pm 0.21 \end{aligned} \tag{5.25}$$

The triangle (which is made up of the decay amplitudes plotted on an Argand diagram with $s_{1/2}$ and $p_{1/2}$ amplitudes as the real and imaginary parts) has two sides almost at right angles, one nearly parallel to the real axis and the other nearly parallel the imaginary axis. The hypotenuse of the would-be triangle (the amplitude for $\Sigma^+ \to p\pi^0$) will only close the triangle if $\alpha \simeq 1.0$. The experimental value of 0.78 ± 0.08 violates this requirement.

Because of the evidence, both consistent with and contradictory to the $\Delta T = 1/2$ rule, it is worthwhile to note that (1) it has no sound theoretical justification; (2) some of its predictions follow also from schemes such as the Sakata model which involve an interaction

$(\bar{p}\Lambda)(\bar{n}p)$ that has both $\Delta T = 1/2$ and $\Delta T = 3/2$ parts* (Okubo, Marshak, and Sudarshan, 1959; Sawyer, 1958); (3) some of the tests are insensitive to violations of the rule because of the detailed dynamics, for example, the slopes of the energy spectra of the odd pion in τ and τ' decay (Sawyer and Wali, 1960; Weinberg, 1960; Ferro-Luzzi et al., 1961); (4) its rigorous application to the current-current interaction necessitates the presence of neutral currents, Eq. (5.9), for which there is no experimental evidence.

5.5 Charged K-Meson Branching Ratios

$K^{\pm}$ mesons decay into six different decay modes with significant intensities. These are summarized in Appendix A, but we wish to go into a little more detail on the experimental branching ratios. Table 6 lists the results of five experiments, two on K^+ decays and three on K^- decays.

Table 6

Reference	Type	$K_{\mu 2}$	$K_{\pi 2}$	τ	τ'	$K_{\mu 3}$	K_{e3}
Barkas et al., 1961	K^- emulsion	57 ± 7	26 ± 7	0 ± 2	3 ± 2	9 ± 4	5 ± 3
Bhowmik, Jain, Mathur, 1961	K^- emulsion	56 ± 13	33 ± 9	0 ± 2	3 ± 3	6 ± 3	3 ± 2
Lichtman et al., 1962	K^- He b. c.	57 ± 4	26 ± 4	5.7 ± 0.5	← 12 ± 2 →		
Bøggild et al., 1961**	K^+ emulsion	59 ± 3	22 ± 3	7.1 ± 0.4	2.4 ± 0.4	5.5 ± 1.1	4.7 ± 1.1
Roe et al., 1961	K^+ Xe b. c.	64.2 ± 1.3	18.6 ± 0.9	5.7 ± 0.3	1.7 ± 0.2	4.8 ± 0.6	5.0 ± 0.5

---

*It turns out that $A_3 \simeq -2\sqrt{2}\,A_1$, so that in Eq. (5.24) the mixture predicts a ratio of 2.0, just as for $|A_1| >> |A_3|$.

**These data are combined results of several emulsion groups.

The relative branching ratios are given as percentages. The reader will notice that there is over-all agreement among the different experiments, but that the recent measurements on K^- in a helium bubble chamber and on K^+ in a Xenon chamber seem to disagree outside stated errors on the relative amounts of the dominant modes, $K_{\mu 2}$ and $K_{\pi 2}$. The values given in Appendix A represent some sort of compromise.

It is possible in a crude way to understand some of the relative rates in Table 6 on the basis of phase space arguments alone, although it will be seen from Table 1 for $K_{\mu 2}$ and $K_{\pi 2}$ that the effective coupling strengths differ significantly. But the relative rates of τ and τ' can, in theory at least, be understood by calculations on the strong-interaction dynamics.

For the K_{e3} and $K_{\mu 3}$ modes, the presence of a lepton pair in each gives hope that the two modes can be related closely. Since they are three-body modes there are spectra and angular or energy correlations available for study, as well as leptonic polarizations. These decay modes differ from the three-body muon decay or the neutron decay in that they involve strongly interacting particles (K and π) with a large energy release. This means that strong interaction effects in the form factors can be explored over a sizable range of momentum transfers.

In Sec. 5.3 we discussed the isospin nature of the three-body leptonic modes. In the following sections we shall consider only the $K^+_{\ell 3}$ modes, concentrating on the kinematic and dynamic effects produced by the strong interactions.

5.6 General Form of the $K_{\ell 3}$ Decay Amplitude*

The decay mode $K^{\pm} \rightarrow \pi^0 + \ell^{\pm} + \nu$ can be described by a Feynman amplitude whose general form is restricted by Lorentz invariance, time-reversal invariance, and the leptonic coupling in a manner already discussed in Sec. 3.4. As usual, we shall assume a local leptonic coupling $[\bar{\ell} O_i (1 + \gamma_5) \nu]$ but shall not immediately restrict the interaction to the vector form. The assumption of locality holds true for beta, muon, and pion decays, and so should have at least approximate validity here.

---

*This and subsequent sections are a somewhat shortened, revised, and updated version of a series of lectures entitled "Leptonic Decay Modes of K Mesons" given by the author at Argonne National Laboratory, April–May, 1961.

The Feynman amplitude will involve a finite number of form factors which, because of the three particles in the final state, will be functions of the momentum transfer to the leptons. The diagram of Fig. 7 indicates the different variables.

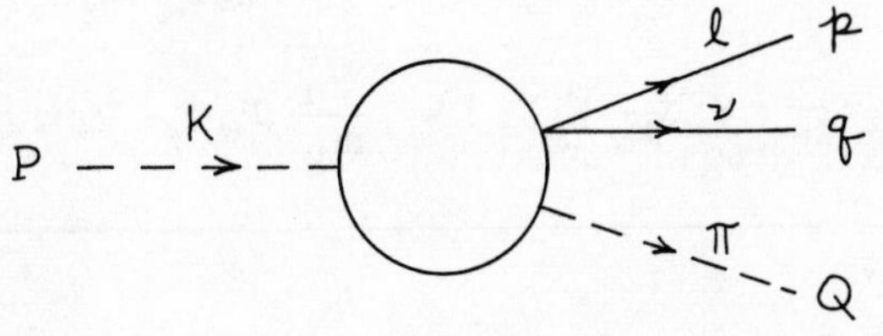

Fig. 7

The momentum transfer is $P - Q = p + q$. The form factors will be functions of $s = -(P - Q)^2 = m_K^2 + m_\pi^2 + 2\,P \cdot Q$. In the rest frame of the K meson, $P \cdot Q = -m_K Q_0$. Thus the form factors are functions of the total pion energy Q_0 in the center-of-momentum frame.

On Lorentz invariance grounds, the amplitude can be written in the general form of Eq. (3.1):

$$\mathcal{M} = \frac{G}{\sqrt{2}} \sum_j F_j \left(\bar{u}_\ell(p) O_j (1+\gamma_5) u_\nu(q)\right) \tag{5.26}$$

As in Sec. 3.1, the various possibilities for F_j can be enumerated for $O_j = S, V, T$. With the understanding that the form factors f_i are scalar functions of s, we have the data in Table 7.

Table 7

Interaction	O_j	$F_j O_j$
Scalar	1	$m_K f_S$
Vector	γ_α	$i(f_1 P_\alpha + f_2 Q_\alpha)$
Tensor	$\sigma_{\alpha\beta} = \frac{1}{2i}(\gamma_\alpha \gamma_\beta - \gamma_\beta \gamma_\alpha)$	$\frac{if_T}{m_K}(P_\alpha Q_\beta - P_\beta Q_\alpha)\sigma_{\alpha\beta}$

(5. 27)

In the scalar and tensor forms, factors of m_K have been inserted in order to make all the f's dimensionless. The f's are real if the interaction is invariant under time reversal.

If one wishes to be general and drop the requirement of $(1 + \gamma_5)$ in the lepton bracket, there will be a total of eight form factors for $K^{\pm}$ decay and another eight for K^0 decay. Thus the most general form will involve 16 complex amplitudes. It seems reasonable, however, to use $(1 + \gamma_5)$ and CP invariance to restrict the number to four real form factors each for the charged and neutral decays ($\Delta T = 1/2$ rule can give relations between the charged and neutral ones).

The equations of motion [e. g., $(i\gamma \cdot p + m_\ell) u_\ell(p) = 0$] can be used to simplify slightly the matrix element. Thus we get

$$\mathcal{M} = \frac{G}{\sqrt{2}} \left(\bar{u}_\ell(p) [\quad] (1 + \gamma_5) u_\nu(q) \right) \tag{5. 28}$$

where the square bracket is the operator,

$$[\quad] = m_K f_S + (f_1 + f_2) i\gamma \cdot P + m_\ell f_2 +$$

$$+ \frac{f_T}{2m_K}\left(\gamma\cdot P\,\gamma\cdot Q - \gamma\cdot Q\,\gamma\cdot P\right)$$

In the rest frame of the K meson this becomes

$$[\ \ ] = m_K\left\{\left(f_S + \frac{m_\ell}{m_K} f_2\right) - (f_1 + f_2)\gamma_4 + \frac{i f_T}{m_K}\gamma_4 \vec{\gamma}\cdot\vec{Q}\right\}$$

There appear to be <u>three</u> distinct operator forms here (1, γ_4, $\gamma_4\vec{\gamma}\cdot\vec{Q}$). But the equations of motion allow us to reduce [ ] in the rest frame to the following:

$$[\ \ ] = m_K\left\{\left(f_S + \frac{m_\ell}{m_K} f_2 + \frac{p_0 - q_0}{m_K} f_T\right) - \left(f_1 + f_2 + \frac{m_\ell}{m_K} f_T\right)\gamma_4\right\} \tag{5.29}$$

This shows that, as far as the spinors are concerned, the structure of the matrix element involves only two operators, 1 and γ_4.

The square of the matrix element, summed over spins (we shall not discuss the lepton polarization), can be evaluated in the standard manner. A general result is

$$\frac{m_\ell m_\nu}{2}\sum_{\text{spins}} \left|\bar{u}_\ell(p)(A - B\gamma_4)(1+\gamma_5)u_\nu(q)\right|^2$$

$$= |A|^2(p_0 q_0 - \vec{p}\cdot\vec{q}) + |B|^2(p_0 q_0 + \vec{p}\cdot\vec{q})$$

$$- 2\,\mathrm{Re}(AB^*)\,m_\ell q_0 \tag{5.30}$$

The square of Eq. (5.28), with Eq. (5.29) inserted, summed over spins is therefore

$$\sum_{\text{spins}} |\mathcal{M}|^2 = \frac{G^2 m_K^2}{m_\ell m_\nu} \Bigg\{ \left| f_S + \frac{m_\ell}{m_K} f_2 + \frac{p_0 - q_0}{m_K} f_T \right|^2 (p_0 q_0 - \vec{p}\cdot\vec{q})$$

$$+ \left| f_1 + f_2 + \frac{m_\ell}{m_K} f_T \right|^2 (p_0 q_0 + \vec{p}\cdot\vec{q})$$

$$- 2\,\mathrm{Re}\left(f_S + \frac{m_\ell}{m_K} f_2 + \frac{p_0 - q_0}{m_K} f_T \right)\left(f_1^* + f_2^* + \frac{m_\ell}{m_K} f_T^* \right) m_\ell q_0 \Bigg\} \tag{5.31}$$

The transition probability is given by Eq. (1.1). There are 9 variables appearing in the rate formula, but the actual number of significant variables is two. The reduction from 9 to 2 occurs as follows: 4 are eliminated by conservation of energy and momentum, and 3 are used up in order to specify the absolute orientation of the whole system in space (Euler angles). The choice of the two variables to be used is arbitrary, but different choices may exhibit certain physical features more clearly than other choices. Some possibilities are:

(1) Pion energy and charged lepton-pion angle
(2) Charged lepton energy and charged lepton-pion angle
(3) Pion energy and neutrino-pion angle
(4) Pion and charged lepton energies

Integration over one of the two variables will give a distribution in the remaining one. Obvious choices here are the charged lepton energy distribution, the pion energy distribution, and the lepton-pion angular correlation. We shall consider choices (3) and (4) in subsequent sections.

5.7 Pion-Neutrion Angular Correlation in $K_{\ell 3}$ (Pais and Treiman, 1957)

In this section we shall consider as independent variables the pion energy and the (π, ν) angle. This is kinematically simplest when dealing with both K_{e3} and $K_{\mu 3}$. The integration over lepton angles in Eq. (1.1) can be accomplished simply. The result for the differential rate is

$$dw = \frac{1}{2(2\pi)^4} \frac{m_\ell m_\nu}{m_K} \sum_{spins} |m|^2 \frac{Q^2 dQ}{Q_0} \frac{q^2 dq}{p_0 q_0} d\Omega_{\pi\nu} \delta(m_K - Q_0 - p_0 - q_0) \tag{5.32}$$

where $p_0 = [m_\ell{}^2 + (\vec{Q} + \vec{q})^2]^{1/2}$ and $d\Omega_{\pi\nu} = 2\pi\, d(\cos\theta)$. The integration over neutrino energy can be performed by using the fact that

$$\delta(m_K - Q_0 - p_0 - q_0) = \frac{p_0}{(m_K - Q_0)(1 + x\cos\theta)} \delta(q - q_0)$$

where

$$q_0 = \frac{(m_K - Q_0)(1 - x^2 - y^2)}{2(1 + x\cos\theta)}$$

$$x = \frac{Q}{m_K - Q_0}$$

$$y = \frac{m_\ell}{m_K - Q_0} \tag{5.33}$$

Then the transition probability is

$$dw = \frac{1}{2(2\pi)^4} \frac{m_\ell m_\nu}{m_K} \sum_{\text{spins}} |\mathcal{M}|^2 \frac{Q q_0 \, dQ_0 \, d\Omega_{\pi\nu}}{(m_K - Q_0)(1 + x\cos\theta)} \tag{5.34}$$

There are various energy-dependent factors in the square of the matrix element of Eq. (5.31). These are:

$$p_0 q_0 - \vec{p}\cdot\vec{q} = q_0 (m_K - Q_0)(1 + x\cos\theta)$$

$$p_0 q_0 + \vec{p}\cdot\vec{q} = q_0 (m_K - Q_0)\left(\frac{y^2 + x^2 \sin^2\theta}{1 + x\cos\theta}\right)$$

$$p_0 - q_0 = (m_K - Q_0)\left(\frac{x^2 + y^2 + x\cos\theta}{1 + x\cos\theta}\right)$$

When all these are inserted into the square of the matrix element, the transition probability can be written as

$$dw = \frac{G^2 m_K}{128\pi^4} \frac{(m_K - Q_0)^3 x (1 - x^2 - y^2)^2}{(1 + x\cos\theta)^4} \{ \; \} \, dQ_0 \, d\Omega_{\pi\nu} \tag{5.35}$$

where

$$\{ \; \} = |f_S'|^2 (1 + x\cos\theta)^2 + |f_V|^2 (x^2 \sin^2\theta + y^2)$$

$$+ |f_T|^2 \left(\frac{Q}{m_K}\right)^2 \left[(x + \cos\theta)^2 + y^2 \sin^2\theta \right] \quad +$$

$$- 2\,\mathrm{Re}(f_S' f_V^*)\, y(1 + x\cos\theta)$$

$$+ 2\,\mathrm{Re}(f_S' f_T^*)\, \frac{Q}{m_K}\,(x + \cos\theta)(1 + x\cos\theta)$$

$$- 2\,\mathrm{Re}(f_V f_T^*)\, \frac{m_\ell}{m_K}\, x\cos\theta\,(1 + x\cos\theta)$$

(5.36)

Here we have denoted

$$f_S' = f_S + \frac{m_\ell}{m_K} f_2$$

and

$$f_V = f_1 + f_2$$

(5.37)

The above expression for the transition rate is rather involved when considered in its complete generality. For the K_{e3} mode considerable simplification occurs, in that we can put $m_\ell \to 0,\ y \to 0$. Then we find

$$\{\ \} = |f_S|^2 (1 + x\cos\theta)^2 + |f_V|^2 x^2 \sin^2\theta$$

$$+ |f_T|^2 \left(\frac{Q}{m_K}\right)^2 (x + \cos\theta)^2$$

$$+ 2\,\mathrm{Re}(f_S f_T^*)\, \frac{Q}{m_K}\,(x + \cos\theta)(1 + x\cos\theta)$$

(5.38)

This is still somewhat complicated, but one might anticipate discriminating between S and T on the one hand and V on the other, on the basis of the rather different angular distributions. This may not be quite as easy as it seems, because of the tendency for backwards peaking exhibited by the common factor $(1 + x\cos\theta)^{-4}$. MacDowell (1962) has discussed these problems by considering the (π,ν) angular correlation in the rest frame of the lepton pair.

Another type of simplification occurs if we assume that only one covariant is present, say V. Then the curly bracket becomes

$$\{\ \} = |f_V|^2 x^2 U(Q,\theta) \tag{5.39}$$

where

$$U(Q,\theta) = \sin^2\theta + \frac{y^2}{x^2}\left|1 - \frac{(m_K - Q_0) f_2}{m_K f_V}(1 + x\cos\theta)\right|^2 \tag{5.40}$$

For the K_{e3} mode, only $\left\{|f_V|^2 x^2 \sin^2\theta\right\}$ survives. Then the transition rate takes the simple form:

$$dw = \frac{G^2 m_K}{128\pi^4}|f_V|^2 (m_K - Q_0)^3 x^3 (1 - x^2)^2 \cdot \frac{\sin^2\theta}{(1 + x\cos\theta)^4}\, d\Omega_{\pi\nu}\, dQ_0 \tag{5.41}$$

with the range of x being $0 \leq x \leq 1$.

Brown et al. (1961) have studied the pion energy spectrum and (π, e) angular correlation in the K^+_{e3} mode. In the approximation of $m_\ell \to 0$, Eq. (5.38) applies equally well to the (π, e) angular distribution as to the (π,ν). Comparison with the pure S, V, or T predictions (using the experimental form factors from the pion energy distributions) for the angular correlation showed that their data were consistent with S or V, but not T. Furthermore, the pion energy spectrum can be fitted by a scalar coupling only if the form factor f_S is very sharply peaked at the upper end of the pion spectrum. For a vector coupling the form factor f_V is found to be sensibly constant. The reason for this difference between f_S and f_V can be seen from Eq. (5.38), where $|f_V|^2$ is multiplied by χ^2 (roughly the square of the pion momentum), while $|f_S|^2$ is not.

In their studies of K_2^0 three-body decay modes, Luers et al. (1961) found from their data on the $(\pi e \nu)$ mode that, independent of the form factors, a pure tensor coupling could be excluded. The scalar and vector couplings were consistent with experiment. But again, the scalar form factor had to vary tremendously with pion energy (roughly by a factor of 14 from pion kinetic energies less than 76 Mev to pion energies greater than 104 Mev), while the vector form factor was more or less constant.

These two experiments strongly suggest that the vector coupling dominates in K_{e3}, although sizable admixtures of scalar and tensor cannot be excluded. Since the leptonic vector coupling is in agreement with all other information on weak interactions, we shall restrict our subsequent discussion to this form.

5.8 Differential Spectrum of Pion and Lepton Energies for $K_{\ell 3}$

To illustrate another choice of variables in $K_{\ell 3}$, we take Q_0 and p_0, the pion and lepton energies. These spectra have been calculated by many people for various possible covariants (Zachariasen, 1958; Okun', 1958; Gatto, 1958; Furuichi, 1958; Fujiiand Kawaguchi, 1959; Brene, Egardt, and Qvist, 1961; etc.). The last-mentioned paper has detailed numerical tables for use with (V - A) coupling and arbitrary form factors.

We shall discuss only the vector coupling, with the two form factors f_1 and f_2. To get the energy spectra, one can return to the original transition rate formula, Eq. (1.1), and integrate out the appropriate variables; or one can transform the angular correlation formulas of Sec. 5.7 by replacing $\cos\theta$ by the lepton energy p_0. In either case, the result for the differential energy spectrum is

$$d\omega = \frac{G^2}{16\pi^3} dp_0 \, dQ_0 |f_V|^2 \Big\{ 2m_K p_0 q_0 - m_K^2 (W_0 - Q_0)$$

$$- \frac{m_\ell^2 q_0}{W_0 - Q_0} + \frac{m_\ell^2}{W_0 - Q_0} \left| q_0 - \frac{f_2}{f_V}(W_0 - Q_0) \right|^2 \Bigg\} \tag{5.42}$$

where $q_o = m_K - Q_o - p_o$ and W_o is the maximum pion energy,

$$W_0 = \frac{m_K^2 + m_\pi^2 - m_\ell^2}{2 m_K}$$

The form factors f_V [Eq. (5.37)] and f_2 are functions of Q_o only. For K_{e3}, only $|f_V|^2$ enters, but for $K_{\mu 3}$ both f_V and f_2 appear.

If we wish to exhibit the spectrum of pion energies or lepton energies, independent of the other energy, we integrate out the unwanted variable. Suppose the pion energy spectrum is desired. We integrate over electron energy between the maximum and minimum values:

$$\left.\begin{matrix} p_{o\,max} \\ \\ p_{o\,min} \end{matrix}\right\} = \frac{(m_K - Q_0 \pm Q)^2 + m_\ell^2}{2(m_K - Q_0 \pm Q)}$$

Then the pion spectrum becomes

$$\frac{dw}{dQ_0} = \frac{G^2}{16\pi^3} |f_V|^2 \frac{Q(W_0 - Q_0)^2}{\left(W_0 - Q_0 + \frac{m_\ell^2}{2m_K}\right)^2} \Bigg\{ \frac{m_K Q^2}{3}$$

$$+ \frac{m_\ell^2}{12} \frac{Q^2}{\left(W_0 - Q_0 + \frac{m_\ell^2}{2m_K}\right)} + \frac{m_\ell^2 (m_K - Q_0)^2}{4\left(W_0 - Q_0 + \frac{m_\ell^2}{2m_K}\right)} \left| 1 - 2\frac{f_2}{f_V} \left(\frac{W_0 - Q_0 + \frac{m_\ell^2}{2m_K}}{m_K - Q_0} \right) \right|^2 \Bigg\} \tag{5.43}$$

For the K_{e3} mode ($m_\ell \to 0$), the pion spectrum takes the simple form,

$$\frac{dw}{dQ_0} = \frac{G^2}{48\pi^3} |f_V|^2 \, m_K Q^3 \tag{5.44}$$

showing a pronounced peaking toward high energies, apart from possible energy variation in $f_V(Q_0)$.

If the lepton spectrum is desired, some assumption needs to be made about the energy dependence of the form factors. In the absence of evidence to the contrary, we can assume that they are sensibly constant over the allowed energy range. Then we can integrate over the pion energies in the interval $Q_{o\,min} \leqslant Q_o \leqslant Q_{o\,max}$, where

$$\left.\begin{matrix} Q_{o\,max} \\ \\ Q_{o\,min} \end{matrix}\right\} = \frac{(m_K - p_0 \pm p)^2 + m_\pi^2}{2(m_K - p_0 \pm p)}$$

The resulting charged lepton spectrum is

$$\frac{dw}{dp_0} = \frac{G^2}{32\pi^3 m_K} \frac{p(w_0 - p_0)^2}{\left(w_0 - p_0 + \frac{m_\pi^2}{2m_K}\right)^2} \cdot$$

$$\cdot \Big\{ |f_V|^2 m_K^2 (m_K p_0 - 2p_0^2 + m_\ell^2) + |f_2|^2 m_\ell^2 (m_K p_0 - m_\ell^2)$$

$$- 2\,\mathrm{Re}(f_V f_2^*)\, m_\ell^2 m_K (m_K - p_0) \Big\} \tag{5.45}$$

where $w_0 = (m_K^2 + m_\ell^2 - m_\pi^2)/2m_K$ is the maximum lepton energy. For the K_{e3} mode ($m_\ell \to 0$), the electron spectrum is

$$\frac{dw}{dp_0} = \frac{G^2}{8\pi^3}|f_V|^2 m_K \frac{p_0^2(w_0-p_0)^2}{m_K-2p_0} \tag{5.46}$$

If the energy variable is chosen as $x = p_o / w_o$, the K_{e3} electron spectrum is

$$\frac{dw}{dx} \sim \frac{x^2(1-x)^2}{\alpha - x}$$

where

$$\alpha = \left(1 - \frac{m_\pi^2}{m_K^2}\right)^{-1} \simeq 1.0810$$

This is a bell-shaped curve, skewed toward higher energies, with a peak at $x \simeq 0.65$.

5.9 Total Decay Rates for K_{e3} and $K_{\mu 3}$ and Relative Values of Form Factors; $K_{\mu 3}$ Muon Spectrum

If the form factors are taken as constants, the remaining integral over the spectrum can be performed to give the total decay rate. For the K_{e3} mode, for example, the total rate is

$$w = \frac{G^2|f_V|^2}{48\pi^3}\int_{m_\pi}^{W_0} Q^3\, dQ_0 = \frac{G^2|f_V|^2 m_K^5}{3072\,\pi^3} F\left(\frac{m_\pi}{m_K}\right) \tag{5.47}$$

where $F(x) = 1 - 8x^2 + 8x^6 - x^8 - 24x^4 \ln x$. For $K^\pm$ meson decay, $m_\pi / m_K = 0.278$ and $F(x) = 0.571$. With the branching ratio given in Appendix A or Table 6 ($\Gamma_{e3} \simeq 4 \times 10^6\ \text{sec}^{-1}$), the numerical value of f_V is $|f_V| \simeq 0.32$.

For the $K_{\mu 3}$ mode, the spectra involve both form factors and are more complicated in their energy dependences. The integration over the spectrum can be done analytically for constant form factors (Fujii and Kawaguchi, 1959), but the results are not very informative. The ratio of the transition rate for $K_{\mu 3}$ to the rate for K_{e3} numerically turns out to be

$$\frac{\Gamma(K^+_{\mu 3})}{\Gamma(K^+_{e3})} = 0.794 - 0.33\, \mathrm{Re}\left(\frac{f_2}{f_V}\right) + 0.075 \left|\frac{f_2}{f_V}\right|^2 \tag{5.48}$$

With the assumption that f_2/f_V is real (time-reversal invariance), the ratio can be plotted as a function of f_2/f_V. This is shown in Fig. 8. The

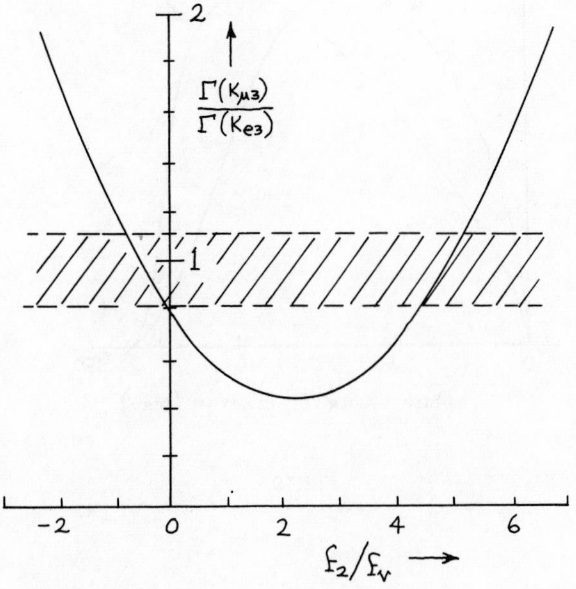

Fig. 8

branching ratio found by Roe et al. (1961) from Table 6 is shown as the shaded area. There are two solutions for f_2/f_V, namely,

$$\frac{f_2}{f_V} = \begin{cases} -0.4 \pm 0.4 \\ +4.8 \pm 0.4 \end{cases} \tag{5.49}$$

With the two solutions for f_2/f_V, two pion or muon spectra can be predicted from Eq. (5.43) or (5.45). These spectra do not differ greatly ($m_\mu/m_K \simeq 0.214$ is the proportionality factor for the interference term between f_2 and f_V). For the muons, examples are shown in Fig. 9. The muon spectra with f_2/f_V large and positive peaks at somewhat higher energies than the one with $f_2 \simeq 0$.

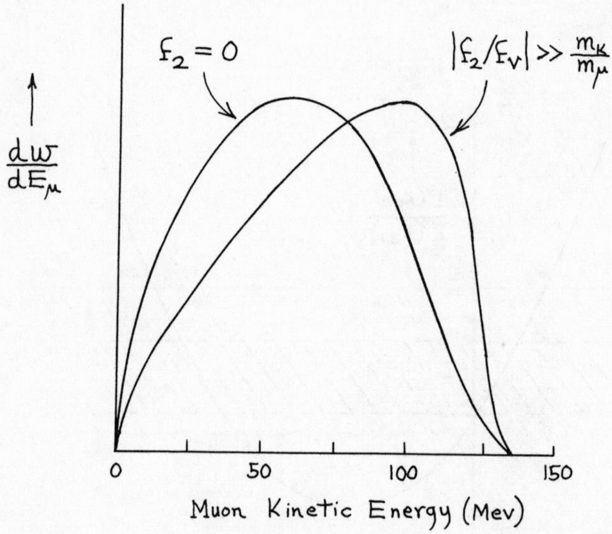

Fig. 9

Two recent experiments have been reported on the $K_{\mu 3}$ spectra (Dobbs et al., 1962; Brown et al., 1962). The first-mentioned experiment was by a University of Pennsylvania group that used a filamentary chamber; the second was by a Berkeley-Michigan group that used a liquid xenon bubble chamber. Observing the upper half of the muon spectrum (K. E. > 50 Mev), the Penn group found their data consistent with the large positive value, $f_2/f_V \simeq 5$, and not consistent with $f_2 \simeq 0$. The xenon bubble chamber group reached precisely the opposite conclusion! They found that the form factor f_V was essentially constant with energy (from Ke3 data), and that f_2 could be taken to be constant, although some energy dependence could not be excluded. With linear forms for f_V and f_2 $[f_i = f_i(0)(1 + \lambda_i s/m_\pi^2)]$, they found $\lambda_V = 0.036 \pm 0.045$, λ_2 unknown within wide limits, and $f_2(0)/f_V(0) = -0.23 \pm 0.30$. With constant form factors, they obtained $f_2/f_V = -0.4 \pm 0.3$.

The conclusion from these two experiments is that we must wait for more data. We shall remark in Sec. 5.12 that the large positive value of f_2/f_V is quite difficult to explain on theoretical grounds. In fact, the simplest model which one can invent uses a π-K current of the form

$$J_{\pi K} = i\left(\frac{\partial \pi^0}{\partial x_\alpha} K^+ - \pi^0 \frac{\partial K^+}{\partial x_\alpha}\right) \tag{5.50}$$

in analogy with the pion current in Eq. (4.7). This gives $f_1 = f_2 =$ constant. On this model we expect $f_2/f_V \simeq +0.5$ and a branching ratio of $w(K_{\mu 3})/w(K_{e3}) \simeq 0.65$.

In the decay $K_2^0 \rightarrow (\pi \ell \nu)$, Luers et al. (1961) found a $K_{\mu 3}/K_{e3}$ branching ratio of 0.79 ± 0.19, somewhat smaller than but consistent with Roe et al. (1961).

5.10 Form Factors in $K_{\ell 3}$ and $\Delta S \neq 0$ Currents

If we wish to go beyond the phenomenological treatment of Secs. 5.6 to 5.9, we can relate the form factors, f_1 and f_2 in Eq. (5.27), to the π-K matrix element of the $\Delta S \neq 0$ adronic current made up from Eq. (5.6), plus possible contributions from Eqs. (5.7) and (5.8). If we denote this current by J_α, then we can write the Feynman amplitude for $K_{\ell 3}$ decay as

$$\mathfrak{M} = i\frac{G}{\sqrt{2}}\langle \pi | J_\alpha(0) | K\rangle \left(u_\ell(p)\gamma_\alpha(1+\gamma_5)u_\nu(q)\right) \tag{5.51}$$

where

$$\langle\pi|J_\alpha(0)|K\rangle = \frac{1}{\sqrt{4P_0Q_0}}\left(f_1(s)P_\alpha + f_2(s)Q_\alpha\right) \tag{5.52}$$

with $s = -(P-Q)^2$.

Statements about the form factors f_1 and f_2 can be made within the framework of the current-current theory, provided that we have some model for the strong interactions. The usual statement that f_1 and f_2 vary slowly with energy is based on the idea that baryon pairs are involved in the intermediate states, as shown in a typical lowest-order diagram (Fig. 10).

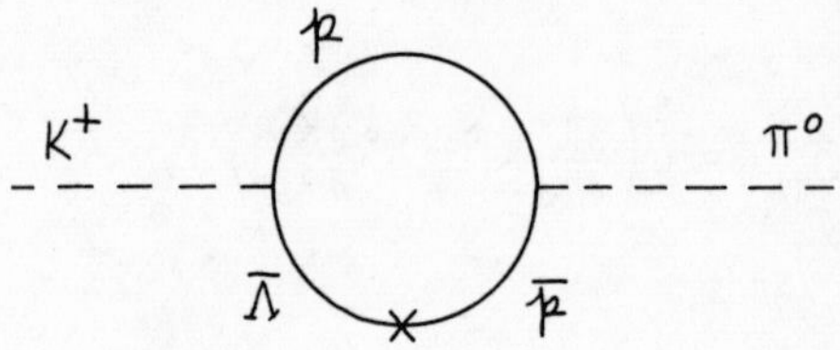

Fig. 10

The cross on the diagram marks the occurrence of the strangeness-changing 4-fermion weak interaction. Since the minimum mass in the intermediate state is $2m_p$, it is expected that the energy variation of f_1 and f_2 with pion energy from m_π to $2m_\pi$ should be slight.

But care must be taken with such arguments. If, for example, the K - π resonance at ~880 Mev is a dominant feature, a diagrammatic description of the strong interaction might be as shown in Fig. 11. This will give form factors exhibiting the influence of the K - π resonance. The tentative assignment of this resonance is as a T = 1/2, J = 1 state. Since its width is small compared to its mass ($\Delta M/M \simeq 6$ per cent), it can be treated approximately as a particle (perhaps one of Gell-Mann's vector

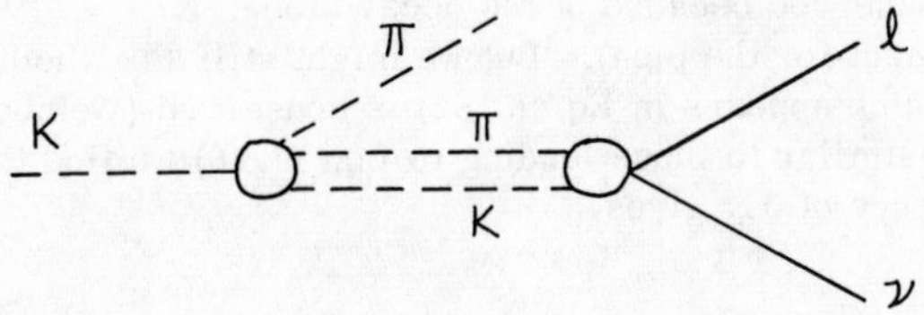

Fig. 11

bosons). A straightforward calculation with the vector boson propagator,

$$\frac{M^2 \delta_{\alpha\beta} + q_\alpha q_\beta}{M^2 + q^2}$$

gives the form factors

$$f_1 = f_1(0) \frac{M^2}{M^2 - s}$$

$$f_2 = \frac{M^2 + m_K^2 - m_\pi^2}{M^2 - m_K^2 + m_\pi^2} \cdot f_1(s) \tag{5.53}$$

With the resonance at 880 Mev, the form factors decrease by ~20 per cent as the pion energy varies from m_π to $Q_{o\,max} \simeq 2m_\pi$. In the spectrum itself this means a variation of nearly 50 per cent, although this is not fully felt since the spectrum peaks strongly at the upper end.

5.11 Partially Conserved $\Delta S \neq 0$ Currents

Because of the success of the conserved and partially conserved current hypotheses for $\Delta S = 0$ decays, it is natural to try out the same ideas in strange particle decays. With the convention that the K meson is pseudoscalar, we know immediately that the $\Delta S = \pm 1$ axial-vector current cannot be conserved because of the decay mode, $K \rightarrow \mu + \nu$ (see Sec. 4.2 for the argument for the pion). But we might still ask whether the vector current which appears in Eq. (5.52) is conserved (Weinberg et al., 1958). By steps similar to those leading to Eq. (4.16) we find that a vanishing divergence of J_α gives

$$\frac{f_2}{f_V} = \frac{m_K}{m_K - Q_0}\left(\frac{1}{1-x^2}\right) \tag{5.54}$$

where x is defined as in Eq. (5.33). Since the range of x is from zero to almost unity, the energy variation of f_2/f_V is tremendous and is probably excluded by the observations discussed in Sec. 5.9. It would be desirable, however, to test some of the unique predictions resulting from Eq. (5.54), such as the pion-neutrino angular correlation, Eqs. (5.39) and (5.40), muon polarization as a function of energy, etc.

Apart from absolute conservation of $\Delta S \neq 0$ currents, the attractive assumption of partially conserved currents needs to be explored. We shall therefore consider what the implications of partial conservation are for the form factors in $K_{\ell 3}$ decay. The π- K matrix element of the divergence of J_α can be obtained from Eq. (5.52):

$$i\sqrt{4P_0Q_0}\,\langle \pi | \partial_\alpha J_\alpha(0) | K \rangle = \left[(m_K^2 - m_\pi^2)\left(\frac{f_1 + f_2}{2}\right) + s\left(\frac{f_1 - f_2}{2}\right) \right] \tag{5.55}$$

The partial conservation assumption is that, in the limit $|s| \rightarrow \infty$, the square bracket vanishes. This can occur under a variety of conditions [e.g., (1) if f_1 and f_2 fall off faster than s^{-1} for large s; (2) if f_1 and f_2 vanish and $(f_1 - f_2)$ falls off faster than s^{-1} for large s], all of which require that the form factors vanish rapidly for large momentum transfers. This in turn means that the form factors may be assumed to satisfy unsubtracted dispersion relations. But, apart from possible relevance in dispersion calculations (see below), the partial-conservation or "gentleness" hypothesis by itself does not allow much to be said about the behavior of the form factors in the physical domain.

The partial-conservation idea and the dominance of a single particle pole has been applied to leptonic K-meson decays by Bernstein and Weinberg (1960). If the π and K parities are the same, the appropriate divergence is that of a vector current. Since this divergence is a Lorentz scalar, the exploitation of a pole term necessitates the existence of a scalar meson (K'), similar to the K meson but of opposite parity. Bernstein and Weinberg conjecture that this scalar "particle" is a sharp s-wave T = 1/2, π - K resonance. Then they can discuss the relative values of the form factors, f_1 and f_2, assuming the dominance of the resonance. Their results will be obtained from dispersion relations in the following section.

5.12 Dispersion-Relation Treatment of Form Factors in $K_{\ell 3}$ Decay

Ever since the pioneering work of Goldberger and Treiman, it has been fashionable to discuss form factors for decay processes by means of dispersion relations. The treatment of $K_{\mu 2}$ decays, involving only the total rate of decay, parallels closely the Goldberger-Treiman discussion of pion decay (Albright, 1959; Sakita, 1959). One can then relate the rate for $K_{\mu 2}$ decay and the rate for hyperon beta decay.

For the K_{e3} and $K_{\mu 3}$ modes, the form factors f_1 and f_2 are functions of the variables $s = -(P - Q)^2 = -(p + q)^2$, with a physical range

$$m_\ell^2 \leqslant s \leqslant (m_K - m_\pi)^2 \tag{5.56}$$

The dispersion-theoretic approach is to write dispersion relations in the variable s for the form factors, taking into account the poles and branch cuts which come from physically allowed intermediate states. Since we start with a K meson (assumed K^+ for definiteness), the strongly interacting particles in the intermediate states must have S = + 1 and zero baryon number. As will be seen below, the lowest mass state is (π K). This means that there is a cut in the complex s plane starting at $s = (m_K + m_\pi)^2$ and extending to infinity along the real axis. Other possible states are ($\pi\pi$ K), (K $\bar{K}$ K), (N $\bar{Y}$), etc., each with its corresponding branch cut. The singularities in the complex s plane will then appear as in Fig. 12.

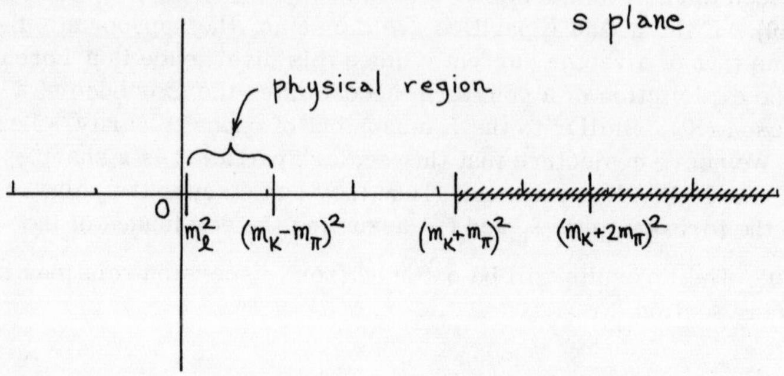

Fig. 12

In units of m_K^2, the physical region extends from near zero to s_{max} = 0.53. The cut due to the (π K) state starts at s = 1.62, while the cuts from more massive states begin at s = 2.4 ($\pi\pi$ K), s = 3.3 ($\pi\pi\pi$ K), etc. The baryon pair cuts are at very large s values [s = 17.2 for ($N\bar{\Lambda}$), etc.].

If the only singularities are those shown above, Cauchy's theorem allows us to write a dispersion relation for the form factors of the form

$$f(s) = \frac{1}{\pi}\int_{(m_K+m_\pi)^2}^{\infty} ds' \frac{\operatorname{Im} f(s')}{s'-s-i\epsilon} \tag{5.57}$$

or perhaps with subtractions at some point such as s = 0. The general philosophy in trying to evaluate f(s) is to assume that only the lowest-mass intermediate states are dynamically important. Thus the cut from the (π K) state is presumed to dominate the present problem, with more remote cuts, such as the baryon pairs, contributing at most a subtraction constant. Once this approximation is made, the equation for f(s) becomes one of the Muskhelishvili-Omnes type, with a solution in terms of the phase shifts for π - K elastic scattering.

Having summarized the general approach, we now outline the formalism for the matrix element of Eq. (5.52). In the standard manner, * the matrix element can be written in terms of a retarded commutator,

$$\langle \pi | J_\alpha(0) | K \rangle =$$

$$\frac{i}{\sqrt{2Q_0}} \int d^4x \, e^{-iQ\cdot x} \langle 0 | \Theta(x_0) [j_\pi(x), J_\alpha(0)] | K \rangle$$

(5. 58)

The current $j_\pi(x)$ is defined by $j_\pi(x) = (m_\pi^2 - \Box^2) \phi_{\pi^0}$. The step function is broken up into odd and even parts in order to give the real (dispersive) and imaginary (absorptive) parts of the matrix element. Thus, we have

$$\mathrm{Im} \sqrt{4P_0Q_0} \langle \pi | J_\alpha(0) | K \rangle =$$

$$\sqrt{\frac{P_0}{2}} \int d^4x \, e^{-iQ\cdot x} \langle 0 | [j_\pi(x), J_\alpha(0)] | K \rangle$$

(5. 59)

To see how this imaginary part enters the dispersion relation of Eq. (5. 57), we insert a complete set of states between the two currents. Then it follows easily that

*See, for example, M. L. Goldberger, in C. DeWitt and R. Omnes (eds.), Dispersion Relations and Elementary Particles, Hermann-Wiley, New York, 1961; or J. D. Jackson, "Introduction to Dispersion Relation Techniques," in G. R. Screaton (ed.), Dispersion Relations, Oliver and Boyd, Edinburgh, 1961.

$$\text{Im}\,\sqrt{4P_0Q_0}\,\langle\pi|J_\alpha(0)|K\rangle = (2\pi)^4\frac{\sqrt{2P_0}}{2}\sum_n \cdot$$

$$\cdot\Big\{\langle 0|j_\pi(0)|n\rangle\langle n|J_\alpha(0)|K\rangle\,\delta^4(p_n - Q)$$

$$-\langle 0|J_\alpha(0)|n\rangle\langle n|j_\pi(0)|K\rangle\,\delta^4(p_n + Q - P)\Big\}$$

(5.60)

The conservation law in the first term demands that $p_n^2 = -m_\pi^2$; hence only the one-pion state can contribute. But its contribution vanishes since $\langle 0|j_\pi(0)|\pi\rangle = 0$. Thus the first term does not contribute at all. In the second term, the 4-momenta p_n must be such that $p_n^2 = (P-Q)^2 = -s$. The state n must evidently have S = + 1 and B = 0. The lowest-mass state is the (π K) state, as already noted. Furthermore, only states with j = 0 [from the time part of $J_\alpha(0)$] and j = 1 [from the space part of $J_\alpha(0)$] can enter.

Because the sum over n divides into a sum over j = 0 states and another over j = 1 states, it is convenient to combine the form factors f_1 and f_2 into decoupled j = 0 and j = 1 amplitudes, as was first done by MacDowell (1959). We denote by a(s) and b(s) the j = 0 and j = 1 amplitudes, respectively. In the coordinate frame where $\vec{p}_n = 0$, the space and time parts of the matrix element $\langle\pi|J_\alpha(0)|K\rangle$ are proportional to the j = 1 and j = 0 amplitudes.

$$\sqrt{4P_0Q_0}\,\langle\pi|\vec{J}(0)|K\rangle = b(s)\,\vec{Q}$$

$$\sqrt{4P_0Q_0}\,\langle\pi|J_0(0)|K\rangle = \sqrt{s}\,a(s)$$

(5.61)

A little algebra shows that, in terms of f_1 and f_2, a and b are

$$a(s) = \frac{1}{2}(f_1 - f_2) + \frac{m_K^2 - m_\pi^2}{2s}(f_1 + f_2)$$

$$b(s) = f_1 + f_2 = f_V$$

(5. 62)

We note that the amplitude a(s) has a pole of kinematic origin at s = 0 with residue $(m_K^2 - m_\pi^2)\, b(0)/2$.

The amplitudes a(s) and b(s) can now be written as dispersion integrals,

$$a(s) = \left(\frac{m_K^2 - m_\pi^2}{2s}\right) b(0) + \frac{1}{\pi}\int_{(m_K+m_\pi)^2}^{\infty} ds' \frac{\operatorname{Im} a(s')}{s' - s - i\epsilon}$$

$$b(s) = \frac{1}{\pi}\int_{(m_K+m_\pi)^2}^{\infty} ds' \frac{\operatorname{Im} b(s')}{s' - s - i\epsilon}$$

(5. 63)

If a subtraction is necessary in b(s), for example, we would have instead

$$b(s) = b(0) + \frac{s}{\pi}\int_{(m_K+m_\pi)^2}^{\infty} ds' \frac{\operatorname{Im} b(s')}{s'(s' - s - i\epsilon)}$$

(5. 64)

The partially conserved current hypothesis implies that at least the j = 0 amplitude satisfies an unsubtracted dispersion relation. *

If only the (πK) state contributes significantly to the sum in Eq. (5.60) for small s, the amplitudes Im a(s') and Im b(s') in the dispersion integrals have known phases, namely, those of the j = 0 and j = 1 scattering states of the π- K system. The dispersion relations are then integral equations of the Muskhelishvili-Omnes type with known solutions (see, for example, the appendix to my Edinburgh lectures, cited earlier in this section). If the j = 0 and j = 1 phase shifts are δ_0 and δ_1, the solutions for b(s) and a(s) are

$$b(s) = b(0) \exp\left[\frac{s}{\pi}\int_{(m_K+m_\pi)^2}^{\infty} ds' \frac{\delta_1(s')}{s'(s'-s-i\epsilon)}\right]$$

$$a(s) = \frac{m_K^2 - m_\pi^2}{2s}\, b(0) \exp\left[\frac{s}{\pi}\int_{(m_K+m_\pi)^2}^{\infty} ds' \frac{\delta_0(s')}{s'(s'-s-i\epsilon)}\right] \tag{5.65}$$

We note a few limiting cases:

1. δ_0 and δ_1 both very small: Then the exponentials are essentially unity and we find $f_1 \simeq f_2$ = constant.

2. Sharp p-wave resonance at s = M^2: Then we have $\delta_0 \simeq 0$ and $\delta_1(s) \simeq \pi\, \Theta\, (s - M^2)$. This gives just the expressions of Eq. (5.53) for the form factors in terms of a vector boson intermediate state.

3. Sharp s-wave resonance at s = M^2: Then we have $\delta_0(s) \simeq \pi\, \Theta\,(s - M^2)$, and $\delta_1 \simeq 0$. This gives

---

*Note that a(s) = (i/s) $\sqrt{4P_oQ_o}\, \langle \pi \,|\, \partial_\alpha J_\alpha(0) \,|\, K \rangle$, from Eq. (5.55).

$$\frac{f_2}{f_V} = \frac{1}{2}\left(1 - \frac{m_K^2 - m_\pi^2}{M^2 - s}\right)$$

which is the Bernstein-Weinberg result discussed on page 361.

MacDowell (1959) examines the results of assuming negligible p wave and a scattering-length approximation for the s-wave phase shift. He concludes that the $K_{\mu 3}$ spectrum will not be very sensitive to the scattering length. This is explicitly verified by Brene, Egardt, and Qvist (1961), who made numerical calculations with the MacDowell formulas.

Various workers have calculated with models which amount to one of the three limiting cases above (Acioli and MacDowell, 1962; Fayyazuddin and Riazuddin, 1962; Chew, 1962; Iizuka, 1961). The net conclusion is that it is difficult to make the exponential terms in Eq. (5.65) vary appreciably in the physical range of s [Eq. (5.56)]. For example, if the s-wave π - K phase shift δ_0 (s) has an average value of the order of $\pi/2$ over the interval $(m_K + m_\pi)^2 \leqslant s \leqslant 2(m_K + m_\pi)^2$ and falls off above that interval, then the exponential in a(s) can be approximated for small s by $(1 + \lambda s)$, where $\lambda \simeq (1/2\, m_K^2)$. This means not more than a 25 per cent variation over the physical range of s.

In addition to concluding that the form factors do not change much with energy in the physical region, we can conclude something about the relative sizes of f_2 and f_V, for which there is conflicting evidence (see Sec. 5.9). From Eq. (5.62) we can obtain f_2/f_V in terms of a/b:

$$\frac{f_2}{f_V} = \frac{1}{2}\left(1 + \frac{m_K^2 - m_\pi^2}{s}\right) - \frac{a(s)}{b(s)} \tag{5.66}$$

The singularity in Eq. (5.66) for s = 0 is only apparent. If we use (5.65) for a/b, we find

$$\frac{f_2}{f_V} = \frac{1}{2}\left[1 + \frac{m_K^2 - m_\pi^2}{s}\left(\frac{E_1 - E_0}{E_1}\right)\right] \tag{5.67}$$

where E_0 and E_1 are the exponentials in Eq. (5.65) involving δ_0 and δ_1, respectively. For small s, $(E_1 - E_0) \propto s$, thereby eliminating the singularity. If we make a linear approximation for E_1 and E_0 for small s—that is, $E_0 \simeq 1 + \lambda_0 s$, $E_1 \simeq 1 + \lambda_1 s$—then Eq. (5.67) can be written approximately as

$$\frac{f_2}{f_V} \simeq \frac{1}{2}\left(\frac{1 + (m_K^2 - m_\pi^2)(\lambda_1 - \lambda_0) + \lambda_1 s}{1 + \lambda_1 s}\right) \tag{5.68}$$

Since the individual λ's are presumably smaller than m_K^{-2} in absolute value (from our example above), one can see from Eq. (5.68) that it is difficult to imagine that f_2/f_V can lie outside the range

$$-0.5 < \frac{f_2}{f_V} < 1.5 \tag{5.69}$$

Consequently, unless there is something very unusual we have not taken into account, we expect the $K_{\ell 3}$ form factor to be slowly varying where observed, the $K_{\mu 3}/K_{e3}$ branching ratio to lie between 0.5 and 1.0, and the muon spectrum to agree with the $f_2 \simeq 0$ curve on p. 356, with the actual values not far from the predictions of the simple model based on Eq. (5.50). We clearly favor the data of Brown et al. (1962) over that of Dobbs et al. (1962).

In the discussion of the last few pages we have ignored the isospin structure of the decay amplitudes. If $(\Delta T, \Delta T_z)$ amplitudes (1/2, 1/2), (3/2, 1/2), (3/2, 3/2) enter in the K decays, the effective form factors for $K^{\pm}$, K_1^0, and K_2^0 decays will involve linear combinations of amplitudes, such as Eq. (5.65), with T = 1/2 and T = 3/2 π- K scattering phase shifts, as discussed in Sec. 5.3. It might be thought that this added freedom could allow a large value of f_2/f_V for K^+ decay, in agreement with Dobbs et al. But it turns out that the existing data are such that mixtures of different isospin amplitudes still leave the effective values of f_2/f_V almost within the interval of Eq. (5.69) for $K^{\pm}$, K_1^0, and K_2^0 decays (Jackson and Schult, unpublished).

6. GUIDE TO THE LITERATURE OF TOPICS NOT COVERED

While a fairly thorough discussion of weak interactions with $\Delta S = 0$ has been given (with the possible exception of nuclear beta decay), only a glimpse has been presented of the decays of strange particles. And even for $\Delta S = 0$ processes, topics such as high-energy neutrino interactions, intermediate vector bosons, etc., have not been mentioned. To remedy these deficiencies we shall list additional topics, together with references to some of the literature. No attempt has been made to give a thorough review of the published work. In particular, reference to papers prior to 1960 is very limited. The reader can consult some of the reviews initially cited on pp. 267-268, or some recent paper, for references to the earlier literature on a particular topic.

The citations will be by author and year, as has been done in earlier chapters; the general bibliography contains the complete references. Papers cited earlier in the notes may be mentioned again here, but reviews will not, unless they are devoted entirely to a topic not treated in the lectures.

6.1 Renormalization of Weak-Interaction Coupling Constants

Balachandran, 1962
Kawakami, 1960
Symanzik, 1959

6.2 Dispersion-Relation Approach to Partially Conserved Currents

Bernstein et al., 1960
Chou, Kuang-Chao, 1961
Dennery and Primakoff, 1962
Gandel'man, 1961
Lannoy and Nuyts, 1962

6.3 Rare Decay Modes of Mu Mesons

Experiment:

Bartlett, Devons, and Sachs, 1962: $e + \gamma$
Conversi, 1962: $\mu^- + N \rightarrow N + e^-$
Crittenden, Walker, and Ballam, 1961: $e + \gamma$, eee, etc.
Frankel et al., 1960: $e + \gamma$
Frankel et al., 1962: $e + \gamma$

Krestinikov et al., 1960: $e + \gamma$
Lee and Samios, 1959: eee, $e \nu \bar{\nu}$ $(e^+ e^-)$
Parker and Penman, 1962: eee

Theory:

Ebel and Ernst, 1960: $e \gamma$ with intermediate boson
Feinberg, 1958: $e \gamma$; if intermediate boson and $\nu_\mu = \nu_e$, rate is large
Nilsson and Marshak, 1961

6.4 Neutrino Reactions

Experiment:

Danby et al., 1962: Columbia-Brookhaven experiment, $\nu_\mu \neq \nu_e$
Reines, 1960

Theory:

Azimov and Shekhter, 1962
Berman, 1961
Cabibbo, 1961
Cabibbo and Gatto, 1960
Lee, 1961
Lee, Markstein, and Yang, 1961
Lee and Yang, 1960
Lee and Yang, 1962
Yamaguchi, 1960
Yamaguchi, 1961

6.5 Intermediate Vector Bosons (W) and Nonlocality in Weak Interactions

Bernstein and Feinberg, 1962: production and decay of W
Cabibbo and Gatto, 1959: general nonlocality
D'Espagnat, 1960: vetons
Dombey, 1961: production of W
Glashow, 1961
Lee and Yang, 1960a: schizons
Lee, Markstein, and Yang,. 1961: ν production of W
Takeda, 1962: 6W's needed if $\Delta Q = - \Delta S$ occurs

6.6 Symmetry Schemes for Weak Interactions: General

Cabibbo and Gatto, 1961a

Królikowski, 1958
Pais, 1960, 1961, 1961a

6.7 Symmetry Schemes: $\Delta T = 1/2$

D'Espagnat and Prentki, 1962: subgroup G of SU_3
Okubo and Marshak, 1961
Salam and Ward, 1960
Radicati and Speiser, 1962
Treiman, 1960a

6.8 Symmetry Schemes: Two Neutrinos

Bludman, 1961
Cabibbo and Gatto, 1961
Feinberg, Gürsey, and Pais, 1961
Feinberg and Weinberg, 1961
Glashow, 1961
Królikowski, 1961, 1962
Lipmanov, 1960

6.9 Symmetry Schemes: $\Delta Q = - \Delta S$

Behrends and Sirlin, 1960, 1962
Takeda, 1962

6.10 Nonleptonic Hyperon Decays

Experiment:

Beall et al., 1961, 1962: Λ and Σ asymmetries and polarization
Cork et al., 1960: Λ and Σ asymmetries
Fowler et al., 1961: Ξ asymmetry
Tripp, Watson, and Ferro-Luzzi, 1962: Σ^- asymmetry
References cited in Secs. 5.1 and 5.4

Theory:

Bose and Marshak, 1962: odd Σ-Λ parity
Feldman, Matthews, and Salam, 1961
Hori, 1960
Iizuka and Oehme, 1962: odd Σ-Λ parity
Maki and Ohnuki, 1961: Sakata model
McCliment and Nishijima, 1962

Okubo, 1960
Okubo, Marshak, and Sudarshan, 1959
Sakita and Oneda, 1960
Singh and Udgaonkar, 1961
Wolfenstein, 1961

6.11 Photonic Hyperon Decays: $Y \rightarrow N + \gamma$

Behrends, 1958
Calucci and Furlan, 1961
Glasser et al., 1961: search for $\Sigma^+ \rightarrow p + \gamma$
Sawamura, 1961
Schneps and Kang, 1961: 3 events of $\Sigma^+ \rightarrow p + \gamma$
Tenaglia, 1960

6.12 Leptonic Hyperon Decays

Experiment:

Bhowmik, 1961: $\Sigma^- \rightarrow e^-$
Bhowmik, Goyal, and Yamdagni, 1961: $\Lambda \rightarrow e^-$
Eisler et al., 1961: $\Lambda \rightarrow \mu^-$
Franzini and Steinberger, 1961: $\Sigma^- \rightarrow e^-$
Galtieri et al., 1962: $\Sigma^+ \rightarrow \mu^+$
Humphrey et al., 1961: $\Sigma^- \rightarrow e^-$, $\Lambda \rightarrow e^-$

Theory:

Bernstein and Oehme, 1961: odd $\Sigma - \Lambda$ parity, $\Delta S = 0$ beta decays
Fayyazuddin and Riazuddin, 1962
Feynman and Gell-Mann, 1958
Harrington, 1961
Norton, 1962
Okun', 1961: $\Delta S = 0$ beta decays and partially conserved A_α.

6.13 Neutral K-Meson Decays

Barshay and Iso, 1962: $K^0 \rightarrow \pi\pi\gamma$ interference effects
Berger and Kazes, 1961: calculation of Δm
Kobzarev and Okun', 1961: suggests experiment to find sign of Δm
Matinyan, 1962: sign of Δm
Nilsson, 1961: calculation of Δm
References to experiments given in Secs. 5.2 and 5.3

6.14 Nonleptonic Charged K-Meson Decays

Barton and Kacser, 1962: dispersion relations in τ decay
Bég and De Celles, 1962: τ decay with p-wave interactions
Ferro-Luzzi et al., 1961: experiment on τ and τ'
Khuri and Treiman, 1960: dispersion relations in τ decay
Lomon et al., 1961: τ decay
Mitra, 1960: τ decay
Pati, Oneda, and Sakita, 1960
Riazuddin and Fayyazuddin, 1961
Sawyer and Wali, 1960: τ decay
Wolf and Zoellner, 1960: dispersion relations in τ decay
References to data on branching ratios given in Sec. 5.5

6.15 Leptonic K-Meson Decays

Brene, et al., 1962: model for form factors
Ivanter, 1958: polarizations of muon in $K_{\mu 3}$
Ivanter, 1959: polarization of muon and spectra in $K_{\mu 3}$
MacDowell, 1957: spectra and polarization
Matinyan and Okun', 1959
Nilsson, 1960: polarization-directional correlation
Okun', 1958a: polarization-directional correlation
Sawyer, 1960: dispersion relations with Q^2 as variable
Werle, 1958: polarization-directional correlation
Zel'dovich, 1961: model for form factors
References cited in Secs. 5.6 through 5.12

6.16 Rare Decay Modes of K Mesons

Cabibbo and Ferrari, 1960: $K^{\pm} \rightarrow \pi^{\pm} e^{+} e^{-}$, $K_1^{0} \rightarrow 2\gamma$
Chadan and Oneda, 1959: K_{e4} $(\pi \pi e \nu)$
Ivanter, 1962: $K \rightarrow (\pi \pi e^{+} e^{-})$
Mathur, 1959: K_{e4}
Neville, 1961: radiative $K_{\mu 3}$ and K_{e3}
Okun' and Rudik, 1961: $K \rightarrow \pi (\ell^{+} \ell^{-})$
Okun' and Shabalin, 1960: K_{e4}
Shabalin, 1961: K_{e4} and $K_{\mu 4}$

APPENDIX A: PARTICLES AND THEIR DECAY MODES

The following table lists all the known particles which are stable in the absence of weak and electromagnetic interactions. The multiple pion resonances are not included. No systematic attempt has been made to give errors on the experimental values, but if a value is quoted to a certain number of significant figures, it can be assumed that there is generally some uncertainty in the last digit. The sources of the information are not listed; Geneva and Rochester Conference reports, plus recent published literature, were utilized.

Note: Entries of the form 1.22 (-8) are to be read as 1.22×10^{-8}.

Decay Properties of Particles

Particle	Mass (Mev)	Lifetime (sec)	Decay Mode	Q (Mev)	Branching ratio	Partial rate (sec^{-1})
ν_e	< 2 (-4)	stable				
ν_μ	<~2	stable				
$e^\pm$	.511	stable				
$\mu^\pm$	105.7	2.21 (-6)	$e + \nu + \nu$	105.2	100%	4.5 (+ 5)
			$e + \gamma$	105.2	$< 10^{-8}$	--
			$e + e + e$	104.1	$< 10^{-7}$	--
π^o	135.0	2 (-16)	$\gamma + \gamma$	135.0	100%	5. (+ 15)
$\pi^\pm$	139.6	2.55 (-8)	$\mu + \nu$	33.9	~100%	3.9 (+ 7)
			$e + \nu$	139.1	$(1.1 \pm 0.2) \times 10^{-4}$	4.3 (+ 3)
			$\pi^o + e + \nu$	4.1	$(1.7 \pm 0.5) \times 10^{-8}$	6. (- 1)
$K^\pm$	493.9	1.22 (-8)	$\mu + \nu$	388.2	~ 60%	49. (+ 6)
			$\pi^\pm + \pi^o$	219.3	~ 22%	18. (+ 6)
			$\pi^\pm + \pi^+ + \pi^-$ (τ)	75.1	~ 6%	5. (+ 6)
			$\pi^\pm + \pi^o + \pi^o$ (τ')	84.3	~ 2%	1.6 (+ 6)
			$\pi^o + \mu + \nu$	253.2	~ 5%	4. (+ 6)
			$\pi^o + e + \nu$	358.4	~ 5%	4. (+ 6)
K_1^o	497.8	1.00 (-10)	$\pi^+ + \pi^-$	218.6	~ 70%	7. (+ 9)
			$\pi^o + \pi^o$	227.8	~ 30%	3. (+ 9)

K_2^o	497.8	7 ± 2 (-8)	$\pi^+ + \pi^- + \pi^o$	83.6	14 ± 2%	~ 2. (+ 6)
			$\pi + e + \nu$	357.7	48 ± 5%	~ 7. (+ 6)
			$\pi + \mu + \nu$	252.6	38 ± 8%	~ 5. (+ 6)
			$\pi^o + \pi^o + \pi^o$	92.8	(probably present)	
n	939.5	1.01 (3)	$p + e^- + \nu$	.783	100%	9.9 (- 4)
p	938.2	stable				
Λ	1115.4	2.5 (-10)	$p + \pi^-$	37.6	64%	2.5 (+ 9)
			$n + \pi^o$	40.9	36%	1.4 (+ 9)
			$p + e^- + \nu$	176.6	~ 0.1%	~ 4.0 (+ 6)
			$p + \mu^- + \nu$	71.5	few events	--
Σ^+	1189.4	.81 (-10)	$p + \pi^o$	116.2	50%	6.1 (+ 9)
			$n + \pi^+$	110.3	50%	6.1 (+ 9)
			$n + \mu^+ + \nu$	144.2	1 event	--
			$n + e^+ + \nu$	249.4	none seen	--
Σ^-	1196.0	1.6 (-10)	$n + \pi^-$	116.9	~100%	6.3 (+ 9)
			$n + e^- + \nu$	255.9	~ .1%	~ 6. (+ 6)
			$n + \mu^- + \nu$	150.8	none seen	--
Σ^o	1191.5	very short	$\Lambda + \gamma$	76.1	--	--
Ξ^-	1318	1.2 (-10)	$\Lambda + \pi^-$	63.4	~100%	8.3 (+ 9)
Ξ^o	1311	?	$\Lambda + \pi^o$	60.6	--	--

APPENDIX B: S-MATRIX SUMMARY AND NOTATION ON DIRAC EQUATION

1. S Matrix

The notation used in these notes for the S-matrix and Feynman amplitudes can be summarized as follows:

In first order the S operator is

$$S \simeq 1 - i\int d^4x \, \mathcal{H}_{int}(x) \tag{B.1}$$

where $\mathcal{H}_{int}(x)$ is the Hamiltonian interaction density. The S matrix between two states, A and B ($A \neq B$), is

$$S_{BA} \equiv \langle B|S|A\rangle \simeq -i\int d^4x \, \langle B|\mathcal{H}_{int}(x)|A\rangle \tag{B.2}$$

The interaction $\mathcal{H}_{int}(x)$ involves products of field operators for bosons and fermions. When these act on the states $|A\rangle$ and $|B\rangle$, certain factors remain, one for each particle created or destroyed. For the fermions there may be various Dirac operators with which spinor products must be made. The conventions on the particle factors are:

Boson:

Destroyed $\qquad \dfrac{1}{\sqrt{2k_0}}\, e^{ik\cdot x}$

Created: $\qquad \dfrac{1}{\sqrt{2k_0}}\, e^{-ik\cdot x}$

(B.3)

Fermion:

Destroyed $\sqrt{\frac{m}{E}}\, u_j(p)\, e^{ip\cdot x}$ on right

Created $\sqrt{\frac{m}{E}}\, \bar{u}_j(p)\, e^{-ip\cdot x}$ on left

(B. 4)

Antifermion:

Destroyed $\sqrt{\frac{m}{E}}\, \bar{v}_j(p)\, e^{ip\cdot x}$ on left

Created $\sqrt{\frac{m}{E}}\, v_j(p)\, e^{-ip\cdot x}$ on right

(B. 5)

In Eqs. (B. 3), (B. 4), and (B. 5) the convention on the Lorentz metric is that 4-vectors are $A_\alpha = (\vec{A}, iA_0)$, with scalar products $(A\cdot B) = \vec{A}\cdot\vec{B} - A_0 B_0$. The notation on spinors, etc., is given below. We note that, for the creation and destruction of antifermions, the spinors appear in the "unnatural" order. Care must be taken of minus signs, which can arise from the anticommutation of the spinor fields in this case.

The integration over d^4x in Eq. (B. 2), with the plane waves which come from the particle factors, yields a 4-dimensional conservation delta function. Hence we define the Feynman amplitude $\mathfrak{M}$ through

$$S_{BA} = -i\,(2\pi)^4 \delta^4(P_B - P_A)\left(\prod_i \frac{m_i}{E_i} \prod_j \frac{1}{2E_j}\right)^{\frac{1}{2}} \mathfrak{M}$$

(B. 6)

The product factors in the square root are just those kinematic factors which appear in Eqs. (B. 3) to (B. 5). The amplitude $\mathcal{M}$ involves spinor products of the fermion spinors, etc. and is a Lorentz invariant quantity, depending on 4-scalar products of the momenta involved.

The transition probability $dw_{B\leftarrow A}$ is

$$dw_{B\leftarrow A} = (2\pi)^4 |\mathcal{M}|^2 \prod_i \frac{m_i}{E_i} \prod_j \frac{1}{2E_j} \delta^4(P_B - P_A) \tag{B. 7}$$

where the product on i is over fermion factors and the one on j is over boson factors. For each particle in the final state we have a density of states, $d^3p/(2\pi)^3$.

2. Dirac Equation

The notation on the Dirac equation is that of Pauli in the Handbuch der Physik, also used by Källén in his lectures. In covariant form the Dirac equation for free particles is

$$\left(\gamma_\alpha \frac{\partial}{\partial x_\alpha} + m\right)\psi = 0 \tag{B. 8}$$

where γ_α are four 4 x 4 Hermitean matrices satisfying the anticommutation rules, $\{\gamma_\alpha, \gamma_\beta\} = 2\delta_{\alpha\beta}$ Explicitly, $\vec{\gamma} = -i\beta\vec{\alpha}$ $\gamma_4 = \beta$, where $\vec{\alpha}$ and β are the Dirac matrices,

$$\vec{\alpha} = \begin{pmatrix} 0 & \vec{\sigma} \\ \vec{\sigma} & 0 \end{pmatrix} \qquad \beta = \begin{pmatrix} 1 & 0 \\ 0 & -1 \end{pmatrix} \tag{B. 9}$$

In Eq. (B. 9) the symbols $\vec{\sigma}$ and 1 are 2 x 2 Pauli operators. In addition to the four γ's and the unit matrix, we shall need $\gamma_5 = \gamma_1\gamma_2\gamma_3\gamma_4$:

$$\gamma_5 = \begin{pmatrix} 0 & -1 \\ -1 & 0 \end{pmatrix} \tag{B. 10}$$

The adjoint field is defined by

$$\overline{\psi} = \psi^{\dagger}\gamma_4 \tag{B. 11}$$

It satisfies the equation of motion,

$$-\frac{\partial\overline{\psi}}{\partial x_\alpha}\gamma_\alpha + m\overline{\psi} = 0 \tag{B. 12}$$

The plane-wave solutions for the free-particle equation (B. 8) can be written

Positive energy

$$u_{1,2}(p) = \sqrt{\frac{E+m}{2m}}\begin{pmatrix} \chi_{1,2} \\ \frac{\vec{\sigma}\cdot\vec{p}}{E+m}\chi_{1,2} \end{pmatrix} \tag{B. 13}$$

Negative energy

$$v_{1,2}(p) = \pm\sqrt{\frac{E+m}{2m}}\begin{pmatrix} \frac{\vec{\sigma}\cdot\vec{p}}{E+m}\chi_{1,2} \\ \chi_{1,2} \end{pmatrix} \tag{B. 14}$$

In Eqs. (B. 13) and (B. 14), the parameter E is positive. The spinor $\chi_{1,2}$ is a 2-element Pauli spinor [$\chi_1 = \binom{1}{0}$, $\chi_2 = \binom{0}{1}$]. The spinor $u_j(p)$ is a positive-energy spinor representing a particle with momentum $\vec{p}$ and spin j. The spinor $v_j(p)$ represents a negative-energy particle with momentum $-\vec{p}$, and spin j. The charge conjugate spinor $v_j^c(p)$ represents a positive-energy antiparticle of momentum $\vec{p}$ and opposite spin [see Eq. (E. 22)].

The plane-wave spinors u(p) and v(p) satisfy the equations of motion,

$$(i\gamma\cdot p + m)u(p) = 0$$
$$(i\gamma\cdot p - m)v(p) = 0 \tag{B. 15}$$

and their adjoints,

$$\bar{u}(p)(i\gamma\cdot p + m) = 0$$
$$\bar{v}(p)(i\gamma\cdot p - m) = 0 \tag{B. 16}$$

The normalization of these spinors is

$$\bar{u}_i(p)u_j(p) = \delta_{ij}$$
$$\bar{u}_i(p)v_j(p) = 0$$
$$\bar{v}_i(p)v_j(p) = -\delta_{ij} \tag{B. 17}$$

The projection operators for positive- and negative-energy states are

$$\Lambda_+(p) \equiv \sum_{j=1}^{2} u_j(p)\bar{u}_j(p) = \frac{m - i\gamma\cdot p}{2m}$$
$$\Lambda_-(p) \equiv \sum_{j=1}^{2} v_j(p)\bar{v}_j(p) = \frac{-m - i\gamma\cdot p}{2m} \tag{B. 18}$$

Note that Λ_- is not a conventional projection operator, since $\Lambda_- v = -v$. But its definition is the appropriate one for performing spin sums.

3. Bilinear Forms

The most general 4 x 4 matrix needs 16 elements to describe it. This general form can be made up of a linear combination of 16 Dirac matrices. These are organized into 5 groups according to their Lorentz transformation properties. The five groups of operators are denoted by O_i, where i = 1, 2, 3, 4, 5 stands for scalar, vector, tensor, axial vector, and pseudoscalar, in that order. Explicitly, the 16 operators are:

i	Name	O_i	
1	S	1	
2	V	γ_α	$\alpha = 1, 2, 3, 4$
3	T	$\sigma_{\alpha\beta} = \frac{1}{2i}(\gamma_\alpha\gamma_\beta - \gamma_\beta\gamma_\alpha)$	$\alpha, \beta = 1, 2, 3, 4$
4	A	$i\gamma_\alpha\gamma_5$	$\alpha = 1, 2, 3, 4$
5	P	γ_5	

(B. 19)

The names are derived from the spatial-transformation properties of the bilinear form, $(\bar{\psi}_1 O_i \psi_2)$, as shown in Appendix E [Eq. (E. 16)]. The bilinear forms transform under proper Lorentz transformations as scalars (S and P), 4-vectors (V and A), and 4-tensors (T). The factors of i appearing in T and A assure that the operator O_i is Hermitean ($O_i = O_i^\dagger$).

The nonrelativistic reduction of the bilinear forms is as follows: Start with $(\bar{\psi} O_i L_i \psi)$, where the L_i are appropriate tensors, namely,

$$L_1 = L$$

$$L_2 = L_\alpha = (\vec{L}, iL_0)$$

$$L_3 = L_{\alpha\beta} = -L_{\beta\alpha}, \text{ with } \begin{array}{l} \vec{L} = \vec{i}L_{23} + \vec{j}L_{31} + \vec{k}L_{12} \\ \vec{L}_0 = \vec{i}L_{14} + \vec{j}L_{24} + \vec{k}L_{34} \end{array}$$

$$L_4 = L_\alpha = (\vec{L}, iL_0)$$

$$L_5 = L$$

(B. 20)

Then the transition from $(\overline{\psi}_1 \, O_i \, L_i \, \psi_2)$ to the nonrelativistic Pauli form, $\langle \chi_1 | O_i^{NR} | \chi_2 \rangle$, yields the following operators O_i^{NR}:

$$O_1^{NR} = L$$

$$O_2^{NR} = i L_0$$

$$O_3^{NR} = \vec{\sigma} \cdot \vec{L}$$

$$O_4^{NR} = -\vec{\sigma} \cdot \vec{L}$$

$$O_5^{NR} = \frac{1}{2mi} \vec{\sigma} \cdot \vec{\nabla} L$$

(B. 21)

We note that S and V reduce to a scalar form (the Fermi interaction of beta decay), while T and A reduce to a spin vector form (the Gamow-Teller interaction of beta decay). P actually has no nonrelativistic limit.

One useful fact about traces of γ matrices involving γ_5 is that

$$\frac{1}{4} \mathrm{Tr}\left[\gamma_5 (\gamma \cdot a)(\gamma \cdot b)(\gamma \cdot c)(\gamma \cdot d) \right] = \det (a\, b\, c\, d)$$

(B. 22)

where det stands for determinant. Traces of less than four other γ's and γ_5 vanish.

APPENDIX C: PHASE SPACE INTEGRALS

In the decay of a system A of mass M_A into a final state B, where there are a total of x bosons and 2y fermions in states A and B together, the dimensionless phase space integral F_{BA} is defined by Eq. (1.6),

$$F_{BA} = (2\pi)^4 M_A^{7-2x-6y} \prod_{\text{final}} \int \frac{d^3 p_i}{(2\pi)^3} \prod_{j=1}^{x} (2E_j)^{-1} \delta^4(P_B - P_A) \tag{C.1}$$

The first product (of integrals) is over all particles in the final state. The second product is over bosons only (but in both states A and B). The integrals are to be evaluated in the rest frame of A ($\vec{P}_A = 0$).

1. Two-Particle Final State

The integrals for two particles are merely over delta functions. There are three separate cases (B → 2F, B → 2B, F → BF, where B and F stand for boson and fermion):

(a) B → 2F:

$$F_{BA} = \frac{1}{16\pi} \sqrt{1 - \left(\frac{m_1 + m_2}{M}\right)^2} \sqrt{1 - \left(\frac{m_1 - m_2}{M}\right)^2} \left[1 - \left(\frac{m_1^2 - m_2^2}{M^2}\right)^2\right] \tag{C.2}$$

where M, m_1, and m_2 are the masses of the initial boson and the two fermions, respectively.

(b) B → 2B :

$$F_{BA} = \frac{1}{16\pi}\sqrt{1-\left(\frac{m_1+m_2}{M}\right)^2}\sqrt{1-\left(\frac{m_1-m_2}{M}\right)^2} \tag{C. 3}$$

(c) F → BF:

$$F_{BA} = \frac{1}{8\pi}\sqrt{1-\left(\frac{m+\mu}{M}\right)^2}\sqrt{1-\left(\frac{m-\mu}{M}\right)^2}\left(1+\frac{m^2-\mu^2}{M^2}\right) \tag{C. 4}$$

where M, m, and μ are the masses of the initial and final fermions and the boson, respectively.

2. Three-Particle Final State: $(M \to m_1, m_2, m_3)$

For three particles in the final state, the phase space integrals are more complicated than for two particles. First of all, there are more possible combinations of bosons and fermions (F → FFF, B → BFF, F → BBF, B → BBB). Secondly, the integration over phase space involves an actual integration over a spectrum. The general case can be expressed in terms of simple functions and elliptic integrals, but the result is not particularly useful. Hence we shall consider a number of special cases which are appropriate for decay processes.

(a) All particles nonrelativistic:

If the energy release $(Q = M - m_1 - m_2 - m_3)$ is small compared to all the masses in the final state, the particles can be treated as nonrelativistic. Then the integration in Eq. (C · 1) is straightforward. The result is

$$F_{BA} = \frac{1}{8\pi^2 M^5} \prod_{j=1}^{x} \left(\frac{M}{2m_j}\right) \left(\frac{m_1 m_2 m_3}{m_1 + m_2 + m_3}\right)^{3/2} Q^2 \tag{C.5}$$

As usual, the product of x factors is for the bosons involved. The energy spectrum of each particle is proportional to $\sqrt{x(1-x)}\,dx$, where x is the ratio of kinetic energy to the maximum kinetic energy, $T_{1,\,max} = (m_2 + m_3)\,Q/(m_1 + m_2 + m_3)$.

(b) Fermion decaying into three relativistic fermions:

For this case the phase space integral reduces to

$$F_{BA} = \frac{1}{4\pi^3}\left(\frac{\Delta}{M}\right)^5 \int_0^1 dx\; x^2\left(1 - x + \frac{x^2}{6}\right) \tag{C.6}$$

where $\Delta = M/2$ is the maximum energy of one of the fermions. The integrand is the phase space energy spectrum of each fermion, with energy in units of the maximum value Δ. The result of the final integration is

$$F_{BA} = \frac{7}{15\,(8\pi)^3} = 2.95 \times 10^{-5} \tag{C.7}$$

(c) Boson decaying into one relativistic boson and two relativistic fermions:

This case differs from the previous one by the presence of a factor 1/2 for the decaying boson, and a factor M/2E for the relativistic boson in the final state. Thus the result for F_{BA} is

$$F_{BA} = \frac{1}{8\pi^3}\left(\frac{\Delta}{M}\right)^5 \int_0^1 dx\, x\left(1 - x + \frac{x^2}{6}\right) \tag{C.8}$$

where the integrand is the energy spectrum of the boson. The final value of F_{BA} is

$$F_{BA} = \frac{5}{12(8\pi)^3} = 2.64 \times 10^{-5} \tag{C.9}$$

We note that this is not very different from the three-fermion value of Eq. (C.7).

Baryonic three-body decay modes involve the emission of leptons (e, ν or μ, ν) and a baryon. Such decays can be divided approximately into two classes:

1. Low Q value, negligible baryon recoil
2. High Q value, baryon recoil

In the first class, the charged lepton mass cannot always be neglected, but the kinetic energy of the baryon can be ignored. Ordinary nuclear beta decay falls in this class. In the second category, the leptons can be taken to have zero mass, but the baryon recoil must be included. Lambda and sigma beta decays are examples of this class.

(d) Baryon decaying into "stationary" baryon, neutrino, and charged lepton:

Let the initial baryon have mass M, the final baryon mass M', and the lepton mass m. Let the maximum energy of the lepton be $\Delta = (M^2 - M'^2 + m^2)/2M \simeq M - M'$. The phase space integral of Eq. (C.1) in this no-recoil approximation is just

$$F_{BA} = \frac{1}{2\pi^3 M^5} \int_m^\Delta dE\; pE(\Delta - E)^2 \tag{C.10}$$

The integrand is the familiar beta spectrum for neutron decay. The integrated result (the f function of ft values) can be written

$$F_{BA} = \frac{1}{60\pi^3}\left(\frac{\Delta}{M}\right)^5 R_o\left(\frac{m}{\Delta}\right) \tag{C. 11}$$

where $R_o(m/\Delta)$ is a reduction factor because of the finite lepton mass,

$$R_o(x) = \sqrt{1-x^2}\left(1 - \frac{9}{2}x^2 + 4x^4\right) + \frac{15}{2}x^4 \ln\left(\frac{1+\sqrt{1-x^2}}{x}\right) \tag{C. 12}$$

For high energies ($m/\Delta \to 0$), $R_o \to 1$ and $F_{BA} \sim \Delta^5$. Eventually, of course, the formula fails because of the neglect of recoil.

For a boson decaying into a "stationary" boson, plus neutrino and and charged lepton, the phase space integral of Eq. (C. 1) is one-quarter of the expression (C. 11).

(e) Baryon decaying into recoiling baryon, neutrino, and relativistic lepton:

In this limiting case of two massless leptons, the phase space integral becomes

$$F_{BA} = \frac{1}{48\pi^3 M^5}\int_{M'}^{\epsilon} dE \; pE \left(3M^2 + M'^2 - 6ME + 2E^2\right) \tag{C. 13}$$

Here the integrand is the energy spectrum of the final fermion of mass M', and $\epsilon = (M^2 + M'^2)/2M$ is its maximum total energy.

If the lepton spectrum is desired, F_{BA} can be written in the alternative form,

$$F_{BA} = \frac{1}{16\pi^3}\left(\frac{\Delta}{M}\right)^5 \int_0^1 dx \frac{x^2(1-x)^2}{\left(\frac{M}{2\Delta} - x\right)^3}\left[\left(\frac{M}{\Delta} - x\right)^2\left(\frac{M}{\Delta} - 1 - x\right) - \frac{x^2}{3}(1-x)\right] \tag{C. 14}$$

where x is the lepton energy in units of its maximum value, $\Delta = (M^2 - M'^2)/2M$. The integrand is the lepton energy spectrum.

The final integration in Eq. (C. 13) or in (C. 14) is elementary, if tedious. The result for F_{BA} can be written in analogy with Eq. (C. 11) as

$$F_{BA} = \frac{1}{60\pi^3}\left(\frac{\Delta}{M}\right)^5 R_1\left(\frac{\Delta}{M}\right) \tag{C. 15}$$

where $R_1(\Delta/M)$ is a recoil correction factor,

$$R_1(z) = \frac{1}{2} - \frac{5}{8z} - \frac{5}{4z^2} + \frac{45}{16z^3} - \frac{15}{16z^4} - \frac{15}{32}\frac{(1-2z)^2}{z^5}\ln(1-2z) \tag{C. 16}$$

$R_1(z)$ varies from 1. 00 at z = 0 to the value 1. 75 at z = 1/2. We see, therefore, that the recoil correction is not of crucial importance in order-of-magnitude estimates. For z = 1/2 we recover the three-relativistic-fermion result of Eq. (C. 7).

(f) Boson decaying into boson and two relativistic fermions:

The case of two massless leptons and a boson in the final state is closely analogous to case (e). The only difference is that the integrand of Eq. (C. 13) is multiplied by the factor M/4E. The phase space integral then becomes

$$F_{BA} = \frac{1}{60\pi^3}\left(\frac{\Delta}{M}\right)^5 R_2\left(\frac{\Delta}{M}\right) \tag{C. 17}$$

where Δ is the maximum lepton energy, as usual, and the boson recoil correction factor is

$$R_2(z) = \frac{5}{64}\left[\frac{9}{z^4} - \frac{15}{z^3} - \frac{2}{z} + \frac{3}{2}\frac{(3-2z)(1-2z)}{z^5}\ln(1-2z)\right] \tag{C. 18}$$

The limiting values of R_2 are 0.25 for z = 0 (negligible boson recoil) and 25/16 = 1.56 for z = 1/2 (boson of zero mass).

The above expressions are all that are needed for the order-of-magnitude considerations of Sec. 1.4. For three-body decays involving a neutrino (but keeping the other lepton's mass finite), the necessary integrals are stated by Fujii and Kawaguchi (1959).

The covariant three-body phase space distribution (corresponding here to the transition B→BBB) is treated in detail in Appendix D. The energy distribution of one of the particles is given by Eq. (D.22) or (D.24).

APPENDIX D: COVARIANT THREE-BODY PHASE SPACE CALCULATIONS

For a transition $A \rightarrow B$ with three particles of masses m_1, m_2, and m_3 in the final state, the transition rate can be written as

$$dw_{BA} \prod_i = F(P, p_1, p_2, p_3) \frac{d^3p_1}{E_1} \frac{d^3p_2}{E_2} \frac{d^3p_3}{E_3} \delta^4(p_1 + p_2 + p_3 - P) \tag{D. 1}$$

where the initial state has total 4-momentum P and the factor $\prod_i$ stands for a product of factors 2E or E/m for the particles in the state A. The function F is a Lorentz invariant function of the scalar products of the various 4-momenta. In fact, both sides of Eq. (D. 1) are Lorentz invariant. The factor $\prod_i$ takes into account the Lorentz-FitzGerald contraction of the normalization volumes in the initial state.

In decay processes or reactions the desired transition rate is often the directional distribution of one of the particles in the final state relative to some axis, such as the direction of the incident beam or the spin of a decaying particle. Hence it is necessary to integrate over two of the three final momenta, subject to the conservation laws. The virtue of Eq. (D. 1) is its Lorentz invariance, which allows us to calculate in some reference frame that is particularly convenient and then generalize the result.

We first note that the density-of-states factor d^3p/E can be written in a manifestly covariant form,

$$\frac{d^3p}{E} = 2\int dp_0 \, \delta(p^2 + m^2) \, d^3p \tag{D. 2}$$

where $p^2 + m^2 = (\vec{p})^2 + m^2 - p_0^2 = E^2 - p_0^2$. This means that the three-dimensional integrations over momenta in Eq. (D. 1) can be replaced by four-dimensional integrations according to Eq. (D. 2).

Let us define the right-hand side of Eq. (D. 1), integrated over $d^3p_1 d^3p_2$, to be $(I\, d^3p_3/E_3)$, where

$$I_j = \iint F_j \frac{d^3p_1}{E_1} \frac{d^3p_2}{E_2} \delta^4(p_1+p_2+p_3-P) \tag{D. 3}$$

Here F_j stands for a particular Lorentz invariant combination of 4-momenta. The simplest forms for F_j will be treated separately below. Using Eq. (D. 2), I_j can be written as

$$I_j = 4\iint d^4p_1\, d^4p_2\, F_j\, \delta(p_1^2+m_1^2)\, \delta(p_2^2+m_2^2)\, \delta^4(p_1+p_2+p_3-P) \tag{D. 4}$$

where $d^4p = d^3p\, dp_o$.

We introduce new variables,

$$K = p_1 + p_2 \qquad p_1 = \frac{K+Q}{2}$$
$$Q = p_1 - p_2 \qquad p_2 = \frac{K-Q}{2} \tag{D. 5}$$

with the properties that $d^4p_1\, d^4p_2 = 2^{-4}\, d^4K\, d^4Q$ and

$$p_1^2 + m_1^2 = \frac{1}{4}(K^2+Q^2+2K\cdot Q) + m_1^2$$

$$p_2^2 + m_2^2 = \frac{1}{4}(K^2+Q^2-2K\cdot Q) + m_2^2$$

Then the product of the two "mass-shell" delta functions becomes

$$\delta(p_1^2+m_1^2)\,\delta(p_2^2+m_2^2) = 4\,\delta(K^2+Q^2+2\mu^2)\,\delta(K\cdot Q+\rho^2) \tag{D. 6}$$

where

$$\mu^2 = m_1^2 + m_2^2$$

$$\rho^2 = m_1^2 - m_2^2 \tag{D. 7}$$

The integral I_j can now be expressed as

$$I_j = \iint d^4K\, d^4Q\, F_j\, \delta(K^2+Q^2+2\mu^2)\,\delta(K\cdot Q+\rho^2)\,\delta^4(K+p_3-P) \tag{D. 8}$$

The integration over d^4K can now be performed trivially to give

$$I_j = \int d^4Q\, F_j\, \delta(K^2+Q^2+2\mu^2)\,\delta(K\cdot Q+\rho^2) \tag{D. 9}$$

In Eq. (D. 9) and below we must remember that $K = P - p_3$.

To perform the remaining integration over d^4Q, we exploit the Lorentz invariance of I_j and choose a convenient coordinate frame for calculation. This frame is the one where $K = (0,\, iK_0)$, namely, the frame where $\vec{p}_1 + \vec{p}_2 = 0$. In this coordinate system,

$$K\cdot Q = -K_0 Q_0 \qquad K^2+Q^2+2\mu^2 = (\vec{Q})^2 - Q_0^2 - K_0^2 + 2\mu^2 \tag{D. 10}$$

Then

$$I_j = \int d^3Q \int dQ_o\, F_j\, \delta\left((\vec{Q})^2 - Q_o^2 - K_o^2 + 2\mu^2\right) \delta\left(K_o Q_o - \rho^2\right) \tag{D. 11}$$

Evidently the integration over dQ_o can now be carried out easily. The result is

$$I_j = \frac{1}{K_o} \int d^3Q\, F_j\left(Q_o = \frac{\rho^2}{K_o}\right) \delta\left[(\vec{Q})^2 - K_o^2\left(1 - \frac{2\mu^2}{K_o^2} + \frac{\rho^4}{K_o^4}\right)\right] \tag{D. 12}$$

Introduction of a new variable,

$$\vec{x} = \frac{\vec{Q}}{K_o\sqrt{1 - \frac{2\mu^2}{K_o^2} + \frac{\rho^4}{K_o^4}}} \tag{D. 13}$$

allows Eq. (D. 12) to be written in the more compact form,

$$I_j = \frac{1}{2}\sqrt{1 - \frac{2\mu^2}{K_o^2} + \frac{\rho^4}{K_o^4}} \int dx \int d\Omega_Q\, F_j\left(Q_o = \frac{\rho^2}{K_o}\right) \delta(x - 1) \tag{D. 14}$$

To proceed further we must specify the detailed dependence of F_j on Q. We shall consider enough special cases so that the method will be clear.

(1) $F_1 = 1$:

For this form, the integration in Eq. (D.14) is trivial. The integral is equal to 4π. We must, however, restore the Lorentz invariance of I_j. Evidently all that need be done is to replace K_o^2 by $-K^2$; hence we find

$$I_1 = 2\pi \sqrt{1 + \frac{2\mu^2}{K^2} + \frac{\rho^4}{K^4}} \tag{D.15}$$

(2) $F_2 = Q^2$:

We can write Q^2 in the notation of Eq. (D.14):

$$Q^2 = (\vec{Q})^2 - Q_o^2 = K_o^2\left(1 - \frac{2\mu^2}{K_o^2} + \frac{\rho^4}{K_o^4}\right)x^2 - \frac{\rho^4}{K_o^2}$$

When this is evaluated at x = 1, the result is

$$Q^2 = K_o^2 - 2\mu^2$$

Consequently the Lorentz invariant generalization is

$$I_2 = (-K^2 - 2\mu^2)\, I_1 \tag{D.16}$$

(3) $F_3 = A \cdot Q$:

In this scalar product the 4-vector A can be any 4-vector which does not depend on Q. Written out, $A \cdot Q$ is

$$A \cdot Q = \vec{A} \cdot \vec{Q} - A_o Q_o = \vec{A} \cdot \vec{Q} - \frac{\rho^2 A_o}{K_o}$$

On integration over angles in Eq. (D.14), the three-vector term vanishes; thus the result in the special coordinate frame is

$$I_3 = -\rho^2 \frac{A_0}{K_0} I_1$$

Evidently the Lorentz invariant generalization is

$$I_3 = -\rho^2 \frac{(A \cdot K)}{K^2} I_1 \qquad \text{(D. 17)}$$

(4) $F_4 = (A \cdot Q)(B \cdot Q)$:

We have explicitly

$$(A \cdot Q)(B \cdot Q) = (\vec{A} \cdot \vec{Q})(\vec{B} \cdot \vec{Q}) + \frac{A_0 B_0 \rho^4}{K_0^2} - \frac{\rho^2}{K_0}\left(A_0 \vec{B} \cdot \vec{Q} + B_0 \vec{A} \cdot \vec{Q}\right)$$

The last term will vanish on integration over angles in Eq. (D. 14), while the first term will average to $1/3\ (\vec{A} \cdot \vec{B})\, Q^2$. Thus the effective integrand in Eq. (D. 14), evaluated at $x = 1$, is

$$(A \cdot Q)(B \cdot Q)_{eff} = \frac{1}{3} \vec{A} \cdot \vec{B} \left(1 - \frac{2\mu^2}{K_0^2} + \frac{\rho^4}{K_0^4}\right) K_0^2 + \frac{A_0 B_0 \rho^4}{K_0^2}$$

This means that the noninvariant result for I_4 is

$$I_4 = \frac{1}{3}\left[(\vec{A} \cdot \vec{B}) K_0^2 \left(1 - \frac{2\mu^2}{K_0^2} + \frac{\rho^4}{K_0^4}\right) + \frac{3A_0 B_0 \rho^4}{K_0^2}\right] I_1$$

The Lorentz invariant generalization is easily found to be

$$I_4 = \frac{1}{3} I_1 \left[(A\cdot K)(B\cdot K)\left(1 + \frac{2\mu^2}{K^2} + \frac{4\rho^4}{K^4}\right) - (A\cdot B)K^2\left(1 + \frac{2\mu^2}{K^2} + \frac{\rho^4}{K^4}\right) \right] \qquad (D.18)$$

For reference purposes we note that I_1, given by Eq. (D. 15), can also be written as

$$I_1 = 2\pi \sqrt{\left(1 + \frac{(m_1+m_2)^2}{K^2}\right)\left(1 + \frac{(m_1-m_2)^2}{K^2}\right)} \qquad (D.19)$$

In this form it bears a remarkable similarity to Eq. (C. 3), to which it is intimately related.

Mu-Meson Decay

In mu-meson decay the two particles whose momenta are integrated over are neutrinos with zero mass. In this circumstance, the results obtained above simplify greatly. For reference we list these special forms:

$$F_1 = 1 \qquad I_1 = 2\pi$$

$$F_2 = Q^2 \qquad I_2 = -2\pi K^2$$

$$F_3 = A\cdot Q \qquad I_3 = 0$$

$$F_4 = (A\cdot Q)(B\cdot Q) \qquad I_4 = \frac{2\pi}{3}\left[(A\cdot K)(B\cdot K) - (A\cdot B)K^2\right] \qquad (D.20)$$

where $K = P - p_3$.

Covariant Statistical Energy Distribution of One Particle in Three

The energy distribution of one particle, assuming F is constant in Eq. (D. 1), can be written down immediately from Eq. (D. 15):

$$d\varpi = 2\pi \frac{d^3p_3}{E_3} \frac{1}{(-K^2)} \sqrt{K^4 + 2\mu^2 K^2 + \rho^4} \tag{D. 21}$$

with $K = P - p_3$, $\mu^2 = m_1^2 + m_2^2$, and $\rho = m_1^2 - m_2^2$. In the center-of momentum frame, after integration over angles, this becomes

$$d\varpi = 8\pi^2 \, p\sqrt{E_0 - E} \left\{ \frac{\sqrt{E_0 - E + \frac{2m_1m_2}{M}}}{E_0 - E + \frac{(m_1+m_2)^2}{2M}} \right\} dE \tag{D. 22}$$

where $p = \sqrt{E^2 - m_3^2}$ is the momentum of the third particle, E its total energy, and

$$E_0 = \frac{M^2 + m_3^2 - (m_1+m_2)^2}{2M} \tag{D. 23}$$

its maximum energy.

The result in Eq. (D. 22) can be cast in various forms. One expression which is useful for comparison with a nonrelativistic limit is in terms of the kinetic energy t of the third particle (e. g., Dalitz, 1956):

$$d\varpi = \frac{16\pi^2 (M m_3)^{\frac{1}{2}}}{M - m_3} \sqrt{t(t_0 - t)} \left\{ \frac{\left(1 + \frac{t}{2m_3}\right)^{\frac{1}{2}} \left(1 - \left(\frac{m_1 - m_2}{M - m_3}\right)^2 - \frac{2Mt}{(M - m_3)^2}\right)^{\frac{1}{2}}}{1 - \frac{2Mt}{(M - m_3)^2}} \right\} dt \tag{D. 24}$$

where $t_o = E_o - m_3$ is the maximum kinetic energy of particle 3. In the nonrelativistic limit, the curly bracket becomes unity, and the familiar $\sqrt{t(t_o - t)}$ spectrum results.

APPENDIX E: SPACE INVERSION, CHARGE CONJUGATION, TIME REVERSAL, AND G CONJUGATION

The symmetry operations of space inversion (P), charge conjugation (C), time reversal (T), and G conjugation (G) are discussed in several places (Wick, 1958; Lüders, 1959; Marshak and Sudarshan, 1961). Consequently, only a brief summary for reference purposes will be given here. The question of arbitrary phase factors will be ignored, and only one simple, consistent choice will be made.

1. Space Inversion

In ordinary quantum mechanics, the invariance of the Hamiltonian under the space inversion transformation, (x, y, z) → (-x, -y, -z), leads to the possibility of classifying states of the system according to a parity quantum number, ± 1. To be precise, there exists a unitary operator P such that all coordinate, momentum, and spin operators transform according to

$$\begin{aligned} \vec{x}' &\equiv P^{-1}\vec{x}P = -\vec{x} \\ \vec{p}' &\equiv P^{-1}\vec{p}P = -\vec{p} \\ \vec{s}' &\equiv P^{-1}\vec{s}P = +\vec{s} \end{aligned} \tag{E. 1}$$

while the state vectors with definite parity satisfy

$$P|\ \rangle = \pm|\ \rangle \tag{E. 2}$$

Equation (E. 1) preserves the commutation relations and equations of motion.

For quantum fields there is a generalization corresponding to Eq. (E. 1) for the field operators. We shall deal with the various cases in turn.

(a) Electromagnetic field:

The charge of a particle is customarily viewed as a true scalar quantity. This then leads in classical electromagnetism to the following spatial-inversion properties for the charge density and current density:

$$\rho'(\vec{x}) = \rho(-\vec{x})$$

$$j_k'(\vec{x}) = -j_k(-\vec{x}) \qquad (k = 1, 2, 3)$$

(E. 3)

From the invariance of Maxwell's equations under space inversion, it can be concluded that the corresponding transformations of the electromagnetic fields are

$$E_k'(\vec{x}) = -E_k(-\vec{x})$$

$$(k = 1, 2, 3)$$

$$B_k'(\vec{x}) = +B_k(-\vec{x})$$

$\vec{E}$ is a polar vector; $\vec{B}$ is an axial vector. The vector potential 4-vector $A_\alpha = (\vec{A}, i\Phi)$ transforms as

$$A_k'(\vec{x}) = -A_k(-\vec{x})$$

$$\Phi'(\vec{x}) = +\Phi(-\vec{x})$$

The quantum-mechanical equivalents of these classical results are all of the form

$$E_k'(\vec{x}) \equiv P^{-1} E_k(\vec{x}) P = -E_k(-\vec{x})$$

(E. 4)

It is useful to note that the two Lorentz invariant combinations of electromagnetic fields, $(E^2 - B^2)$ and $\vec{E} \cdot \vec{B}$, have opposite parities,

$$P^{-1}(E^2 - B^2)P = (E^2 - B^2)$$

$$P^{-1}(\vec{E}\cdot\vec{B})P = -\vec{E}\cdot\vec{B} \tag{E. 5}$$

(b) Scalar and pseudoscalar fields:

Spinless bosons are described by a field operator $\phi(\vec{x}, t)$ which is rotationally invariant. But two choices are possible for the behavior of such a field under space inversion, corresponding to a scalar or pseudoscalar boson. For scalar bosons, the unitary operator P causes the transformation,

$$\phi'(\vec{x}) \equiv P^{-1}\phi(\vec{x})P = +\phi(-\vec{x}) \tag{E. 6}$$

while for pseudoscalar particles, the transformation is

$$\phi'(\vec{x}) \equiv P^{-1}\phi(\vec{x})P = -\phi(-\vec{x}) \tag{E. 7}$$

The pion field is pseudoscalar and behaves according to Eq. (E. 7).

When the field operator is expanded in an orthonormal set, for example, plane waves, then the unitary operator P is assumed to act only on the creation and destruction operators. Thus, if $\phi(x, t)$ is expanded as

$$\phi(\vec{x},t) = \frac{1}{\sqrt{V}}\sum_k \frac{1}{\sqrt{2\omega_k}}\left(a_k e^{i\vec{k}\cdot\vec{x} - i\omega_k t} + b_k^\dagger e^{-i\vec{k}\cdot\vec{x} + i\omega_k t}\right) \tag{E. 8}$$

then the transformed field $\phi'(\vec{x})$ is

$$\phi'(\vec{x},t) = \frac{1}{\sqrt{V}}\sum_k \frac{1}{\sqrt{2\omega_k}}\left(P^{-1} a_k P\, e^{i\vec{k}\cdot\vec{x} - i\omega_k t} + P^{-1} b_k^+ P\, e^{-i\vec{k}\cdot\vec{x} + i\omega_k t}\right)$$

Comparison of this result with $\phi(-\vec{x}, t)$, according to Eq. (E. 6) or (E. 7), shows that the creation and destruction operators transform as

$$P^{-1} a_k P = \eta_P a_{-k} \qquad P^{-1} b_k^+ P = \eta_P b_{-k}^+ \tag{E. 9}$$

and their adjoint forms, where $\eta_P = +1$ for scalar particles and $\eta_P = -1$ for pseudoscalar particles.

(c) Dirac fields:

The single-particle Dirac wave functions have as their space-inversion law the transformation

$$\psi'(\vec{x}) = \beta\psi(-\vec{x}) \tag{E. 10}$$

where $\beta = \gamma_4$. In terms of the plane-wave spinors of Eqs. (B. 13) and (B. 14), this becomes

$$\begin{aligned} u_j'(\vec{p}) &= \beta u_j(\vec{p}) = u_j(-\vec{p}) \\ v_j'(\vec{p}) &= \beta v_j(\vec{p}) = -v_j(-\vec{p}) \end{aligned} \tag{E. 11}$$

For the Dirac spinor field the unitary transformation equivalent to Eq. (E. 10) is

$$\psi'(\vec{x}) \equiv P^{-1}\psi(\vec{x})P = \beta\psi(-\vec{x}) \tag{E. 12}$$

If a plane-wave expansion similar to Eq. (E. 8) is made,

$$\psi(\vec{x},t) = \frac{1}{\sqrt{V}}\sum_{p,j}\left(\frac{m}{E}\right)^{\frac{1}{2}}\left(u_j(p)e^{i\vec{p}\cdot\vec{x}-iEt}\, a_{p,j} + v_j(p)e^{-i\vec{p}\cdot\vec{x}+iEt}\, b^{+}_{p,j}\right) \tag{E. 13}$$

then it is readily found from Eqs. (E. 10) and (E. 11) that the creation and destruction operators transform under space inversion as

$$P^{-1}a_{p,j}P = a_{-p,j} \qquad P^{-1}b^{+}_{p,j}P = -b^{+}_{-p,j} \tag{E. 14}$$

and their adjoint equations. The relative minus sign between the particle and antiparticle forms leads to the conclusion that a particle-antiparticle pair has odd intrinsic parity.

(d) Bilinear forms:

From the transformation law of Eq. (E. 12) for the Dirac field, it is straightforward to show that the bilinear forms $\left(\overline{\psi}_a(\vec{x})\, O_i\, \psi_b(\vec{x})\right)$ transform under space inversion according to the following rule:

$$P^{-1}\left(\overline{\psi}_a(\vec{x})O_{i\alpha}\psi_b(\vec{x})\right)P = \eta^{P}_{i\alpha}\left(\overline{\psi}_a(-\vec{x})O_{i\alpha}\psi_b(-\vec{x})\right) \tag{E. 15}$$

where i = 1, 2, 3, 4, 5 for S, V, T, A, P and the subscript α stands for the appropriate tensor index or indices. The phase factor $\eta^{P}_{i\alpha}$ is

Scalar:	$+1$	
Vector:	-1 for $\alpha = 1, 2, 3;$	$+1$ for $\alpha = 4$
Tensor:	$+1$ for $\alpha, \beta = 1, 2, 3;$	-1 for α or $\beta = 4$
Axial vector:	$+1$ for $\alpha = 1, 2, 3;$	-1 for $\alpha = 4$
Pseudoscalar:	-1	(E. 16)

The spatial components of all these forms transform as expected from their names, the spatial parts of the tensor operator being the Dirac spin operator.

2. Charge Conjugation

The idea of charge conjugation first arose from the symmetry of the Dirac theory of electrons and positrons interacting with the electromagnetic field; but it now has a broader meaning and perhaps should be called particle-antiparticle conjugation, since it applies also to electrically neutral systems (e. g., K^o, $\overline{K}^o$). Nevertheless, it is useful to keep the connection with electric charge in mind.

(a) Charged Scalar or Pseudoscalar field:

A complex scalar or pseudoscalar field $\phi = \phi_1 + i\,\phi_2$, where ϕ_1 and ϕ_2 are Hermitean operators, describes spinless charged particles with an electromagnetic charge-current 4-vector operator,

$$j_\alpha = ie\left[(\partial_\alpha \phi^\dagger)\phi - \phi^\dagger \partial_\alpha \phi\right]$$

where $\phi^\dagger = \phi_1 - i\,\phi_2$. The field $\phi\,(\phi^\dagger)$ destroys (creates) particles and creates (destroys) antiparticles. The unitary operator C which will interchange the roles of particle and antiparticle is evidently such that

$$\phi^c \equiv C^{-1}\phi C = \phi^\dagger$$

$$\phi^{c\dagger} \equiv C^{-1}\phi^\dagger C = \phi \qquad \text{(E. 17)}$$

Clearly, the sign of the 4-vector current will change under such a transformation.

Examples of complex boson fields are those used to describe the charged pions. The usual convention is that the particle is π^+, the antiparticle π^-. Another example is the pair of neutral K-mesons (K^o and $\overline{K}^o$) which differ not in charge but in strangeness.

For the creation and destruction operators in the expansion Eq. (E. 8), the transformation is

$$C^{-1} a_k C = b_k \qquad C^{-1} b_k^{\dagger} C = a_k^{\dagger} \tag{E. 18}$$

and their adjoints.

(b) Self-conjugate scalar or pseudoscalar field:

A neutral particle, such as the neutral pion, with no distinguishing quantum number (e. g., strangeness or baryon number), is described by a Hermitean field, ϕ_o. Then under the charge conjugation operation, ϕ_o transforms into itself:

$$\phi_o^c \equiv C^{-1} \phi_o C = \pm \phi_o \tag{e. 19}$$

For pions the plus sign is chosen in order that the charge-symmetric coupling of pions to nucleons, ($\overline{\psi}\, \underset{\sim}{\tau} \cdot \underset{\sim}{\phi}\, \psi$), is invariant under charge conjugation.

(c) Electromagnetic fields:

From the behavior of the electromagnetic 4-current under charge conjugation, it is evident that the electromagnetic fields and vector potential transform as

$$E_k^c \equiv C^{-1} E_k C = - E_k$$

$$B_k^c \equiv C^{-1} B_k C = - B_k$$

$$A_\alpha^c \equiv C^{-1} A_\alpha C = - A_\alpha \tag{E. 20}$$

These relations imply that the Lorentz invariant combinations $E^2 - B^2$ and $\vec{E} \cdot \vec{B}$ are even under charge conjugation. This can be used as another argument for choosing the plus sign in Eq. (E. 19) for the π° field, since then the effective interaction $(\vec{E} \cdot \vec{B})\ \phi_o$ responsible for the decay $\pi^{\circ} \rightarrow \gamma + \gamma$ is invariant under charge conjugation.

(d) Dirac field:

For the single-particle Dirac equation with electromagnetic interaction, the transformation which changes the sign of the electromagnetic coupling is

$$\psi \longrightarrow \psi' = \gamma_2 \psi^* \tag{E. 21}$$

where the operator γ_2 is peculiar to our representation of Appendix B. In terms of the plane-wave spinors $u_j(p)$ and $v_j(p)$, we have

$$u_1'(p) \equiv \gamma_2 u_1^* = v_2(p)$$

$$u_2'(p) \equiv \gamma_2 u_2^* = v_1(p) \tag{E. 22}$$

and the corresponding relations with the primes reversed.

For the quantized Dirac field there exists a unitary operator C such that the charge-conjugate field is given by

$$\psi^c \equiv C^{-1} \psi C = \gamma_2 \tilde{\psi}^+ \tag{E. 23}$$

In this equation the transpose applies only to the spinors, not to the creation and destruction operators; that is, the symbol $\tilde{\psi}^+$ contains the adjoints of creation and destruction operators and the complex conjugates of spinors and plane-wave exponentials.

If the expansion of Eq. (E. 13) is used, the transformation of Eq. (E. 23) is reflected in the creation and destruction operators as

$$C^{-1} a_{p,1} C = b_{p,2} \qquad C^{-1} a_{p,2} C = b_{p,1}$$

$$C^{-1} b_{p,1}^{+} C = a_{p,2}^{+} \qquad C^{-1} b_{p,2}^{+} C = a_{p,1}^{+} \tag{E. 24}$$

and the adjoint relations.

As a point of notation, we shall sometimes use the notation of a subscript b to mean particle b and $\bar{b}$ to mean the corresponding anti-particle. Then we shall write

$$\psi = \psi_b$$
$$\psi^c = \psi_{\bar{b}} \qquad \text{(E. 25)}$$

(e) Bilinear forms:

By applying the transformation of Eq. (E. 23), or equivalently (E. 24), the charge-conjugation properties of the bilinear covariants can be established to be

$$(\bar{\psi}_{\bar{a}} O_i \psi_{\bar{b}}) \equiv C^{-1}(\bar{\psi}_a O_i \psi_b)C = \eta_i^c (\bar{\psi}_b O_i \psi_a) \qquad \text{(E. 26)}$$

where $\eta_i^c = +1$ for S, A, and P, and $\eta_i^c = -1$ for V and T. In obtaining this relation, it is assumed that the fields anticommute.

3. Time Reversal

Time reversal is somewhat more involved than the previous transformations, because it requires an antiunitary operator rather than a unitary one. An antiunitary operator T is defined by the properties:

$$T|\alpha\rangle = \langle\alpha_T|$$
$$T(c'|\alpha'\rangle + c''|\alpha''\rangle) = c'\langle\alpha'_T| + c''\langle\alpha''_T|$$
$$\langle\beta_T|\alpha_T\rangle = \langle\beta|\alpha\rangle^* \qquad \text{(E. 27)}$$

where the state $|\alpha_T\rangle$ differs from $|\alpha\rangle$ in some manner which depends on T. For time reversal, the state $|\alpha_T\rangle$ has all momenta and angular momenta reversed from the state $|\alpha\rangle$. The necessity of conversion of bras into kets, and vice versa, which amounts to complex conjugation of wave functions, can be understood if we consider a process A → B with S-matrix element $\langle B\ \text{out} | A\ \text{in} \rangle$. The time-reversed situation will be the process B' → A', where A' and B' have spins and momenta reversed, and the relevant amplitude will be $\langle A'\ \text{out} | B'\ \text{in} \rangle$.

For operators it is most convenient to deal with matrix elements. Consider a general operator A and its time-reversed partner, $A' = T^{-1}AT$. Then the last relation in Eq. (E.27) can be used to relate matrix elements of A in time-reversed states to those of A' in the original states. Thus, in the matrix element $\langle \beta_T | A | \alpha_T \rangle$, we write

$$\langle \beta_T | A | \alpha_T \rangle = \langle \beta_T | T T^{-1} A | \alpha_T \rangle$$

and treat $T(T^{-1}A|\alpha_T\rangle)$ as the time-reversed state $|\alpha_T\rangle$ in Eq. (E.27). This leads to

$$\langle \beta_T | A | \alpha_T \rangle = \langle \beta | T^{-1} A | \alpha_T \rangle^* = \langle \beta | A' | \alpha \rangle^* \tag{E.28}$$

If A' and A are simply related, as well as $|\alpha_T\rangle$ and $|\alpha\rangle$, $|\beta_T\rangle$ and $|\beta\rangle$, definite phase relations, etc., emerge (see Sec. 3.4).

In ordinary quantum mechanics of spinless particles the time-reversed wave function is obtained by

$$\psi'(\vec{x},t) = \psi^*(\vec{x},-t) \tag{E.29}$$

while for Pauli spinors the transformation is

$$\psi'(\vec{x},t) = i\sigma_2\, \psi^*(\vec{x},-t) \tag{E.30}$$

For Dirac particles the relativistic generalization of Eq. (E.30) is

$$\psi'(\vec{x},t) = \gamma_3\gamma_1\, \psi^*(\vec{x},-t) \tag{E.31}$$

Here the appearance of $\gamma_3\ \gamma_1$ is peculiar to our representation of Appendix B.

The plane-wave spinors of Eqs. (B.13) and (B.14) transform explicitly as

$$u_1'(\vec{p}) \equiv \gamma_3\gamma_1\, u_1^*(\vec{p}) = -\,u_2(-\vec{p})$$

$$u_2'(\vec{p}) \qquad\qquad = +\,u_1(-\vec{p})$$

$$v_1'(\vec{p}) \qquad\qquad = +\,v_2(-\vec{p})$$

$$v_2'(\vec{p}) \qquad\qquad = -\,v_1(-\vec{p}) \tag{E.32}$$

The operators in ordinary quantum mechanics transform under time reversal as

$$\vec{x}' \equiv T^{-1}\vec{x}\,T = \vec{x}$$

$$\vec{p}' \equiv T^{-1}\vec{p}\,T = -\vec{p}$$

$$\vec{s}' \equiv T^{-1}\vec{s}\,T = -\vec{s} \tag{E.33}$$

For the classical electromagnetic field, the behavior of the charge and current densities under time reversal ($\rho \to \rho$, $j \to -\,j$) implies that the fields and potentials transform as

$$\vec{E}'(\vec{x},t) = +\,\vec{E}(\vec{x},-t)$$

$$\vec{B}'(\vec{x},t) = -\,\vec{B}(\vec{x},-t)$$

$$\vec{A}'(\vec{x},t) = -\,\vec{A}(\vec{x},-t)$$

$$\Phi'(\vec{x},t) = +\,\Phi(\vec{x},-t) \tag{E.34}$$

We shall now turn to the quantized fields.

(a) Scalar or pseudoscalar fields:

The time-reversal operator T transforms a scalar field according to the generalization of Eq. (E. 29):

$$\phi_T(\vec{x},t) \equiv T^{-1}\phi(\vec{x},t)T = \eta_T \phi^{+}(\vec{x},-t) \tag{E. 35}$$

where η_T is a phase factor to be chosen. For pions, $\eta_T = -1$. With the expansion of Eq. (E. 8), it is found that the creation and destruction operators transform as

$$T^{-1} a_k T = \eta_T a^{+}_{-k} \qquad T^{-1} b^{+}_k T = \eta_T b_{-k} \tag{E. 36}$$

and the adjoint relations. We see here the reversal of momenta. But we also turn creation operators into destruction operators, and vice versa. This is in agreement with Eq. (E. 27) where bras were turned into kets, and vice versa, since a creation operator acting on a ket is the dual of a destruction operator acting on a bra.

(b) Electromagnetic fields:

The relations of Eq. (E. 34) have their direct counterpart in quantum electrodynamics. The transformations are of the form

$$\vec{E}_T(\vec{x},t) \equiv T^{-1}\vec{E}(\vec{x},t)T = \vec{E}(\vec{x},-t) \tag{E. 37}$$

and similar relations for B and A_α. Note that the two Lorentz invariants transform as

$$\begin{aligned} T^{-1}(E^2-B^2)T &= +(E^2-B^2) \\ T^{-1}\vec{E}\cdot\vec{B}\,T &= -\vec{E}\cdot\vec{B} \end{aligned} \tag{E. 38}$$

(c) Dirac fields:

The transformation of Eq. (E. 31) is generalized for the spinor field as

$$\psi_T(\vec{x},t) \equiv T^{-1}\psi(\vec{x},t)T = \gamma_3\gamma_1 \tilde{\psi}^{+}(\vec{x},-t) \qquad \text{(E. 39)}$$

where, as in Eq. (E. 23), the transpose acts only on c-number spinors. With the plane-wave expansion of Eq. (E. 13) and the connections of Eq. (E. 32), one finds the time-reversal transformation of the creation and destruction operators to be

$$T^{-1}a_{p,1}T = a^{+}_{-p,2} \qquad T^{-1}b^{+}_{p,1}T = -b_{-p,2}$$

$$T^{-1}a_{p,2}T = -a^{+}_{-p,1} \qquad T^{-1}b^{+}_{p,2}T = +b_{-p,1} \qquad \text{(E. 40)}$$

plus the adjoints of these relations. Again, the antiunitary property of T has turned creation into destruction operators, as well as reversing spins and momenta.

(d) Bilinear forms:

The bilinear combinations of field operators can be shown to transform under time reversal according to

$$(\bar{\psi}_{aT}O_{i\alpha}\psi_{bT}) = \eta^{T}_{i\alpha}(\bar{\psi}_b O_{i\alpha}\psi_a) \qquad \text{(E. 41)}$$

where the notation is similar to Eq. (E. 15). The phase factor $\eta_{i\alpha}^{T}$ has the values,

Scalar: $+1$

Vector: -1 for $\alpha = 1, 2, 3$; $+1$ for $\alpha = 4$

Tensor: -1 for $\alpha, \beta = 1, 2, 3$; $+1$ for α or $\beta = 4$

Axial vector: -1 for $\alpha = 1, 2, 3$; $+1$ for $\alpha = 4$

Pseudoscalar: -1 (E. 42)

Here the spinor fields have been treated as commuting, since the interchange of ψ_a and ψ_b in Eq. (E. 41) is connected with the antiunitarity expressed in Eq. (E. 27).

A somewhat simpler relation occurs if we consider the adjoint of the left-hand side of Eq. (E. 41);

$$\left(\bar{\psi}_{aT} O_i \psi_{bT}\right)^{\dagger} = \eta_i^T \left(\bar{\psi}_a O_i \psi_b\right) \tag{E. 43}$$

where $\eta_i^T = +1$ for S, V, and P, and $\eta_i^T = -1$ for T and A. The adjoint form of Eq. (E. 43) is just what is needed in the connection of Eq. (E. 28) between matrix elements.

Equation (E. 43) can be translated directly into spinor matrix elements as

$$\left(\bar{u}_{aT} O_i u_{bT}\right) = \eta_i^T \left(\bar{u}_a O_i u_b\right)^{*} \tag{E. 44}$$

where u_T is the time-reversed spinor u' of Eq. (E. 32).

4. PCT Theorem

The symmetry operations of P, C, and T can be combined into one operation, which is that of reversing the signs of both space and time coordinates and converting particles into antiparticles. Since this operation commutes with all proper homogeneous Lorentz transformations, any theory possessing Lorentz invariance will necessarily be invariant under the combined PCT operation. This sweeping statement is not quite true. A necessary requirement on the theory is "the customary connection between spin and statistics"; that is, boson fields commute, while spinor fields anticommute. But any theory we are likely to write down is invariant under PCT.

For the creation and destruction operators of the boson field of Eq. (E. 8), the operation PCT transforms them according to

$$\begin{aligned} (PCT)^{-1} a_k (PCT) &= \eta_P \eta_T b_k^{+} \\ (PCT)^{-1} b_k^{+} (PCT) &= \eta_P \eta_T a_k \end{aligned} \tag{E. 45}$$

where $\eta_P = \pm 1$ for scalar (pseudoscalar) bosons and η_T is the time-reversal phase factor in Eq. (E. 35). For the Dirac field of Eq. (E. 13) the equivalent transformations are

$$(PCT)^{-1} a_{p,j} (PCT) = \pm b^{+}_{p,j}$$

$$(PCT)^{-1} b^{+}_{p,j} (PCT) = \pm a_{p,j}$$

(E. 46)

where the $\pm$ sign depends on j = 1, 2. From both Eqs. (E. 45) and (E. 46) it is evident that the PCT operation converts a state with particles of definite momenta and spins into a dual state with antiparticles of the same momenta and spins.

For the bilinear forms, the PCT operation yields, according to Eqs. (E. 16), (E. 26), and (E. 42),

$$(PCT)^{-1} (\bar{\psi}_a O_i \psi_b)(PCT) = \eta_i (\bar{\psi}_{\bar{a}} O_i \psi_{\bar{b}})$$

(E. 47)

where $\eta_i = +1$ for S, T, and P, and $\eta_i = -1$ for V and A. The significant correlation is that even (odd)-rank tensors are even (odd) under PCT. This also holds for higher-rank tensors formed by taking derivatives.

There are many well-known consequences of PCT invariance: (a) the mass of a stable particle is exactly equal to the mass of its antiparticle; (b) the lifetimes of unstable particle and antiparticle are equal; (c) the magnetic moments of particle and antiparticle are equal and opposite.

The most remarkable consequence of PCT invariance is that when a Lagrangian is not invariant under one of the operations of P, C, or T, it is necessarily not invariant under one or both of the other symmetry operations. Thus, the lack of P invariance in weak interactions implies lack of C or T invariance, or both. Another way of looking at this is that T invariance implies PC invariance, etc.

5. G Conjugation

The strongly interacting particles possess the quantum numbers of isotopic spin (T, T_z), implying that the strong interactions are invariant under rotations in isospin space (charge independence). This symmetry property of the strong interactions allows us to introduce a useful new symmetry operation called G conjugation, which combines charge conjugation and rotation in isospin space.

The discussion will be in terms of the pions as an isospin triplet and the nucleons as an isospin doublet. The behavior of the other strongly interacting particles can be inferred from these two; for example, (K^+, K^0) will transform like (p, n), and $(\bar{K}^0, K^-)$ like $(\bar{n}, \bar{p})$.

The charge conjugation properties of nucleons and pions are

$$C^{-1} p C = \bar{p} \qquad C^{-1} n C = \bar{n}$$

$$C^{-1} \pi^{\pm} C = \pi^{\mp} \qquad C^{-1} \pi^0 C = \pi^0 \tag{E.48}$$

where the particle symbol stands for the corresponding field. The pions can be expressed in terms of three Hermitean fields (ϕ_1, ϕ_2, ϕ_3) by

$$\pi^{\pm} = \frac{1}{\sqrt{2}}(\phi_1 \pm i\phi_2) \qquad \pi^0 = \phi_3 \tag{E.49}$$

The three fields can be thought of as the components of a vector field in isospin space. Similarly, the (p, n) doublet can be thought of as the two Pauli spin states in the same space.

The charge conjugation properties of the fields ϕ_i are

$$C^{-1} \phi_1 C = \phi_1$$

$$C^{-1} \phi_2 C = -\phi_2$$

$$C^{-1} \phi_3 C = \phi_3 \tag{E.50}$$

The unitary operator of G conjugation is

$$G = e^{i\pi T_2} C \tag{E.51}$$

that is, charge conjugation, followed by a 180° rotation around the y axis in isospin space. Before considering G, we need to examine the effects of the rotation in isospin space, $R = e^{i\pi T_2}$. For a system with T = 1/2, $\underset{\sim}{T} = 1/2\ \underset{\sim}{\tau}$, where $\underset{\sim}{\tau}$ is the Pauli isospin operator. Then $R = i\,\tau_2$. This means that for the nucleon doublet, the fields transform under R as

$$R^{-1} p R = n \qquad R^{-1} \bar{p} R = \bar{n}$$
$$R^{-1} n R = -p \qquad R^{-1} \bar{n} R = -\bar{p} \tag{E. 52}$$

with $R^2 = -1$. It should be noted that the Pauli spin states for $T_z = \pm 1/2$ are ($|p\rangle$, $|n\rangle$) and ($|\bar{n}\rangle$, $-|\bar{p}\rangle$) for the nucleon and antinucleon doublets. For a system with T = 1, it is simplest to study the effects of R on the Cartesian components of a vector in isospin space. In this way one finds that the "Cartesian" fields ϕ_i transform under R as

$$R^{-1}\phi_1 R = -\phi_1$$
$$R^{-1}\phi_2 R = +\phi_2$$
$$R^{-1}\phi_3 R = -\phi_3 \tag{E. 53}$$

G conjugation combines the results of C and R. From Eqs. (E. 48), (E. 52), and (E. 53) we find that the nucleons and pions transform under G as follows:

$$G^{-1} p G = \bar{n} \qquad G^{-1} \bar{p} G = n$$
$$G^{-1} n G = -\bar{p} \qquad G^{-1} \bar{n} G = -p$$
$$G^{-1} \pi G = -\pi \tag{E. 54}$$

The particularly simple behavior of the pion field under G conjugation makes the concept very useful in discussing multiple pion systems. Other states with zero baryon number and zero strangeness (e. g., $K\bar{K}$ and $N\bar{N}$)

can also be categorized according to their behavior under G.

The behavior of bilinear forms made up of the nucleon fields under G conjugation can be inferred from Eqs. (E. 26) and (E. 52). The result is

$$G^{-1}(\overline{\Psi}_p O_i \Psi_n)G = \eta_i^G(\overline{\Psi}_p O_i \Psi_n)$$

$$G^{-1}(\overline{\Psi}_n O_i \Psi_p)G = \eta_i^G(\overline{\Psi}_n O_i \Psi_p)$$

$$G^{-1}(\overline{\Psi}_p O_i \Psi_p)G = -\eta_i^G(\overline{\Psi}_n O_i \Psi_n) \tag{E. 55}$$

where $\eta_i^G = -\eta_i^C = +1$ for V and T, and $\eta_i^G = -1$ for S, A, and P. For bilinear forms involving hyperons we have results such as

$$G^{-1}(\overline{\Psi}_{\Sigma^+} O_i \Psi_\Lambda)G = \eta_i^G(\overline{\Psi}_\Lambda O_i \Psi_{\Sigma^-})$$

$$G^{-1}(\overline{\Psi}_\Lambda O_i \Psi_{\Sigma^-})G = \eta_i^G(\overline{\Psi}_{\Sigma^+} O_i \Psi_\Lambda)$$

$$G^{-1}(\overline{\Psi}_{\Sigma^+} O_i \Psi_{\Sigma^0})G = -\eta_i^G(\overline{\Psi}_{\Sigma^0} O_i \Psi_{\Sigma^-}) \tag{E. 56}$$

BIBLIOGRAPHY

The bibliography is arranged alphabetically by first author and year. Two papers by the same author in the same year are identified with letters after the year (Gell-Mann, 1958; Gell-Mann, 1958a, etc.).

To save space the journal designations are abbreviated as follows:

B. A. P. S.	Bulletin of the American Physical Society
J. E. T. P.	Soviet Physics, J. E. T. P. (English translation; the volume number and page number are those of the translation only)
N. C.	Nuovo Cimento
N. C. Suppl.	Supplemento del Nuovo Cimento
N. P.	Nuclear Physics
P. L.	Physics Letters
P. R.	Physical Review
P. R. Lett.	Physical Review Letters
P. S. L.	Physical Society (London)
P. T. P.	Progress of Theoretical Physics (Kyoto)
R. M. P.	Reviews of Modern Physics

Acioli, J. L., and S. W. MacDowell, 1962; N. C., 24, 606.
Adams, J. B., 1962; P. R., 126, 1567.
Albright, C. H., 1959; P. R., 114, 1648.
Alexander, Almeida, and Crawford, 1962; P. R. Lett., 9, 69.
Alikhanov et al., 1960; J. E. T. P., 11, 1380.
Allen, J. S., 1959; R. M. P., 31, 791.
Anderson et al., 1959; P. R. Lett., 2, 53.
Anikina et al., 1962; J. E. T. P., 15, 93.
Azimov Ya. I., and V. M. Shekhter, 1962; J. E. T. P., 14, 424.

Backenstoss et al., 1961; P. R. Lett., 6, 415.
Baglin et al., 1960; N. C., 18, 1043.
Balachandran, A. P., 1962; N. C., 23, 429.
Bardin et al., 1960; P. R. Lett., 5, 323.
Bardon, Franzini, and Lee, 1961; P. R. Lett., 7, 23.
Barkas et al., 1961; P. R., 124, 1209.
Barnes, Greenstein, and Nordberg, 1958; P. R. Lett., 1, 328.
Barshay, S., and C. Iso, 1962; P. R., 125, 2168.
Bartlett, Devons, and Sachs, 1962; P. R. Lett., 8, 120.
Barton, G., and C. Kacser, 1962; P. R. Lett., 8, 226.
Beall et al., 1961; P. R. Lett., 7, 285.

Beall et al., 1962; P. R. Lett., 8, 75.
Beg, M. A. B., and P. C. DeCelles, 1962; P. R. Lett., 8, 46.
Behrends, R. E., 1958; P. R., 111, 1691.
Behrends, R. E., and A. Sirlin, 1960; P. R. Lett., 5, 476.
Behrends, R. E., and A. Sirlin, 1962; P. R. Lett., 8, 221.
Berger, V., and E. Kazes, 1961; P. R., 124, 279.
Berman, S. M., 1958; P. R., 112, 267.
Berman, S. M., 1958a; P. R. Lett., 1, 468.
Berman, S. M., 1961; CERN Report 61-22.
Berman, S. M., and A. Sirlin, 1962; Preprint.
Bernstein et al., 1958; P. R., 111, 313.
Bernstein et al., 1960; N. C., 17, 757.
Bernstein, J., and G. Feinberg, 1962; P. R., 125, 1741.
Bernstein, Gell-Mann, and Michel, 1960; N. C., 16, 560.
Bernstein, J., and R. R. Lewis, 1958; P. R., 112, 232.
Bernstein, J., and R. Oehme, 1961; P. R. Lett., 6, 639.
Bernstein, J., and S. Weinberg, 1960; P. R. Lett., 5, 481.
Bertram et al., 1960; P. R. Lett., 5, 61.
Bhowmik, B., 1961; N. C., 21, 567.
Bhowmik, Goyal, and Yamdagni, 1961; N. C., 21, 1066.
Bhowmik, Jain, and Mathur, 1961; N. C., 20, 857.
Bleser et al., 1962; P. R. Lett., 8, 288.
Block et al., 1962; N. C., 23, 1114.
Blokhintsev, L. D., and E. I. Dolinskii, 1962; J. E. T. P., 14, 1410.
Bludman, S., 1961; P. R., 124, 947.
Bøggild et al., 1961; N. C., 19, 621.
Bose, S. K., and R. E. Marshak, 1962; N. C., 23, 556.
Bouchiat, C., and L. Michel, 1957; P. R., 106, 170.
Brene et al., 1962; N. P., 30, 399.
Brene, Egardt, and Qvist, 1961; N. P., 22, 553.
Brown et al., 1961; P. R. Lett., 7, 423.
Brown et al., 1962; P. R. Lett., 8, 450.
Budagov et al., 1959-60; N. P., 14, 339.
Burgy et al., 1958; P. R., 110, 1214.
Burgy et al., 1958a; P. R. Lett., 1, 324.

Cabibbo, N., 1961; N. C., 20, 413.
Cabibbo, N., and E. Ferrari, 1960; N. C., 18, 928.
Cabibbo, N., and R. Gatto, 1959; P. R., 116, 1334.
Cabibbo, N., and R. Gatto, 1960; N. C., 15, 304.
Cabibbo, N., and R. Gatto, 1961; N. C., 19, 612.
Cabibbo, N., and R. Gatto, 1961a; N. C., 21, 872.
Calucci, G., and G. Furlan, 1961; N. C., 21, 677.
Camerini et al., 1962; P. R. (to be published)
Chadan, K., and S. Oneda, 1959; P. R. Lett., 3, 292.
Chew, H., 1962; P. R. Lett., 8, 297.
Chou, K-C., 1961; J. E. T. P., 12, 492.

Conversi, M., 1962; P. R. Lett., 8, 125.
Cork et al., 1960; P. R., 120, 1000.
Cramer et al., 1962; N. C., 24, 546.
Crittenden, Walker, and Ballam, 1961; P. R., 121, 1823.
Culligan et al., 1961; P. R. Lett., 7, 458.

Dalitz, R. H., 1956; P. S. L., A69, 527.
Dalitz, R. H., 1959; R. M. P., 31, 823.
Dalitz, R. H., 1959; Rend. Scuola Intern. Fis. "Enrico Fermi," Varenna, Corso XI, Interazioni Deboli, 299.
Danby et al., 1962; P. R. Lett., 9, 36.
Dennery, P., and H. Primakoff, 1962; P. R. Lett., 8, 350.
DePommier et al., 1962; P. L., 2, 23.
D'Espagnat, B., 1960; N. C., 18, 287.
D'Espagnat, B., and J. Prentki, 1962; N. C., 24, 497.
Dobbs et al., 1962; P. R. Lett., 8, 295.
Dombey, N., 1961; P. R. Lett., 6, 66.
Dunaitsev et al., 1962; P. L., 1, 138.
Durand, Landovitz, and Marr, 1960; P. R. Lett., 4, 620.

Eisler et al., 1961; P. R. Lett., 7, 136.
Egorov et al., 1962; J. E. T. P., 14, 494.
Ely et al., 1962; P. R. Lett., 8, 132.

Falomkin et al., 1962; P. L., 1, 318.
Fayyazuddin and Riazuddin, 1962; N. P., 31, 649.
Feinberg, G., 1958; P. R., 110, 1482L.
Feinberg, Gürsey, and Pais, 1961; P. R. Lett., 7, 208.
Feinberg, G., and S. Weinberg, 1961; P. R. Lett., 6, 381.
Feldman, Matthews, and Salam, 1961; P. R., 121, 302.
Ferro-Luzzi et al., 1961; N. C., 22, 1087.
Feynman, R. P., and M. Gell-Mann, 1958; P. R., 109, 193.
Fischer et al., 1959; P. R. Lett., 3, 349.
Fitch, Piroué, and Perkins, 1961; N. C., 22, 1160.
Fowler et al., 1961; P. R. Lett., 6, 134.
Frankel et al., 1960; P. R., 118, 589.
Frankel et al., 1962; P. R. Lett., 8, 123.
Franzini, P., and J. Steinberger, 1961; P. R. Lett., 6, 281.
Fujii, A., and M. Kawaguchi, 1959; P. R., 113, 1156.
Fujii, A., and H. Primakoff, 1959; N. C., 12, 327.
Furuichi, S., 1958; N. C., 7, 269.

Galtieri et al., 1962; P. R. Lett., 9, 26.
Gandel'man, G. M., 1961; J. E. T. P., 13, 1179.
Gatto, R., 1958; P. R., 111, 1428.
Gatto, R., 1959; Rend. Scuola Intern. Fis. "Enrico Fermi," Varenna, Corso XI, Interazioni Deboli, 336.

Gatto, R., 1959; Fortschr. Physik, 7, 147.
Gatto, R., 1959; N. C. Suppl., 14, 340.
Gell-Mann, M., 1958; P. R., 111, 362.
Gell-Mann, M., 1959; R. M. P., 31, 834.
Gell-Mann, M., and M. Lévy, 1960; N. C., 16, 705.
Gell-Mann, M., and A. H. Rosenfeld, 1957; Ann. Rev. Nuclear Sci., 7, 407.
Gerstein, S. S., and Ya. B. Zeldovich, 1956; J. E. T. P., 2, 576.
Glashow, S. L., 1961; N. P., 22, 579.
Glasser et al., 1961; N. C., 19, 1058.
Goldberger, M. L., 1959; R. M. P., 31, 802
Goldberger, M. L., and S. B. Treiman, 1958; P. R., 110, 1178.
Goldberger, M. L., and S. B. Treiman, 1958a; P. R., 110, 1478.
Goldberger, M. L., and S. B. Treiman, 1958b; P. R., 111, 354.
Good et al., 1961; P. R., 124, 1223.
Gray et al., 1962; B. A. P. S., 7, 4, 348.

Harrington, D. R., 1961; P. R., 124, 1290.
Hildebrand, R. H., 1962; P. R. Lett., 8, 34.
Hori, S., 1960; N. P., 17, 227.
Humphrey et al., 1961; P. R. Lett., 6, 478.
Humphrey, W. E., and R. R. Ross, 1962; P. R., 127, 1305.

Ignatenko et al., 1962; N. P., 32, 563.
Iizuka, J., 1961; P. T. P., 26, 554.
Iizuka, J., and R. Oehme, 1962; P. R., 126, 787.
Ivanter, I. G., 1958; J. E. T. P., 7, 831.
Ivanter, I. G., 1959; J. E. T. P., 8, 79.
Ivanter, I. G., 1962; J. E. T. P., 14, 177.

Jackson, Treiman, and Wyld, 1957; P. R., 106, 517.
Jackson, Treiman, and Wyld, 1957a; N. P., 4, 206.
Jauch, J. M., 1959; CERN Report 59-35.

Kawakami, I., 1960; P. T. P., 24, 27.
Khuri, N. N., and S. B. Treiman, 1960; P. R., 119, 1115.
Kofoed-Hansen, O., 1959; Rend. Scuola Intern. Fis. "Enrico Fermi," Varenna, Corso XI, Interazioni Deboli, 251.
Kobzarev, I. Yu., and L. B. Okun', 1961; J. E. T. P., 12, 426.
Konopinski, E. J., 1959; Ann. Rev. Nuclear Sci., 9, 99.
Krestinikov et al., 1960; J. E. T. P., 10, 622.
Królikowski, W., 1958; N. P., 11, 687.
Królikowski, W., 1961; N. P., 23, 53.
Królikowski, W., 1962; N. C., 24, 52.

Lannoy, F. G., and J. Nuyts, 1962; (Orsay preprint, June).
Lathrop et al., 1961; P. R. Lett., 7, 107.

Lauritsen et al., 1958; P. R. Lett., 1, 326.
Lee, J., and N. P. Samios, 1959; P. R. Lett., 3, 55.
Lee, T. D., 1961; CERN Report 61-22.
Lee, Markstein, and Yang, 1961; P. R. Lett., 7, 429.
Lee, T. D., and C. N. Yang, 1960; P. R. Lett., 4, 307.
Lee, T. D., and C. N. Yang, 1960a; P. R., 119, 1410.
Lee, T. D., and C. N. Yang, 1962; P. R. (to be published)
Leitner et al., 1961; P. R. Lett., 7, 264.
Lichtman et al., 1962; B. A. P. S., 7, 4, 296.
Lipmanov, E. M., 1960; J. E. T. P., 10, 750.
Lipnik et al., 1962; N. P., 30, 312.
Lomon et al., 1961; Ann. Phys., 13, 359.
Lüders, G., 1959; Rend. Scuola Intern. Fis. "Enrico Fermi," Varenna, Corso XI, Interazioni Deboli, 9.
Luers et al., 1961; P. R. Lett., 7, 255.
Lundy et al., 1962; N. C., 24, 549.

MacDowell, S. D., 1957; N. C., 6, 1445.
MacDowell, S. W., 1959; P. R., 116, 1047.
MacDowell, S. W., 1962; Ann. Phys., 18, 171.
Macq, Crowe, and Haddock, 1958; P. R., 112, 2061.
Maier et al., 1961; P. R. Lett., 6, 417.
Maki, Z., and Y. Ohnuki, 1961; P. T. P., 25, 353.
Mann, Miskel, and Bloom, 1958; P. R. Lett., 1, 34.
Mathur, V. S., 1959; N. C., 14, 1322.
Matinyan, S. G., 1962; J. E. T. P., 14, 1072.
Matinyan, S. G., and L. B. Okun', 1959; J. E. T. P., 9, 933.
Mayer-Kuckuk, T., and F. C. Michel, 1961; P. R. Lett., 7, 167.
McCliment, E. R., and K. Nishijima, 1962; P. R. (to be published)
Michel, L., 1950; P. S. L., A63, 514, 1371.
Mitra, A. N., 1960; N. P., 18, 502.
Morita, M., 1959; P. R., 113, 1584.

Nambu, Y., 1960; P. R. Lett., 4, 380.
Neagu et al., 1961; P. R. Lett., 6, 552.
Neagu et al., 1961a; J. E. T. P., 13, 1138.
Neville, D. E., 1961; P. R., 124, 2037.
Nilsson, J., 1960; N. P., 14, 639.
Nilsson, J., 1961; N. C., 22, 414.
Nilsson, J., and R. E. Marshak, 1961; CERN Report 61-22.
Nordberg, Morinigo, and Barnes, 1962; P. R., 125, 321.
Norton, R. E., 1962; P. R., 126, 1216.

Okubo, S., 1960; N. C., 16, 963.
Okubo, S., and R. E. Marshak; 1961; N. C., 20, 791.
Okubo, Marshak, and Sudarshan, 1959; P. R., 113, 944.
Okun', L. B., 1958; J. E. T. P., 6, 409.

Okun', L. B., 1958a; N. P., 5, 455.
Okun', L. B., 1959; Ann. Rev. Nuclear Sci., 9, 61.
Okun', L. B., 1961; J. E. T. P., 12, 154.
Okun', L. B., and A. P. Rudik, 1961; J. E. T. P., 12, 422.
Okun', L. B., and E. P. Shabalin, 1960; J. E. T. P., 10, 1252.

Pais, A., 1960; N. C., 18, 1003.
Pais, A., 1961; R. M. P., 33, 493.
Pais, A., 1961a; P. R., 122, 317.
Pais, A., and S. B. Treiman, 1957; P. R., 105, 1616.
Parker, S., and S. Penman, 1962; N. C., 23, 485.
Pati, Oneda, and Sakita, 1960; N. P., 18, 318.
Plano, R. J., 1960; P. R., 119, 1400.
Polkinghorne, J. C., 1958; N. C., 8, 179 and 781.
Primakoff, H., 1959; R. M. P., 31, 802.
Proceedings of 1958 Conference on High Energy Physics, CERN, Geneva, 1958.
Proceedings of 1960 Conference on High Energy Physics, CERN, University of Rochester, Rochester, 1960.
Proceedings of 1962 Conference on High Energy Physics, CERN, Geneva, 1962.

Radicati, L. A., and D. Speiser, 1962; N. C., 24, 386.
Rainwater, J., 1957; Ann. Rev. Nuclear Sci., 7, 1.
Reines, F., 1960; Ann. Rev. Nuclear Sci., 10, 1.
Reiter et al., 1960; P. R. Lett., 5, 22.
Riazuddin and Fayyazuddin, 1961; P. R. Lett., 7, 464.
Robson, J. M., 1958; Can. J. Phys., 36, 1450.
Roe et al., 1961; P. R. Lett., 7, 346.

Sachs, R. G., and S. B. Treiman, 1962; P. R. Lett., 8, 137.
Sakita, B., 1959; P. R., 114, 1650.
Sakita, B., and S. Oneda, 1960; N. P., 16, 72.
Salam, A., and J. C. Ward, 1960; P. R. Lett., 5, 390.
Sawamura, M., 1961; P. T. P., 26, 505.
Sawyer, R. F., 1958; P. R., 112, 2135.
Sawyer, R. F., 1960; P. R., 118, 618.
Sawyer, R. F., and K. C. Wali, 1960; N. C., 17, 938.
Sawyer, R. F., and K. C. Wali, 1960; P. R., 119, 1429.
Schneps, J., and Y. W. Kang, 1961; N. C., 19, 1218.
Shabalin, E. P., 1961; J. E. T. P., 12, 245.
Singh, V., and B. M. Udgaonkar, 1961; UCRL Report 9863.
Smorodinskii, Ya. A., and Hu Shih-k'e, 1962; J. E. T. P., 14, 438.
Spivak et al., 1961; N. P., 23, 169.
Symanzik, K., 1959; N. C., 11, 269.

Takeda, G., 1962; Ann. Phys., 18, 310.

Taylor, J. C., 1958; P. R., 110, 1216.
Telegdi, V., 1962; P. R. Lett., 8, 327.
Tenaglia, L., 1960; N. C., 17, 423.
Trebukhovskii, Yu. V., 1959; J. E. T. P., 36, 931.
Treiman, S. B., 1960; "The Weak Interactions," Les Houches, Dispersion Relations and Elementary Particles, C. DeWitt and R. Omnes (eds.), Wiley, New York.
Treiman, S. B., 1960a; N. C., 15, 916.
Tripp, Watson, and Ferro-Luzzi, 1962; P. R. Lett., 9, 66.

Vaĭsenberg, Smirnit-skii, and Kolganova, 1961; J. E. T. P., 13, 734.

Weidenmüller, H. A., 1960; P. R. Lett., 4, 299.
Weidenmüller, H. A., 1960a; N. P., 21, 397.
Weinberg, S., 1958; P. R., 112, 1375.
Weinberg, S., 1960; P. R. Lett., 4, 87 and 585(E).
Weinberg, S., 1960a; P. R. Lett., 4, 575.
Weinberg et al., 1958; P. R. Lett., 1, 25.
Werle, J., 1958; N. P., 6, 1.
Werntz, C., 1960; N. P., 16, 59.
Wick, G. C., 1958; Ann. Rev. Nuclear Sci., 8, 1.
Winston, R., and V. L. Telegdi, 1961; P. R. Lett., 7, 104.
Wolf, J., and W. Zoellner, 1962; J. E. T. P., 14, 599.
Wolfenstein, L., 1958; N. C., 8, 882.
Wolfenstein, L., 1961; P. R., 121, 1245.
Wu, C. S., 1959; R. M. P., 31, 783.
Wu, C. S., 1960; "The Neutrino," Theoretical Physics in the Twentieth Century, V. F. Weisskopf and M. Fierz (eds.), Interscience, New York, 249.

Yamaguchi, Y., 1960; P. T. P., 23, 1117.
Yamaguchi, Y., 1961; CERN Report 61-2.

Zachariasen, F., 1958; P. R., 110, 1481 (L).
Zel'dovich, Ya. B., 1961; J. E. T. P., 12, 1232.

GROUP THEORY

AND

APPLICATIONS TO PARTICLE PHYSICS

Christian Fronsdal
University of California, Los Angeles

Notes by the lecturer

CONTENTS

I. INTRODUCTION*

In order to preserve the tradition, I shall start with the obvious remark that our present knowledge of elementary particles consists of a morass of disconnected bits and pieces of information; there are altogether too many "elementary" particles. Actually it cannot be said that there is a shortage of experimental data; rather, we are as yet ignorant as to how it may be put together within the general framework of a theory. That is not to say that there have not been attempts, however, for the literature is flooded with attempts to find symmetries supposedly governing the existence and interactions of elementary particles.

There are two main directions in which we may think our talents best spent, and the choice between them is determined mostly by the amount of pleasure derived from the effort rather than by the degree of optimism one may nurture. One may take the view that an underlying simplicity of nature can be detected by searching diligently enough, although the basic symmetry principles may be hidden from a cursory examination by "symmetry-breaking interactions." Or it may be argued that our main shortcoming is the inability to make reliable computations within the framework of any conjuecture, so that the great challenge is to develop calculational techniques, such as the method of dispersion relations. Although I tend to hold with the second view, it is possible to justify these lectures in two ways: first, because a discussion which is largely phenomenological cannot be completely meaningless—but mainly, because group theory is fun.

Among the various kinds of quantum numbers that have become fashionable in the physics of elementary particles, I want to distinguish sharply a particular set of additive quantities. A <u>diagonal quantum number</u> has two defining properties:

1. Every elementary particle is an eigenstate.
2. The eigenvalue of a composite system is the algebraic sum of the quantum numbers assigned to the constituents.

Electric charge, baryon number, and strangeness are familiar examples.

---

*Some amplification of the material presented here may be found in Rev. Mod. Phys., <u>34</u>, 1 (1962). This paper also contains a large number of references.

Total isotopic spin and parity are nondiagonal quantum numbers.

Diagonal quantum numbers may or may not be conserved. Some are conserved under strong interactions but are not respected by weak or electromagnetic interactions; others seem to be absolutely conserved. It is trivial to determine the greatest possible number of independent diagonal quantum numbers conserved by the strong interactions, on the basis of experimental evidence. We do this by starting with an enormous number of candidates and subsequently reducing these to three independent ones. Introduce a quantum number for every known particle, elementary or not, and use the particle symbol to denote one unit of the respective quantum number. Then the existence of the reaction

$$\mathcal{P} + \mathcal{P} \longrightarrow \mathcal{P} + \mathcal{P} + \pi^{\circ} \tag{1.1}$$

means that there exists the following relation between diagonal quantum numbers:

$$\mathcal{P} + \mathcal{P} = \mathcal{P} + \mathcal{P} + \pi^{\circ} \tag{1.2}$$

This equation is purely algebraic and therefore equivalent to

$$\pi^{\circ} = 0 \tag{1.3}$$

Similarly, the existence of the reaction

$$\mathcal{P} + \mathcal{P} \longrightarrow \mathcal{P} + n + \pi^{+} \tag{1.4}$$

yields

$$\mathcal{P} = n + \pi^{+} \tag{1.5}$$

In this way, every observed reaction gives a linear relation between the quantum numbers. One quickly reaches the conclusion that all diagonal quantum numbers for strongly interacting particles may be expressed in terms of only three of them, for example, as follows:

$$
\begin{aligned}
p &= n + \pi^+ & \Lambda &= n + K^0 \\
\Sigma^- &= n + K^0 - \pi^+ & \pi^0 &= 0 \\
\Sigma^0 &= n + K^0 & \pi^- &= -\pi^+ \\
\Sigma^+ &= n + K^0 + \pi^+ & K^+ &= K^0 + \pi^+ \\
\Xi^0 &= n + 2K^0 & \bar{K}^0 &= -K^0 \\
\Xi^- &= n + 2K^0 - \pi^+ & K^- &= -K^0 - \pi^+
\end{aligned}
\qquad (1.6)
$$

and for any baryon,

$$\bar{B} = -B \qquad (1.7)$$

It is hardly advantageous, though much more conventional, to replace "neutron number," "π^+ number," and "K^0 number" by "baryon number," "charge," and "strangeness," respectively.

The above equations do not, for example, imply that the interactions of Λ and Σ^0 are the same but only that a reaction allowed (forbidden) by conservation of the diagonal quantum numbers remains allowed (forbidden) if Λ is replaced by Σ^0.

The assignment of three independent quantum numbers to the strongly interacting particles admits a picturesque representation. Let the three units n, π^+, and K^0 define three orthogonal coordinate axes; then every elementary particle is represented by a point in a three-dimensional space. The projections in the (π^+, K^0) plane are shown in Fig. 1.

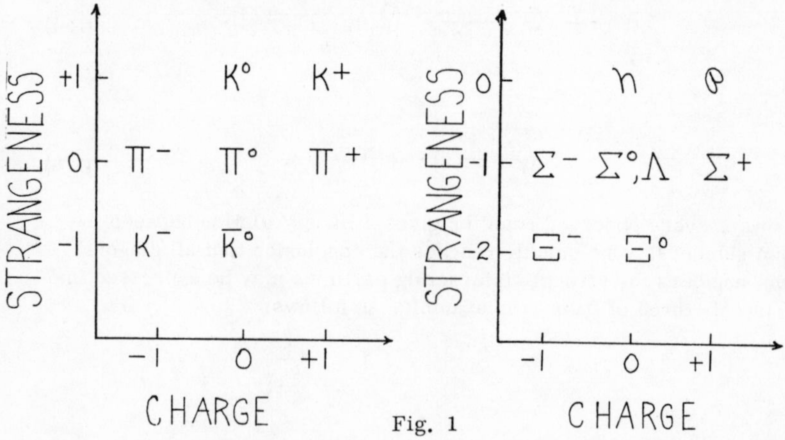

Fig. 1

These pictures have a pleasantly symmetrical aspect, which has led many to a firm belief in a high degree of symmetry in the interactions.

It is in fact true that charge independence, which is a kind of substitution symmetry between particles within the same row, is well supported experimentally. Such symmetry can hardly be exact, because the various particles do not have the same mass; but the observed mass differences, as well as other deviations from pure charge independence, can be imagined to be due to the perturbation of the electromagnetic interactions. Symmetries between particles in the same column must be even less exact, because the mass differences are much larger within a column than within a row. Later we shall discuss the pros and cons of whether symmetries within the columns might show up experimentally.

The diagonal quantum numbers are the simplest kind of quantum numbers, both conceptually and with regard to directness of experimental predictions. Thus conservation laws are simply statements to the effect that a process is or is not allowed. According to the interpretation of quantum mechanics, every observable is the expectation value of a linear hermitian operator, and quantum numbers are the eigenvalues of such operators. If operators are associated with strangeness, baryon number, and charge, we may ask in what representation these operators are diagonal. The definition of a diagonal quantum number guarantees that the operators are diagonal in the occupation-number representation, that is, the representation in which every state has a definite number of physical particles. It is obvious that the three operators associated with strangeness, baryon number, and charge commute with each other, since they can be diagonalized simultaneously.

The next question is whether there exist other quantum numbers that govern the interactions of strongly interacting particles. First, we dispose of the possibility that there might be a fourth diagonal quantum number. In fact, we have already shown that, when we restrict our attention to known particles stable under strong interactions, any diagonal quantum number is a linear combination of η (baryon number), K^0 (strangeness), and π^+ (charge). Therefore a possible fourth conserved diagonal quantum number may be so defined that it has the eigenvalue zero for all known particles. Possible new particles with nonzero eigenvalues can then be created in pairs only, that is, in a kind of associated production. Hence, it may safely be concluded that if new and useful quantum numbers exist they are not diagonal in the occupation-number (or particle) representation.

II. ISOTOPIC SPIN

1. Preliminaries

Charge independence or conservation of isotopic spin is perhaps the simplest generalization of diagonal quantum numbers. While any state with a well defined number of each type of particle is an eigenstate of the latter, the isotopic spin operators T_i (i = 1, 2, 3) are nondiagonal in the particle representation. They may have matrix elements connecting, say, a proton state to a neutron state. The possible energies of a free proton are not the same as those of a free neutron; it follows that the T_i do not commute with the Hamiltonian. Obviously the simplest operators are space- and time-independent, but we see that T_i cannot be both constant and exactly conserved.

In these lectures the mass difference between particles with like baryon number and strangeness will be ignored (except the Λ, Σ^o mass difference). Then constancy and conservation of T_i are not inconsistent, provided nonvanishing matrix elements connect particles with like (within the approximation) mass only. It is perhaps not so unreasonable to consider nonexact conservation laws, since we know that strangeness, though not conserved by weak interactions, is a very useful concept in strong interactions. The prevailing view is that the mass differences we ignore here are due to electromagnetic effects and that T_i is exactly conserved by the purely strong interactions. Another possibility, which so far has not been explored, is that there are exact conservation laws associated with nonconstant operators and that the latter can be fairly well approximated by constant operators.

Because we shall discuss operators that connect particle states within each mass multiplet, it is convenient to represent each multiplet by a single multicomponent wave function. Spin will play a very secondary role, and spin indices may therefore be suppressed. Thus we write:

$$(N_\alpha) = (p, n) \qquad (\Xi_\alpha) = (\Xi^o, \Xi^-) \tag{2.1}$$

$$(K_\alpha) = (K^+, K^o) \qquad (\bar{K}_\alpha) = (\bar{K}^o, -K^-) \tag{2.2}$$

$$(\Sigma_i) = (\Sigma^+, \Sigma^o, \Sigma^-) \tag{2.3}$$

$$(\pi_i) = (\pi^+, \pi^o, \pi^-) \tag{2.4}$$

For easy reference we use the particle symbols to denote the wave functions. Notice that $\bar{K}_\alpha$ is not quite the same as the antiparticle of K_α. This seemingly arbitrary complication of the notation will be justified later.

We shall now see that charge independence follows uniquely from the following postulate: "There exists at least one constant and conserved quantity—say T —that is independent of the diagonal quantum numbers." Clearly T must commute with strangeness because particles with different strangeness have different masses even within our approximation. But T cannot commute with the charge operator Q, because the classification of elementary particles within each multiplet by means of charge is nondegenerate.

The simplest way to state that a quantity is conserved is to say that it commutes with the S matrix. Thus we have by hypothesis

$$[Q, S] = 0 \quad [T, S] = 0 \tag{2.5}$$

$$[Q, T] = iT' \neq 0 \tag{2.6}$$

Now T'commutes with the S matrix:

$$[iT', S] = [Q, [T, S]] + [[Q, S], T] = 0 \tag{2.7}$$

(Jacobi's identity), and therefore T' is conserved. Thus, the commutator of two conserved quantities is conserved. To this we may add that any linear combination of conserved quantities is itself conserved. Taken together, these two properties of operators associated with additively conserved quantities means that they define a Lie algebra; we shall return to this in the next lecture.

Temporarily, we shall restrict ourselves to nucleons. Then all our operators are two-by-two matrices, and the nucleon-number operator is the unit matrix. It is convenient to subtract a multiple of nucleon number (= the unit matrix) from Q to make it traceless. That is, we define

$$T_3 = Q - n/2 = (1/2)\begin{pmatrix} 1 & 0 \\ 0 & -1 \end{pmatrix} = \sigma_3/2 \tag{2.8}$$

Without loss of generality T may be taken traceless, too, and the most general form is

$$T = \sum_i t_i \sigma_i \tag{2.9}$$

where σ_i is a set of hermitian Pauli matrices and the t_i are real numbers. From

$$[\sigma_i, \sigma_j] = 2i\sigma_K, \text{ CYCLICALLY} \tag{2.10}$$

it follows that

$$T' = 2t_1\sigma_2 - 2t_2\sigma_1 \tag{2.11}$$

Thus T' is independent of T and T_3, so that the most general hermitian, traceless, two-by-two matrix is a linear combination of T, T', and T_3 and is thus conserved. This is clearly equivalent to conserving the three quantities

$$T_i = \sigma_i/2 \tag{2.12}$$

They satisfy the commutation relations of angular momentum

$$[T_i, T_j] = T_K, \text{ CYCLICALLY} \tag{2.13}$$

whence the name isotopic "spin."

A theory in which all three T_i are conserved is called "charge-independent." Now we turn to a discussion of the consequences of charge independence for the interactions between nucleons.

2. Charge Independence of Nuclear Forces

For our purpose it is absolutely irrelevant whether we use the formalism of old-fashioned Lagrangian theory or the modern language of abstract field theory. Let us begin by writing down the Lagrangian density for free neutrons and protons:

$$\begin{aligned} L_N &= \bar{n}(\gamma - m)n + \bar{p}(\gamma - m)p \\ &= \Sigma_\alpha \bar{N}_\alpha(\gamma - m)N_\alpha \end{aligned} \tag{2.14}$$

Here the sum consists of only two terms, but for future reference we emphasize that the following remarks are general. We introduce a summation convention for a pair of repeated indices, only when one is a subscript and the other is a superscript. Thus,

$$L_N = \bar{N}^{\alpha} (\gamma - m) N_{\alpha} \tag{2.15}$$

If charge independence holds, then this must be reflected in the form of the Lagrangian, and particularly in the free Lagrangian. In fact, L_N is invariant under the transformation:

$$N_{\alpha} \rightarrow U_{\alpha}^{\beta} N_{\beta} \qquad \bar{N}^{\alpha} \rightarrow \bar{N}^{\beta} U_{\beta}^{+\alpha} \tag{2.16}$$

provided the constant matrix U is unitary:

$$U^{+} = U^{-1} \tag{2.17}$$

Every unitary matrix can be written

$$U = e^{i\varphi} U \tag{2.18}$$

where U is unimodular and φ is a real number. In the special case $U = 1$, Eq. (2.16) reduces to a gauge transformation, which shown that a Lagrangian invariant under Eq. (2.16) conserves baryon number. The special case $\varphi = 0$ is more interesting. Every unimodular matrix U may be written

$$U = e^{iH} \tag{2.19}$$

where H is hermitian (unitarity) and traceless (unimodularity). Suppose that a reaction involving an arbitrary number of particles is compatible with a Lagrangian invariant under Eq. (2.16). Then the amplitude is invariant under Eq. (2.16), which means that the quantity

$$\langle \text{final state} \mid \text{initial state} \rangle$$

is unchanged when the substitutions of Eq. (2.16) are carried out simultaneously on the initial and final states. If both are eigenstates of H, with eigenvalues H_{in} and H_f, then

$$\langle f | i \rangle = \langle f | U^+ U | i \rangle = e^{i(H_{IN} - H_f)} \langle f | i \rangle \tag{2.20}$$

Hence, invariance of the theory under the transformations

$$N_\alpha \rightarrow U_\alpha^\beta N_\beta \,, \quad \bar{N}^\alpha \rightarrow \bar{N}^\beta U_\beta^{+\alpha}$$
$$U = e^{iH} \,, \quad H^+ = H \tag{2.21}$$

has the consequence that H is a conserved quantum number.

Now we specialize with the neutron-proton system. The most general form for H is then

$$H = \Sigma_i t_i T_i \tag{2.22}$$

where T_i are the isotopic spin operators introduced above. Hence invariance under Eq. (2.21) is equivalent to conservation of all three components of isotopic spin.

Whether or not one believes that the Lagrangian is a meaningful concept in strong interactions, it is an experimental fact (existence of OPEP) that an effective coupling between two nucleons and a pion exists. If we suppress all reference to the space-time variables, which cannot lead us astray in the present context, charge independence requires the existence of an "invariant" trilinear form:

$$C_\alpha^{i\beta} \bar{N}^\alpha N_\beta \pi_i \tag{2.23}$$

Since the pions constitute a mere mathematical model as far as nucleon-nucleon interactions are concerned, the meaning of "invariance" in this context is as follows: When the factors $\bar{N}^\alpha$ and N_β are transformed according to Eq. (2.21), the coefficients of π_i are transformed linearly among themselves, and the resulting change in Eq. (2.23) is to be compensated by a linear transformation of the π_i among themselves. Time-reversal invariance requires that Eq. (2.23) be Hermitian, so that the most general form is

$$(\bar{N}^{\alpha} N_{\alpha}) C^{i} \pi_i + (\bar{N} \sigma_j N) C^{ij} \pi_j \tag{2.24}$$

Conservation of charge requires that $C^1 = C^3 = 0$ and that C^{ij} be diagonal. The quantities $(\bar{N} \sigma_i N)$ transform among themselves like the components of a 3-vector (see below), through an angle determined by the coefficients t_i in Eq. (2.22); therefore the three quantities $C^{ij} \pi_j$ must also transform like a vector, while $C^2 \pi_2$ must transform like a scalar. Thus either C^i or C^{ij} must vanish. Experiment shows that $C^{ij} \neq 0$; hence $C^i = 0$. If the pion fields are properly normalized, then Eq. (2.24) induces a pole in the nucleon-nucleon scattering amplitude with the residue

$$(\bar{N} \sigma_j N) C^{ij} \delta_{jk} (\bar{N} \sigma_l N) C^{kl} \tag{2.25}$$

This is invariant only if

$$C^{ij} \delta_{jk} C^{kl} = g^2 \delta^{il} \quad (g = \text{REAL NUMBER}) \tag{2.26}$$

or

$$C^{ij} = g \begin{pmatrix} \pm 1 & & \\ & \pm 1 & \\ & & \pm 1 \end{pmatrix} \tag{2.27}$$

We finally <u>choose</u> the signs of the pion wave functions such that $C^{ij} = g\,\delta^{ij}$, and the invariant coupling is

$$g (\bar{N} \sigma^{i} N) \pi_i \tag{2.28}$$

The main point we wanted to make here is that experiment easily tells us how the pions must transform under isotopic spin "rotations" in order to give us charge independence. After this, we expect to be able to find the transformation properties of the strange particles as well, and the result is obvious: the Ξ, the K, and the $\bar{K}$ transform like the nucleons; the Σ like the pions; and the Λ does not transform at all.

Finally, let us determine the precise transformation properties of the pion in the case of infinitesimal t_i. Then

$$N_\alpha \to (1 + i \Sigma t_k T_k)_\alpha^{\ \beta} N_\beta = N_\alpha + (i/2) t_k \sigma^k{}_\alpha{}^\beta N_\beta \tag{2.29}$$

$$\bar{N}^\alpha \to \bar{N}^\beta (1 - i \Sigma t_k T_k)_\beta^{\ \alpha} = \bar{N}^\alpha - (i/2) t_k \sigma^k{}_\beta{}^\alpha \bar{N}^\beta \tag{2.30}$$

and thus

$$\begin{aligned}(\bar{N}\sigma^i N) &\to (\bar{N}\sigma^i N) + (i/2) t_k \bar{N}(\sigma^i\sigma^k - \sigma^k\sigma^i) N \\ &= (\delta^{ij} + t_k \epsilon^{ijk})(\bar{N}\sigma_j N)\end{aligned} \tag{2.31}$$

The π_i must therefore transform as follows:

$$\pi_i \longrightarrow (1 + i \Sigma t_k T_k')_i^{\ j} \pi_j \tag{2.32}$$

$$(T_k')_i^{\ j} = \epsilon^{ijk} \tag{2.33}$$

The matrices T_k' defined here are three-dimensional and satisfy the same commutation relations as the T_k, which is to say that the transformations of (2.21), (2.29), and (2.30) are two different realizations or representations of the same group. The theory of isotopic spin makes use of the theory of Lie groups and Lie algebras in its most rudimentary form. We shall now take up that subject in a systematic way.

III. STRUCTURE OF CONTINUOUS GROUPS

1. Matrix Groups

I prefer to introduce the subject in terms of groups of matrices because, notwithstanding the formal elegance of the more abstract approach to group theory, only a very thoroughly trained mathematician does not find it necessary to keep a picture of matrices before his inner eye. The finer points of group theory, which are not shared by finite-dimensional matrix groups, are of no interest in the present connection. Besides, the theory of matrix groups is interesting enough in its own right, and we shall find that the specialization leaves us with a field of study more than ample for the limited time at our disposal. For further study, the book "Topological Groups" by Pontriagin is recommended.

Definition. A set of matrices V, V', -- form a matrix group if the following conditions are satisfied:

1. The product of any two matrices of the set exists and is a member of the set.
2. There is one and only one member of the set, called the unit matrix and denoted E, with the property that the product EU equals U for every U.
3. For every U in the set there is a unique inverse, denoted U^{-1}, defined by $UU^{-1} = E$.

A Lie group is distinguished from other matrix groups by a certain property of continuity. The concept of continuity for matrix group could be introduced "without topology," but such a procedure would be reminiscent of the one-time fad among physicists of doing "group theory without group theory."

A d-dimensional square matrix is an array of d^2 complex numbers, or $2d^2$ real numbers. Envisage a $2d^2$-dimensional real space with a Cartesian coordinate system, and associate to each matrix in the group a point in this space, in the obvious way. When every matrix of the group is thus represented, a set of points in $2d^2$-dimensional space that may be continuous or discrete is obtained. Now we take over the terminology we naturally associate with sets of points and apply it to the matrices: thus, we speak of a set of matrices being continuously connected, etc. In this way, a topology can always be added to a matrix group, and a matrix group is a topological group.

Matrix multiplication is continuous: that is, if U and V are varied continuously within the group, then UV also varies continuously. Suppose that a matrix group G consists of several subsets G_1, G_2, -- each of which is continuously connected but disconnected from all the others. Then clearly only one of these subsets — G_1 say — contains the identity E, since E is continuously connected to itself. Thus G_2, G_3, -- cannot be groups.

Theorem. If G_1 has no matrix other than E, then every other set G_2, G_3, -- also contains only one matrix.

Proof. Suppose that G_2 contains two matrices U and V. Then U^{-1} and V^{-1} are also two matrices in G, though not necessarily members of G_2. Since V is continuously connected to U, it follows that VU^{-1} is contained in G_1, contrary to hypothesis.

Theorem. The set G_1 of matrices continuously connected to the identity E is a group.

Proof. If U and V are two matrices in G_1, then UV can be continuously changed to E by continuously changing both U and V to E, since EE = E. Furthermore, U^{-1} is a continuous function of U, and therefore continuously connected to E. Thus, if U and V are in G_1, it follows that UV and U^{-1} are in G_1, which proves the theorem.

Now let U_1, U_2, -- be arbitrary matrices selected from G_1, G_2, -- respectively. Then every matrix in G_2 can be obtained by multiplying some member of G_1 by U_2. Thus the whole group can be obtained from G_1 by multiplying by a certain discrete set of matrices, namely, U_2, U_3, --. Thus every matrix group can be studied by first considering that part which is connected to the identity and then adding a number of discrete matrices. In fact, we shall only study connected matrix groups.

Definition. A connected matrix group is a matrix group in which every matrix is continuously connected to the identity E. The importance of this concept can immediately be made clear by the following observation.

Let two matrices U and V be members of a connected matrix group. Then there exists a one-parameter set of matrices V(t), where t is a real parameter such that U(t) is in the group for all t between 0 and 1 (inclusive), and such that U(0) = U and U(1) = V. Because group multiplication is continuous, the product $U(t')\,U^{-1}(t)$ tends continuously to E as t' tends to t. Hence,

$$\mathcal{U}(t+dt)\,\mathcal{U}^{-1}(t) = E + L(t)\,dt \tag{3.1}$$

Also,

$$\begin{aligned} V = \mathcal{U}(1) &= \mathcal{U}(1-dt)\,\mathcal{U}^{-1}(1-dt)\,\mathcal{U}(1) \\ &= \mathcal{U}(1-dt)\,(E + L(1)\,dt) \\ &= \prod_t (E + L(t)\,dt) \end{aligned} \tag{3.2}$$

Thus every member of a connected matrix group is a product of matrices that differ arbitrarily little from E. That is, <u>every connected matrix group is completely defined by the neighborhood of the identity.</u>

Now we shall see that these topological considerations were useful: we have shown that an important class of matrix groups can be studied in terms of the <u>infinitesimal generators</u> L, defined by

$$\mathcal{U} = E + \epsilon L \tag{3.3}$$

(for infinitesimal ϵ and U in the neighborhood of E), and—perhaps more important—we have found the limitations of the applicability of this method of infinitesimal generators. This restriction is not exactly trivial (consider, for example, the group of all matrices with rational matrix elements).

2. Lie Algebras

We must find the necessary and sufficient conditions on the set of infinitesimal generators L, in order that the set of associated finite matrices U form a connected matrix group. We shall see that the complex multiples of the L must be a Lie algebra.

<u>Definition</u>. A set of matrices L, L', -- form a <u>Lie algebra</u> if the following conditions are satisfied:

1. Every linear combination (with complex coefficients) of matrices in the set belongs to the set.
2. The <u>commutator</u> of two matrices in the set belongs to the set.

<u>Theorem</u>. If the neighborhood of the identity of a connected matrix group is given by $U = E + \epsilon L$, then the complex multiples of the L constitute a Lie algebra.

<u>Proof</u>. Let $U = E + \epsilon L$ and $V = E + \epsilon L'$. Then, to second order,

$$\mathcal{U} V \mathcal{U}^{-1} V^{-1} = E + \varepsilon^2 [L, L'] \tag{3.4}$$

Since the left-hand side of the equation belongs to the group, it follows that [L, L'] belongs to the set of infinitesimal generators. Hence the second condition is satisfied. It is easy to see that the set of generators is continuously connected and that, if L and L' are two generators, so are nL and L + L', where n is an integer. It is not always true that any complex multiple of L is necessarily a generator, but we can extend the set of generators by adding all complex multiples, to obtain a Lie algebra. Here a tremendous simplification is achieved by generalization rather than specialization. The great surprise is that it is possible to determine all possible Lie algebras. All possible connected matrix groups are thereafter obtained by determining the possible continuously connected subsets of the Lie algebras that satisfy the second condition. This is easier than it may seem, and the result is that the only possible specializations that can be introduced are certain reality conditions.

In our applications we shall restrict the U matrices to be unitary. This means that the L matrices must be hermitian, so that cL is a generator only if c is a real number.

Theorem (Inverse). The set of (finite) matrices

$$\mathcal{U} = E + \epsilon L \tag{3.5}$$

and all products of such matrices, where ϵ is infinitesimal and the L form a Lie algebra, is a connected matrix group (= a Lie group). (This is trivial; the nontrivial part is the following.) The generators of this connected matrix group are precisely the Lie algebra from which it was generated.

Proof. We shall give only the simple part of the proof. Consider an arbitrary product (finite or infinite)

$$\mathcal{U} = \prod_K (E + \varepsilon L_K) \tag{3.6}$$

We must prove that, if U is near E,

$$\mathcal{U} = E + \eta L' \tag{3.7}$$

(with η infinitesimal), then L' is in the Lie algebra. Let us expand U in powers of ϵ. If the linear term is nonzero, the result follows from the first condition with which we defined a Lie algebra. If the linear term vanishes and the second-order term does not, then the proof depends on the second property of our definition. The hard part of the proof is to show that it is not necessary to go beyond the second order.

This theorem is very important. It shows that, if the operators associated with a set of conserved quantum numbers form a Lie algebra, then this is a possible complete set of conserved quantum numbers. We have already noted that the existence of two quantum numbers that do not form a Lie algebra implies the existence of a third.

3. Structure Constants

Let L_A, A = 1, 2, --, n be a set of n linearly independent members of a Lie (matrix) algebra such that every other member is linear combination

$$L = \sum_A C_A L_A \tag{3.8}$$

This number n is called the order of the algebra. Then the second condition defining a Lie algebra states that

$$[L_A, L_B] = C_{AB}^{\;\;D} L_D \;; \quad A, B = 1, \cdots, n \tag{3.9}$$

(summation convention.'), where $C_{AB}^{\;\;D}$ are complex numbers. These numbers have two easily established properties. First, since the left-hand side of Eq. (3.9) is antisymmetric in A, B,

$$C_{AB}^{\;\;D} = -C_{BA}^{\;\;D} \tag{3.10}$$

Second, from the Jacobi identity,

$$\sum_{\text{CYCL.PERM.}} [L_A, [L_B, L_D]] = 0 \tag{3.11}$$

we get

$$\sum_{\text{CYCL. PERM.}} C_{AB}^{E} C_{ED}^{F} = 0 \tag{3.12}$$

where the sum is over the three cyclic permutations of A, B, D.

The conditions of Eqs. (3.10) and (3.12) are necessary for the existence of matrices L_A satisfying Eq. (3.9). The proof that they are also sufficient is very simple and yet very instructive. Consider the n-by-n matrices

$$(-C_A)_B{}^D = -C_{AB}{}^D \qquad A = 1, \cdots, n \tag{3.13}$$

in which B labels the rows and D labels the columns. These matrices satisfy Eq. (3.9), because the relation

$$[-C_A, -C_B]_D{}^F = C_{AB}{}^E (-C_E)_D{}^F \tag{3.14}$$

is simply a rearrangement of Eq. (3.12)! In other words, Eq. (3.12) may be interpreted as stating that the matrices $(-C_A)_B{}^D$ are a possible choice of the L_A in (1).

The problem of finding all possible Lie algebras has been solved. This amazing feat was accomplished by successively reducing the problem to a trivial one. The first step in this reduction process is the following.

Definition: The structure of a Lie algebra resides in the structure constants $C_{AB}{}^D$; that is, any two Lie algebras satisfying Eq. (3.9) with the same constants $C_{AB}{}^D$ are said to have the same structure. We shall refer to two different Lie algebras with the same structure constants as two different representations or realizations of the same Lie algebra.

The problem we shall solve here is that of finding all possible Lie algebras—that is, all possible solutions of Eqs. (3.10) and (3.12). Later we shall determine all possible representations of each algebra.

In order to define the structure constants, we had to introduce the basis L_A, A = 1, --, n. Any other set of n linearly independent basis matrices could have been used instead, and the result would have been a different set of structure constants. The main trick that will be used to find all possible solutions of Eqs. (3.10) and (3.12) is to choose that basis which yields the simplest possible form of the structure constants.

Definition. A subalgebra is a subset of the matrices of an algebra, which is itself an algebra. (Thus, if L and L' belong to a subalgebra, so do $\alpha L + \beta L'$ and [L, L'], where α and β are complex numbers.)

Definition. An invariant subalgebra is a subalgebra with the additional property that [L, L'] belongs to the subalgebra if L does, for arbitrary L'.

Definition. An algebra is Abelian if all the structure constants vanish.

Definition. A semisimple algebra has no Abelian invariant subalgebra. A simple algebra has no invariant subalgebra.

If an algebra has an Abelian invariant subalgebra of order $n' < n$, then the basis may be chosen so that the first n' basis matrices, L_1, --, $L_{n'}$ span this subalgebra. Thus, if a,b,c,d take the values 1,2, --, n, and r,s,t,u,v the values n + 1, --, n, the commutation relations take the form

$$[L_a, L_b] = 0 \qquad [L_a, L_r] = C^b_{ar} L_b \tag{3.15}$$

$$[L_r, L_s] = C^a_{rs} L_a + C^t_{rs} L_t \tag{3.16}$$

$$C^r_{ab} = C^c_{ab} = C^s_{ar} = 0 \tag{3.17}$$

From the last set of equations, we get

$$\Sigma_u C^u_{rs} C^v_{ut} = C^u_{rs} C^v_{ut} \tag{3.18}$$

Therefore the Jacobi identity of Eq. (3.12) holds for C^t_{rs} alone, so that these are structure constants for a semisimple algebra. This means that to find all possible algebras with Abelian invariant subalgebras we must first determine all those without. To my knowledge, no complete classification of non-semisimple algebras exists, but for semisimple algebras the results are complete.

4. Cartan's Criterion

It was shown by Cartan that a necessary and sufficient condition for an algebra to be semisimple is that the matrix

$$g_{AB} = C^{E}_{AD} C^{D}_{BE} \tag{3.19}$$

be nonsingular. Sufficiency is easily proved: suppose that there is an Abelian invariant subalgebra whose elements are linear combinations of the first n' < n basis matrices. If subscripts a, b, c, -- are used for these n' basis matrices, then

$$C^{A}_{ab} = 0 \; ; \; C^{B}_{Ab} = 0 \, , \; \text{FOR } B > n' \tag{3.20}$$

and thus

$$g_{Aa} = C^{D}_{AB} C^{B}_{aD} = C^{D}_{Ab} C^{b}_{aD} = C^{d}_{Ab} C^{b}_{ad} = 0 \tag{3.21}$$

Since one column of the matrix g_{AB} vanishes, it is singular.

Necessity is harder to prove. I give here a proof that is instructive because it shows the power of tensor calculus. There are two complementary methods in group theory. One is tensor calculus, by which the basis is kept completely arbitrary and every statement is invariant under a change of basis. The other consists of choosing that basis in which everything becomes as simple as possible. The latter method is the classical one, and it shall be used in the following discussion; but I believe that Cartan's criterion is one of those items that can be carried out more elegantly with tensor calculus.

Actually, we shall be content with proving that if g_{AB} is singular then the algebra is not simple. That it is also not semisimple is left as an exercise.

Consider the transformations

$$L_A \longrightarrow [L_B, L_A] = C^{D}_{BA} L_D \tag{3.22}$$

For every B, this is a mapping of the algebra onto itself. If there exists a subalgebra that gets mapped onto itself, this subalgebra is an invariant subalgebra. If a subalgebra gets mapped onto itself through Eq. (3.22), then it also gets mapped onto itself by

$$L_A \rightarrow L'_A = L_A + i\epsilon^B C_{BA}^{\ \ D} L_D \tag{3.23}$$

and vice versa. This transformation $L_A \rightarrow L_A'$ may be considered a change of basis, and we may determine the commutation relations between the L_A':

$$[L'_A, L'_B] = C'^{\ D}_{AB} L'_D \tag{3.24}$$

If ϵ^B are infinitesimal, we find

$$C'^{\ D}_{AB} = C^{\ D}_{AB} + i\epsilon^E (C_{EA}^{\ \ F} C_{FB}^{\ \ D} + C_{EB}^{\ \ F} C_{AF}^{\ \ D} - C_{EF}^{\ \ D} C_{AB}^{\ \ F}) \tag{3.25}$$

But the bracketed term is just a rearrangement of the left-hand side of Eq. (3.12); hence $C_{AB}^{\ \ D} = C_{AB}'^{\ D}$, and $C_{AB}^{\ \ D}$ is form-invariant under the transformation of Eq. (3.23). Therefore g_{AB} is also form-invariant. Suppose that g_{AB} is singular; then there exists a matrix g^{AB} that satisfies

$$g^{AB} g_{BC} = \Delta^A_C \tag{3.26}$$

where Δ^A_C is a diagonal matrix whose elements are either 1 or zero. Furthermore Δ^A_C is form-invariant. Therefore, the equations

$$\Delta^A_C L_A = 0, \text{ AND } \Delta^A_C L_A = L_C \tag{3.27}$$

are invariant; consequently, the set of solutions of the first equation transform among themselves, as does the set of solutions of the second equation. This, as we have seen, means that the two sets are invariant subalgebras—thereby completing the proof that, if g_{AB} is singular, the algebra is not simple.

5. A Lie Algebra as a Linear Vector Space

The following remarks are not strictly required for the development set forth here, but are meant to put the theory of Lie algebras on a broader base in order to support the intuition.

A linear vector space is any collection of elements (for example, matrices) that is closed under addition and under multiplication by a complex number. According to the first part of the definition, a Lie algebra is a linear vector space. We shall call two elements L and L' orthogonal if the commutator [L, L'] vanishes. Let the matrix L be kept fixed, while L' varies over the algebra. Then, forming the commutator may be interpreted as performing a linear operation on the vector space: that is, every vector (matrix) L' is replaced by the linear combination [L, L'].

Hence, on our linear vector space is defined a set of n operators (say, C_A) that have matrix elements $C_{AB}{}^D$ when referred to a particular basis. A subspace of a linear vector space is a set of vectors that form a linear vector space; hence a subalgebra corresponds to a subspace. A subspace may be invariant under the operators C_A; this means that any member of the subspace remains in the subspace when operated on by the C_A. We see thus that an invariant subalgebra is the same as an invariant subspace.

Now let us use this to show some important properties of invariant algebras.

The orthogonal complement of a subspace consists of all those vectors which are orthogonal to every vector in the subspace. The orthogonal complement of an invariant subalgebra is therefore the set of matrices that commute with every member of the subalgebra.

The orthogonal complement of an invariant subspace is an invariant subspace; hence, the set of all matrices that commute with every member of an invariant subalgebra of a semisimple Lie algebra is an invariant subalgebra. This is also a simple consequence of the Jacobi identity.

We now arrive at the main conclusion of this excursion into the terminology of linear vector spaces. For the student who is not accustomed to the jargon it may be best simply to believe the result, which is after all rather obvious.

By a judicious choice of basis matrices L_1, --, L_n, it can be arranged that the first n' of them span an invariant subspace (when one exists), and the remaining n-n' of them the orthogonal invariant subspace.

If the two parts are not simple the process can be repeated until the semisimple algebra is broken up into simple parts. Thus every semisimple Lie algebra is a sum of simple Lie algebras. Every semisimple Lie algebra is known when every simple Lie algebra is known.

Before turning our attention to simple Lie algebras exclusively let us examine a familiar example of a semisimple algebra. If we use a Euclidean metric (i. e., $x_\mu = \vec{x}, ict$), the commutation relations for generators of infinitesimal Lorentz transformations are

$$[L_{\mu\nu}, L_{\lambda\rho}] = g_{\mu\lambda} L_{\nu\rho} - g_{\mu\rho} L_{\nu\lambda} - g_{\nu\lambda} L_{\mu\rho} + g_{\nu\rho} L_{\mu\lambda} \tag{3.28}$$

That this is semisimple is seen by introducing the following basis:

$$L_A^{\pm} = (L_{BC} \pm L_{A4}) \tag{3.29}$$

where A, B, C is a cyclic permutation of 1, 2, 3. Then the L_A^+ commute with the L_B^-, and each set satisfies the commutation relations of angular momentum. These subalgebras are simple.

6. Importance of Simple Lie Algebras

It may be useful to review, in reverse, the preceding development from general matrix groups to simple Lie algebras.

When all simple Lie algebras have been found, they can be pieced together to give us all semisimple Lie algebras. To this may be added an Abelian invariant subgroup to obtain the most general Lie algebra, though the details of how this is to be done, and precisely what structures are obtained, are not known. The theory of representations, in particular, remains to be worked out for such algebras.

From general Lie algebras, the most general connected matrix group can be obtained after first restricting the parameters as required. On this last point we shall be more specific later.

Finally, the most general matrix group may be obtained by adding discrete matrices to the connected matrix groups. Here again, no systematic procedure is available.

From now on we shall address ourselves almost exclusively to simple

Lie algebras. As far as application to possible generalizations of isotopic spin is concerned, we shall find that this is a much less severe restriction than the above discussion might lead one to expect.

IV. STRUCTURE OF SIMPLE LIE ALGEBRAS

1. Rank of a Simple Lie Algebra

We now set out to solve the equations

$$C_{AB}^{D} + C_{BA}^{D} = 0 \qquad \sum_{\text{CYCL.}} C_{AB}^{E} C_{DE}^{F} = 0 \tag{4.1}$$

for the case of a simple algebra. Since a simple algebra is a special case of a semisimple algebra, we know by Cartan's criterion that the matrix

$$g_{AB} = C_{AD}^{E} C_{BE}^{D} \tag{4.2}$$

is nonsingular. To begin with, we shall rely heavily on this criterion and specialize to simple algebras later.

Keeping in mind the applications, in which the L_A are conserved quantum mechanical operators, we begin by enlisting the largest number of mutually commuting, linearly independent matrices. If H_i, i = 1, 2, --, ℓ is such a set, we may choose our basis so that $L_1 = H_1$, $L_2 = H_2$, --, $L_\ell = H_\ell$. The remaining linearly independent basis vectors will be denoted E_α, where α takes $(n - \ell)$ different values. The number ℓ is called the rank of the algebra. Its great importance stems from the fact that there are only a finite (and small) number of different simple Lie algebras of given rank.

Since

$$[H_i, H_j] = 0 \tag{4.3}$$

it follows that the matrices $C_i = (C_i)_A^{\ B}$ commute. This may be seen

directly from Eq. (4.1), or we may simply remember that the matrices $(-C_A)_B^{\ D}$ satisfy the commutation relations of the L_A. If the H_i are operators representing observables, then they are hermitian; and since they commute, they can be diagonalized simultaneously. Independently of physical arguments, however, it can be shown that:
Important Theorem. In the case of a semisimple algebra the ℓ commuting matrices H_i can always be chosen hermitian, so that they, and in particular the $(C_i)_A^{\ B}$, can always be diagonalized.

From now on, we shall choose the basis where the $(C_i)_A^{\ B}$ are diagonal; then,

$$[H_i, E_\alpha] = C_{i\alpha}^{\ A} L_A = C_{i\alpha}^{\ \alpha} L_\alpha \tag{4.4}$$

We see that the problem of diagonalizing the $(C_i)_A^{\ B}$ is an eigenvalue problem.

2. Root Vectors

Because of Eq. (4.4) we can introduce the real root vectors $r_i(\alpha)$ by

$$[H_i, E_\alpha] = r_i(\alpha) E_\alpha \tag{4.5}$$

Thus, we have

$$C_{ij}^{\ A} = C_{i\alpha}^{\ j} = 0, \quad C_{i\alpha}^{\ \beta} = r_i(\alpha)\delta_\alpha^{\ \beta} \tag{4.6}$$

The root vectors play a central role in what follows. The roots are nondegenerate; that is, there is only one E_α for every $r_i(\alpha)$, but we shall have to skip the proof. We shall sometimes use the notation $\vec{\alpha} = (r_1(\alpha), r_2(\alpha), \ldots, r_\ell(\alpha))$.

There are four special cases of the Jacobi identity, arising from consideration of the following four double commutators: $[H_i, [H_j, H_k]]$ vanishes trivially; $[H_i, [H_j, E_\alpha]]$ leads to the above conclusion that the matrices $(C_i)_A^{\ B}$ commute; $[H_i, [E_\alpha, E_\beta]]$ is the next simplest case and will be explored now.

We have

$$0 = \sum_{CYCL.} C_{i\alpha}^{\ A} C_{\beta A}^{\ B} = C_{i\alpha}^{\ A} C_{\beta A}^{\ B} + C_{\alpha\beta}^{\ A} C_{iA}^{\ B} + C_{\beta i}^{\ A} C_{\alpha A}^{\ B}$$

$$= C_{\beta\alpha}^{\ B} r_i(\alpha) - C_{\alpha\beta}^{\ B} r_i(\beta) + C_{\alpha\beta}^{\ \gamma} C_{i\gamma}^{\ B} \tag{4.7}$$

First setting B = k and then B = δ, we get the following two conditions:

$$C_{\alpha\beta}^{k}(\vec{\alpha} + \vec{\beta}) = 0$$
$$C_{\alpha\beta}^{\delta}(\vec{\delta} - \vec{\alpha} - \vec{\beta}) = 0 \tag{4.8}$$

Thus, we may introduce complex numbers $r^i(\alpha)$ and $N_{\alpha\beta}$ by

$$C_{\alpha\beta}^{i} = r^i(\alpha) \text{ IF } \vec{\alpha} + \vec{\beta} = 0, \text{ AND ZERO OTHERWISE} \tag{4.9}$$

$$C_{\alpha\beta}^{\gamma} = N_{\alpha\beta} \text{ IF } \vec{\gamma} = \vec{\alpha} + \vec{\beta}, \text{ AND ZERO OTHERWISE} \tag{4.10}$$

In terms of commutators, this means that

$$[E_\alpha, E_{-\alpha}] = r^i(\alpha) H_i \tag{4.11}$$

$$[E_\alpha, E_\beta] = N_{\alpha\beta} E_{\alpha+\beta} \tag{4.12}$$

Here $E_{-\alpha}$ is short for E_β when $\vec{\beta} = -\vec{\alpha}$, and $E_{\alpha+\beta}$ is short for E_γ when $\vec{\gamma} = \vec{\alpha} + \vec{\beta}$; that is, the algebraic operations on root vectors are conveniently reflected on the subscripts of the E_α. If $\vec{\alpha} + \vec{\beta}$ does not happen to be a root, then $E_{\alpha+\beta}$ does not exist and $N_{\alpha\beta}$ must vanish. On the other hand, it can easily be proved that $-\vec{\alpha}$ is a root if $\vec{\alpha}$ is a root; hence $E_{-\alpha}$ always exists. To show this, we calculate the tensor g_{AB}, which has a very simple form in the basis that we have introduced.

From Eqs. (4.6), (4.9), and (4.10), we find

$$g_{i\alpha} = C^B_{iA} C^A_{\alpha B} = C^\beta_{i\beta} C^\beta_{\alpha\beta} = 0 \tag{4.13}$$

Hence g_{AB} has no matrix element connecting the first ℓ components with the remaining $(n - \ell)$ components. Again from Eqs. (4.8), (4.9), and (4.10),

$$g_{\alpha\beta} = C^B_{\alpha A} C^A_{\beta B} = C^\alpha_{\alpha i} C^i_{\beta\alpha} + C^{\alpha+\gamma}_{\alpha\gamma} C^\gamma_{\beta,\alpha+\gamma} \tag{4.14}$$

Both terms vanish unless $\vec{\alpha} + \vec{\beta} = 0$. Hence, if $-\vec{\alpha}$ is not a root, we obtain $g_{\alpha A} = 0$, and g_{AB} is singular. By Cartan's criterion this is not possible, and we have proved the theorem: <u>If $\vec{\alpha}$ is a root in a semisimple algebra, then $-\vec{\alpha}$ is also a root.</u>

3. Normalization of the Basis Matrices

Introduce a new basis by $E_\alpha \rightarrow d_\alpha E_\alpha$, where d_α are nonvanishing real numbers. Then $C^\alpha_{i\alpha} = r_i(\alpha) \rightarrow r_i(\alpha)$, $C^i_{\alpha,-\alpha} = r^i(\alpha) \rightarrow d_\alpha d_{-\alpha} r^i(\alpha)$, $C^{\alpha+\beta}_{\alpha\beta} = N_{\alpha\beta} \rightarrow (d_\alpha d_\beta / d_{\alpha+\beta}) N_{\alpha\beta}$, and hence $g_{\alpha,-\alpha} \rightarrow d_\alpha d_{-\alpha} g_{\alpha,-\alpha}$. Choosing $d_\alpha d_{-\alpha} = (g_{\alpha,-\alpha})^{-1}$, we normalize our basis in such a way that $g_{\alpha,-\alpha} = g_{-\alpha,\alpha} = 1$. Thus,

$$g_{AB} = \left(\begin{array}{c|c} g_{ij} & \\ \hline & \begin{array}{cc} 0 & 1 \\ 1 & 0 \end{array} \ddots \end{array}\right) \tag{4.15}$$

where g_{ij} is nonsingular by Cartan's criterion.

We have yet to use Eqs. (4.6), (4.9), and (4.10) to calculate g_{ij}; we shall show that one may take $g_{ij} = \delta_{ij}$ without loss of generality. First,

$$g_{ij} = C^{B}_{iA} C^{A}_{jB} = \sum_{\alpha} r_i(\alpha) r_j(\alpha) \tag{4.16}$$

Thus the condition that g_{ij} be nonsingular means that the vectors $\vec{\alpha} = r_1(\alpha), \ldots, r_\ell(\alpha)$ must span the ℓ-dimensional space. A nonsingular transformation $H_i \rightarrow V_i^{\,j} H_j$ gives $C^{\alpha}_{i\alpha} = r_i(\alpha) \rightarrow V_i^{\,j} r_j(\alpha)$ and $C^{i}_{\alpha,-\alpha} = r^i(\alpha) \rightarrow (V^{-1})^{i}_{j} r^j(\alpha)$, and hence $g_{\alpha,-\alpha} \rightarrow g_{\alpha,-\alpha}$, $g_{ij} \rightarrow V_i^{\,k} V_j^{\,\ell} g_{k\ell}$. Therefore this transformation may be used to reduce g_{ij} to δ_{ij}.

The $r_i(\alpha)$ and $r^i(\alpha)$ are not independent. One might expect a relation of the form

$$r_i(\alpha) = g_{ij} r^j(\alpha) \tag{4.17}$$

This is, in fact, an easy consequence of the normalization

$$1 = g_{\alpha,-\alpha} = C^{B}_{\alpha A} C^{A}_{-\alpha B} \tag{4.18}$$

Namely, using Eq. (4.1) twice,

$$
\begin{aligned}
g_{ij}\, r^{j}(\alpha) &= C^{\gamma}_{i\gamma}\, C^{\gamma}_{j\gamma}\, C^{j}_{\alpha,-\alpha} = C^{B}_{iA}\, C^{A}_{jB}\, C^{j}_{\alpha,-\alpha} \\
&= -C^{B}_{iA}\, [C^{A}_{D\alpha}\, C^{D}_{-\alpha B} + C^{A}_{D,-\alpha}\, C^{D}_{A\alpha}] \\
&= C^{B}_{D\alpha}\, [C^{A}_{-\alpha i}\, C^{D}_{BA} + C^{A}_{B,-\alpha}\, C^{D}_{iA}] - C^{B}_{iA}\, C^{A}_{D,-\alpha}\, C^{D}_{B\alpha} \\
&= C^{A}_{\alpha D}\, C^{D}_{BA}\, C^{B}_{-\alpha i} = C^{-\alpha}_{-\alpha i} = r_i(\alpha)
\end{aligned}
\qquad (4.19)
$$

Having normalized g_{ij} to δ_{ij}, we get $r_i(\alpha) = r^i(\alpha)$. We adopt this normalization and collect the results:

Commutation relations

$$
\begin{aligned}
&[H_i, H_j] = 0, \quad i, j = 1, \cdots, l \\
&[H_i, E_\alpha] = r_i(\alpha)\, E_\alpha \\
&[E_\alpha, E_{-\alpha}] = r^{i}(\alpha)\, H_i \\
&[E_\alpha, E_\beta] = N_{\alpha\beta}\, E_{\alpha+\beta}
\end{aligned}
\qquad (4.20)
$$

Normalization

$$
\begin{aligned}
&r^{i}(\alpha) = r_i(\alpha) \\
&\Sigma_\alpha\, r_i(\alpha)\, r_j(\alpha) = \delta_{ij}
\end{aligned}
\qquad (4.21)
$$

4. Properties of the Roots

We now turn to a systematic investigation of the remaining part of the Jacobi identity, namely,

$$\sum_{\text{CYCL.}} [E_\alpha, [E_\beta, E_\gamma]] = 0 \tag{4.22}$$

This will be done in three steps. First let $\vec{\gamma} = -\vec{\beta}$; then Eq. (4.22) reduces to

$$N_{\alpha\beta} N_{-\beta,\alpha+\beta} = N_{\alpha-\beta,\beta} N_{-\beta,\alpha} + \vec{\alpha}\cdot\vec{\beta} \tag{4.23}$$

If neither $\vec{\alpha} + \vec{\beta}$ nor $\vec{\alpha} - \vec{\beta}$ is a root, then this shows that $\vec{\alpha}$ and $\vec{\beta}$ are orthogonal to each other. To obtain a more general result, consider the <u>strings</u> of matrices

$$[E_\alpha, E_\beta] = N_{\alpha\beta} E_{\alpha+\beta}, [E_{\alpha+\beta}, E_\beta] = N_{\alpha+\beta,\beta} E_{\alpha+2\beta}, \ldots, \tag{4.24}$$

and

$$[E_\alpha, E_{-\beta}] = N_{\alpha,-\beta} E_{\alpha-\beta}, [E_{\alpha-\beta}, E_{-\beta}] = N_{\alpha-\beta,-\beta} E_{\alpha-2\beta}, \ldots, \tag{4.25}$$

Both of these strings must stop—say, after j and k steps, respectively—because there is only a finite number of roots. In Eq. (4.23), replace α by $\alpha + i\beta$ to obtain the recursion relation,

$$\mu_i = \mu_{i-1} + \vec{\beta}\cdot(\vec{\alpha} + i\vec{\beta}) \tag{4.26}$$

where

$$\mu_i = N_{\alpha+i\beta,\beta} N_{-\beta,\alpha+i\beta+\beta} \tag{4.27}$$

in which, by hypothesis, $\mu_i = \mu_{-K-1} = 0$. This not only gives information about the $N_{\alpha\beta}$ but also puts a very strong restriction on the root vectors, for by iteration Eq. (4.26) gives

$$\mu_i = \mu_{i-1} + \vec{\beta}\cdot[\vec{\alpha} - K\vec{\beta} + (i+K)\vec{\beta}]$$
$$= (i+K+1)\vec{\beta}\cdot(\vec{\alpha} - K\vec{\beta}) + \tfrac{1}{2}(i+K)(i+K+1)\vec{\beta}\cdot\vec{\beta} \tag{4.28}$$

Setting i = j,

$$2\vec{\beta}\cdot(\vec{\alpha} - K\vec{\beta}) + (j+K)\vec{\beta}\cdot\vec{\beta} = 0 \tag{4.29}$$

Here $\vec{\beta}\cdot\vec{\beta} = r^i(\beta)\, r_i(\beta) = \sum_i |r_i(\beta)|^2$ cannot vanish; therefore,

$$K - j = 2\vec{\alpha}\cdot\vec{\beta}/\vec{\beta}\cdot\vec{\beta} = g(\alpha/\beta) \quad \text{(SAY)} \tag{4.30}$$

This proves the following fundamental theorem.

Theorem. If $\vec{\alpha}$ and $\vec{\beta}$ are two roots, then $g(\alpha/\beta) = 2\vec{\alpha}\cdot\vec{\beta}/\vec{\beta}\cdot\vec{\beta}$ is an integer, and $\vec{\alpha} - g(\alpha/\beta)\vec{\beta}$ is a root.

A corollary of this theorem is that, if $\vec{\alpha} + \vec{\beta} \neq 1$, $\vec{\alpha}$ and $\vec{\beta}$ are linearly independent.

Corollary. If $\vec{\alpha}$ and $c\,\vec{\alpha}$ are roots in a semisimple algebra, then $c = \pm 1$. (Proof: The theorem easily shows that 2c and 2/c must be integers; hence $c = \pm 1$ or ± 2. The latter case is ruled out below.)

Before exploring further consequences of Eq. (4.28), we shall consider another special case of Eq. (4.22). If we take $\vec{\alpha} + \vec{\beta} + \vec{\gamma} = 0$, the corollary ensures that the three root vectors are not parallel. Equation (4.22) gives

$$N_{\alpha\beta}\vec{\gamma} + N_{\beta\gamma}\vec{\alpha} + N_{\gamma\alpha}\vec{\beta} = 0 \tag{4.31}$$

Hence,

$$N_{\alpha\beta} = N_{\beta,-\alpha-\beta} = N_{-\alpha-\beta,\alpha} \tag{4.32}$$

Using Eqs. (4.28), (4.29), and (4.32), we get

$$\begin{aligned}\mu_0 &= N_{\alpha\beta} N_{-\beta,\alpha+\beta} = N_{\alpha\beta} N_{-\alpha,-\beta} \\ &= (K+1)[\vec{\beta}\cdot\vec{\alpha} - (K/2)\vec{\beta}\cdot\vec{\beta}] = -1/2(K+1)j\,\vec{\beta}\cdot\vec{\beta}\end{aligned} \tag{4.33}$$

If $\vec{\alpha}+\vec{\beta}$ is a root, then j ≥ 1; and since $\vec{\beta}\cdot\vec{\beta}$ cannot vanish, we conclude that $N_{\alpha\beta}$ and $N_{-\alpha,-\beta}$ must both be nonzero. (This completes the proof of the corollary: 2 $\vec{\alpha}$ cannot be a root, since $N_{\alpha\alpha} = 0$.) Under the transformation $E_\alpha \to d_\alpha E_\alpha$, we have

$$N_{\alpha\beta} \to (d_\alpha d_\beta / d_{\alpha+\beta}) N_{\alpha\beta}, \quad N_{-\alpha,-\beta} \to (d_{-\alpha} d_{-\beta} / d_{-\alpha-\beta}) N_{-\alpha-\beta} \tag{4.34}$$

The products $d_\alpha\ d_{-\alpha}$ we have fixed already, but the ratio

$$(N_{\alpha\beta}/N_{-\alpha,-\beta}) \to (d_\alpha/d_{-\alpha})(d_\beta/d_{-\beta})(d_{-\alpha-\beta}/d_{\alpha+\beta})(N_{\alpha\beta}/N_{-\alpha,-\beta}) \tag{4.35}$$

is still at our disposal. We choose $d_\alpha / d_{-\alpha}$ so that this ratio becomes -1:

$$N_{\alpha\beta} = -N_{-\alpha,-\beta} \tag{4.36}$$

Then

$$\mu_0 = -(N_{\alpha/\beta})^2 = -\tfrac{1}{2}(K-1)j\,\vec{\beta}\cdot\vec{\beta} \tag{4.37}$$

and

$$N_{\alpha\beta} = \pm \sqrt{(K+1)(j/2)}\ |\vec{\beta}| \tag{4.38}$$

The signs of the d_α are still at our disposal, so that the signs in Eq. (4.36) are still arbitrary and subject to Eqs. (4.30) and (4.32) and, of course, to $N_{\alpha\beta} = -N_{\beta\alpha}$.

We are now in a position to construct all simple and semisimple algebras of given rank.

5. Lie Algebras of Rank 2; Root Diagrams

From the above fundamental theorem, we have

$$(2\vec{\alpha}\cdot\vec{\beta}/\vec{\beta}\cdot\vec{\beta})(2\vec{\alpha}\cdot\vec{\beta}/\vec{\alpha}\cdot\vec{\alpha}) = 4\cos^2\varphi_{\alpha\beta} = \text{INTEGER} \times \text{INTEGER}$$

where $\varphi_{\alpha\beta}$ is the angle between $\vec{\alpha}$ and $\vec{\beta}$. Thus only the following possibilities can occur:

$$\varphi_{\alpha\beta} = 90^\circ \tag{4.39}$$

$$\varphi_{\alpha\beta} = \pm 60^\circ,\ |\vec{\alpha}|/|\vec{\beta}| = 1 \tag{4.40}$$

$$\varphi_{\alpha\beta} = \pm 45^\circ,\ |\vec{\alpha}|/|\vec{\beta}| = \sqrt{2} \tag{4.41}$$

$$\varphi_{\alpha\beta} = \pm 30^\circ,\ |\vec{\alpha}|/|\vec{\beta}| = \sqrt{3} \tag{4.42}$$

To find all simple and semisimple algebras of rank 2, one starts with two 2-dimensional vectors $\vec{\alpha}$ and $\vec{\beta}$, satisfying one of the four conditions above, and then adds their reflections and all those other root vectors required by the theorem of the previous section. The over-all scale is then fixed by the normalization condition of Eq. (4.21). The results are best displayed by root diagrams, in which all the root vectors are simply drawn with correct directions and magnitudes from a common origin. Then Eqs. (4.39) to (4.42) give Fig. 2a to d, respectively.

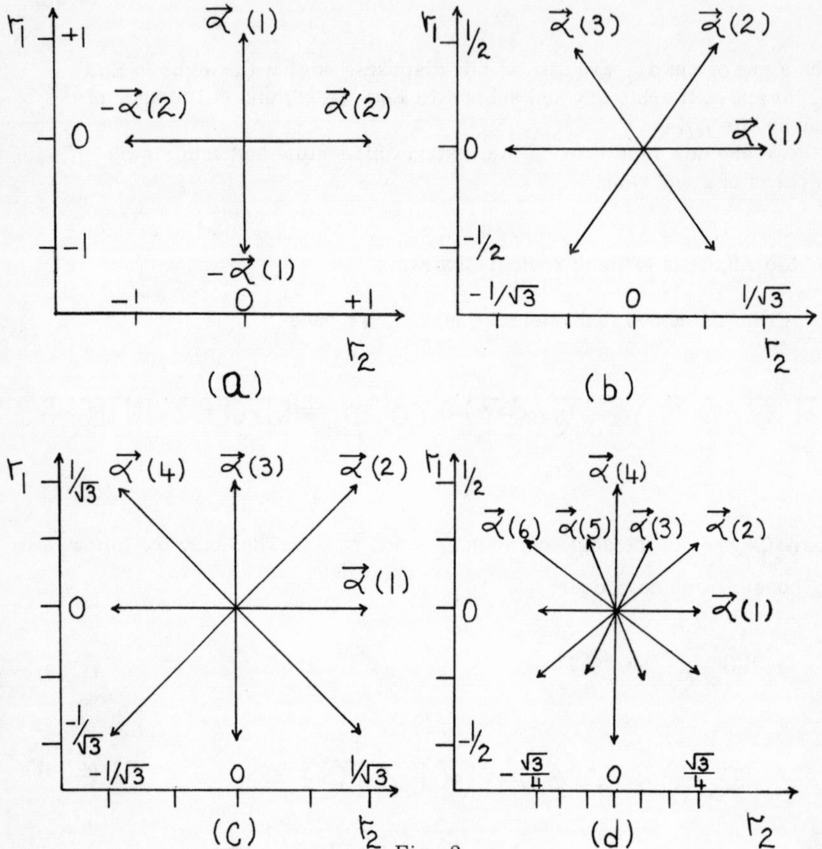

Fig. 2

These algebras are called O_4, A_2, B_2, and G_2, respectively. The first are essentially the infinitesimal Lorentz transformations and are not simple. This is because (refer to the notations in the Figure) the $E_{\pm 1}$ commute with $E_{\pm 2}$, since the corresponding roots are orthogonal. In general, it is true that, if the root vectors separate into mutually orthogonal sets, then the algebra is not simple. Incidentally, we see that the concept of the orthogonal complement of an invariant subalgebra is identical to, and receives a graphical interpretation by, diagonal sets of roots.

The algebras A_2, B_2, and G_2 are simple. The subscript number refers to the rank of the group, the letter to the original classification due to Cartan. The root-diagram technique easily gives all simple algebras of arbitrary rank. The following is a complete list of simple algebras with their respective orders:

$$\begin{array}{lll} A_\ell & \ell = 1, 2, \cdots, & (\ell^2 + 2\ell) \\ B_\ell & \ell = 2, 3, \cdots, & (2\ell^2 + \ell) \\ C_\ell & \ell = 3, 4, \cdots, & (2\ell^2 + \ell) \\ D_\ell & \ell = 4, 5, \cdots, & (2\ell^2 - \ell) \\ \multicolumn{3}{l}{G_2\,(14),\ F_4\,(52),\ E_6\,(78),\ E_7\,(133),\ E_8\,(248)} \end{array} \tag{4.43}$$

The last five are known as "exceptional algebras," while the others correspond to well-known classical groups. Thus A_ℓ is alternatively known as $SU_{\ell+1}$; it may be defined as the set of all hermitian traceless matrices of dimension $\ell + 1$. The algebras B_ℓ are also known as O_n, $n = 2\ell + 1$, which is the set of infinitesimal rotations in an n-dimensional space. The reason why B_1 is excluded from the list is that it is the same as A_1; in fact, anybody who knows anything about spin and angular momentum knows that the infinitesimal rotations in a three-dimensional space may be represented by traceless, hermitian, two-by-two matrices. Rotations in a space of arbitrary dimension may be defined as a set of transformations that leave a <u>symmetric</u> form invariant. The algebras C_ℓ are similarly related to simplectic transformations in a 2ℓ-dimensional space; simplectic transformations leave an <u>antisymmetric</u> form invariant. It happens that C_2 is the same as B_2, while C_1 is the same as A_1. Finally, D_ℓ is the same as O_n, $n = 2\ell$. For $\ell = 1$, this is Abelian; for $\ell = 2$, we have already seen that it is not simple; and for $\ell = 3$, it happens to be the same as A_3.

V. THREE-DIMENSIONAL ROTATIONS

1. Finite Group

As an illustration of the previous sections, as well as preparation for the next one, it is desirable to treat in some detail the most important Lie group of all.

Consider a real Euclidean 3-space, with coordinates x_1, x_2, x_3, and the real linear transformations

$$x_i \to x_i' = R_i^{\ j} x_j \tag{5.1}$$

This is a rotation if the length is preserved. If the x_i are Cartesian coordinates, the square of the invariant length is $\sum_i x_i^2$; but it is convenient to drop the restriction to Cartesian coordinates and to write the invariant squared length as

$$g^{ij} x_i x_j$$

This allows us to use the summation convention. Of course, we require that g^{ij} be nonsingular, so there exists an inverse defined by

$$g^{ij} g_{jk} = \delta_k^i \tag{5.2}$$

The g^{ij} may be used to raise indices, for example, to define $x^i = g^{ij} x_j$. The advantage of using Cartesian coordinates is that $g_{ij} = g^{ij} = \delta_i^{\ j}$, so that there is no need to distinguish between subs and supers. But this is a risky practice, and we shall insist on distinguishing upstairs from downstairs indices. The advantage of this stems from the fact that Cartesian coordinate systems are not always the most convenient ones.

The length is preserved by Eq. (5.1) only if

$$R_i^{\ j} R_k^{\ l} g^{ik} = g^{jl} \tag{5.3}$$

The matrices that satisfy Eq. (5.3) form a group: every $R_i^{\ j}$ has an inverse, namely, $(R^{-1})_k^{\ i} = g^{ij} g_{k\ell} R_j^{\ \ell}$; the unit matrix is in the set; and R R' satisfies Eq. (5.3) if R and R' do.

We first study the topology of this group. The matrices $R_i^{\ j}$ have nine matrix elements; thus each matrix may be associated with a point in a nine-dimensional real space. However, according to Eq. (5.3), only three matrix elements can be chosen arbitrarily; hence the set of all $R_i^{\ j}$ gives only a three-dimensional surface in the nine-dimensional space. Better, therefore, to choose a set of three parameters with which $R_i^{\ j}$ can be specified and to use a three-dimensional topological space. The most convenient choice is based on an elementary theorem from the mechanics of rigid bodies: if a rigid body is rotated, in any manner whatsoever, around a fixed point, then the result can be obtained by a single rotation around a fixed axis. Thus every rotation can be defined by three real numbers: two to give the direction of the axis and one to give the angle of rotation. Of course, this works only for proper rotations, not for reflections, although the simple <u>reflection</u> $R_i^{\ j} = -\delta_i^{\ j}$ satisfies our definition of a rotation. From Eq. (5.3) it is easy to prove that Det $R_i^{\ j} = \pm 1$. A rotation with determinant +1 is called a "proper" rotation, and one with determinant -1 is called "improper." It is clear that the proper rotations are not continuously connected to the improper ones, since there are no rotations with intermediary determinants between +1 and -1. Thus, let G be the set of all rotations, and (G_1, G_2) the set of all proper, improper rotations. Only G_1 contains the identity and is the <u>group</u> of proper rotations. If any member of G_1 (say, $R_i^{\ j}$) is multiplied by the matrix of pure reflections $-\delta_i^{\ j}$, the result has negative determinant and belongs to G_2. Thus the complete rotation group is obtained if the simple reflection is added to the proper rotation group. The latter is that part of the rotation group which is continuously connected to the identity.

Turning now from this digression, we realize that a proper rotation is fully specified by a direction and a number. This number may be restricted to vary between 0 and π, since a rotation of more than π in one direction is a rotation of less than π in the opposite direction. Thus, the set of all proper rotations corresponds to the set of all points in a solid sphere of radius π. But this statement is slightly misleading: consider two rotations around the same axis, but with angles π and $-\pi$. Because the results of these rotations are identical, the matrices are identical; but the corresponding points in the ball are not the same or even close, but are antipodes on the surface. Thus the correct topology is obtained only by positing that antipodal surface points are identical points.

Accordingly, the topology of proper rotations is that of a ball with radius π and with antipodal surface points identified.

Since we have broached the subject of topology, we may now ask this question: Is the proper rotation group (i. e., the above-mentioned ball) simply connected? In other words, can every continuous closed path in the group (i. e., in the ball) be contracted to a single point by continuous deformations, and without ever leaving the group (ball)? Well, were it not for the identifications that had to be made of antipodal surface point, the answer would obviously be yes. Precisely because of these schizophrenic surface points, however, there are paths that cannot be contracted, such as one of those shown in Fig. 3. It is an easy exercise to show that a path which is "broken" (not actually broken, since two points connected by a dotted line are identical) an even number of times can be contracted, and that a path which is "broken" an odd number of times can be continuously contracted until it is broken only once. Thus there are two quite different kinds of paths, and we may say that the topology is doubly connected.

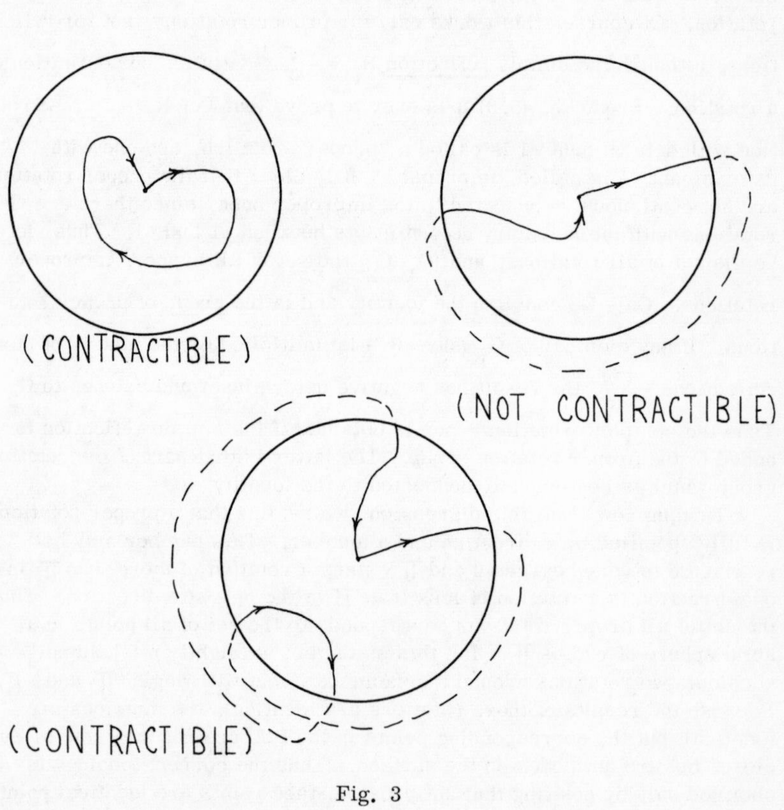

Fig. 3

These topological properties are properties of the group "in the large," and they cannot be discussed if we limit our attention to the neighborhood of the identity (in this case, the neighborhood of the center of the ball). It is well to remember that the study of the Lie algebra of a group (i. e., the infinitesimal transformation) leaves many questions unanswered, and even unasked. Since properties in the large shall be completely ignored in the sections dealing with the other groups, I felt the more compelled to devote extra attention to the topology of the rotation group, the simplest of all simple Lie groups.

The double connectedness of the proper rotations has a direct connection with the two-valuedness of spin transformations. Later we shall study this in detail, but first let us be reminded of the familiar Lie algebra of the rotation group, the angular momentum operators.

2. Lie Algebra

The fact that the finite transformations are completely specified by three parameters is reflected by the fact that there are three linearly independent infinitesimal generators: L_1, L_2, L_3. The commutation relations are well known:

$$[L_A, L_B] = i L_C \qquad \text{CYCLICALLY} \tag{5.4}$$

We immediately suspect that the rank of this algebra is 1, but to make sure let us try to find two commuting matrices:

$$[a^A L_A, b^B L_B] = i\,\vec{a}\times\vec{b}\cdot\vec{L} = 0 \tag{5.5}$$

Thus $\vec{a}$ and $\vec{b}$ must be parallel; but then the two matrices are linearly dependent.

Let us therefore take $H_1 = L_1$ and, in accordance with the general procedure, try to diagonalize $C_{1A}{}^B$. According to Eq. (5.4),

$$C_{1A}{}^{B} = \begin{pmatrix} 0 & 0 & 0 \\ 0 & 0 & i \\ 0 & -i & 0 \end{pmatrix} \tag{5.6}$$

which can be diagonalized, because it is hermitian. Knowing that the eigenvectors of $C_{1A}{}^B$ are $(0, 1, \pm i)$, we complete the basis by introducing

$$E_{\pm 1} = (L_2 \pm i L_3)/\sqrt{2} \tag{5.7}$$

Then Eq. (5.4) gives

$$[H_1, E_{+1}] = E_{+1} \qquad [H_1, E_{-1}] = -E_{-1} \tag{5.8}$$

There are only two roots, $\vec{\alpha} = 1$ and $-\vec{\alpha} = -1$, which are one-dimensional. This is obviously the only possible simple algebra of rank 1, because of the corollary to the theorem in Sec. IV. 4. The normalization in Eq. (5.7) (and in the definition $H_1 = L_1$) has been chosen so that

$$[E_{+1}, E_{-1}] = H_1 \tag{5.9}$$

Thus $r^i(\alpha) = r_i(\alpha)$, as in the general case. The $N_{\alpha\beta}$ do not exist in this case. It may be worth while to emphasize a point we skipped before, namely, that the choice $H_1 = L_1$ is not entirely arbitrary. To be sure, we could have taken $H_1 = L_2$ or $H_1 = L_3$ with impunity, but not any choice of H_1 from all the matrices of the algebra would do. For example, set $H_1 = (L_1 + iL_2)/2$. Then the eigenvalue problem

$$[H_1, a^A L_A] = r a^A L_A \tag{5.10}$$

has no solution. Cartan showed only that a set of H_i can always be found such that the $C_{iA}^{\;\;B}$ can be diagonalized.

This simple algebra is fundamental and occurs as a subgroup of every other simple algebra in several ways. For example, the three matrices E_α, $E_{-\alpha}$, and $H = r^i(\alpha)H_i$ always satisfy the commutation relations:

$$[H, E_{\pm\alpha}] = \pm \vec{\alpha}\cdot\vec{\alpha}\, E_{\pm\alpha} \qquad [E_{+\alpha}, E_{-\alpha}] = H \tag{5.11}$$

By a simple renormalization the factor $\vec{\alpha}\cdot\vec{\alpha}$ is easily eliminated, so that complete agreement with Eqs. (5.8) and (5.9) is obtained.

The root diagram is so simple that it need not take space here; it consists of two antiparallel vectors of unit length, drawn from a common point.

3. Representations

Let $(H_1, E_{\pm 1})$ be any specific set of d-by-d matrices that satisfy the commutation relations of Eqs. (5.8) and (5.9). This is said to constitute a particular representation of the Lie algebra. What must the dimension d be in order that such matrices exist? Can there be several different representations with the same dimension? How does one obtain an explicit construction of these matrices? These questions can be answered not only for the special case at hand but also for every simple or semi-simple Lie algebra!

First, let us say a word about the meaning of "different" representations. Let H_1 and $E_{\pm 1}$ satisfy Eqs. (5.8) and (5.9), and let V be any nonsingular d-by-d matrix. Then one immediately verifies that the matrices $H_1' = VH_1V^{-1}$ and $E'_{\pm 1} = VE_{\pm 1}V^{-1}$ satisfy precisely the same commutation relations. Two different representations related in this way are said to be equivalent. If one representation has been obtained explicitly, it is useless effort to write down the infinity of representations equivalent to it, and we shall in fact regard two representations as distinct only if they are not equivalent. The easiest way to handle this problem is to bring all representations into a standard form, so that two representations are equivalent only (with few exceptions) if they are identical.

Again remembering the quantum mechanical model, we introduce some objects — "state vectors" — on which the matrices can act. We assume that H_1 can be, and has been, diagonalized, so that the state vectors may be characterized by the eigenvalue if H_1 to which they belong and by other "quantum numbers" if H_1 is degenerate. Thus,

$$H_1 \psi(m, \sigma) = m \psi(m, \sigma) \tag{5.12}$$

where σ stands for the "other quantum numbers." The matrices $E_{\pm 1}$ now turn out to be simple creation and destruction operators, whose effect on $\psi(m, \sigma)$ is to produce a state with one more or less unit of m. This is an elementary consequence of the commutation relations of Eq. (5.8), for if

$$E_{+1} \psi(m, \sigma) = \psi' \quad \text{(SAY)} \tag{5.13}$$

then

$$H_1\psi' = H_1 E_{+1}\psi(m,\sigma) = ([H_1, E_{+1}] + E_{+1} H)\psi(m,\sigma)$$
$$= E_{+1}(1 + H_1)\psi(m,\sigma)$$
$$= (m+1)\psi' \tag{5.14}$$

Thus E_{+1} (E_{-1}) raises (lowers) the "spin" of the state or, as we shall call it, the weight of the state.

When E_{+1} is applied repeatedly, we obtain $\psi(m+1,\sigma)$, $\psi(m+2,\sigma)$, -. . . ,- and this must necessarily come to an end if the representation is finite-dimensional. Thus there must be an eigenvalue (say, M), such that

$$E_{+1}\psi(M,\sigma) = 0 \tag{5.15}$$

Conversely, we generate $\psi(M-1,\sigma)$, etc., by means of E_{-1}, and now we pay attention to normalization and write

$$E_{-1}\psi(M-i,\sigma) = \mu_i\psi(M-i-1,\sigma) \tag{5.16}$$

This, too, must eventually come to an end after, say, λ steps; hence,

$$E_{-1}\psi(M-\lambda,\sigma) = 0 \tag{5.17}$$

Having descended from the highest weight (M) to the lowest (M-λ), we may attempt to climb again by means of E_{+1}; for example,

$$E_{+1}\psi(M-1,\sigma) = \psi'(M,\sigma') \tag{5.18}$$

We must show that this new state is the same, up to a factor, as

$\psi(M,\sigma)$. We use the commutation relation of Eq. (5.9) together with Eq. (5.15):

$$\begin{aligned} \mu_0 E_{+1}\psi(M-1,\sigma) &= E_{+1}E_{-1}\psi(M,\sigma) \\ &= [E_{+1},E_{-1}]\psi(M,\sigma) \\ &= M\psi(M,\sigma) \end{aligned} \tag{5.19}$$

For the rest, we use induction:

$$\begin{aligned} \mu_i E_{+1}\psi(M-i-1,\sigma) &= E_{+1}E_{-1}\psi(M-i,\sigma) \\ &= (M-i+E_{-1}E_{+1})\psi(M-i,\sigma) \end{aligned} \tag{5.20}$$

Thus, if $E_{+1}\psi(M-i,\sigma)$ is proportional to $\psi(M-i+1,\sigma)$, it follows that $E_{+1}\psi(M-i-1,\sigma)$ is proportional to $\psi(M-i,\sigma)$. Since this is indeed true for i = 0, it is true for all i.

With that, the whole representation problem is nearly solved, for the $(\lambda+1)$ states we have considered clearly constitute a representation. No other states can be generated by applying the matrices H_1 and $E_{\pm1}$ any number of times. There may be other states differing only in having a different value of σ, but these must again form one or more strings of the same general structure—each structure, each string, being a representation. Thus every representation has the following form:

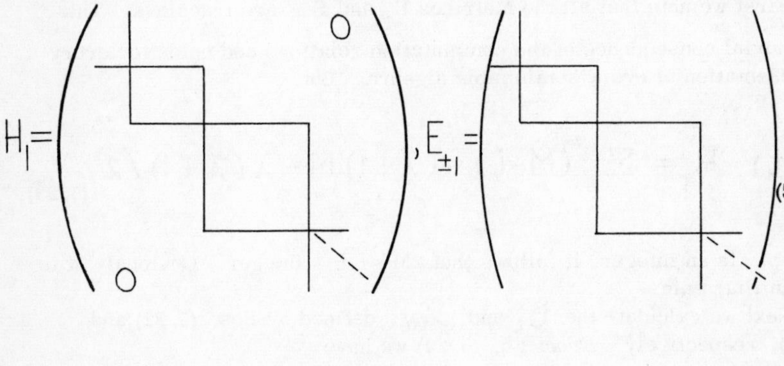

(5.21)

where each block in H_1 has the same size as the corresponding ones in $E_{\pm 1}$, and where each set of submatrices forms a representation of the simple form just discussed.

Quite generally, we may ask of a set of matrices whether or not they may be "diagonalized," or "reduced," to the form (5.21), and we therefore speak of reducible and irreducible representations. Clearly, in a reducible representation each set of submatrices must satisfy the commutation relations; hence the most general reducible representation may be pieced together from irreducible representations. Consequently, in order to find all representations of the algebra, it is sufficient to catalogue the irreducible ones. This is true for all Lie algebras.

There are several criteria for determining whether a representation is irreducible or not, but we are fortunate in that the simplest test of all is easily applicable and effective. Namely, from inspecting the representations of Eq. (5.21), it is obvious that if a representation is reducible there are states which cannot be transformed into each other by applying the matrices any number of times (e.g., the two states corresponding to the first and the last row). It follows that, if every state of a representation can be obtained from one of them by applying the representation matrices, then the representation is irreducible.

Thus we have found, in Eqs. (5.12, (5.12) to (5.17), and (5.20), the most general irreducible representation of the algebra A_1. There remains only to find the possible values of M and λ and to calculate μ_i and ν_i, the latter being defined by the counterpart of Eq. (5.16):

$$E_{+1}\,\psi(M-i) = \nu_i\,\psi(M-i+1) \tag{5.22}$$

The extra "quantum number" σ is omitted here and below; it served only to distinguish the several irreducible representations within one reducible representation.

First we note that all the matrices H_1 and $E_{\pm 1}$ are traceless. This is a trivial consequence of the commutation relations and holds for every representation of every semisimple algebra. But

$$\operatorname{tr} H_1 = \Sigma_i\,(M-i) = (\lambda+1)M - \lambda(\lambda+1)/2 \tag{5.23}$$

Since λ is an integer, it follows that $2M = \lambda$ = integer. Obviously M is the familiar spin.

Next we calculate the ν_i and μ_i, defined by Eqs. (5.22) and (5.16), respectively. From Eq. (5.20) we have

$$\mu_i \nu_{i+1} = \mu_{i-1} \nu_i + \lambda/2 - i \tag{5.24}$$

Clearly the μ_i may be chosen at will, and we choose them so that

$$\mu_i = \nu_{i+1} \geq 0 \tag{5.25}$$

which is consistent with the fact that μ_i is defined for i = 0, 1, ..., λ - 1, while ν_i is defined for i = 1, 2, ..., λ. Then,

$$\begin{aligned} \mu_i^2 &= \mu_{i-1}^2 + \lambda/2 - i \\ &= \lambda(i+1)/2 - i(i+1)/2 \end{aligned} \tag{5.26}$$

or

$$\mu_i = \nu_{i+1} = \sqrt{(i+1)(2-i)/2} \tag{5.27}$$

We reintroduce the more conventional number

$$m = M - i \qquad H_1 \psi(m) = m \psi(m) \tag{5.28}$$

which takes the values

$$\lambda/2, \lambda/2 - 1, \cdots, -\lambda/2$$

Then,

$$\mu_m = \nu_{m-1} = \sqrt{(M-m+1)(M+m)/2} \tag{5.29}$$

Thus there is precisely one irreducible representation for every integer λ, and that representation is

$$H_1 \psi(m) = m\,\psi(m)$$

$$E_{+1}\psi(m) = \sqrt{(M-m)(M+m+1)/2}\;\psi(m+1)$$

$$E_{-1}\psi(m) = \sqrt{(M-m+1)(M+m)/2}\;\psi(m-1)$$

(5. 30)

The dimension of the representation is the number of different values of m (each eigenvalue occurring only once), which is equal to $\lambda + 1 = 2M + 1$.

I have gone through these calculations knowing well that every graduate student knows them all by heart. What may escape him, however, is the great power and generality of the method. Presently we shall see how it may be used to find all representations of all simple Lie algebras.

4. Tensors

The simplest representation of A_1 is obtained by choosing for λ the smallest integer, namely, zero. In this case, $H_1 = E_{\pm 1} = 0$, which is indeed a solution of the commutation relations. This representation is called the trivial or identity representation, because all the finite matrices are equal to the identity matrix. Before turning to the next simplest case, $\lambda = 1$, something should be said about the case $\lambda = 2$.

When $\lambda = 2$, then m takes the values +1, 0, -1. If the three components ψ (m) are ordered according to decreasing m, Eq. (5. 30) gives

$$H_1 = \begin{pmatrix} 1 & 0 & 0 \\ 0 & 0 & 0 \\ 0 & 0 & -1 \end{pmatrix} \qquad E_{+1} = E_{-1}^{T} = \begin{pmatrix} 0 & 1 & 0 \\ 0 & 0 & 1 \\ 0 & 0 & 0 \end{pmatrix}$$

(5. 31)

According to the previous section, there is only one representation of each dimension; therefore Eq. (5. 31) must be equivalent to the regular representation. The latter is the representation

$$L_A = -C_A\,, \quad (C_A)_B^{\;D} = C_{AB}^{\;\;D}$$

(5. 32)

which is clearly three-dimensional. It is very convenient to use a Dirac bracket notation for Eq. (5.32). We use the standard basis (H_i, $E_{\pm\alpha}$) and label the states accordingly: $|i\rangle$ and $|\pm\alpha\rangle$, or in this case $|1\rangle$ and $|\pm 1\rangle$. Then,

$$H_1 = -C^{B}_{1A}|A\rangle\langle B| = |-1\rangle\langle -1| - |+1\rangle\langle +1|$$

$$E_{+1} = -C^{B}_{+1A}|A\rangle\langle B| = |1\rangle\langle +1| - |-1\rangle\langle 1|$$

$$E_{-1} = E^{T}_{+1} \tag{5.33}$$

This is indeed equivalent to Eq. (5.31). Only the states have to be ordered and renormalized as follows: $-|-1\rangle$, $|1\rangle$, $|+1\rangle$. This regular representation, $\lambda = 2$, is of special importance for another reason. The three-dimensional matrices of Eq. (5.31) are precisely those which generate infinitesimal rotations in a three-dimensional space. Thus H_1 is the generator of infinitesimal rotations around the first axis, and L_2 and L_3, defined by $E_{\pm 1} = (L_2 \pm iL_3)/\sqrt{2}$, generate infinitesimal rotations around the other two axes. However, it is not true that a rotation around, say, the first axis is given in terms of Cartesian coordinates by $x_i \to x_i' = x_i + \varepsilon(H_1)_i{}^j x_j$, because in diagonalizing H_1 non-Cartesian coordinates have been introduced. In fact, the basis on which Eq. (5.31) acts is $(x_2 + ix_3)/\sqrt{2}$, x_1, $(x_2 - ix_3)/\sqrt{2}$, and so H_1 generates the transformation

$$\begin{pmatrix} (X_2+iX_3)/\sqrt{2} \\ X_1 \\ (X_2-iX_3)/\sqrt{2} \end{pmatrix} \to \begin{pmatrix} 1+i\varepsilon, & 0, & 0 \\ 0, & 1, & 0 \\ 0, & 0, & 1-i\varepsilon \end{pmatrix} \begin{pmatrix} (X_2+iX_3)/\sqrt{2} \\ X_3 \\ (X_2-iX_3)/\sqrt{2} \end{pmatrix} \tag{5.34}$$

or

$$\begin{aligned} X_1 &\to X_1 \\ X_2 &\to X_2 - \varepsilon X_3 \\ X_3 &\to X_3 + \varepsilon X_2 \end{aligned} \tag{5.35}$$

which is indeed an infinitesimal rotation around the first axis. This representation is the only one which has such a direct physical interpretation.

This representation allows a symmetric invariant form, namely, $g^{ij} x_i x_j$; in fact, the rotations are defined by this property. We found that

$$X_i \longrightarrow X_i' = R_i^{\ j} X_j \tag{5.36}$$

is a rotation if $g^{ij} R_i^{\ k} R_j^{\ \ell} = g^{k\ell}$. If $R = 1 + i\varepsilon L$, this gives

$$g^{ij} L_j^{\ k} + g^{kj} L_j^{\ i} = 0 \tag{5.37}$$

Or, if we use g^{ij} as a metric tensor, defining

$$L^{ik} = g^{ij} L_j^{\ k} \qquad \text{(DEFINITION)} \tag{5.38}$$

then

$$L^{ik} + L^{ki} = 0 \tag{5.39}$$

That is, the L^{ik} must be antisymmetric. Since the number of linearly independent antisymmetric matrices is precisely three, this tallies with the fact that A_1 has three independent basis matrices.

Now let us construct g^{ij} in terms of the representation in Eq. (5.33). If we take $L = H_1$, in Eq. (5.37), we see that g^{ij} can only connect states with equal and opposite eigenvalues of H_1. Thus,

$$g^{ij} = a\{|+1\rangle\langle -1| + |-1\rangle\langle +1|\} + b|1\rangle\langle 1| \tag{5.40}$$

where we have already taken the symmetry of g^{ij} into account.

Next,

$$(g^{ij})E_{+1} = b\,|1\rangle\langle +1| - a\,|+1\rangle\langle 1| \tag{5.41}$$

Because of Eq. (5.37) this must be symmetric; hence a = -b = 1 (the over-all normalization is irrelevant). Hence

$$g^{ij} = -|+1\rangle\langle -1| - |-1\rangle\langle +1| + |1\rangle\langle 1| \tag{5.42}$$

A <u>second-rank tensor</u> is a set of quantities T_{ij}, with i, j = 1, 2, 3, that transform among themselves like the products $x_i x_j$. Thus, if

$$X_i \to X_i' = R_i^{\,j} X_j \tag{5.43}$$

then

$$X_i X_j \to (X_i X_j)' = R_i^{\,k} R_j^{\,\ell} X_k X_\ell \tag{5.44}$$

and hence

$$T_{ij} \to T_{ij}' = R_i^{\,k} R_j^{\,\ell} T_{k\ell} \tag{5.45}$$

In terms of infinitesimal rotations,

$$X_i \to X_i' = X_i + i\epsilon L_i^{\,j} X_j \tag{5.46}$$

$$(X_i X_j) \to (X_i X_j)' = X_i X_j + i\epsilon L_i^{\,k} X_k X_j + i\epsilon L_j^{\,\ell} X_i X_\ell$$

$$T_{ij} \to T_{ij}' = T_{ij} + i\epsilon (L_i^{\,k} \delta_j^{\,\ell} + \delta_i^{\,k} L_j^{\,\ell}) T_{k\ell} \tag{5.47}$$

$$= T_{ij} + i\epsilon L_{ij}^{\,k\ell}\, T_{k\ell} \quad \text{(SAY)} \tag{5.48}$$

This is a new representation of the algebra, for it is trivial to verify that the matrices $L_{ij}^{k\ell}$ (in which both lower indices label and rows and both upper indices label the columns) satisfy the same commutation relations as the $L_i^{\ j}$.

5. Spinors

We now turn to the simplest nontrivial representation of the algebra A_1, the case $\lambda = 1$. Here m takes the values $\pm 1/2$, and the matrices of Eq. (5.30) are

$$H_1 = \begin{pmatrix} 1/2 , & 0 \\ 0 , & -1/2 \end{pmatrix}, \quad E_{+1} = E_{-1}^T = \sqrt{1/2} \begin{pmatrix} 0 , & 1 \\ 0 , & 0 \end{pmatrix} \tag{5.49}$$

or, in terms of L_1, L_2, L_3,

$$L_i = \sigma_i / 2 \tag{5.50}$$

where σ are the Pauli matrices.

We first study some properties of the corresponding finite matrices. Consider an infinitesimal rotation around the third axis,

$$X_i \rightarrow X_i' = X_i + i\, d\varphi\, (H_1)_i^{\ j} X_j \qquad i = 1,2,3 \tag{5.51}$$

where H_1 is the three-dimensional representation given by Eq. (5.31), and the two-dimensional representation of Eq. (5.51):

$$\psi_a \rightarrow \psi_a' = \psi_a + i\, d\varphi\, (H_1)_a^{\ b} \psi_b \qquad a = 1,2 \tag{5.52}$$

where H_1 is given by Eq. (5.49). It is important that the commutation relations for Eqs. (5.31) and (5.49) are precisely the same, so that $d\varphi$ is the same infinitesimal number in Eqs. (5.51) and (5.52).

The finite rotation generated by Eq. (5.49) and the finite transformation generated by Eq. (5.51) are

$$X_i \rightarrow (\mathrm{EXP}\ i\varphi H_1)_i^j X_j \tag{5.53}$$

$$\Psi_a \rightarrow (\mathrm{EXP}\ i\varphi H_1)_a^b \Psi_b \tag{5.54}$$

Now we come back to our topological ball. Let φ increase to π, the surface of the ball. Then we first reaffirm that

$$\left(e^{-i\pi H_1}\right)_i^j = \left(e^{i\pi H_1}\right)_i^j \tag{5.55}$$

because the eigenvalues of $(H_1)_i^j$ are ± 1 or 0. But because the eigenvalues of $(H_1)_a^b$ are $\pm 1/2$,

$$\left(e^{-i\pi H_1}\right)_a^b = -\left(e^{i\pi H_1}\right)_a^b \tag{5.56}$$

Thus if we consider the transformations of Eq. (5.52), then antipodal points on the topological ball are not identical. As long as the parameter φ is less than π, we have precisely the same topology for Eq. (5.51) as for (5.52); but for $\varphi > \pi$, there is a difference. What, then, is the topology of the transformations of Eq. (5.52)?

Consider first an unbroken path through the ball. Then the difference between Eqs. (5.55) and (5.56) never shows up, and with respect to such paths the two topologies are the same. In fact, the only difference is that for every break—that is, every time a surface point is connected to its antipode— the transformation (5.54) receives a minus-sign. After breaking twice, the signs cancel and the relation between the two transformations is the same as for paths with no breaks. This state of affairs may be represented by two topological balls for the transformations of (5.54). For this group a surface point is identified with its antipode on the other ball; thus the paths of Fig. 3 become the paths of Fig. 4. The main difference between the two topologies is that the extended one is simply connected, and all closed paths can be contracted to a point.

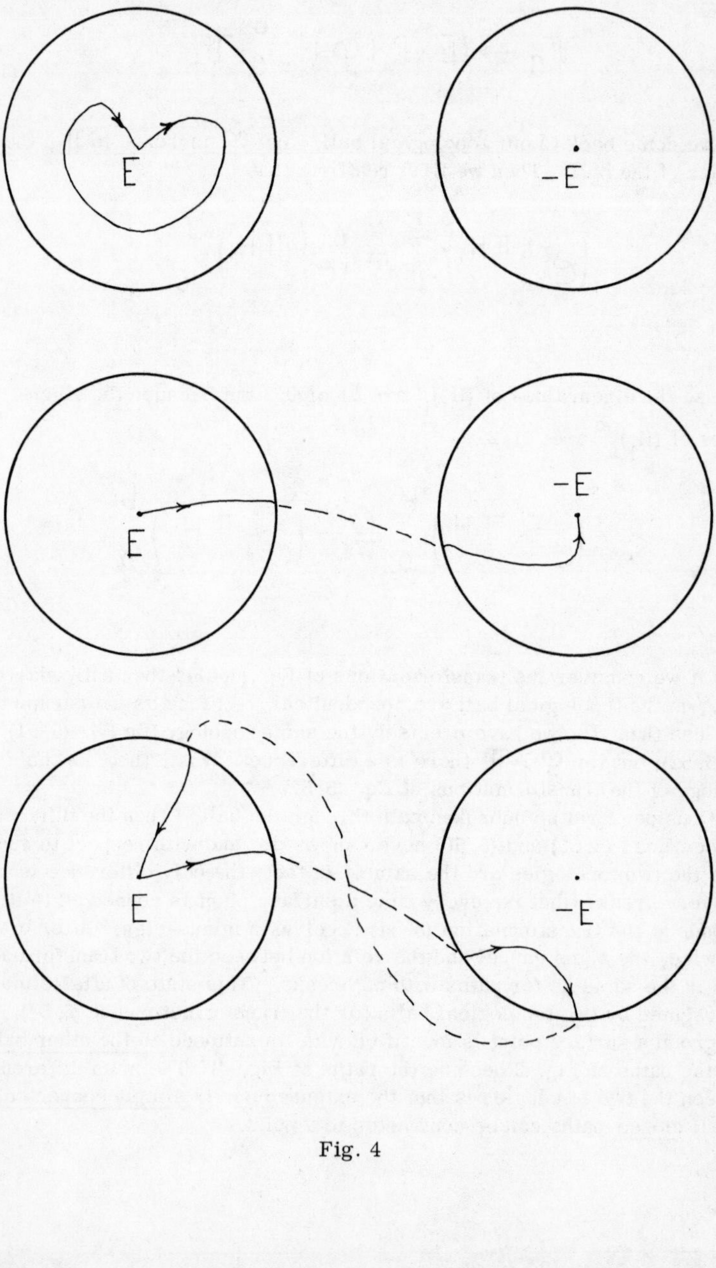

Fig. 4

To every rotation there corresponds not one but two transformations (5.54). These two transformations differ only in over-all sign and are associated with points in different spheres. Thus the identity transformation $\psi_a \to \psi_a$ is the center of one sphere, and its negative is the center of the other sphere.

This relation of a group which is not simply connected to one which is simply connected is general; the simply connected group is said to be the covering group of the multiply (i.e., not simply) connected one. The algebras of groups thus related are identical; for example, the group C_2 of simplectic transformation in four dimensions is the covering group of the group B_2 of rotations in five dimensions.

6. Reduction of Product Representations

The following discussion can with comparative ease be extended to other algebras. For A_1 it is rather trivial and certainly well known, but as a preparation for subsequent sections, it is necessary to obtain a very clear understanding of some fundamental concepts.

Let ψ_a, with a = 1, 2, be a basis for the simplest representation—namely, (5.49)—and consider the transformations

$$\psi_a \to \psi_a' = \psi_a + i\epsilon L_a^{\ b}\psi_b = (1+i\epsilon L)_a^{\ b}\psi_b \tag{5.57}$$

where $L_a^{\ b}$ is some linear combination of the matrices of Eq. (5.49). This transformation induces the following transformation in the four products $(\psi_a\psi_b)$:

$$(\psi_a\psi_b) \to (\psi_a\psi_b)' = (1+i\epsilon L)_a^{\ c}(1+i\epsilon L)_b^{\ d}(\psi_c\psi_d)$$
$$= (\delta_a^{\ c}\delta_b^{\ d} + i\epsilon L_{ab}^{\ cd})(\psi_c\psi_d) \tag{5.58}$$

$$L_{ab}^{\ cd} = \delta_a^{\ c} L_b^{\ d} + L_a^{\ c}\delta_b^{\ d} \tag{5.59}$$

The matrices $L_{ab}{}^{cd}$ (where a, b together label the rows and c, d together label the columns) satisfy the same commutation relations as the $L_a{}^b$; hence the new matrices constitute a representation. Let ψ_{ab} be the basis for this representation; that is, ψ_{ab} is a set of four quantities that transform among themselves exactly like the four products $(\psi_a \psi_b)$. The representation of Eq. (5.59) is called a product representation and is an example of one of the most important operations in group theory.

It is obvious that more general and complicated product representations can be built; Eq. (5.58) shows the general method of construction. In particular, one may construct the n-th rank spinor $\psi_{a_1}, \ldots, a_n$, whose components transform among themselves in the same way as the products $(\psi_{a_1} \cdots \psi_{a_n})$. We shall show that all irreducible representations may be generated in this way, although none of the product representations are actually irreducible.

Nearly everything in this section is independent of the fact that ψ_a is two-dimensional; whereas the fact that the basis matrices $L_a{}^b$ are the set of all traceless matrices is crucial. We have noted that A_ℓ is the set of all traceless matrices in $(\ell + 1)$ dimensions; and since it is easy to leave ℓ arbitrary, we shall do so, specializing to $\ell = 1$ only occasionally in order to point out special simplifications peculiar to this case.

We begin by demonstrating that the representation

$$\psi_{ab} \longrightarrow (\delta_a^c \delta_b^d + i\epsilon L_{ab}{}^{cd})\psi_{cd} \tag{5.60}$$

is reducible. Indeed, notice from Eq. (5.59) that $L_{ab}{}^{cd}$ is symmetric under the simultaneous interchange of both upper and lower indices among themselves. Thus, if ψ_{ab} is symmetric (or antisymmetric) before the transformation, it will also be symmetric (antisymmetric) after. Thus the symmetric components of ψ_{ab} (of which three are linearly independent) never get mixed up with the antisymmetric components. In the special case of A_1, the product representation is reduced by introducing the basis

$$\varphi_1 = \psi_{11}, \; \varphi_2 = (\psi_{12} + \psi_{21})/2, \; \varphi_3 = \psi_{22}, \; \varphi = (\psi_{12} - \psi_{21})/2 \tag{5.61}$$

Since there is only one antisymmetric component, it constitutes a one-dimensional representation. Since the only traceless one-dimensional matrix is zero, φ must be an invariant, as is indeed easily verified. The symmetric part φ_i (with i = 1, 2, 3) on inspection turns out to be the representation of (5. 31).

Returning to the general case, and to spinors of rank n, consider the particular matrices H_i:

$$(H_i)_{a_1 \cdots a_n}^{b_1 \cdots b_n} = \sum_m \delta_{a_1}^{b_1} \cdots (H_1)_{a_m}^{b_m} \cdots \delta_{a_n}^{b_n}$$

(5. 62)

The eigenvalue of $(H_i)_{a_1 \ldots a_n}^{b_1 \ldots b_n}$ is equal to the sum of the eigenvalues of $(H_i)_{a_n}^{b_n}$. Let ψ_1 be the component corresponding to the highest eigenvalue of $(H_i)_a^b$. Then, clearly, $\psi_{111\ldots}$ corresponds to the highest eigenvalue of $(H_i)_{a_1\ldots}^{b_1\ldots}$, and this eigenvalue is precisely n times the eigenvalue associated with ψ_1. The important point is that the highest eigenvalue of $(H_i)_{a_1\ldots}^{b_1\ldots}$ is always associated with the completely symmetric part of the product basis $\psi_{a_1}\ldots$, since in a labeling of the components they are all equal. It follows that, of all the irreducible representations contained in $\psi_{a_1\ldots}$, that with the highest eigenvalue is obtained as follows:

1. Let ψ_1 correspond to the highest eigenvalue of H_i in the original representation, and pick out the component $\psi_{11\cdots 1}$.
2. Apply the matrices of the product representation repeatedly to this component until no new linearly independent components are generated.

<u>Example</u>. Let ψ_a, with a = 1, 2, be a basis for the representation (5. 49). Then from Eq. (5. 62) the highest eigenvalue of H_1 in the product representation is given by

$$H_1 \psi_{1\ldots} = (n/2)\psi_{1\ldots} \tag{5.63}$$

The lowering operator is $\sqrt{1/2}$ times a sum of terms, each of which changes a subscript 1 to a 2 and gives zero when applied to a subscript 2. Thus,

$$E_{-1}\psi_{1\ldots} = \sqrt{1/2}\,(\psi_{211\ldots} + \psi_{121\ldots} + \psi_{112\ldots} + \cdots)$$
$$E_{-1}E_{-1}\psi_{1\ldots} = (1/2)(\psi_{221\ldots} + \psi_{212\ldots} + \psi_{122\ldots} + \cdots) \tag{5.64}$$

Similarly E_{+1} multiplies by $\sqrt{1/2}$, changes a sub 2 to a 1, and annihilates a sub 1:

$$E_{+1}\psi_{1\ldots} = 0$$
$$E_{+1}E_{-1}\psi_{1\ldots} = (n/2)\psi_{1\ldots} \tag{5.65}$$

We have $\psi_{1\ldots} = \psi(n/2)$ and $E_{-1}\psi(n/2) = \mu_0\,\psi\,(n/2-1)$, $E_{+1}\psi\,(n/2-1) = \nu_1\psi\,(n/2)$. Thus $\nu_1^2 = \mu_0^2 = n/2$, $\mu_0 = \sqrt{n/2}$, which agrees with Eq. (5.29), since we have $M = m = n/2$.

It is clear that the components generated in this way are a subset of the completely symmetric part of $\psi_{a_1 \ldots a_n}$. In fact, it is all of the symmetric part, and this is easy to prove for the special case $\ell = 1$. In that case the highest eigenvalue of H_1 in the original representation is 1/2; hence its highest value in the product representation is n/2. We have found that the dimension of the irreducible representation whose highest weight is n/2 is n + 1, which is exactly the number of linearly independent components of the symmetrized n-th rank spinor. Therefore all the components of the symmetric part are needed to make up the irreducible representation with the highest weight. Hence, the basis for the representation $\lambda = n - 1$ is the symmetric part of the n-th rank spinor.

For arbitrary ℓ the same results do not hold, even though it is true that the symmetric part of the n-th rank spinor is always irreducible. In fact, the complete reduction of the product representations of A_ℓ is accomplished by reducing the product basis into its various symmetry classes. This would lead us to the whole theory and technique of Young tableaux, for which we do not have enough time here. Weyl's book "The Classical Groups" contains a good discussion of this topic.

The reduction of product representations is one of the most important problems of group theory, as well as the problem most often confronting us in physical applications. Thus the whole field of addition of angular momenta, fractional parentage, etc., is important for spectroscopy. For elementary particles, it has an important application in constructing invariant interactions and scattering amplitudes, as we have seen and as we shall soon study in more detail.

VI. REPRESENTATIONS OF SIMPLE LIE ALGEBRAS

1. General Tensor Calculus

In the previous section we studied representations in the form of higher-rank spinors. This method is best adapted to the algebras A_ℓ, and for A_1 it yields all representations effortlessly. For other algebras this procedure is more cumbersome, and we shall presently study a more effective one. But he is best prepared who can wield all the tools available, and for this reason I shall give a short orientation in general tensor analysis.

Let $L_a{}^b$ be any representation of any Lie algebra, and ψ_a the basis,

$$\psi_a \rightarrow (1 + i\epsilon L)_a{}^b \, \psi_b \tag{6.1}$$

The contragredient representation has the basis ψ^a and is defined by requiring that $\psi^a \psi_a$ be invariant. Thus,

$$\psi^a \rightarrow (1 - i\epsilon L)^a{}_b \, \psi^b \tag{6.2}$$

The representation in (6.1) is called covariant. All representations come in covariant-contragredient pairs; the first question is whether they are equivalent or not.

Clearly (6.1) and (6.2) are equivalent if (6.1) becomes (6.2) after a change of basis:

$$\psi_a = g_{ab}\psi^b \tag{6.3}$$

where g_{ab} is a nonsingular matrix. When Eq. (6.3) is substituted on the right-hand side of (6.1) and on the left-hand side of (6.2), the two transformations become identical if

$$L^d_{\ b}\, g_{ad} + L^c_{\ a}\, g_{cb} = 0 \tag{6.4}$$

This may be written

$$g_{ab} = (\delta^c_a \delta^d_b + i\epsilon L^{cd}_{ab})\, g_{cd} \tag{6.5}$$

where

$$L^{cd}_{ab} = \delta^c_a L^d_{\ b} + \delta^d_a L^c_{\ b} \tag{6.6}$$

Thus g_{ab} is a form-invariant second-rank tensor. In general, any numerical tensor of whatever rank that is introduced into the game is form-invariant. That is, formally it must be transformed according to the indices (i.e., like products of ψ_a and ψ^a with the same indices, upstairs and downstairs), but the total effect must be to leave the tensor unchanged.

To find out whether or not a pair of contragredient representations are equivalent, one must decide whether a form-invariant g_{ab} exists or not. This depends not only on the structure of the algebra, but also on the particular representation.

The best way to start is to pick the representation of the lowest possible dimension—say, d. If g_{ab} exists and is neither symmetric nor antisymmetric, it can easily be shown that both the symmetric and the antisymmetric part must be nonsingular. Then Eq. (6.4) gives $L_A = 0$. If g_{ab} exists and is symmetric, then Eq. (6.4) is symmetric in (a, b) and imposes d (d + 1)/2 conditions on the $L_a^{\ b}$. Hence the order of the group can be no more than d (d - 1)/2. Similarly, if g_{ab} is antisymmetric one finds that the order cannot exceed d (d + 1)/2. If no g_{ab} exists, the order can be as high as $d^2 - 1$. These three cases correspond to the orthogonal groups (B_ℓ, d = 2ℓ+ 1 for odd d; and D_ℓ, d = 2ℓ for even d), the simplectic groups (C_ℓ, d = 2ℓ, antisymmetric nonsingular g_{ab} can exist for even dimensions only!), and the special unitary groups (A_ℓ, d = ℓ + 1).

We have seen that for A_ℓ, for which no g_{ab} exists, the problem of reducing the tensors is solved by symmetrizing the tensors in their indices. In addition, for mixed tensors like $\psi_{ab}^{\ c}$ that transform like

$$\psi_{ab}^{\ c} \rightarrow \psi_{ab}^{\ c} + i\epsilon (L_a^{\ d} \psi_{db}^{\ c} + L_b^{\ d} \psi_{ad}^{\ c} - L_d^{\ c} \psi_{ab}^{\ d}) \tag{6. 7}$$

the traces, for example, $\psi_{ab}^{\ b}$, transform among themselves and have to be treated separately. For groups with a form-invariant g_{ab} it is not necessary to give special attention to mixed tensors, but g_{ab} and its inverse,

$$g^{ab} g_{bc} = \delta_c^{\ a} \tag{6. 8}$$

may be used to reduce a representation. Thus $g^{ab} \psi_{ab}$ is an invariant; $g^{ab} \psi_{abc}$ transforms like ψ_c; etc. Symmetrization and contraction by means of g^{ab} are the only form-invariant operations available, and the complete reduction of any tensor can be carried out by means of them. If careful not to introduce meaningless quantities, one is always certain that every quantity transforms exactly as its (unsaturated) indices indicate.

For the group G_2, tensor calculus is a bit harder, for in addition to a form-invariant symmetric g_{ab} there exists a form-invariant antisymmetric quantity with three indices, Γ_{abc}, with rather complicated properties.

One or two important simple results may be noted. First, the product of any representation (say, ψ_a) of any group, and the contragredient representation (ψ^a), always contains the regular representation. Let

$(L_A)_a{}^b$ be a basis of the algebra, and construct the quantities $\psi^a (L_A)_a{}^b \psi_b$. Then these transform among themselves according to the regular representation. The regular representation is irreducible if and only if the algebra is simple, as can be seen by looking up the respective definitions. The regular representation always contains a symmetric form-invariant g_{AB}, namely,

$$g_{AB} = C^D_{AC}\, C^C_{BD} \tag{6.9}$$

Hence this representation is equivalent to its contragredient. Finally, the product of the regular representation with itself always contains the regular representation, for we can form $\psi^A\, C^D_{AB}\, \psi_D = \varphi_B$.

I hope that enough tidbits from tensor calculus have been given to inspire further study.

2. Weights

The following is a direct extension to an arbitrary simple algebra of the method we applied to A_1 in the previous section.

In accordance with the Important Theorem of Sec. IV, we take the H_i hermitian. Since they commute, we diagonalize them; thus,

$$H_i \psi(\vec{m}) = m_i \psi(\vec{m}) \qquad i = 1, \cdots, \ell \tag{6.10}$$

where $m = (m_1, \ldots, m_\ell)$ is called a weight or a weight vector and the m_i are real.

A weight is <u>simple</u> if there is only one state $\psi(m)$ of that weight; the number of different states $\psi(\vec{m}), \psi'(\vec{m})$ with the same weight is called the <u>multiplicity</u> of the weight.

It is clear that, if $E_\alpha \psi(m)$ is different from zero, it is a state with weight $\vec{m} + \vec{\alpha}$. This follows directly from $[H_i, E_\alpha] = r_i(\alpha) E_\alpha$, just as in Sec. V. 3. Multiplying the new state by E_α again, the weight $\vec{m} + 2\vec{\alpha}$ is obtained, and so on. This process must stop; therefore, for some integer j,

$$E_\alpha \psi(\vec{m} + j\vec{\alpha}) = 0 \tag{6.11}$$

To this "top" state $\psi(\vec{m} + j\vec{\alpha})$ we apply $E_{-\alpha}$ repeatedly until this comes to a stop:

$$E_{-\alpha} \psi(\vec{m}) = \mu_{\vec{m}} \psi(\vec{m} - \vec{\alpha}), \quad E_{-\alpha} \psi(\vec{m} - K\vec{\alpha}) = 0 \tag{6.12}$$

Then we climb up again,

$$E_\alpha \psi(\vec{m}) = \nu_{\vec{m}} \psi(\vec{m} + \vec{\alpha}) \tag{6.13}$$

and prove by induction, precisely as before, that the set of steps obtained by climbing up again are precisely the same as those by which we came down.

The commutation relation $[E_\alpha, E_{-\alpha}] = r^i(\alpha) H_i$ gives

$$\begin{aligned} \nu_{\vec{m}-\vec{\alpha}} \mu_{\vec{m}} - \nu_{\vec{m}} \mu_{\vec{m}+\vec{\alpha}} &= \vec{\alpha} \cdot \vec{m} \\ &= \vec{\alpha} \cdot (\vec{m} - K\vec{\alpha}) + K \vec{\alpha} \cdot \vec{\alpha} \end{aligned} \tag{6.14}$$

which is precisely of the form encountered in Sec. IV. 4. This recursion relation, together with Eqs. (6. 11) and (6. 12), immediately gives the following theorem, which is completely analogous to that of Sec. IV. 4 (and a simple generalization of the conclusion $2M = \lambda =$ integer for A_1):

Weight Theorem. If $\vec{m}$ is a weight and $\vec{\alpha}$ is a root, then $g(\vec{m}/\vec{\alpha}) = 2\vec{m} \cdot \vec{\alpha} / \vec{\alpha} \cdot \vec{\alpha}$ is an integer and $\vec{m} - g(\vec{m}/\vec{\alpha})\,\vec{\alpha}$ is a weight with the same multiplicity.

This new weight is simply the reflection of m through the hyperplane perpendicular to the root $\vec{\alpha}$. By repeating this operation with all the roots until no new weights are generated, we obtain a set of weight vectors with the same lengths. The weights of such a set are said to be equivalent weights.

One further property of the weights is that

$$\sum \vec{m} = 0 \tag{6.15}$$

which follows from the fact that the H_i are traceless. From these conditions, all possible weights can be found and all representations calculated. But we expect that complicated representations can be best understood as products of simple ones, and this we now proceed to investigate.

3. Classification of Representations

To achieve some ordering of the different weights, we choose the following definitions:

Definition. A weight is positive if the first nonvanishing component is positive. (Thus $m_1 > 0$ or $m_1 = 0$, $m_2 > 0$, etc.) A weight $\vec{m}$ is higher than a weight $\vec{m}'$, if $\vec{m} - \vec{m}'$ is positive. The highest among a set of equivalent weights is called dominant. Thus a dominant weight is one that is higher than any other weight obtained from it by the construction of the theorems of the previous section.

Now we proceed to two very important theorems with surprisingly simple proofs.

Theorem. The highest weight of an irreducible representation is simple.

Proof. Let the highest weight be $\vec{M}$. Because the representation is irreducible, every state may be written $E_\alpha E_\beta \cdots E_\delta \psi(\vec{M})$; and all we shall have to show is that, if such a state has the weight $\vec{M}$, then it is proportional to $\psi(\vec{M})$. First note that $E_\delta \psi(\vec{M}) = 0$ if $\vec{\delta}$ is positive. In the product $E_\alpha E_\beta \cdots E_\delta$, move the matrices with positive roots to the right, picking up terms with commutators $[E_\alpha, E_\beta]$ on the way. When the positive roots arrive at the extreme right they die, and the number of matrices is gradually reduced until no positive roots are left. Then no negative roots are left either, since a succession of negative weights would give a weight $\vec{M} + \vec{\alpha} + \vec{\beta} + \cdots \neq \vec{M}$. Thus, by using the commutation relations only, the state is reduced to a sum of products of the H_i times $\psi(\vec{M})$. This is proportional to $\psi(\vec{M})$; furthermore, for our future benefit, we note that the factor of proportionality depends only on the commutation relations, not on the representation.

Theorem. Two irreducible representations are equivalent if their highest weights are equal.

Proof. Let a representation H_i, E_α be given, and let $\vec{M}$ be the highest weight. Let another representation H_i', E'_α have the same highest weight $\vec{M}$. We must show that, by properly ordering the states, we can make the two sets of matrices equal. From our previous work we know that $E_\alpha E_{-\alpha}\Psi$ is not zero if $E_{-\alpha}\Psi$ is not zero. Thus, if $E_\alpha \cdots E_\delta \Psi(\vec{M}) \neq 0$, then $E_{-\delta} \cdots E_{-\alpha} E_\alpha \cdots E_\delta \Psi(\vec{M})$ is nonzero and proportional to $\Psi(\vec{M})$. Moreover, the constant of proportionality is the same if the E_α be replaced by the E_α'; therefore $E_\alpha' \cdots E_\delta' \Psi(\vec{M})$ is also not zero. Conversely, if $E_\alpha \cdots E_\delta \Psi(\vec{M}) = 0$, then $E_\alpha' \cdots E_\delta' \Psi(\vec{M}) = 0$, which proves that for every weight of one representation there is one in the other, with the same multiplicity. If every state of either representation is normalized by defining it in the form $E_\alpha \cdots E_\delta \Psi(\vec{M})$, then the two will be identical, which proves the theorem.

Now comes the "clincher," and here we shall have to forego the proof for the general case, which is very hard:

Theorem (Cartan). For every simple group of rank ℓ there exist ℓ fundamental irreducible representations whose highest weights — $\vec{M}(1), \cdots, \vec{M}(\ell)$ — are called fundamental dominant weights, with the property that every other highest weight is of the form

$$\sum_{i=1}^{\ell} \lambda_i \vec{M}(i) \tag{6.16}$$

where λ_i are nonnegative integers.

All the fundamental dominant weights can easily be written down, but we shall be content with the case $\ell = 2$, incidentally proving the above theorem for that case.

We have already remarked that, when we form product representations, the highest weight of the product is the sum of the highest weights of the factors. As soon as we have the ℓ fundamental irreducible representations, we may therefore generate the irreducible representations whose weights are given by the expression (6.16). Actually, all irreducible representations can be found from the product representations based on only one single "superfundamental" representation. But it is not sure that this is a great gain, for it is then no longer clear which product representation should be used to obtain the representation with a given weight.

4. Fundamental Representations for $\ell = 2$

The algebra A_2. The positive roots of A_2 (see Fig. 2) are

$$\vec{\alpha}(1) = (1/\sqrt{3}, 0), \quad \vec{\alpha}(2) = (1/2\sqrt{3}, 1/2)$$

$$\vec{\alpha}(3) = (1/2\sqrt{3}, -1/2) \tag{6.17}$$

If $\vec{m} = (m_1, m_2)$, the condition that $2\vec{m} \cdot \vec{\alpha} / \vec{\alpha} \cdot \vec{\alpha}$ be integers is

$$2\sqrt{3}\, m_1 = a, \quad \sqrt{3}\, m_1 + 3m_2 = b, \quad \sqrt{3}\, m_1 - 3m_2 = c \tag{6.18}$$

with a, b, and c integers., Thus,

$$m_1 = (1/2\sqrt{3})(b+c), \quad m_2 = (1/6)(b-c) \tag{6.19}$$

or

$$\begin{aligned} \vec{m} &= (b/6)(\sqrt{3}, 1) + (c/6)(\sqrt{3}, -1) \\ &= b\,\vec{M}(1) + c\,\vec{M}(2) \end{aligned} \tag{6.20}$$

This is the most general weight. To pick out a complete set of dominant weights, we construct the equivalent weights:

$$\vec{m} - 2g(\vec{m}/\vec{\alpha}(1))\,\vec{\alpha}(1) = -c\,\vec{M}(1) - b\,\vec{M}(2)$$

$$\vec{m} - 2g(\vec{m}/\vec{\alpha}(2))\,\vec{\alpha}(2) = -b\,\vec{M}(1) + (b+c)\,\vec{M}(2)$$

$$\vec{m} - 2g(\vec{m}/\vec{\alpha}(3))\,\vec{\alpha}(3) = (b+c)\,\vec{M}(1) - c\,\vec{M}(2) \tag{6.21}$$

This shows that Eq. (6.20) is dominant only if both b and c are positive. This could have been established more easily as follows. Those planes which are normal to a root and which lie closest to the horizontal (first) axis form $\pm 30^{\circ}$ angles with that axis. It is easy to see that a dominant weight must lie between these planes; hence $m_1 > 0$ and $|m_1/m_2| \leq 1/\sqrt{3}$, or $b + c \geq 0$ and $|b - c|/(b + c) \leq 1$. Therefore both b and c must be positive.

We have thus established that the most general dominant weight is of the form

$$\vec{M} = \lambda_1\,\vec{M}(1) + \lambda_2\,\vec{M}(2)$$

$$\vec{M}(1) = (1/6)(\sqrt{3}, 1) \qquad \vec{M}(2) = (1/6)(\sqrt{3}, -1) \tag{6.22}$$

where λ_1 and λ_2 are positive integers or zero. We shall shortly demonstate that there exist representations having $\vec{M}(1)$ and $\vec{M}(2)$ as their highest weights, and then it follows immediately that representations exist having any weight in Eq. (6.22) as its highest weight.

It is useful to draw weight diagrams, analogous to the root diagrams. For every simple algebra, there is only one root diagram, which reveals the structure of the group; but every representation has its own weight diagram. In a weight diagram the end point of every weight vector corresponds to one or more states, and the eigenvalue of H_i of this state is the coordinate m_i of this point. Some weight diagrams for A_2 are shown in Fig. 5. The dotted lines are the hyperplanes perpendicular to the roots. The representation $\lambda_1 = \lambda_2 = 1$ has a weight of multiplicity 2 in the center, while the other weights are simple. This is the regular representation, and the weight diagram is identical to the root diagram. The

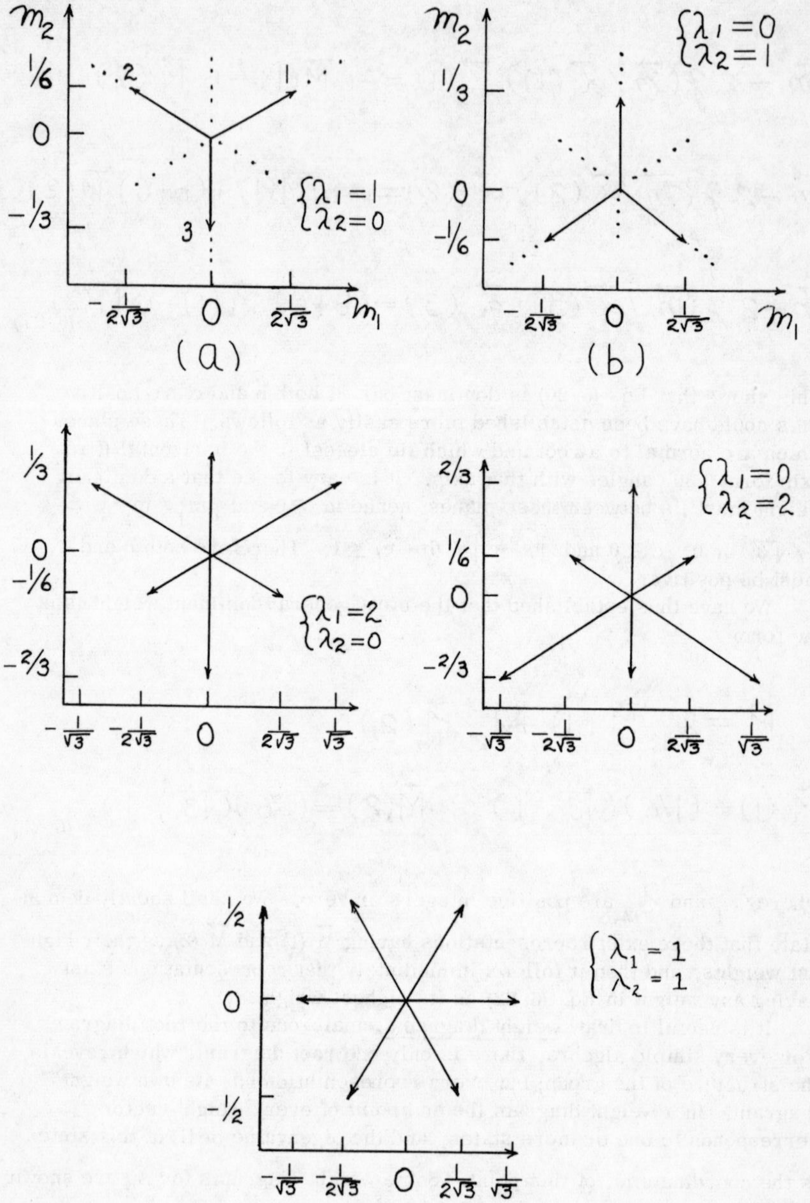

Fig. 5
(A_2)

representations ($\lambda_1 = 1, \lambda_2 = 0$) and ($\lambda_1 = 0, \lambda_2 = 1$) are the three-dimensional representations (6.1) and (6.2), respectively. Later we shall see that it is easy to construct the matrices of a representation from the weight diagram.

The group B_2. In order that $2\vec{m} \cdot \vec{\alpha} / \vec{\alpha} \cdot \vec{\alpha}$ be an integer for every root (see Fig. 2), it is necessary that

$$m_1 = (1/2\sqrt{3})(a+b) \quad , \quad m_2 = (1/2\sqrt{3})\, b \tag{6.23}$$

where a and b are integers. Thus,

$$\vec{M}(\lambda_1, \lambda_2) = (1/2\sqrt{3})\lambda_1 (1,0) + (1/2\sqrt{3})\lambda_2 (1,1) \tag{6.24}$$

where λ_1 and λ_2 are positive integers. The two special weights ($\lambda_1 = 0$, $\lambda_2 = 1$) and ($\lambda_1 = 1$, $\lambda_2 = 0$) are the fundamental dominant weights. The weight diagrams are shown in Fig. 6.

The group G_2. In the same manner as above, we find

$$\vec{M}(\lambda_1, \lambda_2) = (1/2\sqrt{3})\lambda_1 (1,0) + (1/4\sqrt{3})\lambda_2 (3, \sqrt{3}) \tag{6.25}$$

The weight diagrams are shown in Fig. 7.

The weight diagrams are extremely useful, and they will be used extensively throughout the remainder of these lectures. In order to show the connection with what we have learned about matrix representations in previous lectures, we now show how explicit matrix representations are derived from the weight diagrams.

5. Construction of Matrices

In Sec. V.3 we were able to construct the matrices of an arbitrary

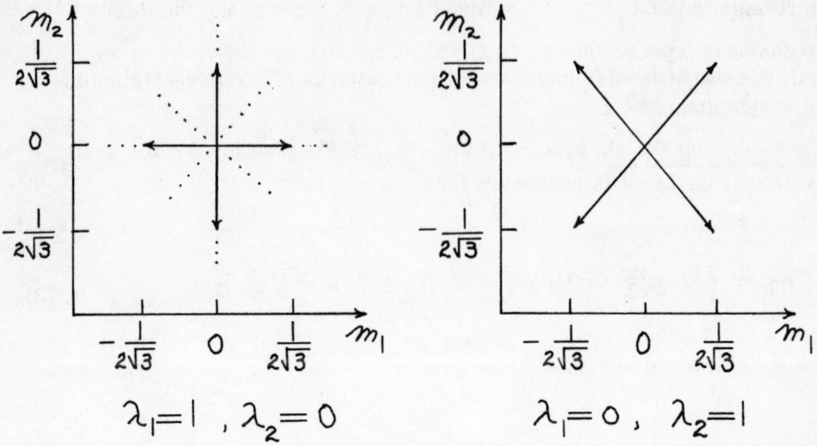

Fig. 6
(B_2)

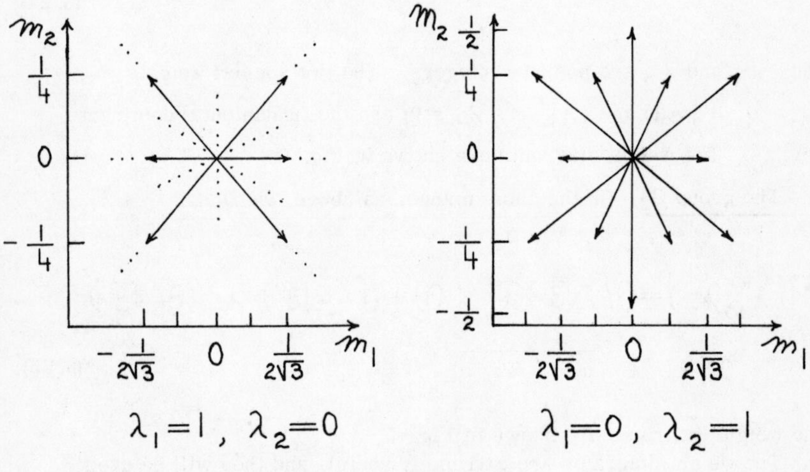

Fig. 7
(G_2)

representation of A_1; now we shall discuss methods whereby this might be achieved for other groups.

The representation whose weight diagram is Fig. 5a is three-dimensional. The weights are all simple, since they are all equivalent to the highest one. We label the weights and the associated states as in Fig. 5a, and the roots as in Fig. 2b. The explicit form of the matrices H_i is obviously given by

$$H_i \psi(\vec{m}) = m_i \psi(\vec{m}) \tag{6.26}$$

The operator E_α increases the weight of a state by the amount $\vec{\alpha}$, that is, $E_\alpha \psi(\vec{m}) \sim \psi(\vec{m} + \vec{\alpha})$. The nonvanishing matrix elements of E_α are those which connect states whose weights may be connected by the vector $\vec{\alpha}$. This is illustrated in Fig. 8; $E_{-\alpha}$ connects the same states

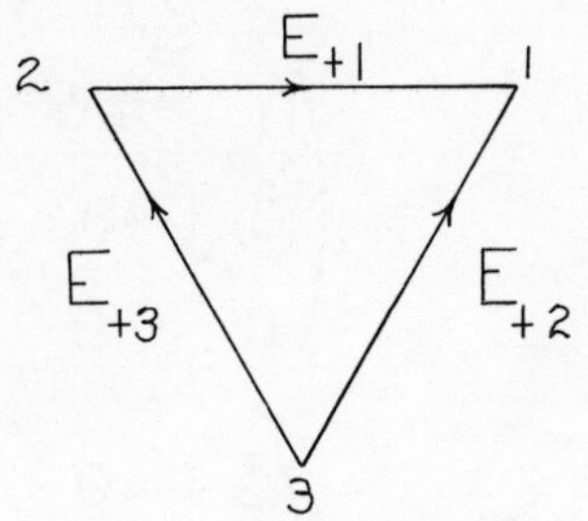

Fig. 8

as E_α, but in the opposite direction.

To find the numerical values of the matrix elements of E_α, we proceed as in Sec. V. 3. We take

$$E_{-\alpha} = E_\alpha^T \tag{6.27}$$

so that the matrix elements of $E_{\pm\alpha}$ are numerically equal. Next,

$$[E_{+1}, E_{-1}]\,\psi(1) = c^2\,\psi(1) = r^i(1)\,H_i\,\psi(1) = (1/\sqrt{3})\,H_1\,\psi(1) = (1/6)\,\psi(1) \tag{6.28}$$

where

$$E_{+1}\,\psi(2) = c\,\psi(1)\;,\quad E_{-1}\,\psi(1) = c\,\psi(2) \tag{6.29}$$

defines the number c. Thus,

$$E_{+1} = E_{-1}^{T} = \begin{pmatrix} 0 & 1/\sqrt{6} & 0 \\ 0 & 0 & 0 \\ 0 & 0 & 0 \end{pmatrix} \tag{6.30}$$

In exactly the same way,

$$E_{+2} = E_{-2}^{T} = \begin{pmatrix} 0 & 0 & 1/\sqrt{6} \\ 0 & 0 & 0 \\ 0 & 0 & 0 \end{pmatrix} \tag{6.31}$$

The signs have been chosen positive, but this is arbitrary. However,

$$[E_{+2}, E_{-1}] = \begin{pmatrix} 0 & 0 & 0 \\ 0 & 0 & -1/6 \\ 0 & 0 & 0 \end{pmatrix} = N_{2,-1}\,E_{+3} \tag{6.32}$$

so that the sign of E_{+3} is determined by the sign of $N_{2,-1}$. The $N_{\alpha\beta}$ were found in Eq. (4.38), which reduces to $N_{\alpha\beta} = \pm 1/\sqrt{6}$. A possible choice is

$$N_{13} = -N_{31} = -N_{-3,-1} = N_{3,-2} =$$

$$N_{-2,1} = N_{2,-3} = N_{-1,2} = 1/\sqrt{6} \tag{6.33}$$

and this gives

$$E_{+3} = E_{-3}^{T} = \begin{pmatrix} 0 & 0 & 0 \\ 0 & 0 & 1/\sqrt{6} \\ 0 & 0 & 0 \end{pmatrix} \tag{6.34}$$

Of course, it is only in a very few simple cases that all the weights are equivalent to the highest weight, but in any case all weights can be obtained by applying the operators E_{α} repeatedly to the state $\psi(\vec{M})$ with the highest weight M. Clearly the first part of our problem is to determine all the weights and their multiplicities for each representation. This we shall do for each algebra of rank 2 in another section. But to obtain the matrices in special cases, even if they be much more complicated than the ones we have just treated, it is often sufficient to apply the methods already at hand. We shall give a general formula that yields a large amount of information about matrix elements, from which with a little ingenuity all the matrices may be constructed.

Let $\vec{M}$ be weight and $\vec{\alpha}$ a root, so that $\vec{M} + \vec{\alpha}$ is not a weight, and consider the string of states $\psi(\vec{M})$, $\psi(\vec{M} - \vec{\alpha})$, $\psi(\vec{M} - 2\vec{\alpha})$, $\cdots$. This string of states is a basis for a representation of the subalgebra $E_{\pm\alpha}$, $r^{i}(\alpha) H_{i}$ (see Sec. V. 2). If we normalize,

$$E'_{\pm\alpha} = (\vec{\alpha}\cdot\vec{\alpha})^{-1/2} E_{\pm\alpha}$$

$$H' = (\vec{\alpha}\cdot\vec{\alpha})^{-1} r^{i}(\alpha) H_{i} \tag{6.35}$$

then the three primed operators have the commutation relations of A_1. The matrix elements of $E_{\pm\alpha}'$ are therefore given by Eq. (5.30) $(m = \vec{M}, \vec{M} - \vec{\alpha}, \cdots)$:

$$E'_{+\alpha}\,\psi(\vec{m}) = \pm\Big[\{\vec{\alpha}\cdot(\vec{M}-\vec{m})/\vec{\alpha}\cdot\vec{\alpha}\}$$

$$\times\{\vec{\alpha}\cdot(\vec{M}+\vec{m}+\vec{\alpha})/\vec{\alpha}\cdot\vec{\alpha}\}\ (1/2)\Big]^{1/2}$$

$$\times\,\psi(\vec{m}+\vec{\alpha}) \tag{6.36}$$

or

$$E_{+\alpha}\,\psi(\vec{m}) = \pm(\vec{\alpha}\cdot\vec{\alpha})^{-1/2}\Big[\vec{\alpha}\cdot(\vec{M}-\vec{m})$$

$$\times\,\vec{\alpha}\cdot(\vec{M}+\vec{m}+\vec{\alpha})/2\Big]^{1/2}\ \psi(\vec{m}+\vec{\alpha})$$

$$E_{-\alpha}\,\psi(\vec{m}) = \pm(\vec{\alpha}\cdot\vec{\alpha})^{-1/2}$$

$$\times\Big[\vec{\alpha}\cdot(\vec{M}-\vec{m}+\vec{\alpha})\ \vec{\alpha}\cdot(\vec{M}+\vec{m})/2\Big]^{1/2}$$

$$\times\,\psi(\vec{m}-\vec{\alpha}) \tag{6.37}$$

We cannot, as in Eq. (5.30), arbitrarily choose the sign. In principle, these formulas should give all matrix elements; but it is necessary to unfurl the complication arising from the fact that the same weight may occur in several different strings, and if the multiplicity is high, a considerable amount of labor is still to be done. But for small representations the present method is quite good.

To illustrate the use of Eq. (6.37), we may construct the simplest representation of G_2, which is ($\lambda_1 = 1$, $\lambda_2 = 0$,); hence the highest weight is $\vec{M} = (1/2\sqrt{3},\ 0)$. In Fig. 7 it is seen that $\vec{M}$ is one of six equivalent weights, and that the only other weight is (0, 0); the multiplicity of this weight is not known to us yet. The nonvanishing matrix elements of the E_α are shown in Fig. 9. First we choose the maximum number of

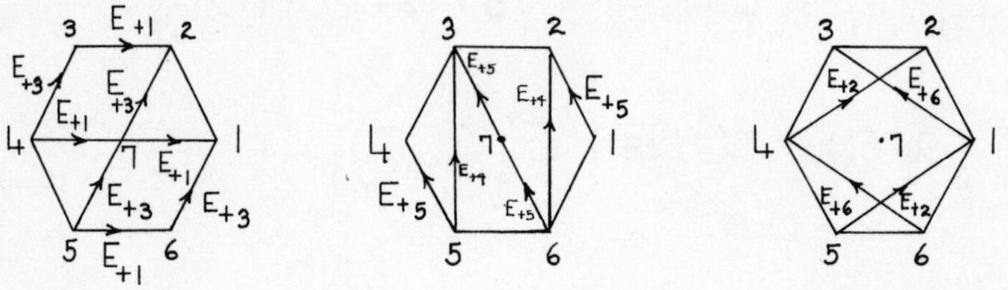

Fig. 9

$E_{+\alpha}$ positive, for example, E_{+1}, E_{+2}, and E_{+4}. Then Eq. (6.26) gives

$$E_{+1} = (1/2\sqrt{3}) \Big[|7\rangle\langle 4| + |1\rangle\langle 7| + (1/\sqrt{2})|2\rangle\langle 3| + (1/\sqrt{2})|6\rangle\langle 5| \Big] \tag{6.38}$$

Now choose a set of $N_{\alpha\beta}$ consistent with Eqs. (4.32), (4.36), and (4.38), for example,

$$N_{-2,4} = N_{2,6} = N_{4,-6} = N_{2,-1} = N_{3,1} = N_{-2,3} = N_{5,-6} = N_{1,6} = N_{-1,5} = N_{3,-4} = N_{-5,4} = N_{-3,5} = 1/\sqrt{8} \tag{6.39}$$

Then,

$$[E_{-2}, E_4]\,\psi(6) = (1/8)\,\psi(4) = N_{-2,4}\, E_6\, \psi(4) = (1/\sqrt{8})\, E_6\, \psi(4),$$

$$[E_{-2}, E_4]\,\psi(1) = -(1/8)\,\psi(3) = N_{-2,4}$$

$$\times E_6\,\psi(1) = -(1/\sqrt{8})\;E_6\,\psi(1), \qquad (6.40)$$

and so

$$E_{+6} = (1/\sqrt{8})\left[\,|4\rangle\langle 6| - |3\rangle\langle 1|\,\right]$$

(6.41)

We find that there is only one state with weight (0, 0); for example,

$$[E_{+1}, E_{-2}]\,\psi(7) = -(1/2\sqrt{3})(1/\sqrt{8})\,\psi(5)$$

$$= N_{1,-2}\,E_{-3}\,\psi(7) \qquad (6.42)$$

and thus $E_{+3}\psi(5)$ is proportional to $\psi(7)$, rather than to some other state with the same weight.

This should suffice to illustrate the method. Fortunately we do not need the explicit representation matrices frequently.

Once the representation matrices have been constructed for the fundamental irreducible representations, those for more complicated representations can be found by forming the appropriate product representation and separating out that part containing the highest weight. This method was discussed in Sec. V. 6, and although the simple case of A_1 was the only example given, the rules are the same in the general case. If the student will take the trouble to work out some concrete examples, he will eventually gain complete versatility with the method. Perhaps the best suggestion is to form the product of the representation of A_2 in this section with itself, extract that part with the highest weight (it is 6-dimensional), and check the commutation relations with the result.

VII. POSSIBLE APPLICATIONS

1. Isotopic Spin; G Conjugation

At this point we shall interrupt the mathematical development for a brief digression into the applications. This will serve to make us more familiar with the Lie algebras of rank 2 and show us what we still have to learn.

First let us review the transformation properties of elementary particles under isotopic spin. A set of particles with the same baryonic number, the same strangeness, and approximately the same mass is called an <u>isotopic spin multiplet</u>. The members of one multiplet transform among themselves according to some representation, irreducible or not, of A_1. Let us accept that the nucleons N_a, with a = 1, 2, transform according to the two-dimensional irreducible representation:

$$N_a \longrightarrow (1 + i\epsilon L)_a^{\ b} N_b \tag{7.1}$$

where $L_a^{\ b}$ is a linear combination of the matrices given by Eq. (5.49). The antinucleons then transform as follows:

$$\overline{N}_a \longrightarrow (1 + i\epsilon L)^{*b}_{a} \overline{N}_b \tag{7.2}$$

In order that the finite transformation matrix be unitary, it is necessary that $\epsilon L_a^{\ b}$ be hermitian; thus,

$$\overline{N}_a \longrightarrow \overline{N}_a - i\epsilon L_b^{\ a} \overline{N}_b \tag{7.3}$$

Here the indices do not quite fit, so that we find it convenient to write $\overline{N}$ with the index upstairs. Then,

$$\overline{N}^a \longrightarrow (1 - i\epsilon L)_b^{\ a} \overline{N}^b \tag{7.4}$$

This is just the contragredient of the transformation (7.1), as we could have anticipated. The restriction to hermitian $\epsilon L_a{}^b$ is equivalent to a restriction to real angles of rotation.

In order to see what particles can be transformed into a nucleon-antinucleon pair, we form the product representation $\bar{N}^a N_b$. This is equivalent to $\bar{N}_a N_b$, because the transformation (7.4) is equivalent to (7.1), as we shall see below. The reduction of this product representation therefore gives an invariant, and the irreducible, three-dimensional regular representation, with the bases

$$\bar{N}^a N_a \quad \text{AND} \quad \bar{N}^a (\sigma_i)^b_a N_b$$

respectively. Thus a particle that can be transformed into a nucleon-antinucleon pair must either be an isotopic singlet (invariant) or a triplet. If there is only one kind of neutral π-meson, then the π-mesons must transform like a triplet π_i (see Sec. II. 2).

The K mesons K^+ and K^o may either be a pair of invariants, or they may transform according to a two-dimensional irreducible representation. Experiments favor the latter possibility. Since all two-dimensional representations of A_1 are equivalent, we can normalize the K_a (a = 1, 2) in such a way that they transform precisely like N_a, that is, according to (7.1). Then the anti-K must transform according to (7.4). But because transformations (7.1) and (7.4) are equivalent, we may normalize the anti-K so that they transform like (7.1). Let $\bar{\bar{K}}_a$ be the two states $\bar{K}^+$ and $\bar{K}^o$, which transform according to (7.3):

$$\bar{K}_a \rightarrow \bar{K}_a - i\epsilon L^a_b \bar{K}_b \tag{7.5}$$

Inserting the most general hermitian $\epsilon L_b{}^a$:

$$\bar{K}_a \longrightarrow \bar{K}_a - i\vec{t}\cdot\vec{\sigma}^a_b \bar{K}_b \tag{7.6}$$

The matrix $i\sigma_2$ has the property

$$(i\sigma_2)\vec{\sigma}(i\sigma_2)^{-1} = -\vec{\sigma}^{\,*} = -\vec{\sigma}^{\,T} \tag{7.7}$$

Therefore, if

$$\bar{K}_a = (i\sigma_2)_a^{\ b}\bar{K}_b = (\bar{K}^0, -\bar{K}^+) = (\bar{K}^0, -K^-) \tag{7.8}$$

then the $\bar{K}_a$ transform exactly like K_a. This is the justification for this definition of $\bar{K}_a$, which we have already introduced in Sec. II. 1.

The relationship between K_a and $\bar{K}_a$,

$$\bar{K}_a = (GK)_a = G_a^{\ b}\bar{K}_b \tag{7.9}$$

is called "G conjugation." The matrix $G_a^{\ b} = (i\sigma_2)_a^{\ b}$ is unitary and may therefore be interpreted as a rotation. In fact, a rotation of 180° around the second coordinate axis is represented by the matrix

$$e^{i\pi T_2} = e^{i\pi\sigma_2/2} = \cos\pi/2 + i\sigma_2\sin\pi/2 = i\sigma_2 \tag{7.10}$$

In general, G conjugation is defined as charge conjugation followed by a rotation of 180° around the second axis. [The special role assigned to the second axis is due to the choice of a special representation among equivalent representations. We have taken σ_1 and σ_3 real, σ_2 imaginary.]

Next we ask what state can be formed from a $\bar{K}$ and a nucleon. We form the product representation $\bar{K}_a N_b$, and this also reduces to a singlet and a triplet. Both correspond to known elementary particles, the

Λ and the Σ, respectively. If a $K\bar{N}\Sigma$ coupling exists, then the Σ must transform precisely like the π_i.

We see that the concept of product representations and the problem of their reduction have important applications.

2. Higher Symmetries?

Two questions should clearly be distinguished:

1. Do higher symmetries among the elementary particles exist in some approximation?
2. Do these symmetries show up experimentally?

If the answer to the second question is a definite no, then the first question is meaningless. But it is quite impossible to give a definite answer to either question; therefore the first should be discussed free of any prejudice incurred by the second.

The most striking suggestion that some high degree of symmetry exists is provided by Fig. 1. What carries the most weight, in my opinion, is the following: Isotopic spin symmetry is well established experimentally, incredible and unmotivated though it may seem. This is a symmetry that mixes particles within the same row only. But Fig. 1 is unchanged if rows and columns are interchanged. Hence, why should not an analogue of isotopic spin symmetry that mixes particles within the same column have the same claim to existence?

Further evidence in favor of higher symmetries comes from the great ease with which the seven mesons and the eight baryons fit into representations of rank-2 algebras. One could have imagined, for example, a world in which all baryons are isospin doublets and all mesons are singlets and/or triplets. In that case, the success of our endeavors would have been much more severely limited. In other words, the material before us lends itself very readily to our game and tempts us to believe that the game has some meaning.

Turning now to the second question, concerning the observability of supposed symmetries, we are faced with the indisputable fact that particles not in the same row of Fig. 1 have quite different masses. This is a very great difficulty indeed, for even in the case of isotopic spin, where the mass differences are small, it is very hard to estimate the magnitude of the deviations from the predictions or pure charge independence. Actually, charge independence does not make any definite predictions at all, either right or wrong, for the predictions are not invariant under a change of reference system (e. g., from C. M. system to Lab. system) and are actually meaningless. This problem is not acute, because the uncertainty can readily be believed to be of the order of a few per cent. But when the mass differences are as large as between the K and the π, the prospects are very grim indeed.

Nevertheless, there are certain experiments, such as scattering at extremely high energies, where it is conceivable that mass differences could be ignored.

If the symmetry is sufficiently apparent that the particles which enjoy it are precisely our elementary particles, then there is good reason to suppose that the same symmetry can be applied nearly as well to the various resonance states. This leads to the prediction of certain as yet unobserved resonances; and in my opinion, a particular symmetry model must live or die according to the success of this kind of prediction.

There is one argument that is sometimes advanced in favor of both the existence and the observability of symmetries between particles of different mass—the so-called "electron-muon universality." But in this connection it is very important to remember that we are dealing with strongly interacting particles, so that, contrary to the situation in weak interactions, observable effects are not simply proportional to the coupling constant. In the absence of a detailed model that allows dependable calculations, a relation between coupling constants cannot be translated into a relation between observable quantities. A good example is the anomalous magnetic moment of the muon. This is some complicated function of the electron and muon masses, and it is only because we are able to calculate this function that we can conclude that the only difference between the electromagnetic properties of the electron and the muon are due to the mass difference. In other words, until we know how to perform satisfactory calculations, it is impossible to prove or disprove most higher-symmetry ideas.

My own conclusion is that it is not at all implausible that higher symmetries exist; what is needed most urgently, however, is to improve our powers of calculation.

3. Schemes for Strong Particles

Clearly the eigenvalues of the two commuting operators H_1 and H_2 must be linear combinations of the two diagonal quantum numbers charge (Q) and strangeness (S). Therefore, by replacing the coordinates Q and S in Fig. 1 by these linear combinations, Fig. 1 must become a weight diagram. Since the latter (1) are symmetric around a line down the middle and (2) have the property that the sum of all the vectors is zero ($\mathrm{tr}\, H_i = 0$), we could use the coordinates $(S + N)/2 = Y$ (hypercharge) and $Q - (S + N)/2 = I_3$, which should now be proportional to H_2 and H_1, respectively. Figure 1, as transformed by using Y and I_3 as coordinates, is shown in Fig. 10. Note that these look strikingly like weight diagrams of simple algebras. Thus. Fig. 10a is the weight diagram of the seven-dimentional representation of G_2 and Fig. 10b is the weight diagram for the eight-dimensional representation of A_2.

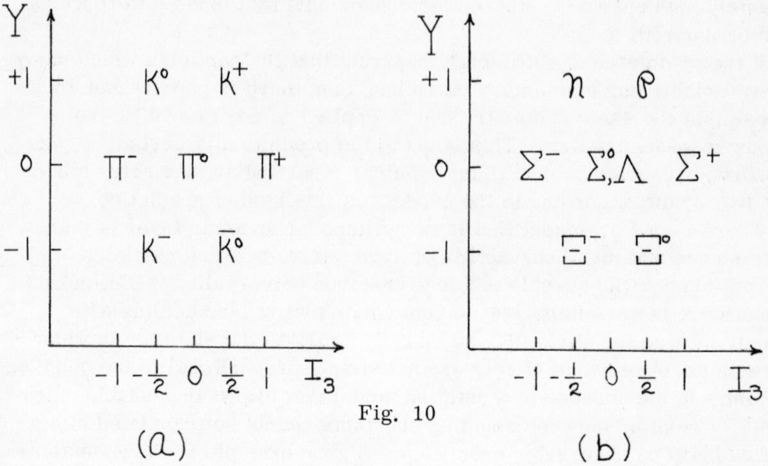

Fig. 10

Of course, in order to couple the mesons to the baryons, both must be representations of the same algebras. If we choose to apply the eight-dimentional representation of A_2 to both sets of particles it is necessary to postulate the existence of one more particle with the same quantum numbers as the π^0 (perhaps the η ?). If, instead, the seven-dimensional representation of G_2 is to fit the baryons, it is necessary to suppose that the Λ does not belong to this representation but is invariant. This is not unreasonable, since the Λ is the only known baryon that is invariant under isotopic spin.

These two assignments are not the only ones possible. Several schemes can be based on the algebra B_2 (C_2), and at least one other scheme based on A_2 is reasonably attractive. I should like to emphasize that experimentalists who try to test predictions have a definite responsibility to be aware of all schemes, or at least all those which have been discussed in the literature. In these lectures, however, I shall limit myself to the above two possibilities.

4. Spin and Parity

For definiteness let us assume that the concept of a strong Lagrangian is meaningful and that the interaction part is strictly invariant under the symmetry transformations. Then the free Lagrangian, which contains the masses of the elementary particles, will break this symmetry because the masses are not the same. This is precisely the situation with regard to the electron-muon universality. But this symmetry-breaking force is invariant under Lorentz transformations and conserves parity; therefore this force cannot affect the spins and parities of the states (that is, if the states are the same with and without the symmetry-breaking force, which we are forced to assume, since otherwise it should be impossible to discover the right symmetry). But the L_A commute with Lorentz transformations and with parity; therefore spin and parity must be the same for all the states within one irreducible representation. This last important conclusion follows from Schuur's Lemma, which is a criterion of irreducibility.

Schuur's Lemma. A set of matrices is irreducible if and only if every matrix that commutes with the set is a multiple of the unit matrix. The proof is extremely simple, and we give a direct argument in the case of parity. If a set of particles does not have the same parity, then the particles can be divided into two subsets, with even and odd parity. Since the matrices of the set commute with parity, they do not change the parity of a state; hence they mix only even-parity states among themselves, and they do not form an irreducible set.

The equality of spins is very easy to satisfy, since all mesons have spin zero and all baryons have spin one-half. The assignment of parities is not so trivial. The pions are known to have the same parity because they are an irreducible representation of isotopic spin. The K_a and $\bar{K}_a$ likewise both have definite parities, and the same parity because of charge-conjugation invariance. The π - K relative parity is a matter of definition, so that we take all known mesons to be pseudoscalars. In the eight-dimensional A_2 scheme it is then necessary to assume the existence of an extra pseudoscalar π°, called $\pi^{\circ\circ}$.

Once the mesons have been taken to be pseudoscalars, the parities of all baryons within each irreducible representation must be the same. This is one of the very few rigorous predictions which can be made. The A_2 scheme requires all parities to be the same; the G_2 scheme allows the Λ to have a parity different from that of the other baryons. The question of the $\Lambda\Sigma$ relative parity is currently the subject of vigorous experimental pursuit. If it turns out to be odd, then the A_2 scheme (Gell-Mann's "eightfold way") will be dead.

5. Couplings and Resonances

An invariant Yukawa coupling between elementary particles is of the form

$$(\bar{B}^a \, \Omega_a^{ib} \, B_b) M_i$$

where B_a is a set of baryons transforming irreducibly under a group, and M_i is an irreducible meson basis. The complex numbers Ω_a^{ib} may or may not exist for given representations B_b and M_i, and to decide on their existence is one of the first questions to be answered, since modern dispersion theoretic techniques allow us to decide whether or not Yukawa couplings exist. This again leads to product representations, for the coefficients of M_i are linear combinations of the product basis $\bar{B}^a B_b$. Since these linear combinations transform among themselves like the contragredient of the M_i representation, we see that the Ω exist if and only if the reduction of the product representation $\bar{B}^a B_b$ contains the contragredient of the M_i representation.

These remarks still hold if the M_i are resonant states rather than stable mesons; therefore the possible sets of resonances can be predicted, and this is in fact one of the more reliable predictions which can be made.

One of the baryon sets, B_b or $\bar{B}^a$, may also be replaced by unstable particles, which would be observed as resonances in meson-baryon scattering.

VIII. CHARACTERS AND GIRDLES

1. Classes and Class Functions

It is possible to introduce the characters and the girdles into the theory of representations of Lie algebras without any prior discussion of the general context in which these concepts first turned up. In doing so, however, I would fail to give any indication of why we are interested in characters and girdles, and the whole subject would seem curiously disconnected from the rest of this course.

First, let us go back to the general matrix group, continuous or discrete. Given two members of the group—say, U and V—we call UVU^{-1} the U conjugate of V. Let V be a fixed matrix, and let U run through the whole group. Then the set of matrices so generated is called the class, or conjugation class, containing V. Clearly, a class is identified by any one of its members. Let V' be a matrix not in the class containing V, that is, such that $V' \neq UVU^{-1}$ for all U in the group. Then the class containing V', namely, $UV'U^{-1}$, has no element in common with the class containing V [for, if $UV'U^{-1} = U'VU'^{-1}$, then $V' = (U^{-1}U')\,V\,(U'^{-1}U) = U''\,V\,U''^{-1}$, contrary to hypothesis]. In this way, a group may be divided into mutually disjoint conjugation classes. In particular, the element E is a class in itself since $UEU^{-1} = UU^{-1} = E$.

The set of eigenvalues of a matrix V are invariant under conjugation, and in particular the trace:

$$\mathrm{tr}\, UVU^{-1} = \mathrm{tr}\, U^{-1}UV = \mathrm{tr}\, V \tag{8.1}$$

We may express this by saying that the trace is a class function: It has the same value for every matrix within a class but may differ from one class to another.

We write

$$\chi(V) = \mathrm{tr}\, V \tag{8.2}$$

thereby associating a complex number with every matrix of the group. The function $\chi(V)$ is called a <u>character</u>. It is, as we have seen, a function over the conjugation classes of the group:

$$\chi(V) = \chi(UVU^{-1}) \tag{8.3}$$

and differs from one representation to another.

For a discrete group, the character has a number of very important properties. Let $\chi_1(V)$ and $\chi_2(V)$ be the characters of two different irreducible representations of the same <u>discrete</u> group. Then,

$$\Sigma_V \chi_1^*(V)\,\chi_2(V) = 0 \tag{8.4}$$

except if the two representations are equivalent. It is, in fact, obvious that $\chi_1(V) = \chi_2(V)$ if the representations are equivalent; but it is also true (though not obvious) that the characters of inequivalent irreducible representations are orthogonal in the sense of Eq. (8. 4), which could also be written

$$\Sigma' n_V \chi_1^*(V)\chi_2(V) = 0 \tag{8. 5}$$

where n_V is the number of elements in a class, and the sum includes only one member of each class.

Now we shall try to extend this concept of the character to continuous groups, immediately specializing to continuously connected Lie groups. Then the discrete sums in Eq. (8. 4), or in (8. 5), have to be replaced by integrals. As an introduction, consider the simplest possible example, a one-parameter Abelian group. Such a group is the group of rotations in two dimensions:

$$\begin{pmatrix} x_1 \\ x_2 \end{pmatrix} \longrightarrow \begin{pmatrix} \cos\varphi, & \sin\varphi \\ -\sin\varphi, & \cos\varphi \end{pmatrix} \begin{pmatrix} x_1 \\ x_2 \end{pmatrix} \tag{8. 6}$$

The Lie algebra consists of a single matrix

$$L_1 = \begin{pmatrix} 0 & i \\ -i & 0 \end{pmatrix} \tag{8. 7}$$

and the multiples thereof. In any representation, L_1 may be diagonalized, so that the irreducible representations are one-dimensional:

$$L_1 = a \tag{8. 8}$$

where a is any real number. The finite transformations, generated from

$$V = E + i\,d\varphi\,a \tag{8. 9}$$

are

$$U_a(\varphi) = e^{ia\varphi} \tag{8.10}$$

Since in the original group a rotation of 360° is the same as no rotation at all, we must have U (2π) = U (0); hence, a must be an integer.

The character is

$$\chi(U) = \text{tr}\, U_a(\varphi) = U_a(\varphi) = e^{ia\varphi} \tag{8.11}$$

or, since the group elements are labeled by φ and the representations by a,

$$\chi(a, \varphi) = e^{ia\varphi} \tag{8.12}$$

Here each transformation is a class, since $UVU^{-1} = V$ for all V. In this case it is obvious what the sum in Eq. (8.4) must be replaced by, for

$$(2\pi)^{-1} \int_0^{2\pi} d\varphi\, \chi^*(a, \varphi)\, \chi(b, \varphi) = \delta_{ab} \tag{8.13}$$

Thus the sum is replaced by the integral over $d\varphi$, no weighting function being necessary. The significance of this is as follows.

The transformation (8.6) is a displacement around a circle. If a point is at the angle φ_0 before the transformation, then it is at an angle $\varphi_0 + \varphi$ afterward. Similarly, the matrices $U_a(\varphi)$ induce displacements within the group itself. The group elements are uniquely labeled by the number φ, with $0 \leq \varphi \leq 2\pi$; the topology of the group is a circle, and to every member of the group there corresponds a point on the circle, and vice versa. The transformations

$$U(\varphi) \rightarrow U(\delta\varphi)\, U(\varphi) = U(\varphi + \delta\varphi) \tag{8.14}$$

are displacements within the group and may be written simply

$$\varphi \to \varphi + \delta\varphi \tag{8.15}$$

The volume element $d\varphi$ in Eq. (8.13) has the property that, under the transformation (8.15),

$$d\varphi \to d\varphi \tag{8.16}$$

that is, the volume element is invariant under the transformations of (8.14).

This is the clue for generalizing Eq. (8.4) or (8.13) to arbitrary Lie groups, in order to find an invariant volume element. Let $V(\vec{n}, \varphi)$ be an arbitrary rotation by the angle φ around the axis $\vec{n}$. Consider the class

$$U V(\vec{n}, \varphi) U^{-1}$$

where U runs through all the rotations. There exists one U that rotates $\vec{n}$ till it is parallel with the X_1 axis without changing φ; therefore every class has a member with $\vec{n}$ parallel to the X_1 axis, say, $V(\varphi)$. Clearly, $V(\varphi)$ and $V(\varphi')$ belong to the same class only if φ and φ' are equal. Consequently, all the classes are labeled by the single real number φ, with $0 \leq \varphi \leq \pi$. Equation (8.6) must take the form

$$\int \chi_1^*(\varphi)\chi_2(\varphi)\mu(\varphi)\, d\varphi = 0 \tag{8.17}$$

where the function $\mu(\varphi)\, d\varphi$ is equal to the "number of rotations" in the classes φ to $\varphi + d\varphi$ — or more properly, $\mu(\varphi)$ is the "density of rotations" in the class φ. To determine $\mu(\varphi)$, we must generalize Eq. (8.14) and demand that $\mu(\varphi)\, d\varphi$ be invariant.

Unfortunately, time does not permit a calculation of $\mu(\varphi)$, either for this simple case or for rank-2 Lie groups. The result is

$$\mu(\varphi) = \xi(0, \varphi)\, \xi^*(0, \varphi) \tag{8.18}$$

where

$$\xi(0, \varphi) = e^{i\varphi/2} - e^{-i\varphi/2}$$

(8.19)

Thus

$$\mu(\varphi) = 4 \sin^2 \varphi/2$$

(8.20)

The reason for splitting $\mu(\varphi)$ into two factors is that Eq. (8.17) achieves a simple form. Since every representation of A_1 is characterized by a single integer λ (= twice the total spin), we indicate the characters by $\chi(\lambda, \varphi)$. Then we introduce the girdle,

$$\xi(\lambda, \varphi) = \chi(\lambda, \varphi)\, \xi(0, \varphi)$$

(8.21)

and Eq. (8.17) becomes

$$\int_0^\pi \xi(\lambda, \varphi)\, \xi(\lambda', \varphi)\, d\varphi = 0 \quad \text{UNLESS } \lambda = \lambda'$$

(8.22)

In general, the girdles are much simpler than the characters.

To calculate the characters, we have only to remember that when H_1 is diagonal it has the eigenvalues

$$\lambda/2\ ,\ \lambda/2 - 1,\ \cdots,\ -\lambda/2$$

Therefore,

$$\chi(\lambda, \varphi) = \operatorname{tr} e^{i\varphi H_1} = e^{i\varphi\lambda/2} + e^{i\varphi(\lambda/2 - 1)} + \cdots + e^{-i\varphi\lambda/2}$$

(8.23)

This geometric series is easily summed:

$$\chi(\lambda,\varphi) = \frac{\left(e^{i\varphi(\lambda+1)/2} - e^{-i\varphi(\lambda+1)/2}\right)}{\left(e^{i\varphi/2} - e^{-i\varphi/2}\right)} \tag{8.24}$$

Hence,

$$\xi(\lambda,\varphi) = e^{i\varphi(\lambda+1)/2} - e^{-i\varphi(\lambda+1)/2} \tag{8.25}$$

Note that the expression for $\chi(\lambda,\varphi)$ has $(\lambda + 1)$ terms; that for $\xi(\lambda,\varphi)$, only 2 terms! The orthogonality of the girdles is now easily checked; in fact,

$$(2\pi)^{-1}\int_0^{\pi} \xi^*(\lambda,\varphi)\,\xi(\lambda',\varphi)\,d\varphi = \delta_{\lambda,\lambda'} \tag{8.26}$$

2. Characters and Girdles for $\ell = 2$

We note that the trace of a matrix V is invariant under conjugation not only by a matrix of the group but also by an arbitrary nonsingular matrix. Since the basis for a simple Lie algebra may be taken as hermitian, any infinitesimal generator —and hence every finite matrix— can be diagonalized; therefore every class must contain a diagonal matrix. The most general diagonal generator is a linear combination of H_1 and H_2; therefore the character function is

$$\chi(V) = \chi(\varphi_1, \varphi_2) = \mathrm{tr}\; e^{i(\varphi_1 H_1 + \varphi_2 H_2)} = \mathrm{tr}\; e^{i\vec{\varphi}\cdot\vec{H}} \tag{8.27}$$

The character is easily calculated from this expression if we know all the eigenvalues or weights of the representation, together with their multiplicities:

$$\chi(\varphi_1, \varphi_2) = \Sigma_{\vec{m}} \gamma_{\vec{m}} e^{i\vec{\varphi}\cdot\vec{m}} \tag{8.28}$$

where $\gamma_{\vec{m}}$ is the multiplicity of the weight $\vec{m} = (m_1, m_2)$.

The problem of invariant group integration— that is, of determining the weight function $\mu(\varphi_1, \varphi_2)$ in

$$\int \chi_1^*(\varphi_1, \varphi_2)\chi_2(\varphi_1, \varphi_2)\mu(\varphi_1, \varphi_2)\, d\varphi_1\, d\varphi_2 = 0 \tag{8.29}$$

again leads us to introduce

$$\mu(\varphi_1, \varphi_2) = \xi(0, 0, \varphi_1, \varphi_2)\xi^*(0, 0, \varphi_1, \varphi_2) \tag{8.30}$$

and

$$\xi(\lambda_1, \lambda_2, \varphi_1, \varphi_2) = \chi(\lambda_1, \lambda_2, \varphi_1, \varphi_2) \times \xi(0, 0, \varphi_1, \varphi_2) \tag{8.31}$$

since every representation is characterized by two integers λ_1 and λ_2. Weyl has found explicit expressions for the girdles $\xi(\lambda_1, \lambda_2, \varphi_1, \varphi_2)$:

$$\xi(\lambda_1, \lambda_2, \varphi_1, \varphi_2) = \Sigma_S \delta_S e^{i(S\vec{K})\cdot\vec{\varphi}} \tag{8.32}$$

where $\vec{K} = \vec{R} + \vec{M}$, $2\vec{R}$ is the sum of the positive roots in the algebra, $\vec{M}$ is the highest weight of the representation, $S\vec{K}$ is a reflection of $\vec{K}$ about a plane normal to a root, and δ_S is the signature of that reflection. The labor of working out this formula explicitly has been carried out and reported [Rev. Mod. Phys., 34, 1 (1962)]. Note that each girdle has only 8 (for B_2), 6 (for A_2), or 12 (for G_2 terms). The characters are now given explicitly by Eq. (8.31); and in particular, the multiplicities $\gamma_{\vec{m}}$ are given by the Fourier decomposition of the character.

We shall show that the character-girdle method furnishes a simple technique to solve several crucial problems. In the next sections, we shall go about the solutions.

Problem 1. In Eqs. (6.10) (6.11) and (6.12) we obtained the highest weights of all irreducible representations of the rank-2 algebras. These and their equivalents are simple, but we do not yet know the multiplicities $\gamma_{\vec{m}}$ of the other weights. To solve this problem, we must carry out the division

$$\chi(\lambda_1, \lambda_2) = \xi(\lambda_1, \lambda_2)/\xi(0,0)$$
$$= \sum \gamma_{\vec{m}}\, e^{i\vec{\varphi}\cdot\vec{m}} \tag{8.33}$$

Problem 2. Let $\chi(\lambda_1, \lambda_2)$ and $\chi(\lambda_1', \lambda_2')$ be the characters of two representations, with bases ψ_a and φ_i. Then the traces in the product representation are

$$\mathrm{tr}\,(v_{ai}^{bj}) = \mathrm{tr}\,(v_a^b\, v_i^j)$$
$$= \mathrm{tr}\,(v_a^b)\ \mathrm{tr}\,(v_i^j) \tag{8.34}$$

The character of a product representation is the product of the characters of the two factors. Furthermore, if a representation is reducible, then the character is clearly the sum of the characters of the irreducible parts.

Since the characters are orthogonal, the expansion

$$\chi(\lambda_1, \lambda_2)\,\chi(\lambda_1', \lambda_2') = \sum_{\mu_1 \mu_2} \times (\lambda_1 \lambda_2 \lambda_1' \lambda_2' \,|\, \mu_1 \mu_2)\,\chi(\mu_1 \mu_2) \tag{8.35}$$

is unique. The coefficients $(\lambda_1\lambda_2\lambda_1'\lambda_2' \,|\, \mu_1\mu_2)$ are integers (positive or zero) that tell us how many times the representation $(\mu_1\mu_2)$ is contained in the product representation. This problem is a generalization of the problem of what spins can be found in a composite system when the constituents have definite spins. Using Eq. (8.31), we get, for example,

$$\chi(\lambda_1 \lambda_2)\,\xi(\lambda_1' \lambda_2') = \sum_{\mu_1 \mu_2} \times (\lambda_1 \lambda_2 \lambda_1' \lambda_2' \,|\, \mu_1 \mu_2)\,\xi(\mu_1 \mu_2) \tag{8.36}$$

This is much simpler than Eq. (8.35). Essentially, it only involves carrying out the product on the left.

Problem 3. We have seen that A_1 is contained in all other simple Lie algebras in several ways, for example, as the subalgebra E_{+1}, E_{-1}, H_1 (except for normalization). Given an irreducible representation $(\lambda_1 \lambda_2)$ of some rank-2 algebra, we may pick out these three matrices, which obviously form a (reducible) representation of A_1. (In the physical applications this means: given a supermultiplet whose members transform according to some representation of a rank-2 algebra, concentrate on isotopic spin transformations.) We may then ask: what irreducible representations of A_1 does this representation reduce to? (What isotopic multiplets does the supermultiplet contain? Example: the eight-dimensional representation of A_2 contains 2 doublets, 1 triplet, and 1 singlet.) The same question could be asked with respect to subgroups other than A_1; thus A_2 is a subgroup of G_2.

The characters of A_1 are simply the trace of H_1, which is obtained from $\chi(\lambda_1\lambda_2)$ by setting $\varphi_2 = 0$. Then,

$$\chi(\lambda_1,\lambda_2,\varphi_1,0)=\Sigma_\mu(\lambda_1,\lambda_2|\mu)\chi(\mu,\varphi_1) \tag{8.37}$$

is a unique expansion, since the $\chi(\mu,\varphi)$ are orthogonal for different μ. The number $(\lambda_1\lambda_2|\mu)$ is the number of times that the representation of A_1 with spin $\mu/2$ is contained in the representation $(\lambda_1\lambda_2)$. Again using Eq. (8.31), we get

$$\left(\lim_{\varphi_2\to 0}\right)\frac{\xi(\lambda_1,\lambda_2,\varphi_1,\varphi_2)}{\xi(0,0,\varphi_1,\varphi_2)}=\Sigma_\mu(\lambda_1\lambda_2|\mu) \times\frac{\xi(\mu,\varphi_1)}{\xi(0,\varphi_1)} \tag{8.38}$$

It is easily seen that $\xi(0,0,\varphi_1,\varphi_2)$ contains $\xi(0,\varphi_1)$ as a factor, and the division of the former by the latter is easy to carry out. Let the ratio be $\Delta(\varphi_1,\varphi_2)$. This has only half as many terms as $\xi(0,0,\lambda_1,\lambda_2)$, and the division in

$$\left(\lim_{\varphi_2\to 0}\right)\frac{\xi(\lambda_1,\lambda_2,\varphi_1,\varphi_2)}{\Delta(\varphi_1,\varphi_2)}=\Sigma_\mu(\lambda_1\lambda_2|\mu) \times\xi(\mu,\varphi_1) \tag{8.39}$$

is easily carried out.

3. Solution of Problems for A_1

The methods will be explained in terms of A_1 and then applied to rank-2 algebras in the following sections.

Problem 1. The character is given by the ratio of $\xi(\lambda, \varphi)$ and $\xi(0, \varphi)$; these are given by Eq. (8.25). Consider the equation

$$\xi(\lambda, \varphi) = \chi(\lambda, \varphi)\, \xi(0, \varphi) \tag{8.40}$$

All three entries in this equation are sums-of-integer or half-odd-integer powers of $e^{i\varphi}$. Let a typical term in $\chi(\lambda, \varphi)$ be $\gamma_m e^{im\varphi}$, and let a typical term in $\xi(0,\varphi)$ be $\gamma_{m'} e^{im'\varphi}$. Then $\xi(\lambda, \varphi)$ is a sum of all terms of the form $\gamma_m \gamma_{m'} e^{i(m+m')\varphi}$; that is, the exponents add, and the multiplicities multiply, as the terms in the two factors are combined in every way and then added.

Every term $\gamma_m e^{im\varphi}$ may be associated with a point on the real line with coordinate m and endowed with a number (multiplicity) γ_m. The product $\gamma_m \gamma_{m'} e^{i(m+m')\varphi}$ is then associated with a point on the real line with coordinate m+m' and endowed with the number (multiplicity) $\gamma_m \gamma_{m'}$. A function such as $\xi(0,\varphi)$ or $\chi(\lambda, \varphi)$ has a whole set of points associated with it, one for every term $\gamma_m e^{im\varphi}$. To multiply all the terms in $\chi(\lambda,\varphi)$ by one term of $\xi(0,\varphi)$ — say, $\gamma_m e^{im\varphi}$ — displace all the coordinates of the points associated with $\chi(\lambda, \varphi)$ by the amount m, while multiplying all the multiplicities by γ_m. Thus the multiplication of $\chi(\lambda, \varphi)$ by $\xi(0,\varphi)$ may be carried out by placing the origin of $\chi(\lambda, \varphi)$ successively on each of the points of $\xi(0\varphi)$, each time multiplying the multiplicities of $\chi(\lambda, \varphi)$ by the multiplicity of the point of $\xi(0,\varphi)$, and finally adding algebraically multiplicities that are associated with the same point.

Two examples of diagrams associated with $\chi(\lambda, \varphi)$ are shown in Fig. 11, together with the <u>girdle diagram</u> (or simply <u>girdle</u>) associated with $\xi(0, \varphi)$. In general, the coordinate of the extreme right (left) point of $\chi(\lambda, \varphi)$ is $\lambda/2$ ($-\lambda/2$), and the intervals between points are all unity. The multiplicities, as is seen from Eq. (8.23), are all +1 for $\chi(\lambda, \varphi)$. For $\xi(0,\varphi)$ we obtain the multiplicities from Eq. (8.25), setting $\lambda = 0$.

When we carry out the multiplication of Fig. 11a by Fig. 11c in the way just explained, we see that every half-odd-integer point between $-\lambda/2$ and $\lambda/2$ receives a multiplicity +1 from placing the origin of Fig. 11c to the left of it, and a multiplicity -1 from placing the origin of Fig. 11c to the right of it. Therefore all these multiplicities cancel each

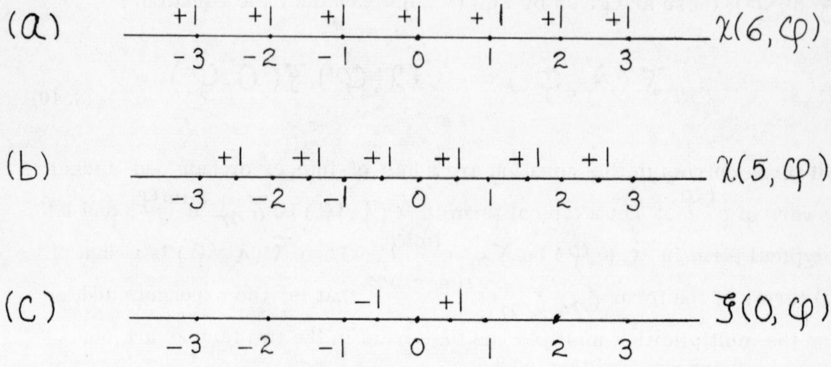

Fig. 11

other, and what remains is shown in Fig. 12. The two points have coordinates $\pm(\lambda + 1)/2$, so that the result does indeed agree with Eq. (8.25).

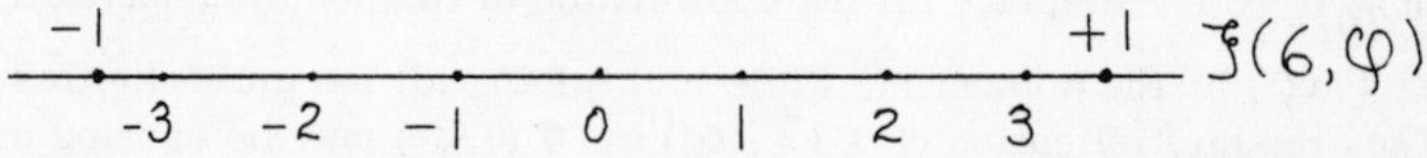

Fig. 12

The geometric multiplication may be inverted, so that $\chi(\lambda, \varphi)$ is obtained by geometrically dividing $\xi(\lambda, \varphi)$ by $\xi(0, \varphi)$. This is carried out precisely in the way of ordinary division of a many-digit number by a shorter one. First we place Fig. 11c on Fig. 12, with the origin on the point with coordinate $\lambda/2$ (= 3). This gives the point $\lambda/2$ as one term in the answer but introduces an unwanted multiplicity of -1 at the point $(\lambda-1)/2$ (= 5/2). To cancel this. Fig. 11c is again superimposed on Fig. 12, this time with its origin on the point $\lambda/2 - 1$ (= 2). This cancels out the unwanted multiplicity at $(\lambda-1)/2$, gives the point $(\lambda-1)/2$ as one term in the answer, and introduces another unwanted multiplicity of -1 at the position $(\lambda-3)/2$. This process continues until the extra multiplicity of -1 occurs at the position $-(\lambda+1)/2$, where it enjoys a happy union with the -1 of Fig. 12. In the process, Fig. 11c has been placed on all the points $-\lambda/2$, $-\lambda/2-1, \ldots, \lambda/2$, and only once on each of these points. Thus the answer is Fig. 11a, as anticipated.

I have gone into considerable detail to explain these geometrical operations only to obviate the necessity for repeating it all in the less trivial case of rank-2 algebras. In that case, the individual terms are of the form $\gamma_{\vec{m}}\, e^{i\vec{m}\cdot\vec{\varphi}}$, and the single coordinate m along a line is replaced by two coordinates in a plane. The product of two terms $\gamma_{\vec{m}}\, e^{i\vec{m}\cdot\vec{\varphi}}$ and $\gamma_{\vec{m}}\, e^{i\vec{m}'\cdot\vec{\varphi}}$ now has as coordinates the components of the vector sum $\vec{m}+\vec{m}'$; but except for this, the extension is verbatim.

Problem 2. Suppressing λ_2, λ'_2, and μ_2 in Eq. (8.36), we have

$$\chi(\lambda)\, \xi(\lambda') = \sum_{\mu} (\lambda\lambda'|\mu)\, \xi(\mu) \tag{8.41}$$

where $(\lambda\lambda'|\mu)$ is an integer (positive or zero), which tells us how many times the representation with spin $\mu/2$ is contained in the product of representations with spin $\lambda/2$ and $\lambda'/2$.

The answer is clearly symmetrical in λ and λ', and it is convenient to take $\lambda' \geq \lambda$. With $\lambda' = 5$ and $\lambda = 2$, the multiplication is carried out in Fig. 13.

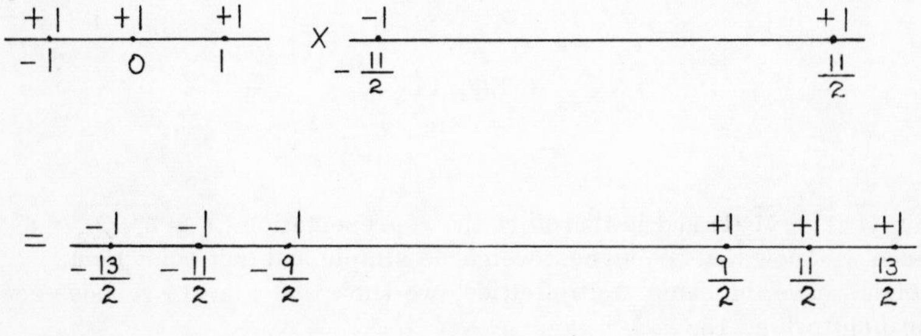

Fig. 13

The result is evidently a sum of girdles, each girdle $\xi(\lambda+\lambda', \varphi)$, $\xi(\lambda+\lambda'-1, \varphi), \ldots, \xi(\lambda'-\lambda, \varphi)$ appearing exactly once. Thus

$$(\lambda\lambda'|\mu) = 1, \qquad \mu = \lambda+\lambda', \lambda+\lambda' \; 1, \ldots, |\lambda'-\lambda|$$
$$= 0, \quad \text{OTHERWISE} \tag{8.42}$$

which is indeed a familiar result. Problem 3 has no application to A_1.

4. Examples of Geometric Operations for $\ell = 2$

The lowest-dimensional representations of any simple rank-2 Lie algebra are the three-dimensional representations of A_2. These may be denoted $(1, 0) = 3$ and $(0, 1) = \bar{3}$ and have the weight diagrams of Fig. 5a and b. The product of Fig. 5a with itself is shown in Fig. 14. We already happen to know that the product is reducible, reducing to a 6- and a 3-dimensional representation. The former has the highest weight

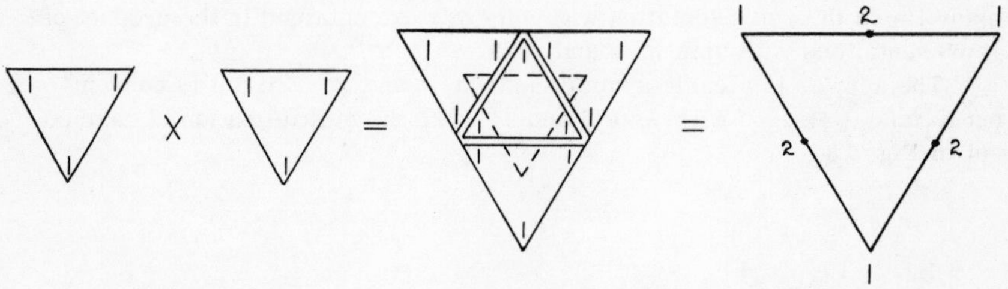

Fig. 14

$\vec{M} = \vec{M}(1) + \vec{M}(1)$ and is therefore the representation $\lambda_1 = 2$, $\lambda_2 = 0$. Since we know that the highest weight is simple and that equivalent weights have the same multiplicities, we know that Fig. 14 reduces according to Fig. 15.

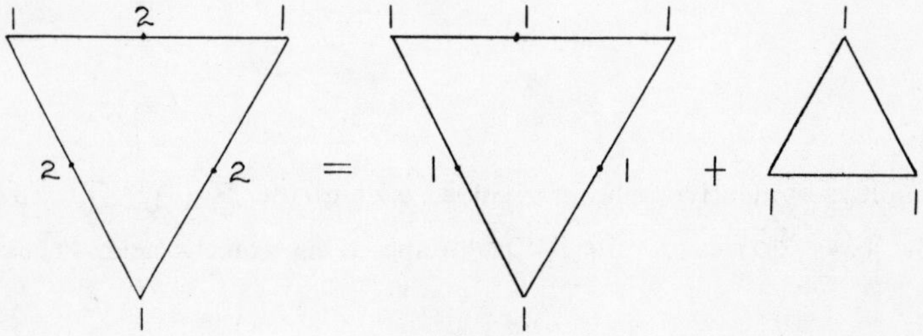

Fig. 15

Notice that the three-dimensional representation is not (1, 0) = 3 but (0, 1) = $\bar{3}$, the contragredient. That the product representation, whose basis is ψ_{ab}, contains the contragredient representation ψ^c can be verified by noting that the Levi-Civita symbol ε^{abc} is form-invariant and may be used to transform two covariant indices into one contravariant index:

$$\psi^c = \varepsilon^{abc}\psi_{ab} \tag{8.43}$$

This simply says that the vector product of two vectors (which is anti-symmetric) is an axial vector.

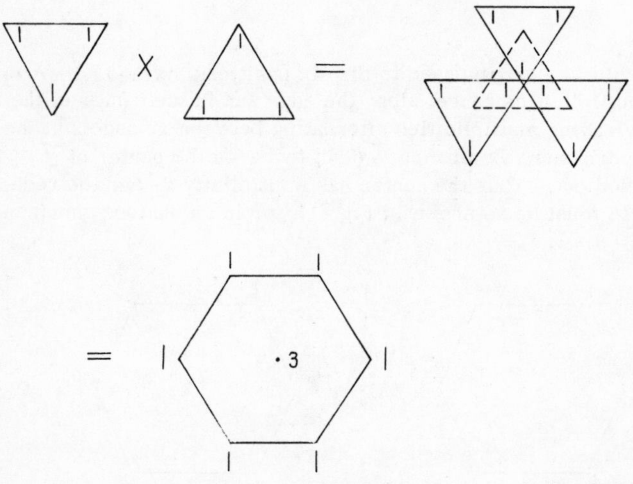

Fig. 16

In order to carry out the reduction of Fig. 15, we had to know in advance that the product in Fig. 14 reduces to a 3- and a 6-dimensional representation. Now let us use the girdle method to deduce the decomposition of the product 3 x $\bar{3}$ (Fig. 16). The point at the center has multiplicity 3, and we have to figure out how many of these three states belong to the representation with the highest weight (1, 1). To this end we may calculate the character of this representation by means of Eq. (8.33):

$$X(1,1) = \frac{\xi(1,1)}{\xi(0,0)}$$

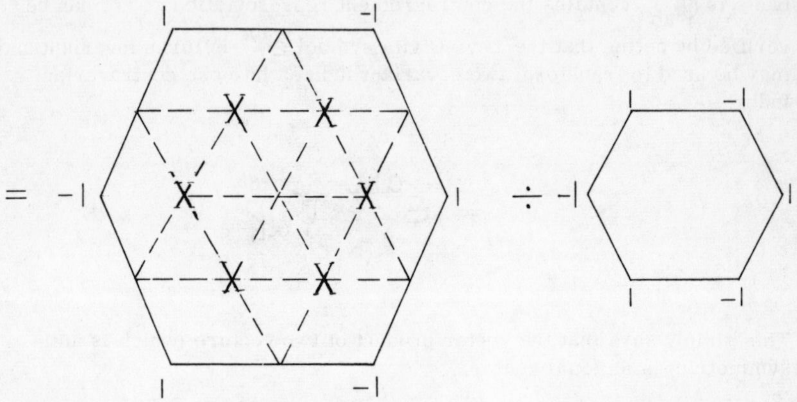

If $\xi(0,0)$ is superimposed in the six positions marked with crosses, then the multiplicities cancel along the edge and in the center of the figure, while leaving multiplicities alternating between +2 and −2 at the positions of the crosses. By placing $\xi(0,0)$ twice on the center of $\xi(1,1)$ these are canceled out. Thus the center has multiplicity 2, and the reduction of Fig. 16 must be as shown in Fig. 17, or in an obvious shorthand: $3 \times \bar{3} = 8 + 1$.

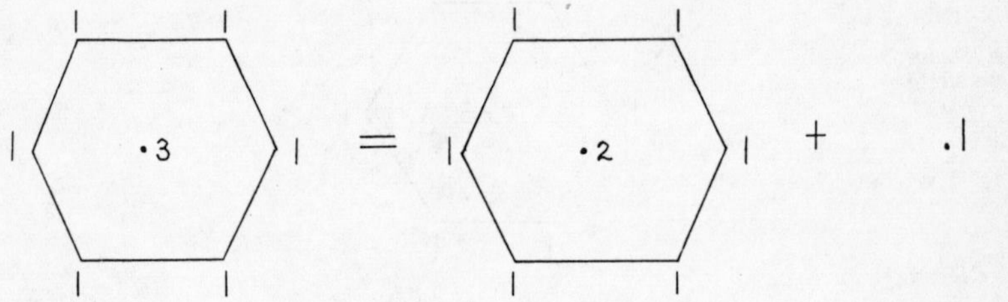

Fig. 17

5. Some General Results

Contents of A_2. If $(E_{\pm 1}, H_1)$ is the subgroup that is interpreted as isotopic spin, and H_2 is hypercharge, we may ask which isotopic multiplets of each hypercharge comprise a representation (λ_1, λ_2). The pedestrian way to answer this question is to construct the entire weight diagram and then to analyze each row, a row corresponding to a definite value of H_2, and hence of hypercharge. A row is then a sum of characters of A_1, and it is relatively easy to analyze this sum.

There is, however, an easier way. If $\chi(\lambda_1, \lambda_2)$ is multiplied by $\xi(0, \varphi)$, then the A_1 characters in every row are converted into A_1 girdles. Thus, we write

$$\chi(\lambda_1, \lambda_2)\, \xi(0, \varphi_1) = \sum_{m_2, \mu} e^{i m_2 \varphi_2}$$

$$\times\ (\lambda_1 \lambda_2 | m_2 \mu)\, \xi(\mu, \varphi_1) \tag{8.44}$$

where the coefficient $(\lambda_1 \lambda_2 | m_2 \mu)$ tells us the number of isotopic multiplets with spin $\mu/2$ having hypercharge m_2. (Hypercharge is not measured in the same unit as m_2, but the factor of proportionality may be presumed known.) To find this number, we note that $\xi(0, 0)$ may be factored as in Fig. 18:

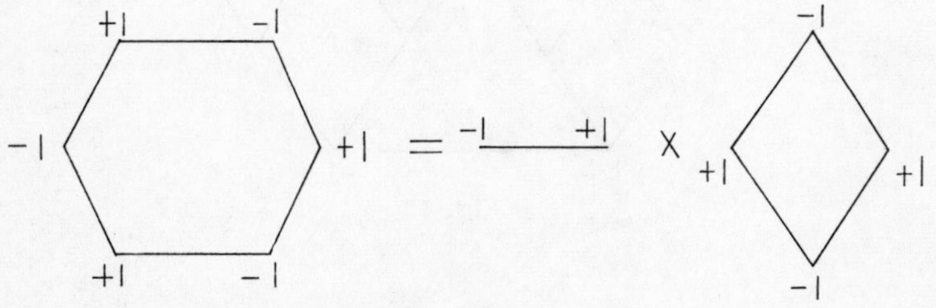

Fig. 18

Thus,

$$\chi(\lambda_1, \lambda_2)\, \xi(0, \varphi_1) = \frac{\xi(\lambda_1, \lambda_2)}{\xi(0,0)}\, \xi(0, \varphi_1)$$

$$= \frac{\xi(\lambda_1, \lambda_2)}{\Delta(\varphi_1, \varphi_2)} \tag{8.45}$$

Accordingly, to find $(\lambda_1\ \lambda_2 | m_2 \mu)$ it is only necessary to divide $\xi(\lambda_1\ \lambda_2)$ by $\Delta(\varphi_1 \varphi_2)$. Because of the simplicity of the latter figure, this is easily carried out (Fig. 19).

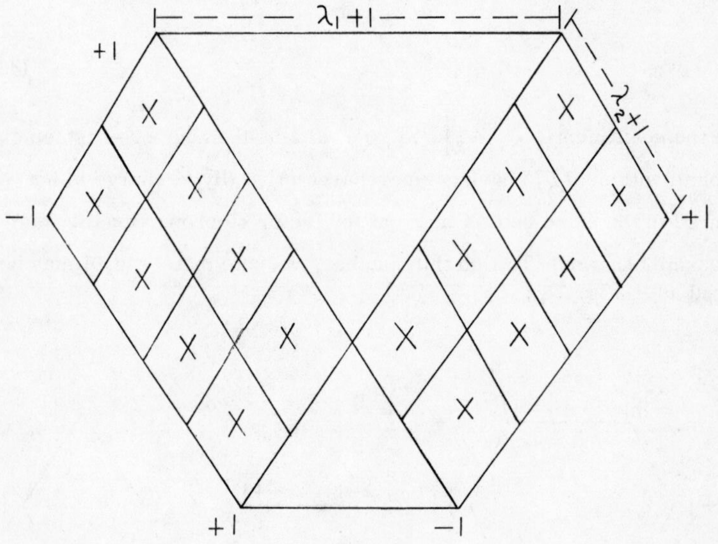

Fig. 19

Clearly the crosses on the left have multiplicities of -1, and those on the right of +1. Comparing Fig. 19 with Eq. (8.44), we see that every cross on the right-hand side of the figure corresponds to one isotopic multiplet, whose spin (hypercharge) is determined by its horizontal (vertical) coordinate. If we are interested in the total number of multiplets, regardless of hypercharge, we simply count the number of crosses in a column. Thus, in Fig. 19 there are one singlet, two doublets, two triplets, two quadruplets, and one quintuplet. It is easy to write the general formula in closed form:

$$(\lambda_1 \lambda_2 | m_2 \mu) = 1 \tag{8.46}$$

if $(\mu + m_2)/2 + (\lambda_1 - \lambda_2)/3$ and $(\mu - m_2)/2 - (\lambda_1 - \lambda_2)/3$ are nonnegative integers not larger than λ_1 and λ_2, respectively; otherwise, $(\lambda_1 \lambda_2 / m_2 \mu) = 0$, and

$$\sum_{m_2} (\lambda_1 \lambda_2 | m_2 \mu) = (\lambda_1 \lambda_2 | \mu) = (\lambda_1 + \lambda_2 + 2 - |\mu - \lambda_1| - |\mu - \lambda_2|)/2 \tag{8.47}$$

However, I think that it is easier to read the results off the diagram than to use these formulas.

Weights of A_2. Actually, Fig. 19 tells us everything about the representations of A_2; in particular, the weight diagram is obtained immediately by dividing by $\xi(0, \varphi_1)$, and the result is shown in Fig. 20. It is best to use oblique coordinates (60°); then the weights lie at the grid points. It is also useful to shift the origin as indicated. The girdle may be written

$$\xi^{A2}(\lambda_1, \lambda_2, \sqrt{3}\,\varphi_1, \sqrt{3}\,\varphi_2) = (XZ)^{-(2\lambda_1 + \lambda_2)/3} \times \sum (\pm) X^{\bar{m}_1} Z^{\bar{m}_2}$$

$$X = e^{i\varphi_1} \qquad Z = e^{i(\varphi_1 + \sqrt{3}\,\varphi_2)/2} \tag{8.48}$$

$$\sum(\pm)\, X^{\overline{m}_1} Z^{\overline{m}_2} = X^{\lambda_1+\lambda_2+1} Z^{\lambda_1} - X^{\lambda_1} \times Z^{\lambda_1+\lambda_2+1} - X^{-1} Z^{\lambda_1+\lambda_2+1} - X^{-1} Z^{\lambda_1} + X^{\lambda_1} Z^{-1} - X^{\lambda_1+\lambda_2+1} Z^{-1} \tag{8.49}$$

Here a factor $\sqrt{3}$ has been incorporated into φ_1 and φ_2 in order that the weights be integers when measured from the new origin at

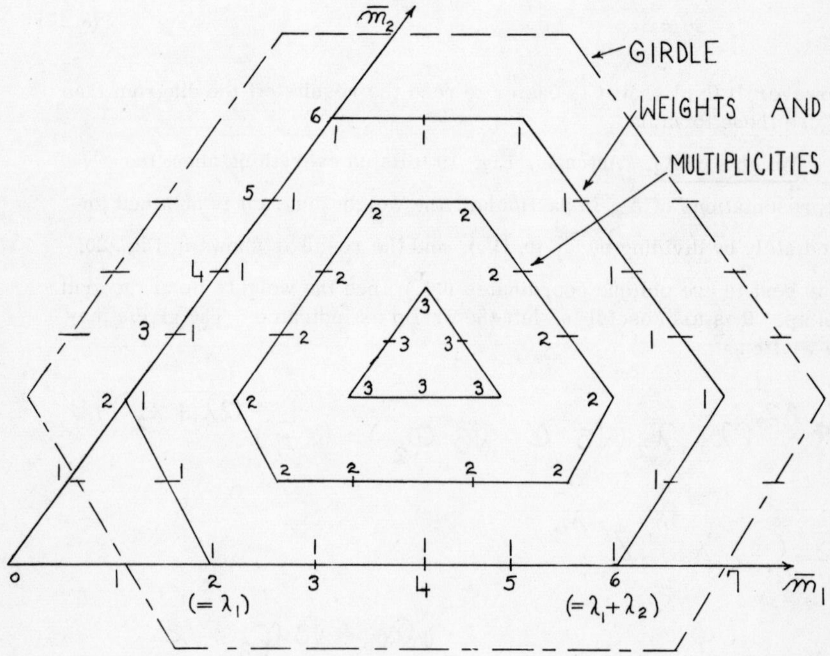

Fig. 20

$(ZX)^{-(2\lambda_1+\lambda_2)/3}$. The weights are distributed among hexagons, and the rule for the multiplicities is extremely simple: it is 1 on the largest hexagon, increases by 1 from one hexagon to the next smaller hexagon or triangle, and is the same on all triangles.

Reduction of G_2. The algebra G_2 contains A_2 as a subgroup. The girdles of G_2 are dodecahedrons, and that includes $\xi^{G_2}(0,0)$. The divisions would therefore be very long and cumbersome if no simplification could be found. In fact, it is easy to see that

$$\xi^{G_2}(0,0,2\sqrt{3}\varphi_1, 2\sqrt{3}\varphi_2) = \xi^{A_2}(0,0,\sqrt{3}\varphi_1, \sqrt{3}\varphi_2)\,\xi^{A_2}(0,0,3\varphi_2, 3\varphi_1) \tag{8.50}$$

This factorization is shown in Fig. 21, together with another amusing factorization.

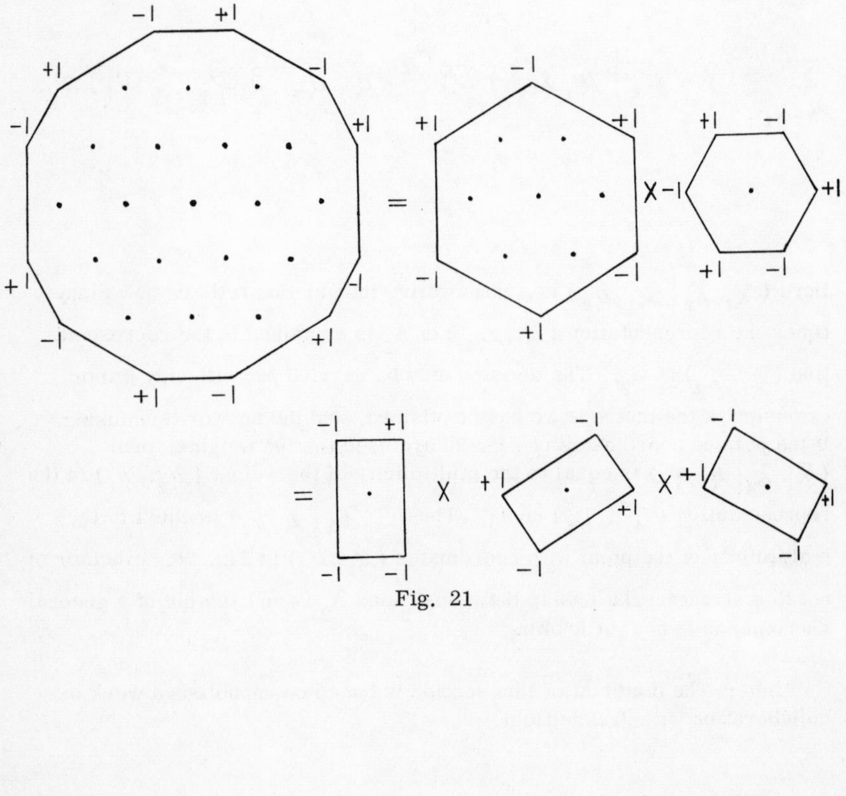

Fig. 21

To find out how many times each representation of A_2 is contained in a given representation of G_2, we write

$$\chi^{G_2}(\lambda_1, \lambda_2, 2\sqrt{3}\,\varphi_1, 2\sqrt{3}\,\varphi_2) = \sum_{\mu_1\mu_2} (\lambda_1 \lambda_2 | \mu_1 \mu_2)$$

$$\times \chi^{A_2}(\mu_1, \mu_2, 3\varphi_2, 3\varphi_1)$$

or, multiplying by ξ^{A2} $(0, 0; 3\varphi_2, 3\varphi_1)$:

$$\frac{\xi^{G_2}(\lambda_1, \lambda_2, 2\sqrt{3}\,\varphi_1, 2\sqrt{3}\,\varphi_2)}{\xi^{A_2}(0, 0, \sqrt{3}\,\varphi_1, \sqrt{3}\,\varphi_2)} =$$

$$\sum_{\mu_1\mu_2} (\lambda_1 \lambda_2 | \mu_1 \mu_2)\, \xi^{A_2}(\mu_1 \mu_2, 3\varphi_2, 3\varphi_1)$$

Here $(\lambda_1, \lambda_2 | \mu_1 \mu_2)$ is a nonnegative integer that tells us how many times the representation (μ_1, μ_2) of A_2 is contained in the representation (λ_1, λ_2) of G_2. The division may be carried out with only minor extension of the methods we have explained, and the answer is amusing. If the oblique coordinates of Fig. 20 are used for the weights, then $(\lambda_1, \lambda_2 | \mu_1 \mu_2)$ is equal to the multiplicity of the weight (μ_2, μ_1) in the representation (λ_1, λ_2) of A_2. Thus $(\lambda_1 \lambda_2 | \mu_1 \mu_2)$ is equal to the multiplicity of the point with coordinates (μ_2, μ_1) in Fig. 20. Whether or not this strange relationship between G_2 and A_2 is an example of a general phenomenon is not yet known.

Note: The material of this section is based on unpublished work in collaboration with J. Dreitlein.